Fundamentals of Abstract Algebra

Neal H. McCoy

Professor Emeritus of Mathematics, Smith College
Visiting Professor of Mathematics, Baylor University

ALLYN AND BACON, INC. BOSTON

To my sister DOROTHY

© Copyright 1972 by Allyn and Bacon, Inc., 70 Atlantic Avenue, Boston, Massachusetts. All rights reserved. Printed in the United States of America. No part of the material protected by this copyright notice may be reproduced or utilized in any form or by any means, electronic or mechanical, including photocopying, recording, or by any informational storage and retrieval system, without written permission from the copyright owner.

Library of Congress Catalog Card No. 72-183215
Printed in the United States of America

CONTENTS

iii

*13   FIELD EXTENSIONS   308

14   SYSTEMS OF LINEAR EQUATIONS   328

15   DETERMINANTS   355

16   LINEAR TRANSFORMATIONS AND MATRICES   379

PREFACE

This is an expanded version of my book, *Introduction to Modern Algebra*, Allyn and Bacon, Inc., Revised edition 1968; hereafter referred to as ITMA.

In common with ITMA, this book is intended for use as a text for students who are just beginning the study of abstract mathematics. However, the present version includes considerably more material than ITMA and should hopefully meet the needs of those instructors who desire to go more deeply into certain topics or to include a somewhat wider range of topics.

For ease of comparison, in the table of contents those sections or complete chapters which treat material not covered in ITMA are indicated by asterisks. It will be noted that there are four new chapters and five additional new sections in other chapters. It is not necessary to list here the new topics inasmuch as a glance at the table of contents will reveal this information.

In addition to new material, in this version there are a few modifications in the order of presentation of certain topics. Thus, products of mappings and inverse mappings are introduced in the first chapter instead of postponing these concepts until groups are studied. Moreover, some material on linear transformations (Section 12.7) is presented in the chapter on vector spaces, well in advance of the later chapter devoted to a more detailed study of linear transformations and matrices.

The new last chapter includes several independent topics which can be presented in almost any order or, if desired, most of them can just as well come fairly early in the course. For example, Section 17.5 on Zorn's Lemma and the second example illustrating its use (the existence of a basis for an arbitrary vector space) can be inserted along with the treatment in Chapter 12 of bases for vector spaces of finite dimension. Except for the last chapter, new material is introduced as soon as suitable background is available and can be studied at the point it occurs in the text or at any later point, or omitted as desired. It may be well to point out explicitly that the second new chapter on groups (The Sylow Theorems) is independent of the first new chapter on groups (Finite Abelian Groups), and these two chapters may be studied in either order.

It is unlikely that any two instructors will agree completely on just what topics should be covered in a first course in abstract algebra. However, it is hoped that the flexibility attained by the presence of a number of optional topics—for use as desired—will justify the appearance of still another introduction to this subject.

A selected bibliography occurs at the end of the text, and there are notes and references to the bibliography at the ends of several chapters. Interested students should therefore find it easy to supplement the text by additional reading as desired.

I wish to express my thanks to Thomas R. Berger, Richard L. Faber and Kenneth E. Hummel, who read an essentially final version of all of the manuscript except the last chapter. Each of them made several valuable suggestions and caught a number of slips, thus helped to improve the accuracy or clarity at various points in the text.

Northampton, Mass.   NEAL H. McCOY

SOME FUNDAMENTAL CONCEPTS

The outstanding characteristic of modern algebra, and indeed also of many other branches of modern mathematics, is its extensive use of what is known as the axiomatic or postulational method. The method itself is not new, since it was used by Euclid (about 300 B.C.) in his construction of geometry as a deductive science. However, in many ways the modern viewpoint is quite different from Euclid's, and the power of the method did not become apparent until this century.

We shall not attempt to give here any description or analysis of the postulational method, but the material of the next few chapters will illustrate the ideas involved. This first brief chapter will present a few basic concepts to be used repeatedly, and will introduce some convenient notation. Although the reader may have previously met some, or even all, of these concepts, they are so fundamental for our purposes that it seems desirable to start off by presenting them in some detail. Many more illustrations of each concept will appear in later chapters.

1.1 SETS

The concept of *set* (class, collection, aggregate) is fundamental in mathematics as it is in everyday life. A related concept is that of *element* of a set. We make no attempt to define these terms but shall presently give some examples that will illustrate the sense in which they are being used.

First of all, we may say that a set is made up of elements. In order to give an example of a set we need, therefore, to exhibit its elements or to give some rule that will specify its elements. We shall often find it convenient to denote sets by capital letters and elements of sets by lower-case letters. If a is an element of the set A, we may indicate this fact by writing $a \in A$ (read, "a is an element of A"). Also, $a \notin A$ will mean that a is not an element of the set A. If both a and b are elements of the set A, we may write $a, b \in A$.

If P is the set of all positive integers, $a \in P$ means merely that a is a positive integer. Certainly, then, it is true that $1 \in P$, $2 \in P$, and so on. If B is the set of all triangles in a given plane, $a \in B$ means that a is one of the triangles in this plane. If C is the set of all books in the Library of Congress, then $a \in C$ means that a is one of these books. We shall presently give other examples of sets.

If $a, b \in A$ and we write $a = b$, it is always to be understood that these are identical elements of A. Otherwise expressed, a and b are merely different symbols designating the same element of A. If $a, b \in A$ and it is not true that $a = b$, we may indicate this fact by writing $a \neq b$ and may say that a and b are *distinct* elements of A.

If A and B are sets with the property that every element of A is also an element of B, we call A a *subset* of B and write $A \subseteq B$ (read, "A is contained in B"). This is also sometimes written in the form $B \supseteq A$. Perhaps we should point out that for every set A it is true that $A \subseteq A$ and hence, according to our definition, one of the subsets of A is A itself. If $A \subseteq B$ and also $B \subseteq A$, then A and B have exactly the same elements and we say that these sets are *equal*, and indicate this by writing $A = B$. If it is not true that $A = B$, we may write $A \neq B$. If $A \subseteq B$ and $A \neq B$, then we say that A is a *proper subset* of B and indicate this fact by the notation $A \subset B$ (read, "A is properly contained in B"). Clearly, $A \subset B$ means that every element of A is an element of B and, moreover, B contains at least one element which is not an element of A.

Sometimes, as has been the case so far, we may specify a set by stating in words just what its elements are. Another way of specifying a set is to exhibit its elements. Thus, $\{x\}$ indicates the set which consists of the single element x, $\{x, y\}$ the set consisting of the two elements x and y, and so on. We may write $A = \{1, 2, 3, 4\}$ to mean that A is the set whose elements are the positive integers 1, 2, 3, and 4. If P is the set of all positive integers, by writing

$$K = \{a \mid a \in P, a \text{ divisible by } 2\},$$

we shall mean that K consists of all elements a having the properties indicated after the vertical bar, that is, a is a positive integer and is divisible by 2. Hence, K is just the set of all *even* positive integers. We may also write

$$K = \{2, 4, 6, 8, \cdots\},$$

the dots indicating that all even positive integers are included in this set. As another example, if

$$D = \{a \mid a \in P, \, a < 6\},$$

then it is clear that $D = \{1, 2, 3, 4, 5\}$.

Whenever we specify a set by exhibiting its elements, it is to be understood that the indicated elements are distinct. Thus, for example, if we write $B = \{x, y, z\}$, we mean to imply that $x \neq y$, $x \neq z$, and $y \neq z$.

For many purposes, it is convenient to allow for the possibility that a set may have no elements. This fictitious set with no elements we shall call the *empty set*. According to the definition of subset given above, the empty set is a subset of every set. Moreover, it is a proper subset of every set except the empty set itself. The empty set is often designated by $\varnothing$, and thus we have $\varnothing \subseteq A$ for every set A.

If A and B are sets, the elements that are in both A and B form a set called the *intersection* of A and B, denoted by $A \cap B$. Of course, if A and B have no elements in common, $A \cap B = \varnothing$.

If A and B are sets, the set consisting of those elements which are elements either of A or of B (or of both), is a set called the *union* of A and B, denoted by $A \cup B$.

As examples of the concepts of intersection and union, let $A = \{1, 2, 3\}$, $B = \{2, 4, 5\}$, and $C = \{1, 3, 6\}$. Then we have

$$A \cap B = \{2\}, A \cap C = \{1, 3\}, B \cap C = \varnothing,$$
$$A \cup B = \{1, 2, 3, 4, 5\}, A \cup C = \{1, 2, 3, 6\}, \text{ and}$$
$$B \cup C = \{1, 2, 3, 4, 5, 6\}.$$

Although we have defined the intersection and the union of only *two* sets, it is easy to extend these definitions to any number of sets, as follows. The *intersection* of any number of given sets is the set consisting of those elements which are in all the given sets, and the *union* is the set consisting of those elements which are in at least one of the given sets.

If A, B, and C are sets, each of the following is an immediate consequence of the various definitions which we have made:

$A \cap B \subseteq A$ and $A \cap B \subseteq B$.
$A \subseteq A \cup B$ and $B \subseteq A \cup B$.
$A \cap B = A$ if and only if $A \subseteq B$.
$A \cup B = A$ if and only if $B \subseteq A$.
If $B \subseteq C$, then $A \cup B \subseteq A \cup C$ and $A \cap B \subseteq A \cap C$.

In working with sets, so-called Venn diagrams are sometimes used to give a purely symbolic, but convenient, geometric indication of the relationships involved. Suppose, for the moment, that all sets being considered are subsets of some fixed set U. In Figures 1 and 2, the points within the square represent elements of U. If A and B are subsets of U, then the elements of A and B may be represented by the points within indicated circles (or any other closed regions). The intersection and the union of the sets A and B are then represented in an obvious way by the shaded regions in Figures 1 and 2, respectively.

Of course, the use of a Venn diagram is not meant to imply anything about the nature of the sets being considered, whether or not indicated intersections are nonempty, and so on. Moreover, such a diagram cannot in itself constitute a proof of any fact, but it may be quite helpful in suggesting a proof.

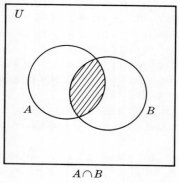

$A \cap B$

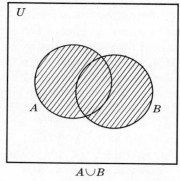

$A \cup B$

Figure 1   **Figure 2**

Let us make the following remarks by way of emphasis. A problem of frequent occurrence is that of proving the equality of two sets. Suppose that C and D are given sets and it is required to prove that $C = D$. By definition of equality of sets, we need to show that $C \subseteq D$ and that $D \subseteq C$. Sometimes one or both of these conditions follow easily from given facts. If not, the standard procedure is to start with an arbitrary element of C and show that it is an element of D, and then do the same thing with C and D interchanged. When we write "let $x \in C$" or "$x \in C$," we mean that x is to represent a completely arbitrary element of the set C. Hence, to show that $C \subseteq D$, we only need to show that "if $x \in C$, then $x \in D$." Of course, any other symbol could be used in place of x. Let us now give an example by way of illustration.

EXAMPLE.   If A, B, and C are sets, prove that

$$A \cup (B \cap C) = (A \cup B) \cap (A \cup C).$$

SOLUTION.   First, let us take advantage of the opportunity to give another illustration of a Venn diagram. If we think of the

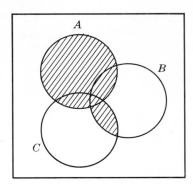

Figure 3

meaning of $A \cup (B \cap C)$ as consisting of all elements of A together with all elements that are in both B and C, we see that the set $A \cup (B \cap C)$ may be represented by the shaded portion of the Venn diagram in Figure 3. We leave it to the reader to verify that this same shaded region also represents the set $(A \cup B) \cap (A \cup C)$.

We now proceed to give a formal proof of the required formula. Clearly, $B \cap C \subseteq B$, so $A \cup (B \cap C) \subseteq A \cup B$. Similarly, $B \cap C \subseteq C$, and hence $A \cup (B \cap C) \subseteq A \cup C$. It follows that

$$A \cup (B \cap C) \subseteq (A \cup B) \cap (A \cup C),$$

and we have obtained inclusion one way. To obtain inclusion the other way, let $x \in (A \cup B) \cap (A \cup C)$ and let us proceed to show that $x \in A \cup (B \cap C)$. Now $x \in A \cup B$ and also $x \in A \cup C$. If $x \in A$, then surely $x \in A \cup (B \cap C)$. If $x \notin A$, then $x \in B$ and $x \in C$, so that $x \in B \cap C$, and again we have that $x \in A \cup (B \cap C)$. This shows that $(A \cup B) \cap (A \cup C) \subseteq A \cup (B \cap C)$, and the proof is therefore complete.

The final concept to be introduced in this section may be illustrated by the familiar idea of coordinates of a point in a plane. A point is determined by an ordered pair (x, y) of real numbers. The word *ordered* is meant to imply that the order of writing the two numbers x and y is important; that is, that (x, y) is to be considered as a different pair than (y, x) unless, of course, x and y happen to be equal real numbers. If **R** denotes the set of all real numbers, the set of all ordered pairs of elements of **R** is frequently called the *Cartesian product* of **R** by **R** and designated by $\mathbf{R} \times \mathbf{R}$. More generally, if A and B are any sets, the set of all ordered pairs (a, b), where $a \in A$ and $b \in B$, is the *Cartesian product* of A by B, designated by $A \times B$. It may happen, of course, that A and B are identical sets, as in the illustration given above. It is obvious how to define the Cartesian product of more than two sets. Thus, for example, the set $A \times B \times C$ is the set of all ordered triples (a, b, c), where $a \in A$, $b \in B$, and $c \in C$.

As another example of a product set, if $A = \{1, 2, 3\}$, and $B = \{u, v\}$, then

$$A \times B = \{(1, u), (1, v), (2, u), (2, v), (3, u), (3, v)\}.$$

EXERCISES

1. If $A = \{a, b, c\}$, $B = \{c, x, y\}$, and $C = \{x, z\}$, determine each of the following sets: $A \cap B$, $A \cap C$, $B \cap C$, $A \cup B$, $A \cup C$, $B \cup C$, $A \times B$, $A \times C$, $B \times C$.

2. Let P be the set of all positive integers, and define subsets of P as follows:

$$F = \{a \mid a \in P,\ a < 10\},$$
$$G = \{a \mid a \in P,\ a > 5\},$$
$$H = \{a \mid a \in P,\ a \text{ divisible by } 3\}.$$

Determine each of the following sets: $F \cap G$, $F \cap H$, $G \cap H$, $F \cup G$, $F \cup H$, $G \cup H$.

3. Exhibit the four different subsets of a set with two elements. How many subsets does a set with three elements have? A set with four elements?

4. If k is a positive integer, show that a set with $k + 1$ elements has twice as many subsets as a set with k elements. Then find a formula for the number of subsets of a set with n elements, where n is an arbitrary positive integer.

5. If A, B, and C are sets, draw Venn diagrams to illustrate and then give a formal proof that $A \cap (B \cup C) = (A \cap B) \cup (A \cap C)$.

6. If X is a subset of a set U, let us denote by X' the *complement* of X in U, that is, the set of all elements of U which are not in subset X. If A and B are subsets of U, prove each of the following: $(A \cap B)' = A' \cup B'$, $(A \cup B)' = A' \cap B'$.

1.2 MAPPINGS

As a first illustration of the concept to be introduced in this section, let C be the set of all books in the Library of Congress and P the set of all positive integers. Corresponding to each book there is a unique positive integer; namely, the number of pages in the book. That is, to each element of C there corresponds in this way a unique element of P. This is an example of a mapping of the set C into the set P. As another illustration, let N be the set of all names occurring in a given telephone directory, and L the set of the twenty-six letters of the alphabet. We may then associate with each name the first letter of the surname, and this then defines a mapping of N into L. Additional examples will be given after the following definition.

1.1   Definition.   A *mapping* of a set A into a set B is a correspondence that associates with each element a of A a unique element b of B. The notation $a \rightarrow b$ is sometimes used to indicate that b is the element of B that is associated with the element a of A under a given mapping. We may say that a *maps into b* or that b is the *image* of a under this mapping.

Let us now give an example of a mapping of the set $S = \{1, 2, 3, 4\}$ into the set $T = \{x, y, z\}$. To specify such a mapping, we merely need to select an element of T to be the image of each element of S. Thus

1.2 $$1 \rightarrow x, \quad 2 \rightarrow y, \quad 3 \rightarrow x, \quad 4 \rightarrow y$$

defines a mapping of S into T in which x is the image of 1, y the image of 2, and so on. Note that although every element of S is required to have an image in T, it need not be true that every element of T occurs as the image of at least one element of S.

Before proceeding, let us observe that a *function*, as the term is often used, is just a mapping of the set **R** of all real numbers (or of some subset of **R**) into the same set **R**. For example, the function f defined by $f(x) = x^2 + x + 1$ is the mapping $x \rightarrow x^2 + x + 1$ which associates with each real number x the real number $x^2 + x + 1$. In this setting, the mapping is denoted by f and the image of the number x under the mapping f by $f(x)$.

Although we are now concerned with arbitrary sets (not just sets of real numbers), the function notation of the preceding paragraph could be, and frequently is, used for mappings. However, we shall adopt an alternate notation which is also of fairly wide use in algebra and which will have some advantages later on. Mappings will henceforth usually be denoted by Greek letters, such as α, β, γ, $\cdots$. If α is a mapping of A into B, the image of an element a of A will be denoted by $a\alpha$. Note that α is here written on the right and without parentheses, rather than on the left as in the more familiar function notation $\alpha(a)$. For example, let β be the mapping 1.2 of S into T. Then, instead of writing 1.2 we might just as well write

1.3 $1\beta = x, \quad 2\beta = y, \quad 3\beta = x, \quad 4\beta = y.$

Another mapping γ of S into T is defined by

1.4 $1\gamma = x, \quad 2\gamma = y, \quad 3\gamma = y, \quad 4\gamma = z.$

We shall presently use these mappings to illustrate certain additional concepts.

It is customary to write $\alpha: A \to B$ to indicate that α is a mapping of the set A into the set B. We may also sometimes write $a \to a\alpha$, $a \in A$, to indicate this mapping, it being understood that for each $a \in A$, $a\alpha$ is a uniquely determined element of B. If we have mappings $\alpha: A \to B$ and $\beta: A \to B$, we naturally consider these mappings to be *equal*, and write $\alpha = \beta$, if and only if $a\alpha = a\beta$ for every $a \in A$. Thus, for the mappings $\beta: S \to T$ and $\gamma: S \to T$ exhibited above, we have $\beta \neq \gamma$ since, for example, $3\beta = x$ and $3\gamma = y$.

In order to avoid some trivial special cases, whenever we consider a mapping of a set A into a set B we shall always tacitly assume that the sets A and B are not empty.

In studying mappings it is sometimes suggestive to make use of a geometrical diagram. Figure 4 is supposed to suggest that α is a mapping of A into B and that under this mapping each element a of A has image $a\alpha$ in B.

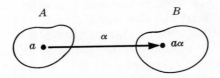

Figure 4

In the particular mapping $\beta: S \to T$ given by 1.3, the element z of T does not occur as the image of any element of S. However, in the mapping $\gamma: S \to T$, defined in 1.4, every element of T is the image of at least one element of S. The language for stating this essential difference between these mappings is given in the following definition.

1.5   Definition.   A mapping α of A into B is said to be a mapping of A *onto* B if and only if every element of B is the image of at least one element of A under the mapping α.

Thus, γ is a mapping of S onto T, whereas β is not a mapping of S onto T. It is important to observe that "into" is *not* the opposite of "onto." According to our language, every mapping is a mapping of some set into some set. That is, "onto" is a special case of "into," and if $\alpha: A \to B$ is a mapping of A *onto* B, it is perfectly correct to say that it is a mapping of A into B (although this doesn't give the maximum amount of available information).

If $\alpha: A \to B$ is a mapping of A into B, let us denote by $A\alpha$ the set of all elements of B that occur as images of elements of A under the mapping α, that is,

$$A\alpha = \{a\alpha \mid a \in A\} .$$

Thus α is an onto mapping if and only if $A\alpha = B$. In any case, an arbitrary mapping $\alpha: A \to B$ may be considered as defining a mapping of A *onto* the subset $A\alpha$ of B. Thus, associated with each mapping is an onto mapping if we suitably restrict the set in which the images lie.

There is one additional concept which plays an important role in the study of mappings. In the mapping $\beta: S \to T$, defined by 1.3, we see that both 1 and 3 have x as image. Similarly, $\gamma: S \to T$, defined by 1.4 is such that both 2 and 3 have y as image. Now let $T = \{x, y, z\}$ as above, and let $U = \{r, s, t, u\}$. Then the mapping $\theta: T \to U$ defined by

1.6
$$x\theta = t, \quad y\theta = r, \quad z\theta = u$$

is such that every element of U which occurs as an image of some element of T is the image of exactly one element of T. This property has a name which we proceed to introduce.

1.7 Definition. A mapping $\alpha: A \to B$ is said to be a *one-one* mapping of A into B if and only if distinct elements of A have distinct images in B or, equivalently, if $a_1, a_2 \in A$ such that $a_1\alpha = a_2\alpha$, then $a_1 = a_2$.

The mapping $\theta: T \to U$ defined by 1.6 is an example of a one-one mapping. Note, however, that it is not an onto mapping. Hence a one-one mapping may or may not be an onto mapping. Clearly, also, an onto mapping need not be a one-one mapping.*

We now give some additional examples to illustrate these concepts.

EXAMPLE 1. Let C be a nonempty subset of the set D. The mapping $\phi: C \to D$ defined by $c\phi = c$ for each $c \in C$ is a one-one mapping of C into D. It is an onto mapping if and only if $C = D$.

---

* Some other terms will be found in the literature as follows. An onto mapping is also called a *surjection;* a one-one mapping may be called an *injection*. A mapping which is both one-one and onto is also called a *bijection*.

EXAMPLE 2.   Let $\alpha: A \times B \to A$ be defined by $(a, b)\alpha = a$ for each $(a, b) \in A \times B$. This is certainly an onto mapping. However, if b_1, $b_2 \in B$ with $b_1 \neq b_2$, then $(a, b_1)\alpha = (a, b_2)\alpha$ with $(a, b_1) \neq (a, b_2)$, so the mapping is not a one-one mapping. It will be a one-one mapping if and only if B has exactly one element. The mapping α of this example is called the *projection* of $A \times B$ onto A. Similarly, one can define the projection of $A \times B$ onto B.

EXAMPLE 3.   Let $\mathbf{Z}$ be the set of all integers and $\alpha: \mathbf{Z} \to \mathbf{Z}$ be defined by $i\alpha = 2i + 1$, $i \in \mathbf{Z}$. In contrast to most of our previous examples, this is an example of a mapping of the set $\mathbf{Z}$ into the same set $\mathbf{Z}$. To determine whether α is an onto mapping, let j be an arbitrary element of $\mathbf{Z}$ and let us find whether j is the image of some element. That is, we need to determine whether there exists an integer i such that $2i + 1 = j$. Clearly, there will be no such integer i if j is even since $2i + 1$ is odd for every integer i. Thus, α is not an onto mapping. Is it a one-one mapping? To answer this question, suppose that i_1, $i_2 \in \mathbf{Z}$ such that $i_1\alpha = i_2\alpha$, that is, such that $2i_1 + 1 = 2i_2 + 1$. It follows that $i_1 = i_2$ and α is therefore a one-one mappings.s

It will probably seem reasonable, and it is indeed true although we shall not discuss this fact here, that if set C has n elements for some positive integer n, then there will exist a one-one mapping of C onto D if and only if D also has n elements.

EXERCISES

1.   Let $\mathbf{Z}$ be the set of all integers, and $i \in \mathbf{Z}$. Determine in each case whether the indicated mapping α of $\mathbf{Z}$ into $\mathbf{Z}$ is an onto mapping and whether it is a one-one mapping.

   (a) $i\alpha = i + 3$,   (d) $i\alpha = 2i - 1$,
   (b) $i\alpha = i^2 + i$,   (e) $i\alpha = -i + 5$,
   (c) $i\alpha = i^3$,   (f) $i\alpha = i - 4$.

2.   Let $\mathbf{R}$ be the set of all real numbers, and $x \in \mathbf{R}$. Determine in each case whether the indicated mapping α of $\mathbf{R}$ into $\mathbf{R}$ is an onto mapping and whether it is a one-one mapping.

   (a) $x\alpha = 2x + 1$,   (d) $x\alpha = x^3$,
   (b) $x\alpha = 1 - x$,   (e) $x\alpha = x^2 + x$,
   (c) $x\alpha = x^2$,   (f) $x\alpha = 4x$,

   (g) $x\alpha = \begin{cases} x \text{ if } x \text{ is rational,} \\ 2x \text{ if } x \text{ is irrational.} \end{cases}$

3. Let P be the set of all positive integers, and $n \in P$. Determine in each case whether the indicated mapping of P into P is an onto mapping and whether it is a one-one mapping.

   (a) $n\alpha = 2n$,   (c) $n\alpha = n^2$,
   (b) $n\alpha = n + 1$,   (d) $1\alpha = 1, n\alpha = n - 1$ for $n > 1$.

4. Give an example of a mapping of the set P of all positive integers into the set P such that every element of P is the image of exactly two elements.

5. If $\mathbf{R}$ is the set of all real numbers, use the fact that every cubic equation with real coefficients has a real root to show that the mappng α of $\mathbf{R}$ into $\mathbf{R}$ defined by $x\alpha = x^3 - x$, $x \in \mathbf{R}$, is a mapping of $\mathbf{R}$ onto $\mathbf{R}$. Is it a one-one mapping?

6. If $\mathbf{R}$ is the set of all real numbers, why doesn't the formula $x\alpha = \dfrac{1}{x}$, $x \in \mathbf{R}$, define a mapping of $\mathbf{R}$ into $\mathbf{R}$?

7. If $A = \{1, 2, 3\}$ and $B = \{x, y\}$, verify that there exist eight mappings of A into B and nine mappings of B into A. How many mappings of A onto B are there?

8. Let A be a set with m elements, and B a set with n elements (m and n positive integers). Formal proofs are not required, but in each of the following give some indication why you believe your conclusion to be correct.

   (a) Determine the number of mappings of A into B.
   (b) If $n \geq m$, determine the number of one-one mappings of A into B.
   (c) If $m = n$, determine the number of one-one mappings of A onto B.

9. Let $\mathbf{R}$ be the set of all real numbers, and let $x \in \mathbf{R}$. Use any calculus methods which you know to determine whether each of the following mappings α of $\mathbf{R}$ into $\mathbf{R}$ is an onto mapping and whether it is a one-one mapping:

   (a) $x\alpha = e^x$,   (c) $x\alpha = x + \sin x$,
   (b) $x\alpha = \sin x$,   (d) $x\alpha = \dfrac{x}{2} + \sin x$.

1.3 PRODUCTS OF MAPPINGS

Under certain conditions, two or more mappings may be combined in a natural way to form a new mapping. Suppose that A, B, and C are sets and that we have given mappings $\alpha\colon A \to B$ and $\beta\colon B \to C$. It is then easy to define in a natural way a mapping of A into C. If $a \in A$, we first take the image $a\alpha$ of a under the mapping α. Now $a\alpha \in B$, so $(a\alpha)\beta$ is a uniquely determined element of C. Thus $a \to (a\alpha)\beta$, $a \in A$, defines a mapping of A into C determined by the given mappings α and β. We denote this mapping by $\alpha\beta$ and call it the *product* (or *composition*) of α by β. More formally, the definition of the mapping $\alpha\beta\colon A \to C$ is as follows:

1.8
$$a(\alpha\beta) = (a\alpha)\beta, \qquad a \in A.$$

We may point out that, according to the definition just given, $\alpha\beta$ means "first perform α, then perform β." It is here that it makes an essential difference in notation whether we denote the image of a under the mapping α by $a\alpha$ or by the function notation $\alpha(a)$. Had we adopted the latter notation, the mapping which we have denoted by $\alpha\beta$ would map an element a of A into the element $\beta(\alpha(a))$ of C, and it would be natural to denote it by $\beta\alpha$. Both notations are widely used and in reading other books the student must be prepared to find either one.

As a simple illustration of Definition 1.8, let $A = \{1, 2, 3, 4\}$, $B = \{x, y, z\}$, $C = \{r, s\}$, and let $\alpha\colon A \to B$ and $\beta\colon B \to C$ be defined, respectively, as follows:

$$1\alpha = y, \quad 2\alpha = x, \quad 3\alpha = x, \quad 4\alpha = z;$$
$$x\beta = s, \quad y\beta = r, \quad z\beta = s.$$

Then the mapping $\alpha\beta\colon A \to C$ is obtained by the following calculations:

$$1(\alpha\beta) = (1\alpha)\beta = y\beta = r,$$
$$2(\alpha\beta) = (2\alpha)\beta = x\beta = s,$$
$$3(\alpha\beta) = (3\alpha)\beta = x\beta = s,$$
$$4(\alpha\beta) = (4\alpha)\beta = z\beta = s.$$

It should be clear that in defining the product of two mappings a certain condition on the sets involved is necessary. Thus, if α is a mapping of A into B, $\alpha\beta$ is defined only if β is a mapping of the set B into some set.

We now take one more step as follows. Let A, B, C, and D be sets, and suppose that we have mappings $\alpha\colon A \to B$, $\beta\colon B \to C$, and $\gamma\colon C \to D$. Then $\alpha\beta$ is a mapping of A into C, and $(\alpha\beta)\gamma$ is a mapping of A into D. In like manner, $\alpha(\beta\gamma)$ is seen to be a mapping of A into D. It is an important fact that these two mappings are equal; that is, that

1.9
$$(\alpha\beta)\gamma = \alpha(\beta\gamma).$$

By the definition of equality of mappings, we shall prove 1.9 by verifying that

1.10
$$a((\alpha\beta)\gamma) = a(\alpha(\beta\gamma))$$

for every element a of A.

First, we observe that by the definition of the product of the mappings $\alpha\beta$ and γ, we have

$$a((\alpha\beta)\gamma) = (a(\alpha\beta))\gamma.$$

Then, by the definition of the product $\alpha\beta$, it follows that

$$(a(\alpha\beta))\gamma = ((a\alpha)\beta)\gamma,$$

and so the left side of 1.10 is equal to $((a\alpha)\beta)\gamma$. In like manner, by applying the definition of the product of α by $\beta\gamma$, and then the definition of the product $\beta\gamma$, we obtain

$$a(\alpha(\beta\gamma)) = (a\alpha)(\beta\gamma) = ((a\alpha)\beta)\gamma.$$

Since both sides of 1.10 are equal to $((a\alpha)\beta)\gamma$, we have proved 1.10 and also 1.9.

The fact that 1.9 holds whenever the indicated products are defined is usually expressed by saying that multiplication of mappings is *associative*. This property of associativity will appear frequently in various settings throughout this book.

For each set A, the *identity mapping on A* will be denoted by ϵ_A. That is, $\epsilon_A: A \to A$ is defined by $a\epsilon_A = a$ for each $a \in A$. If $\alpha: A \to B$, then for $a \in A$ we have $a\alpha = (a\epsilon_A)\alpha = a(\epsilon_A\alpha)$. Thus $\alpha = \epsilon_A\alpha$. Similarly, it may be verified that $\alpha\epsilon_B = \alpha$.

If $\alpha: A \to B$ and $\beta: B \to A$ are such that $\alpha\beta = \epsilon_A$, we say that β is a *right inverse* of α and that α is a *left inverse* of β. The following theorem gives conditions under which a mapping has a right or a left inverse.

1.11 Theorem. *Let $\alpha: A \to B$ be a given mapping. Then each of the following is true:*

  (i)   *The mapping α has a right inverse if and only if it is a one-one mapping.*

  (ii) *The mapping α has a left inverse if and only if it is an onto mapping.*

  (iii) *If α has a right inverse $\beta: B \to A$ and a left inverse $\gamma: B \to A$, then $\beta = \gamma$.*

Proof of (i): Suppose, first, that $\beta: B \to A$ is a right inverse of α, so that $\alpha\beta = \epsilon_A$. For each $a \in A$, we have that

$$(a\alpha)\beta = a(\alpha\beta) = a\,\epsilon_A = a.$$

Hence, if a_1, a_2, $\in A$ such that $a_1\alpha = a_2\alpha$, it follows that $(a_1\alpha)\beta = (a_2\alpha)\beta$, and thus that $a_1 = a_2$. This shows that α is a one-one mapping.

Conversely, let us assume that α is a one-one mapping, and define a mapping $\beta\colon B \to A$ such that $\alpha\beta = \epsilon_A$. Now $A\alpha$ may well be a proper subset of B, but for each $b \in A\alpha$, the fact that α is one-one assures us that there is exactly *one* element a of A such that $b = a\alpha$. If $b \in A\alpha$, we define $b\beta = a$, where $b = a\alpha$. For each $b \in B$ with b not in $A\alpha$, we choose a fixed element a_1 of A and define $b\beta = a_1$. Then β is defined on all of B and for $a \in A$, we have $a(\alpha\beta) = (a\alpha)\beta = a$. That is, $\alpha\beta = \epsilon_A$ and β is a right inverse of α.

Proof of (ii): Suppose that α has a left inverse $\gamma\colon B \to A$, so that $\gamma\alpha = \epsilon_B$. Then for each $b \in B$, we see that $(b\gamma)\alpha = b(\gamma\alpha) = b$, and clearly α is an onto mapping.

Conversely, let us assume that $\alpha\colon A \to B$ is an onto mapping. For each $b \in B$, choose * one element a of A such that $a\alpha = b$ and define $b\gamma = a$. This defines a mapping $\gamma\colon B \to A$ and clearly $b(\gamma\alpha) = (b\gamma)\alpha = b$ for each $b \in B$. Thus, $\gamma\alpha = \epsilon_B$, and γ is indeed a left inverse of α.

Proof of (iii): Under our assumptions, we have that $\alpha\beta = \epsilon_A$ and that $\gamma\alpha = \epsilon_B$. The reader is asked to justify each step in the following proof of the desired result:

$$\beta = \epsilon_B\beta = (\gamma\alpha)\beta = \gamma(\alpha\beta) = \gamma\epsilon_A = \gamma.$$

If there exists a mapping $\delta\colon B \to A$ which is both a right inverse and a left inverse of the mapping $\alpha\colon A \to B$, δ is said to be an *inverse* of α. A special case of part (iii) of the preceding theorem, applied to the situation in which both β and γ are inverses of α, shows that if a mapping has an inverse, it is *unique*. The unique inverse (if it exists) of a mapping α is usually denoted by α^{-1}. In view of the theorem, we see that a mapping $\alpha\colon A \to B$ has an inverse if and only if it is a one-one and onto mapping. It is clear that if $\alpha\colon A \to B$ is a one-one mapping of A onto B, then $\alpha^{-1}\colon B \to A$ is a one-one mapping of B onto A. The simple relationship between the mappings α and α^{-1} may possibly be suggested by the diagram of Figure 5. The reader should carefully observe that the mapping α^{-1}, as here defined, exists if and only if α is a one-one mapping of A onto B, since in any mapping of B into A *every* element of B must have exactly *one* image in A.

---

* The possibility of making such a choice of one element from each of a possibly infinite number of sets involves an interesting and profound assumption called the "Axiom of Choice". We here simply assume that this is permissible. Discussions of this axiom may be found, for example, in Wilder [51], Kurosh [10] and Birkhoff [45] as listed in the bibliography at the end of this book.

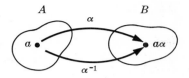

Figure 5

Clearly, a one-one mapping of A onto B may be thought of as a pairing of the elements of A and the elements of B. In view of the mutual relationship between A and B, a one-one mapping of A onto B (or of B onto A) is sometimes called a *one-to-one correspondence between A and B*.

EXERCISES

1. Given mappings $\alpha\colon A \to B$ and $\beta\colon B \to C$, prove each of the following:

    (i) If both α and β are one-one mappings, then $\alpha\beta$ is a one-one mapping.

    (ii) If both α and β are onto mappings, then $\alpha\beta$ is an onto mapping.

    (iii) If $\alpha\beta$ is a one-one mapping, then α is a one-one mapping.

    (iv) If $\alpha\beta$ is an onto mapping, then β is an onto mapping.

2. Suppose that $\alpha\beta$ is defined. If α has a right inverse α_1 and β has a right inverse β_1, prove that $\alpha\beta$ has $\beta_1\alpha_1$ as a right inverse.

3. Suppose that $\alpha\beta$ is defined. If α has a left inverse α_2 and β has a left inverse β_2, prove that $\beta_2\alpha_2$ is a left inverse of $\alpha\beta$.

4. If $\alpha\beta$ is defined, and α has the inverse α^{-1}, and β has the inverse β^{-1}, prove that $\beta^{-1}\alpha^{-1}$ is defined and is the inverse of $\alpha\beta$.

5. Let $A = \{1, 2, 3\}$, and define mappings $\alpha\colon A \to A$ and $\beta\colon A \to A$ as follows:

$$1\alpha = 2, \quad 2\alpha = 1, \quad 3\alpha = 3,$$
$$1\beta = 2, \quad 2\beta = 3, \quad 3\beta = 1.$$

Compute each of the following mappings of A into A: $\alpha\beta$, $\beta\alpha$, α^{-1}, β^{-1}, and $(\alpha\beta)^{-1}$. Verify that

$$(\alpha\beta)^{-1} = \beta^{-1}\alpha^{-1} \neq \alpha^{-1}\beta^{-1}.$$

1.4   EQUIVALENCE RELATIONS

The concept of an equivalence relation, to be defined presently, plays a very important role in modern algebra. Accordingly, we present it in this preliminary chapter even though we shall not have need of it until the last section of Chapter 4. Before giving the definition, let us briefly explain what we mean by a relation.

If $\mathbf{Z}$ is the set of all integers, and $i < j$ has the usual meaning for $i, j \in \mathbf{Z}$, then "$<$" is an example of a relation defined on $\mathbf{Z}$. This statement only means that for every ordered pair (i, j) of elements of $\mathbf{Z}$, $i < j$ is either true or false. With the usual meanings of these symbols, "$\leq$" and "$=$" are other relations defined on $\mathbf{Z}$.

In general, let A be a given set. We say that a *relation* "$\sim$" is defined on A if for each ordered pair (a, b) of elements of A, a $\sim b$ is either true or false. We may write $a \nsim b$ to indicate that $a \sim b$ is false.* For the present, we are not concerned with relations in general but only with those relations which have the particular properties stated in the following definition.

1.12   Definition.   A relation "$\sim$" defined on a set A is called an *equivalence relation* if it has the following three properties, where a, b, and c are arbitrary elements of A:

(1) $a \sim a$ (*reflexive property*).
(2) If $a \sim b$, then $b \sim a$ (*symmetric property*).
(3) If $a \sim b$ and $b \sim c$, then $a \sim c$ (*transitive property*).

If "$\sim$" is an equivalence relation, we may find it convenient to read $a \sim b$ as "a is equivalent to b."

The relation "$<$" on the set $\mathbf{Z}$ of all integers is not an equivalence relation since it has neither the reflexive property nor the symmetric property. The relation "$\leq$" has the reflexive property and the transitive property, but not the symmetric property. Of course, "$=$" is an equivalence relation on $\mathbf{Z}$ (or on any other set), as is perhaps suggested by the word "equivalence."

We shall now give a few examples of equivalence relations, but many more will occur in later chapters of this book. Let T be the set of all triangles in a fixed plane, and let a and b be arbitrary elements of T. Then "$\sim$" is an equivalence relation on T if we agree to define "$\sim$" in any one of the following ways:

---

* Given a relation "$\sim$" on a set A, we may associate with it the uniquely determined subset T of the Cartesian product $A \times A$ consisting of all ordered pairs (a, b) such that $a \sim b$. Conversely, given a subset T of $A \times A$, we may use it to define a relation "$\sim$" on A by agreeing that $a \sim b$ if and only if the ordered pair (a, b) is an element of T. Thus a relation on a set A is uniquely associated with a subset of $A \times A$. For this reason, a relation on a set A is frequently *defined* to be simply a subset of $A \times A$.

(i) $a \sim b$ to mean "a is congruent to b,"
(ii) $a \sim b$ to mean "a is similar to b,"
(iii) $a \sim b$ to mean "a has same area as b,"
(iv) $a \sim b$ to mean "a has the same perimeter as b."

As another example of an equivalence relation, let $\mathbf{Z}$ be the set of all integers, and let us define $a \equiv b$ to mean that $a - b$ has 3 as a factor; that is, that there exists an integer n such that $a - b = 3n$. It is then readily verified that "$\equiv$" has the three defining properties of an equivalence relation. Furthermore, every integer is equivalent to one of the three integers 0, 1, 2. In this connection, consider the following three subsets of $\mathbf{Z}$:

$$J = \{\cdots, -9, -6, -3, 0, 3, 6, 9, \cdots\},$$
$$K = \{\cdots, -8, -5, -2, 1, 4, 7, 10, \cdots\},$$
$$L = \{\cdots, -7, -4, -1, 2, 5, 8, 11, \cdots\}.$$

It will be observed that every integer is in exactly one of these subsets. In other words, the union of these three subsets is $\mathbf{Z}$ and the intersection of any two of them is the empty set. Moreover, J can be characterized as the set of all elements of $\mathbf{Z}$ that are equivalent to 0 (or to any other element of J), and similar characterizations can be given for K and L. The sets J, K, and L are examples of a concept which we proceed to define.

1.13   Definition.   Let A be a set and "$\sim$" an equivalence relation defined on A. If $a \in A$, the subset of A which consists of all elements x of A, such that $x \sim a$ is called an *equivalence set*. This equivalence set will frequently be denoted by $[a]$.

This definition of the equivalence set $[a]$ can be written formally as follows:

1.14 $$[a] = \{x \mid x \in A, x \sim a\}.$$

In the above example, note that $J = [0]$, $K = [1]$, and $L = [2]$; also that $[0] = [3] = [6]$, and so on. Hence there are just the three different equivalence sets.

To return to the general definition, let us consider a few properties of equivalence sets. First, since $a \sim a$ by the reflexive property of an equivalence relation, we always have $a \in [a]$; that is, $[a]$ is the equivalence set which contains a. This shows that every element of A is in at least one equivalence set. Other important properties of equivalence sets are the following, where a and b are elements of the set A:

1.15
    (i) $[a] = [b]$ if and only if $a \sim b$,
    (ii) If $[a] \cap [b] \neq \varnothing$, then $[a] = [b]$.

As a first step in proving 1.15(i), let us assume that $[a] = [b]$ and show that $a \sim b$. It has been pointed out that $a \in [a]$, and hence we have $a \in [b]$. By definition of the equivalence set $[b]$, it follows that $a \sim b$, as we wished to show. Conversely, let us now assume that $a \sim b$. If $x \in [a]$, then $x \sim a$ by definition of $[a]$. Now we have $x \sim a$ and $a \sim b$, so the transitive property of an equivalence relation assures us that $x \sim b$. This then implies that $x \in [b]$, and we have therefore proved that $[a] \subseteq [b]$. We leave as an exercise the similar proof that $[b] \subseteq [a]$, from which we conclude that $[a] = [b]$, as desired.

We now prove 1.15(ii). Since $[a] \cap [b] \neq \varnothing$, there exists at least one element s of A such that $s \in [a]$ and also $s \in [b]$. It follows that $s \sim a$ and $s \sim b$. (Why?) By the symmetric property of an equivalence relation, we have $a \sim s$. Since $a \sim s$ and $s \sim b$, the transitive property assures us that $a \sim b$. The fact that $[a] = [b]$ then follows at once from 1.15(i).

A collection of subsets of a set A is often called a *partition* of A if A is the union of these subsets and any two of the subsets have empty intersection. In view of 1.15(ii), together with the fact that every element of A is in some equivalence set, we see that the different equivalence sets relative to an equivalence relation defined on A form a partition of A. Conversely, it may be verified that a given partition of A determines an equivalence relation on A if we *define* elements in the same subset to be equivalent.

1.5   OPERATIONS

There is just one other term that we wish to introduce in this preliminary chapter. First, we consider a familiar concept as follows. Let $\mathbf{Z}$ be the set of all integers. Associated with each ordered pair (i, j) of elements of $\mathbf{Z}$ there is a uniquely determined element $i + j$ of $\mathbf{Z}$. Accordingly, we say that addition, denoted by "$+$," is an operation on $\mathbf{Z}$. More precisely, we may call it a *binary* operation to emphasize that it is defined for each ordered *pair* of elements of $\mathbf{Z}$. The general definition is as follows.

1.16   **Definition.***   Let A be a given set. A *binary operation* "$\circ$" on A is a correspondence that associates with each ordered pair (a, b) of elements of A a uniquely determined element $a \circ b$ of A.

---

* Expressed more formally, this definition merely asserts that a binary operation "$\circ$" on A is a mapping of $A \times A$ into A. The image of an element (a, b) of $A \times A$ under this mapping is then denoted by $a \circ b$.

Later on we shall seldom have occasion to use any unfamiliar symbol to denote an operation. For the most part, we shall find it convenient to call an operation "addition" or "multiplication," and to use the familiar notations, $a + b$ and $a \cdot b$ (or simply ab). However, for the moment we continue to use the symbol "∘" for a binary operation on a set A. We may emphasize that saying that "∘" is a binary operation on A asserts that $a \circ b$ is a uniquely determined element of A for *every* $a \in A$ and *every* $b \in A$. Some important concepts are introduced in the following definition.

1.17 Definition. Let "∘" be a binary operation defined on the set A. Then

(i) The operation "∘" is said to be a *commutative* operation, if and only if $a \circ b = b \circ a$ for all $a, b \in A$.

(ii) The operation "∘" is said to be an *associative* operation if and only if $(a \circ b) \circ c = a \circ (b \circ c)$ for all $a, b, c \in A$.

(iii) An element e of A is said to be an *identity* for the operation "∘" if and only if $a \circ e = e \circ a = a$ for every $a \in A$.

As examples of these concepts, let us again consider the set $\mathbf{Z}$ of all integers. For the present, we assume as known the familiar properties of addition and multiplication on $\mathbf{Z}$; in particular, that they are both commutative and associative. Moreover, since $a + 0 = 0 + a = a$ for every $a \in \mathbf{Z}$, we see that 0 is the identity for addition; and clearly 1 is the identity for multiplication.

On the same set $\mathbf{Z}$, let us define $a \circ b = a - b$. Since $3 \circ 2 = 1$ and $2 \circ 3 = -1$, we see that this operation is not commutative. Note that just *one* instance in which $a \circ b \neq b \circ a$ implies that the operation is not commutative. The reader may verify that neither is this operation associative. Does there exist an identity for this operation? Since $a \circ 0 = a - 0 = a$ for every integer a, it might appear at first glance that 0 is an identity. However, $0 \circ a = -a$ and the definition of an identity is not met.

EXERCISES

1. If "∼" is an equivalence relation on a set A, carefully prove each of the following:

(i) If $a, b \in A$ such that $a \not\sim b$, then $[a] \cap [b] = \varnothing$.

(ii) If $a, b, c, d \in A$ such that $c \in [a]$, $d \in [b]$ and $[a] \neq [b]$, then $c \not\sim d$.

2. If a and b are integers, let us define $a \equiv b$ to mean that $a - b$ has 5 as a factor. Verify that "$\equiv$" is an equivalence relation on the set $\mathbf{Z}$ of all integers, and exhibit all the different equivalence sets.

3. If $A = \{x, y\}$ and we define $x \sim x$, $x \nsim y$, $y \nsim x$, $y \nsim y$, verify that the relation "$\sim$" has exactly two of the three defining properties of an equivalence relation.

4. Find an example of a relation on some set which is reflexive and symmetric, but not transitive.

5. In each of the following, "$\circ$" is the specified binary operation on the set $\mathbf{Z}$ of integers. Determine in each case whether the operation is commutative, whether it is associative, and whether there is an identity for the operation.

    (i) $a \circ b = b$,

    (ii) $a \circ b = a + b + ab$,

    (iii) $a \circ b$ is the larger of a and b,

    (iv) $a \circ b = 2a + 2b$,

    (v) $a \circ b = a + b - 1$,

    (vi) $a \circ b = a + ab$.

RINGS

In this chapter we shall introduce the important class of algebraic systems that are called *rings*, give a large number of examples, and then establish some fundamental properties of any ring. All the properties that are used to define a ring are suggested by simple properties of the integers, and we begin by pointing out some of these properties. The following section is therefore of a preliminary nature and is merely intended to furnish a partial motivation of the material to follow.

This chapter is merely an introduction to the theory of rings. Additional material on this subject will be presented in later chapters.

2.1 FORMAL PROPERTIES OF THE INTEGERS

The simplest numbers are the numbers 1, 2, 3, $\cdots$, used in counting. These are called the "natural numbers" or the "positive integers." Addition and multiplication of natural numbers have simple interpretations if we consider a natural number as indicating the number of elements in a set. For example, suppose that we have two piles of stones, the first one containing m stones and the second one n stones. If the stones of the first pile are placed on the second pile, there results a pile of $n + m$ stones. If, instead, the stones of the second pile are placed on the first pile, we get a pile of $m + n$ stones. It thus seems quite obvious that

$$m + n = n + m$$

for every choice of m and n as natural numbers, that is, that addition of natural numbers is commutative. This property of the natural numbers is an example of what is sometimes called a *law* or a *formal property*. Another example is the associative law of addition.

Multiplication of natural numbers may be introduced as follows. If one has m piles, each of which contains n stones, and all the stones are placed in one pile, the resulting pile will contain mn stones. It is also a familiar fact that multiplication of natural numbers is both commutative and associative. Moreover, addition and multiplication are such that the so-called *distributive law* holds:

$$m(n + k) = mn + mk,$$

where m, n, and k are arbitrary natural numbers.

Historically, the natural numbers were no doubt used for centuries before there was any consideration of their formal properties. However, in modern algebra it is precisely such formal properties that are of central interest. Some of the reasons for this changed viewpoint will become evident later on in this chapter as well as in succeeding chapters.

Of course, if m and n are natural numbers, there need not be a natural number x such that $m + x = n$. In order to be able to solve all equations of this kind, we need to have available the negative integers and zero along with the positive integers. The properties with which we shall be concerned in the next section are suggested by well-known properties of the system of *all* the integers (positive, negative, and zero). Near the end of the next chapter we shall be ready to give what may be called a characterization of the system of all integers although, for the most part, we shall merely assume a familiarity with the simpler properties of this system. In later chapters, the other number systems of elementary algebra will be discussed in some detail. However, even before they are presented in a logical way we shall not hesitate to illustrate parts of our general theory by examples from these familiar number systems.

2.2 DEFINITION OF A RING

The concepts to be presented in this section are of fundamental importance, although a full realization of their generality will probably not become apparent until the examples of the following section are carefully studied.

We begin with a nonempty set R on which there are defined two binary operations, which we shall call "addition" and "multiplication," and for which we shall use the familiar notation. Accordingly, if a, $b \in R$, then $a + b$ and ab (or $a \cdot b$) are uniquely determined elements of the set R. We now assume the following properties or laws, in which a, b, and c are arbitrary elements, distinct or identical, of R.

P₁: $a + b = b + a$ (*commutative law of addition*).

P₂: $(a + b) + c = a + (b + c)$ (*associative law of addition*).

P₃: There exists an element 0 of R such that $a + 0 = a$ for every element a of R (*existence of a zero*).

P₄: If $a \in R$, there exists $x \in R$ such that $a + x = 0$ (*existence of additive inverses*).

P₅: $(ab)c = a(bc)$ (*associative law of multiplication*).

P₆: $a(b + c) = ab + ac, \ (b + c)a = ba + ca$ (*distributive laws*).

Under all these conditions R is said to be a *ring*. Let us repeat this definition in the following formal way.

2.1   **Definition.**   If R is a nonempty set on which there are defined binary operations of addition and multiplication such that Properties P₁–P₆ hold, we say that R is a *ring* (with respect to these definitions of addition and multiplication).

Let us make a few remarks about the defining properties of a ring. First, we may emphasize that we should not think of the elements of a ring as necessarily being *numbers*. Moreover, addition and multiplication are not assumed to have any properties other than those specified. The element "0", whose existence is asserted in P₃, and which we call a *zero*, is actually an identity for the operation of addition since, by P₁, $0 + a = a + 0$ and therefore we also have $0 + a = a$. We do not assume that there is only *one* identity for addition, but later on we shall prove this to be true. Again, we should not think of 0 as being the familiar *number* zero, it is merely an identity for the operation of addition. Finally, we point out that P₄ does not assert that there is only *one* $x \in R$ such that $a + x = 0$, but this fact will also be proved eventually.

All the properties used to define a ring are certainly familiar properties of the integers. Hence, with the usual definitions of addition and multiplication, the set of all integers is a ring. Henceforth, this ring will be denoted by **Z**. For this ring, the zero whose existence is asserted in P₃ is the familiar number zero.

Now let E be the set of all *even* integers (positive, negative, and zero). Using, of course, addition and multiplication as already defined in **Z**, we see that the sum of two elements of E is an element of E, and similarly for the product of two elements. Hence, the operations of addition and multiplication, originally defined on the larger set **Z**, are also operations *on the set E*. This fact is often expressed by saying that E is *closed* under these operations. It is easy to verify that E is itself a ring.

If all elements of a ring S are contained in a ring R, it is natural to call S a *subring* of R. It is understood that addition and multiplication of elements of S are to coincide with addition and multiplication of these elements considered as elements of the larger ring R. Naturally, a set S of elements of R cannot possibly be a subring of R unless S is closed under the operations of addition and multiplication on R since, otherwise, we would not have operations *on the set S*. We see that E, as defined above, is a subring of the ring $\mathbf{Z}$. However, the set of all odd integers cannot be a subring of $\mathbf{Z}$ since this set is not closed under addition; that is, the sum of two odd integers is not always (in fact, is never) an odd integer.

It is important to observe that the definition of a ring does not require that the operation of multiplication be commutative. However, we shall frequently want to consider this property, so let us give it a number as follows:

P_7: If $a, b \in R$, then $ab = ba$ \qquad (*commutative law of multiplication*).

A ring which has property P_7 is called a *commutative* ring. If P_7 does not hold, that is, if there exist at least two elements c and d of R such that $cd \neq dc$, then R is said to be a *noncommutative* ring.

We may also point out that in a ring there need not be an identity for the operation of multiplication. If in a ring R there exists an identity for multiplication, we shall usually call it a *unity* of R and say that R is a *ring with unity*. For convenience of reference, let us give this property a number as follows:

P_8: There exists an element e of R such that $ea = ae = a$ for every element a of R \qquad (*existence of a unity*).

We may emphasize that a ring need not have either of the properties P_7 or P_8. However, many of the rings that we shall study in detail will have both of these properties. The ring $\mathbf{Z}$ is an example of a commutative ring with unity, whereas the ring E of all even integers is a commutative ring without a unity. A few cases of noncommutative rings will occur among the examples of the next section. Naturally, they will have to be quite different from the familiar number systems.

2.3 EXAMPLES OF RINGS

In order to give an example of a ring R, it is necessary to specify the elements of R and to define the operations of addition and multiplication on R so that Properties P_1–P_6 hold. The ring $\mathbf{Z}$ of integers has been mentioned as a well-known example of a ring. Other examples are the ring of all real numbers and the ring of all complex numbers, with the usual definitions of addition and multiplication. It will be recalled that the *rational numbers* are those numbers which can be expressed in the form m/n, where m and n are integers with $n \neq 0$. With respect to the familiar definitions of addition and multiplication of rational numbers, the set of all rational numbers is also a ring. Clearly, the ring $\mathbf{Z}$ is a subring of the ring of all rational numbers; the ring of all rational numbers is a subring of the ring of all real numbers; and the ring of all real numbers is a subring of the ring of all complex numbers. All these number systems will be considered in detail in later chapters.

We proceed to give some other, less familiar, examples of rings. For the most part, we shall not write out the verifications of the Properties P_1–P_6. Some of these verifications will be required in the next list of exercises. The purpose of these examples is to clarify the concept of a ring and to show that there are rings of many different kinds.

EXAMPLE 1. Let S be the set of all real numbers of the form $x + y\sqrt{2}$, where $x, y \in \mathbf{Z}$, with addition and multiplication defined in the usual way. It may be verified that S is closed under these operations. Actually, S is a commutative ring with unity. Of course, it is a subring of the ring of all real numbers.

EXAMPLE 2. Let T be the set of all real numbers of the form $u + v\sqrt[3]{2} + w\sqrt[3]{4}$, where u, v, and w are rational numbers. Using the usual definitions of addition and multiplication, T is a commutative ring with unity.

EXAMPLE 3. Let $R = \{u, v, w, x\}$; that is, R consists of just these four elements. We define addition and multiplication in R by means of the following tables.

$(+)$	u	v	w	x
u	u	v	w	x
v	v	u	x	w
w	w	x	u	v
x	x	w	v	u

$(\cdot)$	u	v	w	x
u	u	u	u	u
v	u	v	w	x
w	u	w	w	u
x	u	x	u	x

These we read as follows. For example, we find $v + x$ by looking in the addition table at the intersection of the row which contains v as its left-hand element and the column which contains x at the top. Since w appears in this position, we have $v + x = w$. Other examples are: $w + w = u$, $x + w = v$, $vw = w$, $xx = x$. It would take too much calculation to verify the associative laws and the distributive laws, and we shall now merely state that they do hold. From the addition table, it is seen that the zero of the ring R is the element u; and from the multiplication table it follows that v is the unity. The reader may verify that this is a commutative ring. This ring R differs from previous examples in that it has only a finite number (four) of elements.

EXAMPLE 4.   Let C be the set of all functions which are continuous on the closed interval $0 \leq x \leq 1$, with the usual definitions of addition and multiplication of functions. Since a sum or product of two continuous functions is a continuous function, C is closed under these operations. It can be shown that C is a ring. What is the zero of C? Does it have a unity?

EXAMPLE 5.   The set $T = \{0\,,\,e\}$ is a ring of two elements if addition and multiplication are defined by the following tables.

$(+)$	0	e		$(\cdot)$	0	e
0	0	e		0	0	0
e	e	0		e	0	e

Clearly, 0 is the zero of this ring and e is the unity. Hence, this ring has *only* a zero and a unity.

EXAMPLE 6.   Let $K = \{a, b, c, d\}$ with addition and multiplication defined by the following tables.

$(+)$	a	b	c	d		$(\cdot)$	a	b	c	d
a	a	b	c	d		a	a	a	a	a
b	b	a	d	c		b	a	b	c	d
c	c	d	a	b		c	a	a	a	a
d	d	c	b	a		d	a	b	c	d

The ring K is our first example of a noncommutative ring. From the multiplication table we see, for example, that $cd = a$, whereas $dc = c$. Does this ring have a unity? What is the zero?

We may emphasize that in this example, as in others in which addition and multiplication of more than two elements are defined by tables, it would be exceedingly tedious to verify the associative and distributive laws. Of course, the tables have not been written down at random but have been obtained by methods not yet available to the student. At present, the associative and distributive laws will have to be taken on faith but there is no real difficulty in verifying the other defining properties of a ring.

EXAMPLE 7.   For later reference, we give still another example of a ring with four elements a, b, c, and d. In this case, we define addition and multiplication as follows:

(+)	a	b	c	d
a	a	b	c	d
b	b	a	d	c
c	c	d	a	b
d	d	c	b	a

(·)	a	b	c	d
a	a	a	a	a
b	a	b	c	d
c	a	c	d	b
d	a	d	b	c

It will be observed that the addition table coincides with the addition table of the preceding example. However, the multiplication table is quite different. This ring is another example of a commutative ring.

EXAMPLE 8. Let L be the set $\mathbf{Z} \times \mathbf{Z} \times \mathbf{Z}$. That is, L is the set of all ordered triples (a, b, c), where $a, b, c \in \mathbf{Z}$. We make the following definitions:

$$(a, b, c) + (d, e, f) = (a + d, b + e, c + f),$$
$$(a, b, c)(d, e, f) = (ad, bd + ce, cf).$$

To avoid any possible confusion, we may again state that we consider two elements of a set to be equal only if they are identical. Hence, if (a, b, c) and (d, e, f) are elements of L, then $(a, b, c) = (d, e, f)$ means that $a = d$, $b = e$, and $c = f$.

It is easy to verify that $(0, 0, 0)$ is the zero of the ring L, and that $(1, 0, 1)$ is a unity. This is another noncommutative ring since, for example,

$$(0, 1, 0)(1, 0, 0) = (0, 1, 0),$$

whereas

$$(1, 0, 0)(0, 1, 0) = (0, 0, 0).$$

Let us verify one of the distributive laws for this ring. If (a, b, c), (d, e, f), and (g, h, i) are elements of L, let us show that

$$(a, b, c)((d, e, f) + (g, h, i)) = (a, b, c)(d, e, f) + (a, b, c)(g, h, i).$$

The equality of these expressions is a consequence of the following simple calculations:

$$(a, b, c)((d, e, f) + (g, h, i)) = (a, b, c)(d + g, e + h, f + i)$$
$$= (a(d + g), b(d + g) + c(e + h), c(f + i)),$$

and

$$(a, b, c)(d, e, f) + (a, b, c)(g, h, i)$$
$$= (ad, bd + ce, cf) + (ag, bg + ch, ci)$$
$$= (ad + ag, (bd + ce) + (bg + ch), cf + ci).$$

The right sides of these equations are equal in view of certain simple properties of the integers. What properties are involved?

EXAMPLE 9.   Let W be the set of all symbols of the form

$$\begin{bmatrix} a & b \\ c & d \end{bmatrix},$$

where a, b, c, and d are arbitrary elements of **Z**. Our definitions of addition and multiplication are as follows:

$$\begin{bmatrix} a & b \\ c & d \end{bmatrix} + \begin{bmatrix} e & f \\ g & h \end{bmatrix} = \begin{bmatrix} a+e & b+f \\ c+g & d+h \end{bmatrix},$$

$$\begin{bmatrix} a & b \\ c & d \end{bmatrix} \cdot \begin{bmatrix} e & f \\ g & h \end{bmatrix} = \begin{bmatrix} ae+bg & af+bh \\ ce+dg & cf+dh \end{bmatrix}.$$

With respect to these definitions of addition and multiplication, W is a ring. It is called the *ring of all matrices of order two over the integers*. The reader may verify, by examples, that the commutative law of multiplication does not hold and hence that W is a noncommutative ring.

We may point out that the elements of W are quadruples of elements of **Z**, and could just as well have been written in the form (a, b, c, d). However, the above notation is more convenient and is the traditional one.

If we modify this example by letting a, b, c, and d be rational (or real, or complex) numbers instead of integers, we obtain *the ring of all matrices of order two over the rational (or real or complex) numbers*. More general matrices will be considered in a later chapter.

EXAMPLE 10.   This final example is of a type quite different from any of the previous examples. Let A be a given set, and let R be the set of *all* subsets of A, including the empty set and the entire set A. We shall now denote elements of R by lower-case letters— even though they are sets of elements of A.

Our definitions of addition and multiplication are as follows. If $a, b \in R$, $a + b$ is the set of all elements of A that are in subset a or in subset b, *but not in both*. Also, we define $ab = a \cap b$, the intersection of a and b; in other words, it is the set of elements in both a and b. We may observe that $a + b$ is not, in general, the union of the sets a and b, but it will be this union whenever $a \cap b$ is the empty set. In the Venn diagram shown in Figure 6, region 1 represents those elements of A which are in neither subset a nor subset b, region 2, those elements of A which are in a but not in b, and so on. Hence ab is represented by region 4 and $a + b$ by regions 2 and 3.

We now assert that with the above definitions of addition and multiplication, R is a commutative ring with unity.

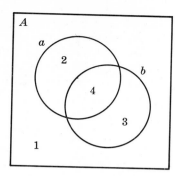

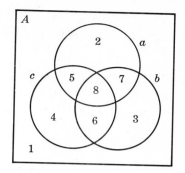

Figure 6

Figure 7

The commutative laws of addition and multiplication are obvious, as is also the associative law of multiplication. Let us briefly consider the associative law of addition, and let a, b, and c be arbitrary elements of R. In Figure 7, $a + b$ is represented by regions 2, 3, 5, and 6. Since c is made up of regions 4, 5, 6, and 8, it follows that $(a + b) + c$ is represented by regions 2, 3, 4, and 8. This pictorial representation suggests that $(a + b) + c$ consists of those elements of A which are in exactly one of the subsets a, b, and c; together with those which are in all three. To complete the verification of the associative law of addition by means of Venn diagrams, we need to characterize the set $a + (b + c)$. We omit the details, but it is not difficult to verify that we again get the set represented by regions 2, 3, 4, and 8. Hence, $(a + b) + c = a + (b + c)$, as we wished to show. In an exercise below the reader is asked to consider how one could turn this geometrical argument into a formal proof.

If we denote the empty set by "0," it follows that $a + 0 = a$, and the empty set is the zero of the ring R. Moreover, the subset of A consisting of A itself is the unity of the ring. (Why?) If $a \in R$, it is interesting to observe that $a + a = 0$, and thus a is its own additive inverse. Another unusual property of this ring is that $a \cdot a = a$ for every element a of R. We shall refer to this ring as the *ring of all subsets of the set A*.

We conclude this section not by giving still another example of a ring but by presenting a simple, but quite useful, way to construct new rings from given rings. Suppose that R and S are rings, distinct or identical, and let us consider the Cartesian product $R \times S$ whose elements are the ordered pairs (r, s), $r \in R$, $s \in S$. On this set $R \times S$, we define addition and multiplication as follows:

$$(r_1, s_1) + (r_2, s_2) = (r_1 + r_2, s_1 + s_2),$$
$$(r_1, s_1)(r_2, s_2) = (r_1 r_2, s_1 s_2).$$

It is understood, of course, that r_1, $r_2 \in R$ and that s_1, $s_2 \in S$. Moreover, although the same symbol for addition is used in both rings,

$r_1 + r_2$ is the sum of r_1 and r_2 in the ring R, and $s_1 + s_2$ is the sum of s_1 and s_2 in the ring S (and similarly for products). We leave as an exercise the proof that with respect to the above definitions the set $R \times S$ becomes a ring. In spite of the "product" notation for the set, this ring is usually called the *direct sum* of the rings R and S, and frequently denoted by $R \oplus S$. What conditions on R and S will assure us that $R \oplus S$ is commutative? That it has a unity?

EXERCISES

In these exercises, it is to be assumed that the real numbers (in particular, the rational numbers and the integers) have all the familiar properties which are freely used in elementary algebra.

1.   Which of the following are rings with respect to the usual definitions of addition and multiplication? In this exercise, the ring of all even integers is denoted by E.

   (a)   The set of all positive integers.

   (b)   The set of all integers (positive, negative, and zero) that are divisible by 3.

   (c)   The set of all real numbers of the form $x + y\sqrt{2}$, where $x, y \in E$.

   (d)   The set of all real numbers of the form $x + y\sqrt[3]{2}$, where $x, y \in \mathbf{Z}$.

   (e)   The set of all real numbers of the form $x + y\sqrt[3]{2} + z\sqrt[3]{4}$, where $x, y, z \in \mathbf{Z}$.

   (f)   The set of all real numbers of the form $x + y\sqrt{3}$, where $x \in E$ and $y \in \mathbf{Z}$.

   (g)   The set of all rational numbers that can be expressed in the form m/n where $m \in \mathbf{Z}$ and n is a positive odd integer.

2.   What is the additive inverse of each element of the ring R of Example 3?

3.   Verify that the subset $S = \{u, w\}$ of the ring R of Example 3 is a subring of R. Show that, except for the notation employed, this is the ring of Example 5.

4.   For the ring R of Example 3, use the tables to verify each of the following:

$$(u + v) + w = u + (v + w),$$
$$(v + w) + x = v + (w + x),$$
$$w(v + x) = wv + wx,$$
$$(w + v)x = wx + vx,$$
$$(xv)w = x(vw).$$

5. For the ring L of Example 8, verify the other distributive law and the associative law of multiplication.

6. For the ring W of Example 9, verify the associative law of multiplication and the distributive laws. What is the zero of this ring? Verify that

$$\begin{bmatrix} 1 & 0 \\ 0 & 1 \end{bmatrix}$$

   is a unity of W. Give examples to show that W is a noncommutative ring.

7. For the ring R of Example 10, consider how a formal proof of the associative law of addition could be given without use of Venn diagrams, and write out at least a part of the proof.

8. For the ring R of Example 10, use Venn diagrams to verify that if $a, b, c \in R$, then $a(b + c) = ab + ac$. How do you know without further calculation that the other distributive law must also hold?

9. Using the notation for complements as in Exercise 6 of Section 1.1, show that the addition used in Example 10 could have been defined as follows: $a + b = (a \cap b)' \cap (a \cup b)$.

10. In Example 10, why would we not obtain a ring if we were to define $ab = a \cap b$ and $a + b = a \cup b$?

11. On the set $S = \mathbf{Z} \times \mathbf{Z}$, let us define addition and multiplication as follows:

$$(a, b) + (c, d) = (a + c, b + d),$$
$$(a, b)(c, d) = (ac + 2bd, ad + bc).$$

   Prove that S is a commutative ring wiith unity.

12. It can be shown that the set $\{a, b, c, d\}$ is a ring if addition and multiplication are defined by the following tables.

(+)	a	b	c	d		(·)	a	b	c	d
a	a	b	c	d		a	a	a	a	a
b	b	c	d	a		b	a	c	a	c
c	c	d	a	b		c	a	a	a	a
d	d	a	b	c		d	a	c	a	c

Is this a commutative ring? Does it have a unity? What is the zero of this ring? What is the additive inverse of each element of this ring?

13. Show that neither of the following can possibly be the addition table for a ring consisting of the set $\{a, b, c, d\}$ of four elements.

(+)	a	b	c	d
a	a	b	c	a
b	b	c	d	a
c	c	d	a	b
d	a	a	b	c

(+)	a	b	c	d
a	a	b	c	d
b	b	c	a	d
c	c	a	d	b
d	b	c	d	a

14. Define addition of integers in the usual way, but define the "product" of any two integers to be zero. Is the set of all integers a ring with respect to addition and this new "multiplication"?

15. If a and b are integers, let us define $a \oplus b$ to be ab, and $a \odot b$ to be $a + b$. Is the set of all integers a ring with respect to the operations "$\oplus$" of "addition" and "$\odot$" of "multiplication"?

16. A set $A = \{x\}$ with one element has just two subsets, and so the ring of all subsets of A, as defined in Example 10, is a ring with two elements. Make addition and multiplication tables for this ring, and compare it with the ring of Example 5.

17. Make addition and multiplication tables for the ring of all subsets of the set $A = \{1, 2\}$. Verify that by a proper choice of notation, this ring is the ring of Example 3.

18. The following is an addition table and part of the multiplication table for a ring with three elements. Make use of the distributive laws to fill in the rest of the multiplication table.

(+)	a	b	c
a	a	b	c
b	b	c	a
c	c	a	b

($\cdot$)	a	b	c
a	a	a	a
b	a	b	$-$
c	a	$-$	$-$

Is this a commutative ring? Does it have a unity?

19. Do the same as in the preceding exercise, using the following addition table and partial multiplication table for a ring with four elements.

$(+)$	a	b	c	d
a	a	b	c	d
b	b	a	d	c
c	c	d	a	b
d	d	c	b	a

$(\cdot)$	a	b	c	d
a	a	a	a	a
b	a	$-$	$-$	a
c	a	$-$	c	$-$
d	a	b	c	$-$

Is this a commutative ring? Does it have a unity?

20. If a and b are any integers let us give the following new definitions of "addition" and "multiplication," indicated respectively by "$\oplus$" and "$\odot$":

$$a \oplus b = a + b - 1, \quad a \odot b = a + b - ab.$$

Verify that with respect to these definitions of "addition" and "multiplication," the set of all integers is a commutative ring with unity. What is the zero of this ring?

21. If R and S are rings, give a detailed proof that the direct sum $R \oplus S$ is a ring.

22. (i) If the ring R has m elements and the ring S has n elements (m and n being positive integers), how many elements are there in the direct sum $R \oplus S$?

    (ii) Give an example of a commutative ring with 16 elements and an example of a noncommutative ring with 16 elements.

    (iii) Give an example of a ring with 32 elements which does not have a unity.

2.4 SOME PROPERTIES OF ADDITION

So far we have given the definition of a ring and have presented a number of examples of rings of many different kinds. It should by now be clear that when we think of an arbitrary ring we should not necessarily think of one of our familiar number systems. Accordingly, we cannot consider any properties of a ring as being obvious, except those actually used in the definition. In this section and the next we shall give proofs of a number of properties of any ring. In the present section, we consider only properties of addition, and hence will use in our proofs only the properties P_1–P_4.

First, let us prove the following result.

2.2 Theorem. *The zero of a ring R, whose existence is asserted by P_3, is unique.*

By this statement, we mean the following. If $0, 0' \in R$ such that for every element a of R,

$$a + 0 = a, \tag{1}$$

and also

$$a + 0' = a, \tag{2}$$

then $0 = 0'$. The proof is as follows. Since Equation (1) is true for every element a of R, we may replace a in this equation by $0'$. Hence, we have that

$$0' + 0 = 0'. \tag{3}$$

In like manner, it follows from Equation (2) that

$$0 + 0' = 0. \tag{4}$$

Since, by the commutative law of addition, $0' + 0 = 0 + 0'$, it follows from Equations (3) and (4) that $0 = 0'$, and the proof is complete.

In view of this result, we are justified in speaking of *the* zero of a ring. An element which is not the zero may naturally be called a *nonzero* element.

We next prove the following theorem.

2.3   Theorem.   (Cancellation Laws of Addition)

If a, b, and c are elements of a ring R, the following are true:

(*i*)   *If $a + c = b + c$, then $a = b$.*

(*ii*)   *If $c + a = c + b$, then $a = b$.*

We proceed to prove the first statement of this theorem. Let us therefore assume that

$$a + c = b + c. \tag{5}$$

By P_4, there exists an element t of R such that

$$c + t = 0. \tag{6}$$

Now it follows from Equation (5) that

$$(a + c) + t = (b + c) + t. \tag{7}$$

But

$$
\begin{aligned}
(a + c) + t &= a + (c + t) &&(\textit{assoc. law}),\\
&= a + 0 &&(\textit{Equation (6)},\\
&= a &&(\textit{definition of 0}).
\end{aligned}
$$

Similarly,

$$
\begin{aligned}
(b + c) + t &= b + (c + t)\\
&= b + 0 = b.
\end{aligned}
$$

From these calculations, and Equation (7), we see that $a = b$, as we wished to show.

In view of the commutative law of addition, part (ii) of the theorem follows at once from part (i), and we therefore omit the proof.

Although the definition of the zero requires that $a + 0 = a$ for *every* element a of a ring R, we can now observe that the zero of a ring is completely determined by any *one* element. By this statement, we mean that *if d is some one element of R and $d + z = d$, then we must have* $z = 0$. Of course, this fact is an immediate consequence of the preceding theorem. For $d + z = d$ and $d + 0 = d$ imply that $d + z = d + 0$, from which it follows that $z = 0$.

The next result is also an almost immediate consequence of the preceding theorem.

2.4 Corollary. *The additive inverse of an element a of a ring R, whose existence is asserted by Property P_4, is unique.*

To prove this statement, suppose that $a + x = 0$ and also that $a + y = 0$. Then $a + x = a + y$, and one of the cancellation laws of addition shows at once that $x = y$.

Since each element a of R has exactly one additive inverse, we shall find it convenient to denote this additive inverse by $-a$, and shall also often write $b + (-a)$ in the form $b - a$. It may be helpful to have in mind a verbal definition of $-a$ as follows, "$-a$ is the element of R which when added to a gives 0." That is, if $a + x = 0$ (or, equally well, $x + a = 0$), it follows that $x = -a$.

Since $a + (-a) = 0$, we see also that a is the additive inverse of $-a$, that is, that $-(-a) = a$. We have thus established the first of the following, where a, b, and c are arbitrary elements of a ring:

2.5
(i) $\qquad -(-a) = a,$
(ii) $\qquad -(a + b) = -a - b,$
(iii) $\qquad -(a - b) = -a + b,$
(iv) $\qquad (a - b) - c = a - (b + c).$

Let us next prove the second of these statements. Now $-(a +b)$ is, by definition, the additive inverse of $a + b$, and we proceed to verify as follows that also $-a - b$ is the additive inverse of $a + b$:

$$
\begin{aligned}
(a + b) + (-a - b) &= (a + b) + ((-a) + (-b)) & \text{(\textit{notation}),}\\
&= [(a + b) + (-a)] + (-b) & \text{(\textit{assoc. law}),}\\
&= [a + (b + (-a))] + (-b) & \text{(\textit{assoc. law}),}\\
&= [a + (-a + b)] + (-b) & \text{(\textit{comm. law}),}\\
&= [(a + (-a)) + b] + (-b) & \text{(\textit{assoc. law}),}\\
&= (0 + b) + (-b) & \text{(\textit{def. of} $-a$),}\\
&= b + (-b) & \text{(\textit{def. of} 0),}\\
&= 0 & \text{(\textit{def. of} $-b$).}
\end{aligned}
$$

We therefore see that both $-(a + b)$ and $-a - b$ are additive inverses of $a + b$. Hence, the uniqueness of the additive inverse implies that

$$-(a + b) = -a - b,$$

and the proof is complete. The proofs of the other two parts of 2.5 will be given as exercises in the next list of exercises.

The final theorem of this section is the following.

2.6   Theorem.   *If a and b are elements of a ring R, the equation $a + x = b$ has in R the unique solution $x = b - a$.*

It is easy to verify that $x = b - a$ *is* a solution. For

$$
\begin{aligned}
a + (b - a) &= a + (-a + b) & \text{(\textit{comm. law}),}\\
&= (a + (-a)) + b & \text{(\textit{assoc. law}),}\\
&= 0 + b = b.
\end{aligned}
$$

The *uniqueness* of the solution follows from one of the cancellation laws. For if we have $a + x = b$ and $a + y = b$, then $a + x = a + y$, and this implies that $x = y$.

2.5   SOME OTHER PROPERTIES OF A RING

In this section we shall establish some properties of a ring that involve multiplication only, and some that involve both addition and multiplication.

First, we prove the following result.

2.7   Theorem.   *A ring can have at most one unity.*

The proof is much like the proof of the uniqueness of the zero. Suppose that e, $e' \in R$ such that for every element a of R,

$$ea = ae = a, \tag{1}$$

and also

$$e'a = ae' = a. \tag{2}$$

In particular, Equation (1) must hold for $a = e'$, that is, we must have

$$ee' = e'e = e'. \tag{3}$$

Similarly, by setting $a = e$ in Equation (2), we obtain

$$e'e = ee' = e. \tag{4}$$

Equations (3) and (4) then imply that $e = e'$, and there is only one unity. If a ring has a unity, we may therefore properly speak of *the* unity of a ring.

We next make the following definition.

2.8   Definition.   Let a be an element of a ring R with unity e. If there exists an element s of R such that

$$as = sa = e,$$

then s is called a *multiplicative inverse* of a.

One of the defining properties of a ring states that every element has an additive inverse. However, simple examples show that the situation may be quite different for multiplicative inverses. In the ring of all real numbers it is true that every nonzero element has a multiplicative inverse. In the ring $\mathbf{Z}$ of all integers there are exactly two elements that have multiplicative inverses, namely, 1 and -1. In the ring of all subsets of a given set A (Example 10), the only element that has a multiplicative inverse is the unity e of the ring; that is, the subset consisting of the entire set A. For if a and b are elements of this ring, ab (which we defined to be $a \cap b$) is a proper subset of A if either a or b is a proper subset of A. Hence, $ab = e$ only if $a = e$ and $b = e$.

In view of these examples, it is clear that we must never take it for granted that an element of a ring necessarily has a multiplicative inverse. However, the following result is easy to establish.

2.9   Theorem.   *If an element a of a ring R with unity e has a multiplicative inverse, it is unique.*

Suppose that both s and t are multiplicative inverses of the element a. Then, using the fact that $sa = e$ and the associative law of multiplication, we see that

$$s(at) = (sa)t = et = t.$$

But since $at = e$, it is also true that

$$s(at) = se = s,$$

and it follows that $s = t$.

In case a has a multiplicative inverse, it is customary to designate this multiplicative inverse by a^{-1}.

It will be recalled that the zero of a ring has been defined in terms of addition only. However, we shall now prove the following theorem, which has a familiar form.

2.10   Theorem.   *For each element a of a ring R, we have*
$$a \cdot 0 = 0 \cdot a = 0.$$

Since $a + 0 = a$, it follows that

$$a(a + 0) = a \cdot a.$$

But, by one of the distributive laws,

$$a(a + 0) = a \cdot a + a \cdot 0.$$

Hence,

$$a \cdot a + a \cdot 0 = a \cdot a.$$

Now we know that $a \cdot a + 0 = a \cdot a$ and, by Theorem 2.3, we conclude that $a \cdot 0 = 0$.

In case R is a commutative ring, it follows from what we have just proved that also $0 \cdot a = 0$. If R is not commutative, a proof that $0 \cdot a = 0$ can easily be given using the other one of the distributive laws. This proof will be left as an exercise.

The following can now be verified in turn for arbitrary elements a, b, and c of a ring:

	(i)	$a(-b) = -(ab),$
	(ii)	$(-a)b = -(ab),$
2.11	(iii)	$(-a)(-b) = ab,$
	(iv)	$a(b-c) = ab - (ac),$
	(v)	$(b-c)a = ba - (ca).$

The proof of (i) goes as follows. We have

$$a(b + (-b)) = a \cdot 0 = 0.$$

However, by one of the distributive laws, we know that

$$a(b + (-b)) = ab + a(-b).$$

Hence,

$$ab + a(-b) = 0.$$

But since ab has a unique additive inverse $-(ab)$, it follows that $a(-b) = -(ab)$. The proofs of the other parts of 2.11 will be left as exercises.

In view of 2.11(i) and (ii), we see that

$$-(ab) = (-a)b = a(-b).$$

Accordingly, in later sections we shall usually write simply $-ab$ for any one of these equal expressions.

Let us now make a few remarks about the concept of *subring*. If S is a subring of the ring R, then not only is S a subset of R but the operations of addition and multiplication on S coincide with those operations as defined in the ring R. In particular, it follows that the zero of R is also the zero of S and, moreover, the additive inverse of an element of the subring S is identical with the additive inverse of this element considered as an element of R. (Why?) The following theorem, whose proof will be left as an exercise, furnishes a convenient way to determine whether a set of elements of R is actually a subring of R.

2.12   Theorem.   *Let R be a ring and S a nonempty subset of the set R. Then S is a subring of R if and only if the following conditions hold:*

(i)   *S is closed under the operations of addition and multiplication defined on R.*

(ii) *If $a \in S$, then $-a \in S$.*

EXERCISES

1. Prove 2.5(iii) and (iv).

2. If a and b are elements of the ring of all subsets of a given set (Example 10), show that (i) $a = -a$, and (ii) the equation $a + x = b$ has the solution $x = a + b$.

3. Complete the proof of Theorem 2.10 by showing that $0 \cdot a = 0$ for every element a of any ring.

4. Prove 2.11(ii)–(v).

5. If a, b, c, and d are elements of a ring, prove each of the following:

   (i) $(a + b)(c + d) = (ac + ad) + (bc + bd)$,
   (ii) $(a + b)(c + d) = (ac + bc) + (ad + bd)$,
   (iii) $(a - b)(c - d) = (ac + bd) - (bc + ad)$,
   (iv) $(a + b)(c - d) = (ac + bc) - (ad + bd)$,
   (v) $(a - b)(c + d) = (ac + ad) - (bc + bd)$,
   (vi) $(a(-b))(-c) = a(bc)$.

6. Verify that every nonzero element of the ring of Example 7 has a multiplicative inverse.

7. Show that an element (a, b, c) of the ring L of Example 8 has a multiplicative inverse if and only if $a = \pm 1$ and $c = \pm 1$.

8. (i) Find the multiplicative inverse of each of the following elements of the ring W of Example 9:

$$\begin{bmatrix} 2 & 5 \\ 1 & 3 \end{bmatrix}, \quad \begin{bmatrix} 2 & 7 \\ 1 & 3 \end{bmatrix}, \quad \begin{bmatrix} 6 & 1 \\ 17 & 3 \end{bmatrix}.$$

   (ii) Show that the element

$$\begin{bmatrix} 1 & 2 \\ 0 & 3 \end{bmatrix}$$

   of the same ring W does not have a multiplicative inverse in W.

9. Let R be a ring with unity. If a and b are elements of R that have multiplicative inverses, show that ab has a multiplicative inverse by verifying that $(ab)^{-1} = b^{-1}a^{-1}$.

10. Give an example of elements a and b of some ring such that a^{-1} and b^{-1} exist, but $(ab)^{-1} \neq a^{-1}b^{-1}$.

11. Suppose that a, c, and d are elements of a ring R and that a has a multiplicative inverse in R. Prove that if $ac = ad$ (or $ca = da$), then $c = d$. Show how Theorem 2.9 may be considered to be a special case of this result.

12. Prove Theorem 2.12.

13. If R and S are rings verify that the set of elements of the direct sum $R \oplus S$ of the form $(a, 0)$, where $a \in R$ and 0 is the zero of S, is a subring of $R \oplus S$.

14. Give an example of a ring R having a subring S such that
    (i) R has a unity and S does not have a unity,
    (ii) R does not have a unity but S has a unity,
    (iii) R and S have the same unity,
    (iv) R and S both have unities, but they are different,
    (v) R is a noncommutative ring and S is commutative.

15. Show that the set of all elements of the ring W of Example 9 of the form
$$\begin{bmatrix} x & 0 \\ y & z \end{bmatrix},$$
where x, y, $z \in \mathbf{Z}$ is a subring of the ring W.

16. If S and T are subrings of a ring R, show that $S \cap T$ is a subring of R. Give an example to show that $S \cup T$ need not be a subring.

17. (i) Give the addition table and multiplication table for a ring with exactly one element.
    (ii) If a ring R has more than one element and has a unity e, show that $e \neq 0$.

18. Let R be an arbitrary ring and $a \in R$. Prove that the set $\{x \mid x \in R, ax = 0\}$ is a subring of R.

2.6 GENERAL SUMS AND PRODUCTS

The operations of addition and multiplication are *binary* operations, that is, they apply to *two* elements only. Let us now consider how we can give a meaning to sums or products of three or more elements of a ring.

If a_1, a_2, and a_3 are elements of a ring, let us define $a_1 + a_2 + a_3$ as follows:

2.13 $$a_1 + a_2 + a_3 = (a_1 + a_2) + a_3.$$

However, by the associative law of addition, it then follows that

2.14 $$a_1 + a_2 + a_3 = a_1 + (a_2 + a_3),$$

and therefore a sum of three elements is independent of the way parentheses might be introduced to indicate the manner of association of the elements.

Now that we have defined a sum of three elements of a ring, let us define a sum of four elements as follows:

2.15 $$a_1 + a_2 + a_3 + a_4 = (a_1 + a_2 + a_3) + a_4.$$

The associative law of addition then shows that

2.16 $$a_1 + a_2 + a_3 + a_4 = (a_1 + a_2) + (a_3 + a_4),$$

and also that

2.17 $$a_1 + a_2 + a_3 + a_4 = a_1 + (a_2 + a_3 + a_4).$$

These calculations verify that the sum of four elements is also independent of the way in which the elements may be associated.

It seems fairly clear that similar statements hold for sums of more than four elements. A general proof can be given by the method of mathematical induction. This method of proof will be discussed in the next chapter, at which time we shall return to a further consideration of the material of this section. Although we shall not now give a proof, we proceed to formulate a statement which generalizes what we have said about sums of three or four elements, as well as some similar statements also involving products.

We have in 2.13 and 2.15 defined the sum of three or four elements of a ring. In general, if k is a positive integer such that

$$a_1 + a_2 + \cdots + a_k$$

has been defined, we define

2.18 $$a_1 + a_2 + \cdots + a_k + a_{k+1} = (a_1 + a_2 + \cdots + a_k) + a_{k+1}.$$

It should then appear that this gives us a definition of the sum of any number n of elements of a ring. Such a definition is called a *recursive* definition, and definitions of this kind will be considered more carefully in the next chapter.

We shall not write out the details, but in precisely the same way it is possible to give a recursive definition of a product of any number n of elements of a ring.

We now state the following theorem, which generalizes several of the properties used in the definition of a ring.

2.19   Theorem.   *Let n be an arbitrary positive integer, and let $a_1, a_2, \cdots, a_n$ be elements of a ring R.*

(i)   Generalized associative laws. *For each positive integer r such that $1 \leq r < n$, we have*

2.20
$$(a_1 + a_2 + \cdots + a_r) + (a_{r+1} + \cdots + a_n) = a_1 + a_2 + \cdots + a_n,$$

and

2.21
$$(a_1 a_2 \cdots a_r)(a_{r+1} \cdots a_n) = a_1 a_2 \cdots a_n.$$

(ii)   Generalized distributive laws. *If $b \in R$, we have*

2.22
$$b(a_1 + a_2 + \cdots + a_n) = ba_1 + ba_2 + \cdots + ba_n,$$

and

2.23
$$(a_1 + a_2 + \cdots + a_n)b = a_1 b + a_2 b + \cdots + a_n b.$$

(iii)   Generalized commutative laws. *If $i_1, i_2, \cdots, i_n$ are the integers $1, 2, \cdots, n$ in any order, then*

2.24
$$a_{i_1} + a_{i_2} + \cdots + a_{i_n} = a_1 + a_2 + \cdots + a_n.$$

In case R is a commutative *ring, we have also*

2.25
$$a_{i_1} a_{i_2} \cdots a_{i_n} = a_1 a_2 \cdots a_n.$$

It will be observed that if $n = 3$ in 2.20, then necessarily $r = 1$ or $r = 2$ and the truth of 2.20 in these cases is asserted by 2.14 and 2.13. Similarly, if $n = 4$, it follows that $r = 1, 2,$ or 3. These three cases of 2.20 have been verified in 2.17, 2.16, and 2.15.

Let us explain the notation used in the generalized commutative laws. As an example, let $n = 3$, and let $i_1 = 3$, $i_2 = 1$, $i_3 = 2$. Then 2.24 states that

$$a_3 + a_1 + a_2 = a_1 + a_2 + a_3.$$

This special case can readily be verified as follows:

$$
\begin{aligned}
a_3 + a_1 + a_2 &= (a_3 + a_1) + a_2 && \textit{(def.),}\\
&= a_3 + (a_1 + a_2) && \textit{(assoc. law),}\\
&= (a_1 + a_2) + a_3 && \textit{(comm. law),}\\
&= a_1 + a_2 + a_3 && \textit{(def.).}
\end{aligned}
$$

As stated above, a general proof of any part of the above theorem requires the use of mathematical induction, and this method of proof will be discussed later. However, the theorem should seem fairly obvious; for the time being we shall merely assume it without proof. In particular, Theorem 2.19(i) assures us that we can introduce parentheses in a sum or product to indicate association in any way we wish without changing the value of the respective sum or product. Accordingly, we shall henceforth usually omit such parentheses entirely. Some special cases of the theorem will be assigned as exercises at the end of this section.

We next observe that positive integral exponents may be defined in any ring R in the usual way. If a is an arbitrary element of R, we may define $a^1 = a$, $a^2 = a \cdot a$, and, in general, if k is a positive integer such that a^k has been defined, we define $a^{k+1} = a^k \cdot a$. The following familiar laws of exponents now hold, where m and n are arbitrary positive integers.

2.26   (i) $a^m \cdot a^n = a^{m+n},$
           (ii) $(a^m)^n = a^{mn}.$

Suppose, now, that a, $b \in R$. Then $(ab)^2 = (ab)(ab)$, and if $ba \neq ab$, $(ab)^2$ may not be equal to $a^2 b^2$. However, if $ba = ab$, it does follow that $(ab)^2 = a(ba)b = a(ab)b = a^2 b^2$. In general, it is not difficult to show that if R is a *commutative* ring and m is any positive integer, then

2.27 $(ab)^m = a^m \cdot b^m.$

We may remark that *negative* integral exponents can be defined if we restrict attention to elements which have multiplicative inverses. However, we shall postpone any consideration of negative exponents until a later chapter.

We now introduce a convenient notation for *multiples* that parallels the exponent notation for *powers*. If $a \in R$, let us define $1a = a$, $2a = a + a$, and, in general, if k is a positive integer such that ka has been defined, we define $(k + 1)a = ka + a$. If 0 is the zero integer, we define $0a$ to be the zero element of R. Actually, there will be no confusion if the same symbol is used to designate the zero integer and the zero of the ring. Since every element of a ring has an additive inverse, we can easily introduce negative multiples as well as positive multiples. If m is a positive integer, we define $(-m)a$ to be $m(-a)$. Then $(-m)a$ is also seen to be equal to $-(ma)$. Thus, for example,

$$(-2)a = 2(-a) = -a - a = -(a + a) = -(2a).$$

The reader may easily convince himself of the truth of the following, it being understood that m and n are any integers (positive, negative, or zero) and that a and b are arbitrary elements of any ring R:

2.28

(i)	$ma + na = (m + n)a,$
(ii)	$m(na) = (mn)a,$
(iii)	$m(a + b) = ma + mb,$
(iv)	$m(ab) = (ma)b = a(mb),$
(v)	$(ma)(nb) = (mn)(ab).$

It should perhaps be emphasized that ma is a convenient way of indicating a certain sum of elements of R. However, since the integer m is not necessarily itself an element of R, it is not correct to think of ma as the product of two elements of R. Hence, for example, 2.28(iii) is not necessarily a consequence of one of the distributive laws.

Again, complete proofs of 2.26, 2.27, and 2.28 require the use of mathematical induction.

We may reiterate our present point of view as follows. Except where explicitly stated, as in a later section where we consider formal proofs of some of the facts mentioned here, we shall henceforth assume the truth of 2.19, 2.26, 2.27 and 2.28. In particular, we shall consider it permissible to write sums or products of more than two elements without use of parentheses.

EXERCISES

1. Verify the truth of 2.20 for the case in which $n = 5$, and therefore $r = 1, 2, 3,$ or 4.

2. Verify 2.22 for the case in which $n = 3$.

3. Verify 2.24 for the case in which $n = 4$, $i_1 = 3$, $i_2 = 1$, $i_3 = 4$, $i_4 = 2$.

4. If R is a commutative ring, verify 2.27 for the case in which $m = 3$.

5. If a is any element of the ring of Example 3, verify that $2a = 0$. (The zero of the ring is u.)

6. In the ring W of Example 9, let
$$A = \begin{bmatrix} 1 & 2 \\ 0 & 0 \end{bmatrix},$$
and
$$B = \begin{bmatrix} 0 & 1 \\ 0 & 1 \end{bmatrix}.$$
Verify that $(AB)^2 \neq A^2B^2$.

7. If x and y are any elements of the ring K of Example 6, verify that $(xy)^2 = x^2y^2$, even though this is not a commutative ring.

8. Show that, by a suitable change of notation, 2.26(i) can be considered to be a special case of 2.21.

9. Show that, by a suitable change of notation, 2.28(i) can be considered to be a special case of 2.20.

10. Show that, by a suitable change of notation, 2.28(iv) can be obtained from 2.22 and 2.23.

11. A ring R is called a *Boolean ring* if $a^2 = a$ for every element a of R. If R is a Boolean ring and $a \in R$, prove that $2a = 0$. Then prove that R is necessarily a commutative ring. [Hint: Consider $(a + b)^2$.]

12. Prove that the direct sum $R \oplus S$ of two rings R and S is a Boolean ring if and only if both R and S are Boolean rings.

13. Give an example of a Boolean ring with 32 elements and an example of a ring with 32 elements which is not a Boolean ring.

14. Let R be an arbitrary ring and consider matrices
$$\begin{bmatrix} a & b \\ c & d \end{bmatrix},$$
where $a, b, c, d \in R$. If addition and multiplication are defined as in Example 9, prove that we obtain a ring. This ring is called the ring of all matrices of order two over the ring R.

15. Prove that if a ring R contains elements s and t such that $st \neq 0$, then the ring of all matrices of order two over R is a noncommutative ring.

2.7 HOMOMORPHISMS AND ISOMORPHISMS

The concepts to be introduced in this section play an exceedingly important role in modern algebra. Before giving formal definitions, we illustrate the ideas by several examples.

EXAMPLE 1. Let $\mathbf{Z}$ be the ring of integers and T the ring of Example 5 of Section 2.3, whose addition and multiplication tables we here reproduce for convenience.

$(+)$	0	e		$(\cdot)$	0	e
0	0	e		0	0	0
e	e	0		e	0	e

Now let $\theta: \mathbf{Z} \to T$ be the mapping defined as follows for $i \in \mathbf{Z}$:

$$i\theta = \begin{cases} 0 & \text{if } i \text{ is even,} \\ e & \text{if } i \text{ is odd.} \end{cases}$$

Thus, for example, $4\theta = 0$ and $7\theta = e$. We next observe that

$$(4 + 7)\theta = 11\theta = e = 4\theta + 7\theta,$$

and also that

$$(4 \cdot 7)\theta = 28\theta = 0 = (4\theta)(7\theta).$$

Actually, it may be verified that similar results always hold. That is, if $i, j \in \mathbf{Z}$, then

$$(i + j)\theta = i\theta + j\theta$$

and

$$(ij)\theta = (i\theta)(j\theta).$$

As a matter of fact, the addition and multiplication tables for T are just those which we would get if we thought of 0 as standing for "even" and e for "odd." Thus, for example, $e + e = 0$ and "odd" + "odd" = "even."

What we have observed is that in this example "the image of a sum is the sum of the images." More precisely, if we take the sum of i and j in the ring $\mathbf{Z}$, the image of this sum is the sum in the ring T of the respective images of i and j. This fact is often expressed by saying that the operation of *addition is preserved under the mapping θ*. Similarly, the operation of multiplication is also preserved under this mapping θ.

Now the mapping θ of this example is clearly a mapping of $\mathbf{Z}$ *onto* T, and we have indicated that both the operations of addition and multiplication are preserved under this mapping. According to the definition to be given below, the mapping θ is an example of a *homomorphism* of the ring $\mathbf{Z}$ onto the ring T.

EXAMPLE 2. Let R and S be arbitrary rings, and let $\phi\colon R \times S \to R$ be the *projection* of the set $R \times S$ onto R, as defined in Example 2 of Section 1.2. Since the set $R \times S$ becomes a ring $R \oplus S$ under natural definitions of addition and multiplication, ϕ may be considered as a mapping of the ring $R \oplus S$ onto the ring R defined by

$$(r, s)\phi = r, \qquad (r, s) \in R \oplus S.$$

We assert that the operations of addition and multiplication are preserved under the mapping ϕ. That this is true for addition is a consequence of the following simple calculations:

$$[(r_1, s_1) + (r_2, s_2)]\phi = (r_1 + r_2, s_1 + s_2)\phi = r_1 + r_2$$
$$= (r_1, s_1)\phi + (r_2, s_2)\phi.$$

A similar calculation will verify that multiplication also is preserved under the mapping ϕ. Hence ϕ is a homomorphism of $R \oplus S$ onto R.

EXAMPLE 3. Let $K = \{a, b, c, d\}$ be the ring of Example 6 of Section 2.5 with addition and multiplication tables which we here reproduce.

(+)	a	b	c	d		(·)	a	b	c	d
a	a	b	c	d		a	a	a	a	a
b	b	a	d	c		b	a	b	c	d
c	c	d	a	b		c	a	a	a	a
d	d	c	b	a		d	a	b	c	d

Now let $L = \{i, j, k, l\}$, with addition and multiplication on L defined by the following tables.

(+)	i	j	k	l
i	k	l	i	j
j	l	k	j	i
k	i	j	k	l
l	j	i	l	k

(·)	i	j	k	l
i	i	j	k	l
j	k	k	k	k
k	k	k	k	k
l	i	j	k	l

It can be proved that L is a ring with respect to these definitions of addition and multiplication. At first glance, the rings K and L may seem quite different, but it is not difficult to verify that they are identical except for the notation used. If, in the tables for K we replace a by k, b by i, c by j, and d by l, the tables will coincide except for the order in which the elements are written down. Let us state this fact in a more precise way as follows. Let $\psi: K \to L$ be the mapping defined by

$$a\psi = k, \quad b\psi = i, \quad c\psi = j, \quad d\psi = l.$$

Then not only is ψ a *one-one* mapping of K onto L but also the operations of addition and multiplication are preserved under the mapping ψ. Thus ψ is a homomorphism of K onto L which is a one-one mapping (in contrast to the homomorphisms of the two preceding examples). Such a homomorphism is given the special name of an *isomorphism*.

Let us now give formal definitions of the concepts which have been introduced in the above examples.

2.29   Definition.   A mapping $\theta: R \to S$ of a ring R into a ring S is called a *homomorphism* if and only if the operations of addition and multiplication are preserved under θ, that is, if and only if for arbitrary elements a, b, of R, the following hold:

2.30 $$(a + b)\theta = a\theta + b\theta, \quad (ab)\theta = (a\theta)(b\theta).$$

If there exists a homomorphism of R onto S, we may say that R is *homomorphic* to S or that S is a *homomorphic image* of R.

The following special case is of such importance that we give it a separate definition.

2.31   Definition.   A homomorphism which is a one-one mapping is called an *isomorphism*. If there exists an isomorphism of R onto S, we may say that R is *isomorphic* to S or that S is an *isomorphic image* of R.

We may emphasize that, for the sake of generality, we have not required a homomorphism or isomorphism to be an onto mapping.

However, whenever we say that R is homomorphic (isomorphic) to S or that S is a homomorphic (isomorphic) image of R, we do mean to imply that it is an onto mapping. Although the more general concept is useful in certain parts of the theory, we shall seldom have occasion to refer to homomorphisms (isomorphisms) that are not onto mappings. The reader should watch carefully to see whether the word "onto" is used.*

It may be worth observing that there always exists a trivial homomorphism of any ring R into any ring S. We have only to define the image of every element of R to be the zero element of S. Of course, this does not assert that S is a homomorphic image of R.

If the mapping $\theta: R \to S$ is an isomorphism of the ring R onto the ring S, it may be verified that the mapping $\theta^{-1}: S \to R$, as defined in Section 1.2, is an isomorphism of S onto R. Accordingly, if R is isomorphic to S, then S is isomorphic to R, and we may sometimes simply say that R and S are *isomorphic rings*. As suggested by the last example above, it should be clear that isomorphic rings may be considered as differing only in the notation used to indicate the elements of the rings. Accordingly, isomorphic rings are sometimes said to be *abstractly identical*.

The symbol $\cong$ is widely used for "is isomorphic to". Thus, if R and S are rings and we write $R \cong S$, it means that there exists an isomorphic mapping of R onto S. Using this notation, we have just shown in the preceding paragraph that if $R \cong S$, then $S \cong R$. We may emphasize that the homomorphic mapping of R into S whose existence is asserted by writing $R \cong S$ is both a one-one and an onto mapping.

The most fundamental properties of homomorphisms are stated in the following theorem. It should be kept in mind that an isomorphism is a special case of a homomorphism, so that isomorphisms certainly have the stated properties.

2.32 Theorem. *Let $\theta: R \to S$ be a homomorphism of the ring R into the ring S. Then each of the following is true:*

   (*i*)   *If 0 is the zero of R, then 0θ is the zero of S.*

   (*ii*)   *If $a \in R$, then $(-a)\theta = -(a\theta)$.*

   (*iii*) *If R has a unity e and θ is an onto mapping, then S has $e\theta$ as unity.*

   (*iv*)   *Suppose that R has a unity and that θ is an onto mapping. If a is an element of R having a multiplicative inverse, then $(a^{-1})\theta = (a\theta)^{-1}$.*

   (*v*)   *If R is a commutative ring and θ is an onto mapping, then S is a commutative ring.*

---

* A homomorphism that is a one-one mapping is also called a *monomorphism*. Likewise, a homomorphism that is an onto mapping is sometimes called an *epimorphism*. In this new language an *isomorphism* is both a monomorphism and an epimorphism, and thus means the same as our symbol $\cong$ to be introduced presently.

Proof of (iii). We need to show that $s(e\theta) = (e\theta)s = s$ for every element s of S. Let s be an arbitrary element of S. Since θ is an onto mapping, there exists at least one element r of R such that $r\theta = s$. Now e is a unity of R, and therefore $re = er = r$. Hence $(re)\theta = (er)\theta = r\theta$. Since multiplication is preserved under the mapping θ, it follows that $(r\theta)(e\theta) = (e\theta)(r\theta) = r\theta$, or $s(e\theta) = (e\theta)s = s$, as required.

We leave the proof of the other parts of the theorem as an exercise.

EXERCISES

In these exercises the examples referred to are those of Section 2.3.

1. Prove Theorem 2.32 (i), (ii), (iv), and (v).

2. In the ring K of Example 6, show that $\{a , b\}$ is a subring of K which is isomorphic to the ring of Example 5.

3. If $\theta: R \rightarrow S$ is a homomorphism of the ring R into the ring S, prove that the set T of all images of elements of R is a subring of S.

4. Exhibit a homomorphism of the ring of Example 3 onto the ring of Example 5.

5. If R and S are rings, verify that the subring of $R \oplus S$ consisting of all elements of the form $(r , 0)$, $r \in R$, is isomorphic to R.

6. Show that the set of all elements of the ring L of Example 8 of the form $(x , 0 , x)$, $x \in \mathbf{Z}$, is a subring of L which is isomorphic to $\mathbf{Z}$.

7. If L is the ring of Example 8, show that the mapping $\theta: L \rightarrow \mathbf{Z}$ defined by $(a , b , c)\theta = a$ is a homomorphism of L onto $\mathbf{Z}$.

8. It was shown in a previous exercise that the set P of all elements of the ring W of Example 9 of the form

$$\begin{bmatrix} x & 0 \\ y & z \end{bmatrix}, \qquad x, y, z \in \mathbf{Z},$$

is a subring U of W. Show that the mapping $\theta: U \rightarrow L$ defined by

$$\begin{bmatrix} x & 0 \\ y & z \end{bmatrix}\theta = (x , y , z), \qquad x, y, z \in \mathbf{Z},$$

is an isomorphism of U onto the ring L of Example 8.

9. Does the ring of Exercise 12 of Section 2.3 have a subring isomorphic to the ring of Example 5?

10. If R and S are rings, prove that $R \oplus S \cong S \oplus R$.

11. If $\theta: R_1 \to R_2$ and $\phi: S_1 \to S_2$ are, respectively, homomorphisms of R_1 onto R_2 and of S_1 onto S_2, exhibit a homomorphism of $R_1 \oplus S_1$ onto $R_2 \oplus S_2$.

12. Give examples of a ring R without unity and a ring S with unity such that S is a homomorphic image of R.

13. Give examples of a noncommutative ring R and a commutative ring S such that S is a homomorphic image of R.

14. Exhibit a pair of rings, each with four elements, which are not isomorphic. Do the same thing for rings with eight elements.

15. Let R be a ring without unity. On the set $R \times \mathbf{Z}$ let us define addition and multiplication as follows:

$$(a, i) + (b, j) = (a + b, i + j),$$
$$(a, i)(b, j) = (ab + ja + ib, ij).$$

    Prove that with respect to this addition and multiplication $R \times \mathbf{Z}$ is a ring with unity and that this ring contains a subring which is isomorphic to R.

16. Let R be the ring of Exercise 20 of Section 2.3. Then as *sets* R and $\mathbf{Z}$ are identical, but they are distinct as *rings* since the operations are different. Show that the mapping $\theta: \mathbf{Z} \to R$ defined by $a\theta = 1 - a$, $a \in \mathbf{Z}$, is an isomorphism of $\mathbf{Z}$ onto R.

INTEGRAL DOMAINS

The properties which we used to define a ring were suggested by simple properties of the integers. However, since we have had numerous examples of commutative rings with unity that bear little resemblance to the ring of integers, it is clear that the system of integers must have some other properties in addition to those which make it a commutative ring with unity. Accordingly, in order to specify in some sense *all* the properties of the ring of integers, we need to consider some properties not mentioned in the previous chapter. In the present chapter we proceed to restrict the rings studied and, eventually, shall have enough properties listed that, in a sense to be described precisely later on, the *only* system which has all these properties is the ring of integers. We may then say that we have obtained a characterization of the ring of integers.

One of the properties that we shall require in characterizing the ring of integers is a property which leads in a natural way to the method of proof by mathematical induction. Accordingly, we shall introduce this important method of proof and use it to establish a few of the results that were stated without proof in Section 2.6.

We shall conclude the chapter with a few remarks about an alternate method of approaching the study of the integers in which all the familiar properties are derived from a few simple properties of the *positive* integers only.

3.1 DEFINITION OF INTEGRAL DOMAIN

We have proved that if 0 is the zero of a ring R, then $a \cdot 0 = 0 \cdot a = 0$ for every element a of R. Of course, this is a familiar property of our elementary number systems. However, in some of the rings previously mentioned there exist elements c and d, both of which are different from zero, such that $cd = 0$. For example, in the ring of Example 3 of Section 2.3 we have $wx = u$, where u is the zero. As another example, consider the ring of all subsets of a given set (Example 10). The empty set is the zero of this ring and, by the definition of multiplication in this ring, if c and d are subsets whose intersection is the empty set, then $cd = 0$. In discussing elements of the type just mentioned, it will be convenient to make the following definition.

3.1   Definition.   An element a of a ring R is said to be a *divisor of zero in R* if there exists a *nonzero* element c of R such that $ac = 0$ or a *nonzero* element d of R such that $da = 0$.

It is trivial that the zero of a ring R is a divisor of zero (provided R has more than one element and therefore has a nonzero element to play the role of c or d in the above definition). The elementary number systems have no divisors of zero except the zero or, as we shall say, have no nonzero divisors of zero. An alternate way of stating that a ring R has no nonzero divisors of zero is to say that it has the following property:
   If $r, s \in R$ such that $rs = 0$, then $r = 0$ or $s = 0$.
   We next prove the following simple result.

3.2   Theorem.   (Cancellation Laws of Multiplication).

If a is not a divisor of zero in a ring R, then each of the following holds:

(i)   If $b, c \in R$ such that $ab = ac$, then $b = c$.
(ii) If $b, c \in R$ such that $ba = ca$, then $b = c$.

Let us prove part (i) of this theorem. If $ab = ac$, it follows that $a(b - c) = 0$. Then, since a is not a divisor of zero, we must have $b - c = 0$ or $b = c$. Of course, part (ii) follows by a similar argument.
   It is important to keep in mind that the cancellation laws of multiplication hold *only if a is not a divisor of zero*.
   In most of this chapter we shall be studying rings without nonzero divisors of zero. In such a ring the cancellation laws of multiplication as stated in Theorem 3.2 always hold provided only that $a \neq 0$. Moreover, in order to restrict ourselves for the present to rings more like the ring of integers, we shall also require our rings to be commutative and to have a unity. The next definition gives a convenient way to refer to rings having all of these properties.

3.3 Definition. A ring D with more than one element is called an *integral domain* if it is commutative, has a unity, and has no nonzero divisors of zero.

The most familiar examples of integral domains are the ring of integers, the ring of real numbers and the ring of complex numbers. The reader may verify that the rings of Examples 1, 2, 5, and 7 of Section 2.3 are integral domains, whereas the rings of Examples 3, 4, 6, and 10 are not integral domains.

3.2 ORDERED INTEGRAL DOMAINS

One important property of the integers that has not been mentioned so far is that they can be *ordered*. If we think of the integers as being exhibited in the following way

$$\cdots, \; -4, \; -3, \; -2, \; -1, \; 0, \; 1, \; 2, \; 3, \; 4, \; \cdots,$$

and a and b are integers, we say that "a is greater than b" if a occurs to the right of b in the above scheme. It is clear that "a is greater than b" means merely that $a - b$ is a positive integer. This observation suggests that the concept of "order" can be defined in terms of the concept of "positive." We therefore make the following definition.

3.4 Definition. An integral domain D is said to be an *ordered integral domain* if D contains a subset D^+ with the following properties:

(i)   If $a, b \in D^+$, then $a + b \in D^+$ (*closed under addition*).
(ii) If $a, b \in D^+$, then $ab \in D^+$ (*closed under multiplication*).
(iii) For each element a of D exactly *one* of the following holds:

$$a = 0, \qquad a \in D^+, \qquad -a \in D^+ \qquad (\textit{trichotomy law}).$$

The elements of D^+ are called the *positive* elements of D. The nonzero elements of D that are not in D^+ are called the *negative* elements of D.

In view of the definition of an integral domain, the cancellation laws of multiplication (as stated in Theorem 3.2) are always valid in an integral domain so long as $a \neq 0$.

We may emphasize that D^+ is just the notation used to designate a particular subset of an ordered integral domain D. No significance is to be attached to the use of the symbol "$+$" in this connection.

Obviously, the set $\mathbf{Z}^+$ of positive integers has the properties required of D^+ in the above definition, and hence $\mathbf{Z}$ is an ordered integral domain. However, there are other ordered integral domains such as, for example, the integral domain of all rational numbers or the integral domain of all real numbers. However, not all integral domains are ordered integral domains. For example, we shall prove later on that the integral domain of all complex numbers has no subset with the three properties listed in the preceding definition, and therefore this integral domain is not ordered. See also Exercise 14 at the end of this section.

Now let D be any ordered integral domain, and let D^+ be the set of positive elements of D, that is, the set having the three properties stated in the preceding definition. If $c, d \in D$, we *define* $c > d$ (or $d < c$) to mean that $c - d \in D^+$. Then it is clear that $a > 0$ means that $a \in D^+$, that is, that a is a positive element of D. Similarly, $a < 0$ means that $-a \in D^+$ or that a is a negative element of D. The three properties of Definition 3.4 can then be restated in the following form:

3.5
    (i)   If $a > 0$ and $b > 0$, then $a + b > 0$.
    (ii) If $a > 0$ and $b > 0$, then $ab > 0$.
    (iii) If $a \in D$, then exactly one of the following holds:

$$a = 0, \quad a > 0, \quad a < 0.$$

It is now not difficult to verify the following additional properties of inequalities:

3.6
    (i)   If $a > b$, then $a + c > b + c$ for every $c \in D$.
    (ii) If $a > b$ and $c > 0$, then $ac > bc$.
    (iii) If $a > b$ and $c < 0$, then $ac < bc$.
    (iv) If $a > b$ and $b > c$, then $a > c$.
    (v) If $a \neq 0$, then $a^2 > 0$.

The proof of the first of these is as follows. If $a > b$, we have $a - b > 0$. However, $a + c - (b + c) = a - b$ and we see at once that $a + c - (b + c) > 0$, that is, that $a + c > b + c$.

Let us now prove 3.6(v). If $a \neq 0$, then by the form 3.5(iii) of the trichotomy law, either $a > 0$ or $-a > 0$. If $a > 0$, it follows from 3.5(ii) that $a^2 > 0$. If $-a > 0$, the same argument shows that $(-a)^2 > 0$. Since, by 2.11(iii), $(-a)^2 = a^2$, it follows again that $a^2 > 0$.

Proofs of the other parts of 3.6 will be left as exercises.

It is obvious that one can define $a \geq b$ (or $b \leq a$) to mean that either $a = b$ or $a > b$, without specifying which. We shall henceforth use this notation whenever convenient to do so. If $a \geq 0$, it is sometimes convenient to say that a is *nonnegative*. By writing $a < b < c$, we shall mean that $a < b$ and that also $b < c$.

In any ordered integral domain it is possible to introduce the concept of absolute value in the usual way as follows.

3.7 Definition. Let D be any ordered integral domain and $a \in D$. The *absolute value* of a, written as $|a|$, is defined as follows:

(i) If $a \geq 0$, then $|a| = a$.

(ii) If $a < 0$, then $|a| = -a$.

From this definition it follows that $|0| = 0$ and that if $a \neq 0$, then $|a| > 0$.

EXERCISES

1. If a is a divisor of zero in a commutative ring R, show that ar also is a divisor of zero for every element r of R.

2. Let N be the set of all elements of an arbitrary ring R which are *not* divisors of zero. Prove that N is closed under multiplication, and verify by an example that N need not be closed under addition.

3. Prove that if a has a multiplicative inverse a^{-1} in a ring R, then a is not a divisor of zero in R.

4. Verify that each of the following is a divisor of zero in the ring of all matrices of order two over $\mathbf{Z}$:

$$\begin{bmatrix} 0 & 1 \\ 0 & 0 \end{bmatrix}, \begin{bmatrix} 1 & 2 \\ 0 & 0 \end{bmatrix}, \begin{bmatrix} 1 & 2 \\ 2 & 4 \end{bmatrix}.$$

5. Prove 3.6(ii), (iii), (iv).

In Exercises 6–12, the letters a, b, c, and d represent elements of an ordered integral domain.

6. Prove that if $a > b$, then $-a < -b$.

7. Prove that if $a > b$ and $c > d$, then $a + c > b + d$.

8. Prove that if a, b, c, and d are all positive with $a > b$ and $c > d$, then $ac > bd$.

9. Prove that if $a > 0$ and $ab > ac$, then $b > c$.

10. Prove that $|ab| = |a| \cdot |b|$.

11. Prove that $-|a| \leq a \leq |a|$.

12. Prove that $|a + b| \leq |a| + |b|$.

13. Prove: There cannot be a greatest element in an ordered integral domain D (that is, for each $d \in D$ there exists $c \in D$ such that $c > d$).

14. Use the result of the preceding exercise to give a convincing argument (a formal proof is not required) why an integral domain with a finite number of elements cannot be an ordered integral domain.

15. If Property 3.2(i) holds for every nonzero element a of a ring R, prove that R has no nonzero divisor of zero.

16. If Property 3.2(i) holds for every nonzero element a of a ring R, prove that Property 3.2(ii) also holds for every nonzero element a of R.

17. Prove that in a Boolean ring, as defined in Exercise 11 of Section 2.6, every nonzero element except the unity (if it has a unity) is a divisor of zero.

18. Prove that an isomorphic image of an integral domain is an integral domain.

3.3 WELL-ORDERING AND MATHEMATICAL INDUCTION

We need one further condition to characterize the ring of integers among the ordered integral domains. Let us first make the following general definition.

3.8 Definition. A set S of elements of an ordered integral domain is said to be *well-ordered* if each nonempty subset U of S contains a least element, that is, if for each nonempty subset U of S there exists an element a of U such that $a \leq x$ for every element x of U.

It is apparent that the set of all positive integers is well-ordered, and we shall presently find that this property is precisely what distinguishes the ring of integers from other ordered integral domains. The rational numbers will be considered in detail later on in this book, but we may observe now that the set of positive rationals is not well-ordered. In fact, the set of all positive rational numbers has no least element. For if r is any positive rational number, then $r/2$ is also a positive rational number and $r/2 < r$. Hence there can be no least positive rational number.

Let us pause to clarify our point of view about the ring of integers. We have not *proved* any property of the integers, instead we have from time to time merely assumed that they have certain properties. We are now able to state precisely as follows just what properties of the integers we do wish to consider as known. *We assume that the ring of integers is an ordered integral domain in which the set of positive elements is well-ordered.* Accordingly, when we shall henceforth speak of a proof of any property of the integers we shall mean a proof based on this assumption only. The theorem of the next section will indicate why no other properties are required.

The following theorem, which is the basis of proofs by mathematical induction, is just as "obvious" as the fact that the set of positive integers is well-ordered. However, in accordance with our chosen point of view, we shall give a proof of this result.

3.9 Theorem. *Let K be a set of positive integers with the following two properties:*

(i) $1 \in K$.

(ii) *If k is any positive integer such that $k \in K$, then also $k + 1 \in K$.*

Then K consists of the set of all *positive integers.*

To prove this theorem, let us assume that there is a positive integer not in K, and obtain a contradiction. Let U be the set of all positive integers not in K and therefore, by our assumption, U is not empty. Then, by the well-ordering property, U must contain a least element m. Since, by (i), we have $1 \in K$, clearly $m \neq 1$ and it follows that $m > 1$ and therefore $m - 1 > 0$. Moreover, $m - 1 \in K$ since m was chosen to be the least element of U. Now, by (ii) with $k = m - 1$, we see that $m \in K$. But $m \in U$, and we have obtained the desired contradiction. The proof is therefore complete.

The most frequent application of Theorem 3.9 is to a proof of the following kind. Suppose that there is associated with each positive integer n a *statement* (or proposition) S_n, which is either true or false, and suppose we wish to prove that the statement S_n is true for every positive integer n. Let K be the set of all positive integers n such that S_n is a true statement. If we can show that $1 \in K$, and that whenever $k \in K$, then also $k + 1 \in K$, it will follow from Theorem 3.9 that K is the set of all positive integers. Since $n \in K$ merely means that S_n is true, we may reformulate these remarks in the following convenient form.

3.10 Induction Principle. *Suppose that there is associated with each positive integer n a statement S_n. Then S_n is true for every positive integer n provided the following hold:*

(*i*) S_1 *is true.*

(*ii*) *If k is any positive integer such that S_k is true, then also S_{k+1} is true.*

A proof making use of the Induction Principle (or of Theorem 3.9) is usually called a proof by induction or a proof by mathematical induction.

We may remark that there is another useful form of the Induction Principle in which condition (ii) is replaced by a somewhat different condition. (See Exercise 9 at the end of this section.)

As a first illustration of the language and notation just introduced, we consider a simple example from elementary algebra. If n is a positive integer, let S_n be the statement that

$$2 + 4 + 6 + \cdots + 2n = n(n + 1),$$

it being understood that the left side is the sum of the first n positive even integers. We now prove that S_n is true for every positive integer n, by verifying (i) and (ii) of 3.10. Clearly, S_1 is true since S_1 merely states that $2 = 1 \cdot 2$. Suppose, now, that k is any positive integer such that S_k is true, that is, such that the following is true:

$$2 + 4 + 6 + \cdots + 2k = k(k + 1).$$

Then, by adding the next even integer, $2(k + 1)$, to both sides we obtain

$$2 + 4 + 6 + \cdots + 2k + 2(k + 1) = k(k + 1) + 2(k + 1)$$
$$= (k + 1)(k + 2).$$

However, this calculation shows that S_{k+1} is true, and hence we have verified both (i) and (ii) of 3.10. The Induction Principle then assures us that S_n is true for every positive integer n.

We now consider again part of the material of Section 2.6, and we first illustrate by a simple example how a recursive definition really involves the Induction Principle. The recursive definition of a^n, which was given earlier, may be stated in the following formal way.

3.11 Definition. *If a is an element of a ring R, we define $a^1 = a$. Moreover, if k is a positive integer such that a^k is defined, we define $a^{k+1} = a^k \cdot a$.*

Now let S_n be the statement, "a^n is defined by 3.11." The Induction Principle then shows that S_n is true for every positive integer n, that is, that a^n is defined by 3.11 for every positive integer n.

Let us now prove (2.26(i)) that if m and n are arbitrary positive integers, then

3.12
$$a^m \cdot a^n = a^{m+n}.$$

Let S_n be the statement that for the positive integer n, 3.12 is true for *every* positive integer m. Then, by definition of a^{m+1}, we see that $a^m \cdot a^1 = a^{m+1}$, and hence S_1 is true. Let us now assume that k is a positive integer such that S_k is true, that is, such that

3.13
$$a^m \cdot a^k = a^{m+k}$$

for every positive integer m. Then

$$
\begin{aligned}
a^m \cdot a^{k+1} &= a^m \cdot a^k \cdot a && \text{(by def. of } a^{k+1}\text{)}, \\
&= a^{m+k} \cdot a && \text{(by 3.13)}, \\
&= a^{m+k+1} && \text{(by def. of } a^{(m+k)+1}\text{)}.
\end{aligned}
$$

We have now shown that S_{k+1} is true, and the Induction Principle then assures us that S_n is true for every positive integer n. Thus we have given a formal proof of the very familiar law of exponents stated in 3.12. In the above proof we have tacitly made use of the associative law of multiplication. As a matter of fact, it was pointed out in the preceding chapter that 3.12 is actually a special case of the generalized associative law of multiplication.

As a further illustration of the use of mathematical induction in proving the results stated in Section 2.6, we shall prove the generalized associative law of addition (2.20). For convenience of reference, let us first restate in a slightly different notation the recursive definition (2.18) of a sum of more than two elements of a ring. If l is a positive integer and $b_1, b_2, \cdots, b_{l+1}$ are elements of a ring such that

$$b_1 + b_2 + \cdots + b_l$$

is defined, we define

3.14
$$b_1 + b_2 + \cdots + b_{l+1} = (b_1 + b_2 + \cdots + b_l) + b_{l+1}.$$

Now let S_n be the statement that for arbitrary elements $a_1, a_2, \cdots, a_n$ of a ring and for each positive integer r such that $1 \leq r < n$, we have

3.15 $(a_1 + \cdots + a_r) + (a_{r+1} + \cdots + a_n) = a_1 + a_2 + \cdots + a_n.$

To establish the generalized associative law of addition, we need to prove that S_n is true for every positive integer n. Clearly, S_1 and S_2 are true, and we verified S_3 and S_4 in Section 2.6. We complete the proof by showing that if k is a positive integer such that S_k is true, then also S_{k+1} is true. Otherwise expressed, if S_k is true and r is an integer such that $1 \leq r < k + 1$, we shall show that

3.16 $(a_1 + \cdots + a_r) + (a_{r+1} + \cdots + a_{k+1})$
        $= a_1 + a_2 + \cdots + a_{k+1}.$

The case in which $r = k$ is true at once by definition (3.14) of the right side of 3.16. Suppose, then, that $r < k$. As a special case of 3.14, we have

$$a_{r+1} + \cdots + a_{k+1} = (a_{r+1} + \cdots + a_k) + a_{k+1}.$$

This is used in the first step of the following calculation:

$(a_1 + \cdots + a_r) + (a_{r+1} + \cdots + a_{k+1})$
    $= (a_1 + \cdots + a_r) + ((a_{r+1} + \cdots + a_k) + a_{k+1})$
    $= ((a_1 + \cdots + a_r) + (a_{r+1} + \cdots + a_k)) + a_{k+1}$ *(by assoc. law)*,
    $= (a_1 + \cdots + a_k) + a_{k+1}$ *(by S_k)*,
    $= a_1 + \cdots + a_{k+1}$ *(by 3.14)*.

This calculation establishes 3.16 and completes the proof.

In a similar manner the other results that were stated in Section 2.6 can be established by induction. Some of them are listed in the following set of exercises.

EXERCISES

1.   Prove the generalized distributive law (2.22):

$$b(a_1 + a_2 + \cdots + a_n) = ba_1 + ba_2 + \cdots + ba_n.$$

2.   Prove (2.26(ii)) that for arbitrary positive integers m and n,

$$(a^m)^n = a^{mn}.$$

3.   If a and b are elements of a commutative ring, prove (2.27) that $(ab)^m = a^m b^m$ for every positive integer m.

4. If n is a positive integer and $a_1, a_2, \cdots, a_n$ are elements of an integral domain such that $a_1 a_2 \cdots a_n = 0$, show that at least one of the a's is zero.

5. If $\theta: R \to S$ is a homomorphism of the ring R into the ring S and $a \in R$, prove that $a^n \theta = (a\theta)^n$ for every positive integer n.

6. Prove (2.28(iii)) that if a and b are elements of a ring, for every integer m (positive, negative, or zero),

$$m(a + b) = ma + mb.$$

7. Prove (2.28(iv)) that if a and b are elements of a ring, for every integer m,

$$m(ab) = (ma)b + a(mb).$$

8. Prove (2.28(i)) that if a is an element of a ring, for all integers m and n,

$$ma + na = (m + n)a.$$

[Hint: Make a number of cases as follows: either m or n is zero; both m and n are positive; one of m, n is positive and the other negative; both m and n are negative.]

9. Use the fact that the set of positive integers is well-ordered to prove the following alternate form of the Induction Principle:

Suppose that there is associated with each positive integer n a statement S_n. Then S_n is true for every positive integer n provided the following hold:

(i) S_1 is true.

(ii) If k is positive integer such that S_i is true for every positive integer $i < k$, then also S_k is true.

3.4 A CHARACTERIZATION OF THE RING OF INTEGERS

The purpose of this section is to prove the following theorem.

3.17 Theorem. *Let both D and D' be ordered integral domains in which the set of positive elements is well-ordered. Then D and D' are isomorphic.*

Since we are assuming that $\mathbf{Z}$ is an ordered integral domain in which the set of positive elements is well-ordered, this theorem will show that $\mathbf{Z}$ is the *only* ring with these properties (if we do not consider isomorphic rings as "different" rings).

As a first step in the proof, we shall prove a lemma. In the statement of this lemma, and henceforth whenever it is convenient to do so, we shall make use of the notation introduced in Definition 3.4 and let Z^+ denote the set of all positive integers.

3.18 Lemma. *Let D be an ordered integral domain in which the set D^+ of positive elements is well-ordered. If e is the unity of D, then*

$$D^+ = \{me \mid m \in Z^+\},$$

and

$$D = \{ne \mid n \in Z\}.$$

Moreover, if n_1, $n_2 \in Z$ such that $n_1 e = n_2 e$, then $n_1 = n_2$.

We recall that $a \in D^+$, can also be expressed by writing $a > 0$. It is clear that $e > 0$ since $e^2 = e$, and $e^2 > 0$ by 3.6(v). For each positive integer n, let S_n be the statement that $ne > 0$. Since, by definition, $1e = e$, we have just verified the truth of S_1. If, now, k is a positive integer such that S_k is true, it follows from 3.5(i) that $(k + 1)e = ke + e > 0$, and therefore that S_{k+1} is true. We have therefore proved by mathematical induction that $me > 0$ for every positive integer m. That is, $me \in D^+$ for every positive integer m. We now proceed to show that all elements of D^+ are of this form.

First, since D^+ is well-ordered, D^+ itself has a least element. Actually, e is this least element. For suppose that c is the least element of D^+, and that $0 < c < e$. It follows by 3.6(ii) that $0 < c^2 < c$, since $ce = c$. Hence $c^2 \in D^+$ and $c^2 < c$. However, this violates the assumption that c is the least element of D^+, and it follows that the least element of D^+ is the unity e.

We can now complete the proof that every element of D^+ is of the form me for some positive integer m. Suppose that this is false, and let U be the nonempty set of elements of D^+ that are not of this form. Then U must have a least element, say d. We have proved that e is the least element of D^+, and hence we must have $d > e$, or $d - e > 0$. Hence, $d - e \in D^+$ and, since $e > 0$, it follows that $d - e < d$ and hence that $d - e \notin U$; therefore $d - e = m_1 e$ for some positive integer m_1. It then follows that $d = e + m_1 e = (1 + m_1)e$, and $1 + m_1$ is a positive integer. But d, being an element of U, is *not* of this form, and we have a contradiction. It follows that U must be the empty set, that is, that every element of D^+ is of the required form.

It is now easy to complete the proof of the first statement of the lemma. If $a \in D$, and $a \notin D^+$, then 3.4(iii) implies that $a = 0$ or $-a \in D^+$. If $a = 0$, then $a = 0 \cdot e$. If $-a \in D^+$, then by what we have just proved, $-a = m_2 e$ for some positive integer m_2. It follows that

$a = (-m_2)e$, and so every element of D is of the form ne, where n is an integer (positive, negative, or zero).

Now suppose that n_1, $n_2 \in \mathbf{Z}$ such that $n_1e = n_2e$. If $n_1 \neq n_2$, we can assume that the notation is so chosen that $n_1 > n_2$. It follows that $n_1 - n_2 > 0$ and, by the part of the lemma already proved, $(n_1 - n_2)e \in D^+$. Hence $(n_1 - n_2)e \neq 0$, or $n_1e \neq n_2e$. Thus the assumption that $n_1 \neq n_2$ leads to a contradiction, and we conclude that $n_1 = n_2$. This completes the proof of the lemma.

It is now easy to prove Theorem 3.17. If e and e' are the respective unities of D and of D', the lemma shows that

$$D = \{ne \mid n \in \mathbf{Z}\},$$

and

$$D' = \{ne' \mid n \in \mathbf{Z}\}.$$

Moreover, the last statement of the lemma asserts that the elements of D are *uniquely* expressible in the form ne, $n \in \mathbf{Z}$. Of course, the elements of D' are likewise uniquely expressible in the form ne', $n \in \mathbf{Z}$.

We now assert that the mapping $\theta: D \to D'$ defined by

$$(ne)\theta = ne', \qquad\qquad n \in \mathbf{Z},$$

is the desired isomorphism of D onto D'. By the uniqueness property just obtained, θ is a one-one mapping of D onto D'. Moreover, under this mapping we have

$$(n_1e + n_2e)\theta = [(n_1 + n_2)e]\theta = (n_1 + n_2)e' = n_1e' + n_2e'$$
$$= (n_1e)\theta + (n_2e)\theta,$$

and

$$[(n_1e)(n_2e)]\theta = [(n_1n_2)e]\theta = (n_1n_2)e' = (n_1e')(n_2e')$$
$$= [(n_1e)\theta][(n_2e)\theta].$$

Hence, addition and multiplication are preserved and we indeed have an isomorphism. This completes the proof of the theorem.

3.5 THE PEANO AXIOMS (OPTIONAL)

So far, we have merely *assumed* that the system of all integers has the properties of an ordered integral domain in which the set of positive elements is well-ordered. In this section we shall briefly indicate how it is possible to assume as a starting point only a few simple properties of the natural numbers (positive integers) and then to *prove* all the other properties that are required. This program was first carried out by the Italian mathematician, G. Peano, and the simple properties with which we start are therefore called Peano's Axioms. If we denote by N the set of all natural numbers, these axioms are often stated as follows.*

AXIOM 1. $1 \in N$.

AXIOM 2.   To each element m of N there corresponds a unique element m' of N called the *successor* of m.

AXIOM 3.   For each $m \in N$ we have $m' \neq 1$. (That is, 1 is not the successor of any natural number.)

AXIOM 4.   If m, $n \in N$ such that $m' = n'$, then $m = n$.

AXIOM 5.   Let K be a set of elements of N. Then $K = N$ provided the following two conditions are satisfied:

(i) $1 \in K$.
(ii) If $k \in K$, then $k' \in K$.

This last axiom is essentially our Theorem 3.9 and is the basis of proofs by mathematical induction. In this approach to the study of the natural numbers it is taken as one of the defining properties or axioms.

Using only these five simple axioms, it is possible to *define* addition and multiplication on N and then to *prove* that N has all the properties of an integral domain except that it does not have a zero and its elements do not have additive inverses. We proceed to give the definitions of addition and multiplication, but shall not carry out the rest of the program. The details can be found in many algebra texts.

The definition of addition is as follows.

3.19 Definition. Let m be an arbitrary element of N. First, we define $m + 1 = m'$. Moreover, if $k \in N$ such that $m + k$ is defined, we define $m + k' = (m + k)'$.

By Axiom 5, it follows that the set of all elements n of N such that $m + n$ is defined by 3.19 is the set of *all* elements of N. In other words, an operation of addition is now defined on N.

---

* In more modern language, Axioms 2, 3, and 4 simply assert that there exists a one-one mapping of N into N with the property that the element 1 does not occur as an image. Using Axiom 5, it is easy to show that every other element of N is an image.

The operation of multiplication is defined in a similar way as follows.

3.20 Definition. Let m be an arbitrary element of N. First, we define $m \cdot 1 = m$. Moreover, if $k \in N$ such that $m \cdot k$ is defined, we define $m \cdot k' = m \cdot k + m$.

It is also possible to define an order relation on N as follows. If m, $n \in N$, we define $m > n$ to mean that there exists an element k of N such that $m = n + k$. It can then be proved that ">" has all the properties that we would expect it to have when applied to the positive elements of an ordered integral domain. Moreover, the set N is well-ordered according to our Definition 3.8 of this concept.

Up to this point we have outlined a program for using Peano's Axioms to establish all the familiar properties of the natural numbers or positive integers. In order to obtain the *ring* of all integers we still have to introduce into the system the negative integers and zero. This can be done by a method quite similar to that which we shall use in Chapter 5 to construct the rational numbers from the integers. Accordingly, we postpone any further discussion of this program until Section 5.7 at the end of Chapter 5.

NOTES AND REFERENCES

A discussion of the development of the integers from a set of axioms for the natural numbers (the set of Peano or some other set) will be found, e.g., in the following books listed in the bibliography: Landau[47], Dubisch[4], and in an appendix in Johnson [9].

IV

SOME PROPERTIES OF THE INTEGERS

Now that we have obtained a characterization of the ring **Z** of integers, in this chapter we proceed to establish a number of simple properties of this system. In giving illustrative examples we shall naturally make use of our familiar decimal notation, but the proofs will be based only on the fact that the ring of integers is an ordered integral domain in which the set of positive elements is well-ordered. In particular, mathematical induction will play a central role in many of the proofs, although we shall frequently omit some of the details.

4.1   DIVISORS AND THE DIVISION ALGORITHM

We begin with the following familiar definition.

4.1   Definition.   If $a, d \in \mathbf{Z}$ with $d \neq 0$, d is said to be a *divisor* (or *factor*) of a if there exists an element a_1 of **Z** such that $a = a_1 d$. If d is a divisor of a, we say also that d *divides* a or that a is *divisible by* d or that a is a *multiple* of d.

We could just as well allow d to be zero in the above definition, but this case is unimportant and it is convenient to exclude it.

We shall often write $d|a$ to indicate that d divides a. We now list as follows a number of simple facts involving the concept of divisor.

   (i)   *If $d|a$ and $a|b$, then $d|b$.*
   (ii)   *$d|a$ if and only if $d|(-a)$.*
   (iii)   *$d|a$ if and only if $(-d)|a$.*
   (iv)   *$\pm 1|a$ for every integer a.*

    (v)   *$d|0$ for every nonzero integer d.*

4.2 *(vi)*   *If $a \neq 0$ and $d|a$, then $|d| \leq |a|$. Moreover, if $a \neq 0$, $d|a$, and $d \neq \pm a$, then $|d| < |a|$.*

    (vii) *If $d| \pm 1$, then $d = \pm 1$.*

    (viii) *If $a|b$ and $b|a$, then $a = \pm b$.*

    (ix)   *If $d|a$ and $d|b$, then $d|(ax + by)$ for arbitrary integers x and y.*

    We shall prove a few of these statements and leave the proof of the others as an exercise.

PROOF OF 4.2*(vi)*. Let us first point out that one part of the proof of Lemma 3.18 implies the not surprising fact that the unity 1 of **Z** is the smallest positive integer. Now if $d|a$, there exists an integer a_1 such that $a = a_1 d$, and $a \neq 0$ implies that $a_1 \neq 0$ and $d \neq 0$. Hence $|a_1| \geq 1$ and $|a_1| \cdot |d| \geq |d|$. However, using the well-known result of Exercise 10 of Section 3.2, it follows that $|a| = |a_1 d| = |a_1| \cdot |d| \geq |d|$. This completes the proof of the first statement of 4.2(vi). The second statement follows from the part just proved and the observation that $|d| = |a|$ if and only if $d = \pm a$.

PROOF OF 4.2*(vii)*. If $d|\pm 1$, then 4.2(vi) shows that $|d| \leq |\pm 1| = 1$. Since $d \neq 0$, we must have $|d| = 1$, or $d = \pm 1$.

PROOF OF 4.2*(ix)*. Since $d|a$ and $d|b$, there exist integers a_1 and b_1 such that $a = a_1 d$ and $b = b_1 d$. Hence, if $x, y \in$ **Z**, we have $ax + by = (a_1 x + b_1 y)d$ and therefore $d|(ax + by)$.

    The following concept is an important one in studying divisibility properties of the integers.

4.3 **Definition.** A nonzero integer p other than 1 or -1 is called a *prime* if its only divisors are ± 1 and $\pm p$.

    If $n > 1$, it follows from this definition that n is *not* a prime if and only if there exist positive integers n_1 and n_2, with $1 < n_1 < n$ and $1 < n_2 < n$, such that $n = n_1 n_2$.

    It is obvious that $-p$ is a prime if and only if p is a prime. The first few positive primes are

$$2, 3, 5, 7, 11, 13, 17, 19, \cdots.$$

One of the principal reasons for the importance of the primes is that every integer other than 0, 1, and -1 is a prime or can be expressed as a product of primes. This is sometimes taken for granted in arithmetic, and no doubt seems almost obvious. However, the fact that any integer can be so expressed and in only one way, in a sense to be made precise later, is not trivial to prove and is so important that it is often called the "Fundamental Theorem of Arithmetic." We shall return to this theorem in a later section of this chapter.

We proceed to a consideration of the following result.

4.4   Division Algorithm. *If $a, b \in \mathbf{Z}$ with $b > 0$, there exist unique integers q and r such that*

4.5 $a = qb + r,$ $0 \leq r < b.$

Before giving a detailed proof, we can make the existence of q and r appear plausible by use of a geometric argument. Consider a coordinate line with the multiples of b marked off as in Figure 8.

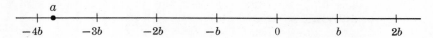

Figure 8

Then if a is marked off, it either falls on a multiple of b, say qb, or it falls between two successive multiples of b, say qb and $(q + 1)b$. (In the figure, $q = -4$.) In either case, there exists an integer q such that $qb \leq a < (q + 1)b$. If we set $r = a - qb$, then $a = qb + r$ and it is clear that $0 \leq r < b$.

Let us now give a proof which does not make use of geometric intuition. An outline of the proof is as follows. Since 4.5 can be written in the form $r = a - qb$, we consider those nonnegative integers of the form $a - xb$, where $x \in \mathbf{Z}$, and shall show that one of them is necessarily less than b. This one we shall then identify with the integer r, whose existence we wish to establish. In order to carry out the details, let S be the set of integers defined as follows:

$$S = \{a - xb \mid x \in \mathbf{Z}, a - xb \geq 0\}.$$

First, we show that the set S is not empty. Now $b \geq 1$, since b is assumed to be a positive integer. It follows that $|a| \cdot b \geq |a|$, and hence that $a + |a| \cdot b \geq a + |a| \geq 0$. Hence, by using $x = -|a|$, we see that S contains the integer $a + |a| \cdot b$, and is therefore not empty. If $0 \in S$, clearly 0 is the least element of S. If $0 \notin S$, S is a nonempty set of positive integers and therefore has a least element, since the set of positive integers is well-ordered. Hence, in either case, S has a least element, say r. There must then exist an integer q such that $a - qb = r$.

We therefore have $a = qb + r$, where $0 \leq r$, and we proceed to show that also $r < b$. Let us suppose, on the contrary, that $r \geq b$. Then $r - b \geq 0$ and, since $r - b = a - (q + 1)b$, we see that $r - b \in S$. But since $b > 0$, $r - b < r$ and we have a contradiction of the fact that r is the least element of S. Hence, $r < b$, and this completes the proof that there exist integers q and r satisfying 4.5. It remains to be proved that they are unique.

Suppose that q and r satisfy 4.5, and that also

$$a = q_1 b + r_1, \qquad\qquad 0 \leq r_1 < b.$$

Then $qb + r = q_1 b + r_1$, and it follows that

4.6 $$b(q - q_1) = r_1 - r.$$

Using the fact that the absolute value of a product is equal to the product of the absolute values, and that $|b| = b$, we obtain

$$b \cdot |q - q_1| = |r_1 - r|.$$

But, since $0 \leq r < b$ and $0 \leq r_1 < b$, we must have $|r_1 - r| < b$ and it follows that $b \cdot |q - q_1| < b$. Since $|q - q_1|$ is a nonnegative integer, this implies that $|q - q_1| = 0$, that is, that $q = q_1$; and 4.6 then shows that also $r = r_1$. We have therefore proved the uniqueness of the integers q and r satisfying 4.5.

The unique integers q and r which satisfy 4.5 are called, respectively, the *quotient* and the *remainder* in the division of a by b. It is important to observe that a is divisible by b if and only if the remainder in the division of a by b is zero.

In a numerical case, at least if $a > 0$, the actual calculation of q and r can be carried out by the familiar process of long division. The method is easily adapted also to the case in which a is negative.

EXERCISES

1. Prove 4.2(i)–(v), (viii).

2. Show that if $x = y + z$ and d is a divisor of any two of the integers x, y, and z, it is also a divisor of the third.

3. Let b and m be positive integers. If q is the quotient and r is the remainder when the integer a is divided by b, show that q is the quotient and mr is the remainder when ma is divided by mb.

4. If p and q are positive primes such that $p|q$, show that $p = q$.

5. If n is a positive integer and p_1, p_2, $\cdots$, p_n are distinct positive primes, show that the integer $(p_1 p_2 \cdots p_n) + 1$ is divisible by none of these primes.

6. For each of the following pairs of integers find the quotient and the remainder in the division of the first integer by the second, and verify Equation 4.5:

(i) 1251, 78   (iii) 4357, 418

(ii) 31, 158   (iv) -168, 15.

7. Prove the following generalized form of the Division Algorithm. If a, $b \in \mathbf{Z}$ with $b \neq 0$, there exist unique integers q and r such that $a = qb + r, 0 \leq r < |b|$. [Hint: Make use of the case already proved in which b was assumed to be positive.]

8. Give a formal proof that if $i \in \mathbf{Z}$, the largest integer which is less than i is $i - 1$, that is, that there exists no integer j such that $i - 1 < j < i$.

9. Let a, b, and c be integers with $b > 0$ and $c > 0$. If q is the quotient when a is divided by b and q' is the quotient when q is divided by c, prove that q' is the quotient when a is divided by bc.

4.2 DIFFERENT BASES (OPTIONAL)

In this section we make use of the Division Algorithm to prove a result which, although independent of the rest of this book, is of some interest in itself.

It is customary to use the integer 10 as the base of our number system. By this we mean that when we write 4371, for example, it is understood to stand for $4 \cdot 10^3 + 3 \cdot 10^2 + 7 \cdot 10 + 1$. The numbers 4, 3, 7, and 1 are called the *digits* of this number. The possible digits of a number are then the ten integers 0, 1, 2, $\cdots$, 9. Actually, any positive integer greater than 1 can be used as a base in the way in which we ordinarily use 10. By this statement we mean the following.

4.7 Theorem. *Let b be a positive integer greater than 1. Then every positive integer a can be expressed uniquely in the form*

4.8 $$a = r_m b^m + r_{m-1} b^{m-1} + \cdots + r_1 b + r_0,$$

where m is a nonnegative integer and the r's are integers such that

$$0 < r_m < b \text{ and } 0 \leq r_i < b \text{ for } i = 0, 1, \cdots, m - 1.$$

If 4.8 holds, it will be convenient to say that the right side of 4.8 is "a representation of a, using the base b." We shall first sketch a proof that every positive integer has such a representation, and then prove the uniqueness. In the proof we shall use the form of the Induction Principle given in Exercise 9 of Section 3.3.

If $a < b$, then 4.8 holds with $m = 0$ and $r_0 = a$; hence every positive integer less than b has a representation, using the base b. In particular, the integer 1 has such a representation. To complete the proof by induction, let us assume that every positive integer less than a has a representation, and show that a must then have a representation. By the remarks above, the case in which $a < b$ has already been disposed of, so we may assume that $a \geq b$. By the Division Algorithm, we have that

4.9 $$a = qb + r, \qquad 0 \leq r < b,$$

with $q > 0$ since $a \geq b$, and clearly $q < a$ since $b > 1$. Therefore, by our assumption, q has a representation, using the base b. That is, we may write

$$q = s_k b^k + \cdots + s_1 b + s_0,$$

where k is a nonnegative integer, $0 < s_k < b$, and $0 \leq s_i < b$ for $i = 0, 1, \cdots, k - 1$. If we substitute this expression for q in Equation 4.9, we obtain

$$a = s_k b^{k+1} + \cdots + s_1 b^2 + s_0 b + r,$$

and it may be verified that this is a representation of the required form (with the m of 4.8 being $k + 1$). The Induction Principle thus shows that every positive integer has a representation, using the base b.

Let us now establish the *uniqueness* of the representation of a, using the base b. If $a < b$, a representation 4.8 must reduce merely to $a = r_0$ (that is, $m = 0$), and it is clear that there is no other representation. Accordingly, let us suppose that $a \geq b$ and for the purposes of our induction proof let us now assume that for every positive integer less than a there is a unique representation, using the base b. If 4.8 is one such representation for a, we may write

$$a = (r_m b^{m-1} + \cdots + r_1)b + r_0,$$

and since $0 \leq r_0 < b$, we see that r_0 is the remainder and that $r_m b^{m-1} + \cdots + r_1$ is the quotient in the division of a by b. Moreover, the quotient is greater than zero since $a \geq b$. Suppose, now, that in addition to 4.8 we have the following representation of a, using the base b:

$$a = t_n b^n + \cdots + t_1 b + t_0,$$

with the appropriate restrictions on these various numbers. Then, by the same argument as applied above to 4.8, we see that t_0 is the quotient and $t_n b^{n-1} + \cdots + t_1$ is the quotient in the division of a by b. However, in the division algorithm the quotient and the remainder are unique. Hence $r_0 = t_0$; also we have

$$r_m b^{m-1} + \cdots + r_1 = t_n b^{n-1} + \cdots + t_1,$$

and the two sides of this equation give representations, using the base b, of a positive integer less than a. But, by our assumption, it follows that these representations must be identical. Hence we conclude that $m = n$ and that $r_i = t_i$ for $i = 1, 2, \cdots, m$. Since we already know that $r_0 = t_0$, we see that our two representations of a are identical, and the proof of uniqueness is completed by an application of the Induction Principle.

Just as we omit the powers of 10 in the usual notation, we may specify a number a, using the base b, by giving in order the "digits" $r_m, r_{m-1}, \cdots, r_1, r_0$. In order to indicate the base being used, let us specify the number a, given by 4.8, by writing $(r_m r_{m-1} \cdots r_1 r_0)_b$. If no base is indicated, it will be understood that the base is 10. For example, $(3214)_5$ really means

$$3 \cdot 5^3 + 2 \cdot 5^2 + 1 \cdot 5 + 4,$$

and it is readily verified that $(3214)_5 = 434$. The proof of the uniqueness part of the above theorem suggests an easy way to obtain the representation of a given number a, using the base b. That is, r_0 is the remainder in the division of a by b, r_1 is the remainder in the division of the preceding quotient by b, and so on. We exhibit the calculations for 434, using the base 5. Here the remainders in the successive divisions are written off to the right, and the divisions are carried out until the last quotient is less than 5. We conclude, therefore, that $434 = (3214)_5$, which agrees with our previous calculations.

$$
\begin{array}{r|rr}
5 & 434 & \\
\hline
5 & 86 & 4 \\
\hline
5 & 17 & 1 \\
\hline
 & 3 & 2
\end{array}
$$

It is possible to carry out all the usual operations of arithmetic using entirely some fixed base other than 10. As an illustration, let us use base 5. In order to add or multiply any two numbers we need only learn addition and multiplication tables for the integers less than 5. In designating an integer less than 5, it is not necessary to indicate whether the base is 5 or 10. However, we have $5 = (10)_5$, $3 + 4 = (12)_5$, $3 \cdot 4 = (22)_5$, and so on. The reader may verify the addition and multiplication given below, following the usual procedure of arithmetic but using base 5 throughout.

$$
\begin{array}{r}
(3204)_5 \\
(23)_5 \\
\hline
(20122)_5 \\
(11413)_5 \\
\hline
(134302)_5
\end{array}
$$

$$
\begin{array}{r}
(3142)_5 \\
(1224)_5 \\
\hline
(4421)_5
\end{array}
$$

ADDITION   MULTIPLICATION

Of course, any other base can be used just as well as 5. However, the only base other than 10 that is in use to any extent is the base 2, and this system is called the *binary* system. The possible "digits" in the binary system are just 0 and 1, and expressing a number in this system involves expressing it as a sum of *different* powers of 2. For example, $(1011)_2 = 2^3 + 2 + 1$. The binary system is a most convenient one for use with many of the modern high-speed computing machines. Some of these machines are so constructed that information can be fed into the machine in the usual decimal system. The machine then expresses the given numbers in the binary system, carries out the calculations in the binary system, changes the results back into the decimal system, and automatically prints the answers.

EXERCISES

1. Write each of the following numbers using the base 5 and also using the base 2:

   24,   116,   412,   3141,   2384.

2. Carry out the following additions using the indicated base:

$$
\begin{array}{r}
(1130)_5 \\
(432)_5 \\
\hline
\end{array}
\qquad
\begin{array}{r}
(2143)_5 \\
(1434)_5 \\
\hline
\end{array}
\qquad
\begin{array}{r}
(101101)_2 \\
(11011)_2 \\
\hline
\end{array}
$$

3. Carry out the following multiplications using the indicated base:

$$
\begin{array}{r}
(143)_5 \\
(244)_5 \\
\hline
\end{array}
\qquad
\begin{array}{r}
(4312)_5 \\
(324)_5 \\
\hline
\end{array}
\qquad
\begin{array}{r}
(10101)_2 \\
(1101)_2 \\
\hline
\end{array}
$$

4. Prove that every positive integer a can be expressed in the form

$$3^m + a_{m-1}3^{m-1} + \cdots + a_13 + a_0,$$

where m is a nonnegative integer and each of the integers a_{m-1}, $\cdots$, a_1, a_0 has the value 0, 1, or -1.

4.3   GREATEST COMMON DIVISOR

We next make the following definition.

4.10   Definition.   If a and b are nonzero integers, the *greatest common divisor* (g.c.d.) of a and b is the unique *positive* integer d with the following two properties:

   (i) $d|a$ and $d|b$.
   (ii)   If c is an integer such that $c|a$ and $c|b$, then $c|d$.

We shall presently prove the existence of the g.c.d. of two nonzero integers a and b. However, it is easy to see that if there is a positive integer which satisfies conditions (i) and (ii), it is unique. For if d and d_1 satisfy both these conditions, it follows that $d|d_1$ and $d_1|d$. Then, since they are positive, 4.2(viii) shows that $d = d_1$.

In proving the existence of the g.c.d. we shall make use of the following concept.

4.11   Definition.   If $a, b \in \mathbf{Z}$ we say that an integer of the form

$$ax + by, \qquad\qquad x, y \in \mathbf{Z},$$

is a *linear combination* of a and b.

The existence of the g.c.d., and also one of its important properties, will be established in the following theorem.

4.12   Theorem.   *If a and b are nonzero integers, the least positive integer which is expressible as a linear combination of a and b is the g.c.d. of a and b. That is, if d is the g.c.d. of a and b, there exist integers x_1 and y_1 such that*

$$d = ax_1 + by_1,$$

and d is the smallest positive integer which is expressible in this form.

For convenience of reference, let us define the set S as follows:

$$S = \{ax + by | x, y \in \mathbf{Z}, \, ax + by > 0\}.$$

Hence S is just the set of all positive integers that are expressible as linear combinations of a and b. Since, for example, $a^2 + b^2$ is an element of S, it is clear that S is not empty. Accordingly, there must exist a smallest positive integer d in the set S. Since $d \in S$, there exist integers x_1 and y_1 such that

4.13
$$d = ax_1 + by_1.$$

We next show that d is a divisor of a. By the Division Algorithm, there exist integers q and r such that

$$a = qd + r, \qquad\qquad 0 \le r < d.$$

Using Equation 4.13, we then find that

$$r = a - qd = a - q(ax_1 + by_1)$$
$$= a(1 - qx_1) + b(-qy_1).$$

It is now clear that if $r > 0$, then $r \in S$. But since $r < d$ and d is the least element of S, we conclude that $r = 0$. Hence, $a = qd$, and d is a divisor of a. In a similar way it can be shown that d is a divisor of b. Hence, d satisfies condition 4.10(i).

It is quite easy to see that d also satisfies condition 4.10(ii). For, suppose that c is a common divisor of a and of b, and hence that $a = a_1 c$, $b = b_1 c$ for certain integers a_1 and b_1. Then, using Equation 4.13, we obtain

$$d = a_1 c x_1 + b_1 c y_1 = (a_1 x_1 + b_1 y_1)c,$$

and c is a divisor of d. This completes the proof of the theorem.

Although the preceding theorem establishes the existence of the g.c.d., its proof does not suggest a method for actually computing the g.c.d. of two given integers. We next present a procedure, known as the *Euclidean Algorithm*, which will be useful in this connection.

If d is the g.c.d. of the integers a and b, then, by 4.2(ii) and (iii), it is also the g.c.d. of $-a$ and b, of a and $-b$, and of $-a$ and $-b$. Accordingly, without loss of generality, we now assume that a and b are positive integers. By the Division Algorithm, we may write

$$a = qb + r, \qquad\qquad 0 \le r < b.$$

If $r = 0$, then $b|a$ and the g.c.d. of a and b is b, so henceforth we assume that $r \ne 0$. We now divide b by r, getting

$$b = q_1 r + r_1, \qquad\qquad 0 \le r_1 < r.$$

If $r_1 \neq 0$, we divide r by r_1, and obtain

$$r = q_2 r_1 + r_2, \qquad\qquad 0 \leq r_2 < r_1,$$

and repeat this process. Since $r > r_1 > r_2 > \cdots$, and all these remainders are nonnegative integers, we must eventually get a zero remainder. If r_{k+1} is the first zero remainder, we then have the following system of equations:

4.14

$$
\begin{aligned}
a &= qb + r, & 0 &< r < b, \\
b &= q_1 r + r_1, & 0 &< r_1 < r, \\
r &= q_2 r_1 + r_2, & 0 &< r_2 < r_1, \\
r_1 &= q_3 r_2 + r_3, & 0 &< r_3 < r_2, \\
&\;\;\cdots & &\;\;\cdots \\
r_{k-2} &= q_k r_{k-1} + r_k, & 0 &< r_k < r_{k-1}, \\
r_{k-1} &= q_{k+1} r_k.
\end{aligned}
$$

We now assert that r_k (the last nonzero remainder) is the g.c.d. of a and b. To establish this fact, we need to verify the two properties (i) and (ii) of Definition 4.10. First, let us show that r_k is a common divisor of a and b. We do so by starting with the last of Equations 4.14 and working back to the first as follows. It is clear from the last equation that r_k is a divisor of r_{k-1}. Since now r_k is a common divisor of r_k and r_{k-1}, the next-to-last equation shows that it is also a divisor of r_{k-2}. Proceeding in this way, when we get to the second equation we will know that r_k is a common divisor of r_1 and r, and hence is also a divisor of b. The first equation then shows that r_k is also a divisor of a. Hence, r_k is a common divisor of a and b, and 4.10(i) is established. To establish 4.10(ii), let c be any common divisor of a and b. We now use Equations 4.14 in the other order. The first equation shows that c is a divisor of r, the next that it is a divisor of r_1, and so on. Eventually, we find that it is a divisor of r_k, and the proof is complete.

Let us now give a numerical example. Suppose that we desire to compute the g.c.d. of the integers 26 and 382. By ordinary division we find that Equations 4.14 take the following form:

$$
\begin{aligned}
382 &= 14 \cdot 26 + 18, \\
26 &= 1 \cdot 18 + 8, \\
18 &= 2 \cdot 8 + 2, \\
8 &= 4 \cdot 2.
\end{aligned}
$$

In this case, 2 is the g.c.d. since it is the last nonzero remainder.

Not only is the Euclidean Algorithm useful in computing the g.c.d. of two integers, but it is also useful in expressing the g.c.d. of two integers as a linear combination of these integers. Actually, *each* of the remainders in Equations 4.14 can be expressed, in turn, as a linear combination of a and b. From the first of Equations 4.14, we see that

4.15 $$r = a - qb,$$

and hence r is a linear combination of a and b. Substituting this expression for r in the second equation, and solving for r_1, we get

4.16 $$r_1 = b - q_1(a - qb) = (1 + q_1q)b - q_1a,$$

and hence r_1 is a linear combination of a and b. Now substituting from 4.15 and 4.16 into the third of Equations 4.14, we obtain

$$\begin{aligned} r_2 = r - q_2r_1 &= (a - qb) - q_2[(1 + q_1q)b - q_1a] \\ &= (1 + q_2q_1)a - (q + q_2 + q_2q_1q)b, \end{aligned}$$

so that r_2 is a linear combination of a and b. By continuing in this way, we see that each remainder and, in particular, the g.c.d. r_k is expressible as a linear combination of a and b (see Exercise 8 below). We are not here interested in general formulas which express these remainders as linear combinations of a and b since, in a numerical case, it is easy to compute, in turn, each of these linear combinations.

As an example, let us carry out the calculations for the case in which $a = 382$ and $b = 26$. The Euclidean Algorithm has been applied above to these two integers to find that their g.c.d. is 2. Let us now use the equations previously exhibited to express each of the remainders as a linear combination of 382 and 26. For simplicity, we shall write a in place of 382 and b in place of 26. The calculations are as follows:

$$\begin{aligned} 18 &= a - 14b, \\ 8 &= b - 18 = b - (a - 14b) = 15b - a, \\ 2 &= 18 - 2 \cdot 8 = a - 14b - 2(15b - a) \\ &= 3a - 44b. \end{aligned}$$

Hence,

$$2 = 3(382) - 44(26),$$

and we have expressed the g.c.d. of 382 and 26 as a linear combination of these two integers.

We shall sometimes find it convenient to let (a, b) designate the g.c.d. of a and b. Thus, for example, we have that $(382, 26) = 2$. There can be no possible confusion with other uses of the number pair notation since the context will make it clear that we are considering the g.c.d. of two integers and not, for example, the coordinates of a point in the plane.

We shall frequently need to refer to a pair of integers with 1 as their g.c.d. Accordingly, it is convenient to make the following definition.

4.17 Definition.   The integers a and b are said to be *relatively prime* if and only if their g.c.d. is 1; that is, if and only if $(a, b) = 1$.

EXERCISES

Unless otherwise specified, the letters represent arbitrary nonzero integers.

1. Find the g.c.d. of each of the following pairs of integers and express it as a linear combination of the two integers: (i) 52 and 38, (ii) 81 and 110, (iii) 320 and 112. (iv) 7469 and 2387, (v) 10,672 and -4147.

2. Show that a and b are relatively prime if and only if 1 is expressible as a linear combination of a and b.

3. If $d = (a, b)$ and $a = a_1 d$, $b = b_1 d$, show that $(a_1, b_1) = 1$.

4. If m is a positive integer, show that $(ma, mb) = m(a, b)$.

5. Show each of the following:

    (i) If p is a positive prime and a is a nonzero integer, then either $(a, p) = 1$ or $(a, p) = p$.

    (ii) If p and q are distinct positive primes, then 1 is expressible as a linear combination of p and q.

6. If $x = yz + t$, prove that $(x, z) = (z, t)$.

7. Prove that $(a, bc) = 1$ if and only if $(a, b) = 1$ and $(a, c) = 1$.

8. Write out a formal proof that every remainder in Equations 4.14 is expressible as a linear combination of a and b. [Hint: Assume that this is false, and obtain a contradiction.]

9. If a, b, and n are given, prove that n is expressible as a linear combination of a and b if and only if $(a, b)|n$.

10. (i) Define the g.c.d. of *three* nonzero integers.

(ii) Establish the existence of the g.c.d. of three integers by proving a result analogous to Theorem 4.12.

(iii) If d is the g.c.d. of a, b, and c, show that $d = ((a, b), c) = ((a, c), b) = (a, (b, c))$.

(iv) Let d be the g.c.d. of a, b, and c. If $a = a_1 d$, $b = b_1 d$, and $c = c_1 d$, show that 1 is the g.c.d. of the three integers a_1, b_1, and c_1.

4.4 THE FUNDAMENTAL THEOREM

The principal theorem to be proved in this section has to do with the factorizations of an integer into a product of primes. We begin with the following important preliminary result.

4.18 Lemma. *If a and b are nonzero integers and p is a prime such that $p|ab$, then $p|a$ or $p|b$.*

To prove this lemma, let us suppose that p does not divide a, and show that $p|b$. Since p is a prime which is not a divisor of a, the definition of a prime implies that $(a, p) = 1$. Then Theorem 4.12 shows that there exist integers x and y such that $1 = ax + py$. Multiplying by b, we obtain

$$b = abx + bpy.$$

Since we are given that $p|ab$, clearly p divides the right member of this equation, and therefore divides b.

It is almost obvious that the preceding lemma can be generalized to apply to a product of more than two integers. For future reference we now state this more general result.

4.19 Lemma. *Let p be a prime and m an arbitrary positive integer. If a_1, a_2, $\cdots$, a_m are nonzero integers such that $p|(a_1 a_2 \cdots a_m)$, then $p|a_i$ for at least one i, $1 \leq i \leq m$.*

This lemma is easily established by induction, and the proof will be left as an exercise. The case in which $m = 2$ is covered by the preceding lemma.

It is easy to verify, for example, that $60 = 2 \cdot 2 \cdot 3 \cdot 5$, and hence that 60 can be expressed as a product of positive primes. We could also write $60 = 2 \cdot 5 \cdot 3 \cdot 2$, but we shall not consider these two factorizations as essentially different since they differ only in the order in which the prime factors are written down. With this understanding, it is true that 60 has only one factorization into a product of positive primes. This is a special case of the following important theorem.

4.20 Fundamental Theorem of Arithmetic. *Every positive integer $a > 1$ can be expressed as a product of positive primes in one and only one way (except for the order of the factors).*

In the statement of the theorem it is to be understood that, as a special case, a "product" of primes may consist of a single prime. This agreement is to take care of the case in which a is itself a prime.

First, we shall show that every positive integer $a > 1$ can be expressed, in at least one way, as a product of positive primes. Let K be the set of all integers greater than one that can *not* be so expressed. If K is not the empty set, there is a least integer c in K, and clearly c is not a prime. Hence, $c = c_1 c_2$, where $1 < c_1 < c$ and $1 < c_2 < c$. Since c is the least element of K, we have $c_1 \notin K$ and $c_2 \notin K$. This implies that both c_1 and c_2 can be expressed as products of primes, and since $c = c_1 c_2$ it is clear that c can also be expressed. However, this contradicts the fact that $c \in K$, and therefore K must be the empty set. In other words, every integer $a > 1$ can be expressed as a product of positive primes.

There remains to prove the *uniqueness* of the representation of an integer as the product of primes. A good many different proofs of this fact are known, but we shall here assume that there exists an integer a which can be expressed as a product of primes in two different ways, and obtain a contradiction. Suppose, then, that $a = p_1 p_2 \cdots p_r$, and that $a = q_1 q_2 \cdots q_s$, where the p's and q's are positive primes and that the p's are not identical with the q's. From the equation

$$p_1 p_2 \cdots p_r = q_1 q_2 \cdots q_s,$$

we cancel all primes that occur on both sides and, by a suitable choice of notation, obtain an equation

4.21 $$p_1 p_2 \cdots p_i = q_1 q_2 \cdots q_j.$$

Now we must have $i \geq 1$ and $j \geq 1$ since 1 does not have a prime factor. The preceding equation then shows that $p_1 | (q_1 q_2 \cdots q_j)$ and Lemma 4.19 implies that p_1 divides some one of $q_1, q_2, \cdots, q_j$. But since the p's and q's are positive primes, we conclude that p_1 must equal some one of these q's. However, this contradicts the fact that, by the way Equation 4.21 was obtained, the same prime cannot occur on both sides of this equation. This contradiction completes the proof of the theorem.

Of course, the primes occurring in a factorization of an integer into prime factors need not all be distinct. By combining the equal primes, we see that every integer $a > 1$ can be expressed uniquely in the form

4.22 $$a = p_1^{n_1} p_2^{n_2} \cdots p_k^{n_k},$$

where the p's are distinct positive primes and each of $n_1, n_2, \cdots, n_k$ is a positive integer. The right side of 4.22 may conveniently be called the *standard form* of the integer a. As an example, $2^2 \cdot 3 \cdot 5$ is the standard form of the integer 60.

Throughout this section we have considered positive integers only. However, this is no essential restriction as we can see as follows. If $a < -1$, then $-a > 1$ and the Fundamental Theorem shows that $-a$ can be expressed uniquely as a product of positive primes. It follows that a itself is then expressible uniquely as -1 times a product of positive primes. For example, $-60 = (-1) \cdot 2^2 \cdot 3 \cdot 5$.

4.5   SOME APPLICATIONS OF THE FUNDAMENTAL THEOREM

If a and c are positive integers and c is a divisor of a, then $a = cd$ for some positive integer d. If c and d are expressed as products of prime factors, then clearly a is a product of all prime factors of c times all prime factors of d. Moreover, the Fundamental Theorem then states that this gives the unique factorization of a as a product of prime factors. It follows that the only possible prime factors of c (or of d) are the primes that are factors of a. If then a is expressed in the standard form 4.22, any divisor c of a is necessarily of the form

$$c = p_1^{m_1} p_2^{m_2} \cdots p_k^{m_k},$$

where $0 \le m_i \le n_i$ $(i = 1, 2, \cdots, k)$. Conversely, any integer c of this form is clearly a divisor of a.

It is now easy to obtain the g.c.d. (a, b) of two integers a and b if both a and b are expressed in standard form. Clearly, (a, b) is the product of those primes which are factors of both a and b, each such prime occurring to the smaller of the two powers to which it occurs in a and in b. For example, $60 = 2^2 \cdot 3 \cdot 5$ and $252 = 2^2 \cdot 3^2 \cdot 7$. It follows that $(60, 252) = 2^2 \cdot 3$.

We have previously had a method for computing the g.c.d. of two integers by the use of Euclid's algorithm—a method which does not involve finding any prime factors of the given integers. From a computational point of view, the previous method may involve much less work than the present one since it may be exceedingly difficult to find the prime factors of fairly large numbers, and therefore difficult to express them in standard form.

We shall not have much occasion to use the concept we now define, but we include it here for the sake of completeness.

4.23 Definition. The *least common multiple* (l.c.m.) of two nonzero integers a and b is the positive integer m with the following two properties:

(i) $a|m$ and $b|m$.

(ii) If c is an integer such that $a|c$ and $b|c$, then $m|c$.

It is easy to verify the *uniqueness* of the l.c.m., and its existence may be established in various ways. (See Exercises 3 and 5 below.)

We conclude this section by giving a formal proof of the following well-known result. We shall show that there do not exist nonzero integers a and b such that

4.24
$$a^2 = 2b^2.$$

Let us suppose, on the contrary, that there do exist such integers, which we may obviously assume to be positive. If $d = (a, b)$, by Exercise 3 of the preceding set, we have $a = da_1$, $b = db_1$, where $(a_1, b_1) = 1$. Substituting in 4.24, and dividing by a^2, we find that

$$a_1^2 = 2b_1^2.$$

This equation implies that $2|a_1^2$ and Lemma 4.18 (or the Fundamental Theorem) shows that $2|a_1$. But then $4|a_1^2$ and therefore $4|2b_1^2$. This implies that $2|b_1^2$ and we must have $2|b_1$. Thus 2 is a common divisor of a_1 and b_1. We have therefore obtained a contradiction of the fact that $(a_1, b_1) = 1$, and hence there can be no nonzero integers satisfying 4.24. The proof is therefore complete.

Another, perhaps more familiar, way of stating the result just proved is to say that $\sqrt{2}$ is not a rational number; that is, it is not expressible in the form a/b, where a and b are integers.

EXERCISES

1. Express 120 and 4851 in standard form, and find their g.c.d. and their l.c.m.

2. Do the same for 970 and 3201.

3. Explain how one can find the l.c.m. of any two integers if their standard forms are known.

4. (i) Using a method similar to that used in the proof of Lemma 4.18, show that if a is a divisor of bc and $(a, b) = 1$, then a is a divisor of c.

   (ii) Prove the same result by use of the Fundamental Theorem.

5. If $a = a_1 d$ and $b = b_1 d$, where $d = (a, b)$, show that the l.c.m. of a and b is $a_1 b_1 d$.

6. Show that a positive integer $a > 1$ is a perfect square (that is, is the square of an integer) if and only if in the standard form of a all the exponents are even integers.

7. Show that if b and c are positive integers such that bc is a perfect square and $(b, c) = 1$, then both b and c are perfect squares.

8. Prove that there do not exist nonzero integers a and b such that $a^2 = 3b^2$.

9. If n is a positive integer which is not a perfect square, prove that there do not exist nonzero integers a and b such that $a^2 = nb^2$.

10. For each positive integer n, show that there are more than n positive primes. [Hint: Use the result of Exercise 5, Section 4.1.]

11. Prove Lemma 4.19.

4.6 PYTHAGOREAN TRIPLES (OPTIONAL)

If x, y, and z are *positive* integers such that

4.25 $$x^2 + y^2 = z^2,$$

we shall call the ordered triple (x, y, z) a *Pythagorean triple*. Clearly, (x, y, z) is a Pythagorean triple if and only if there exist right triangles whose sides have respective lengths x, y, and z units. Well-known examples of Pythagorean triples are $(3, 4, 5)$, $(6, 8, 10)$, and $(5, 12, 13)$. In this section we shall determine all Pythagorean triples.

First, we observe that we can limit our problem somewhat. If (x, y, z) is a Pythagorean triple, then so is (kx, ky, kz) for every positive integer k. Conversely, let (x, y, z) be a Pythagorean triple and suppose that d is a common divisor of x, y, and z. If we write $x = x_1 d$, $y = y_1 d$, and $z = z_1 d$, we can cancel d^2 from each term of the equation

$$(x_1 d)^2 + (y_1 d)^2 = (z_1 d)^2,$$

and find that (x_1, y_1, z_1) is also a Pythagorean triple. If it happens that d is the g.c.d. of the *three* integers x, y, and z (see Exercise 10, Section 4.3), then x_1, y_1, and z_1 have 1 as their g.d.c. Let us say that a Pythagorean triple (a, b, c) is a *primitive* Pythagorean triple if a, b, and c have 1 as their g.c.d. Then the observations that we have just made assure us that *every* Pythagorean triple is of the form (ra, rb, rc), where (a, b, c) is a primitive Pythagorean triple and r is a positive integer. Our general problem is therefore reduced to the problem of finding all primitive Pythagorean triples.

Now let (x, y, z) be a primitive Pythagorean triple. It is easy to see that *each pair* of the numbers x, y, and z must be relatively prime. If, on the contrary, two of these numbers were not relatively prime, they would have a common prime factor p. Then Equation 4.25 would show that p is also a factor of the third, which would contradict the assumption that (x, y, z) is primitive. As a special case of what we have just proved, we see that x and y cannot both be even. We next show that, also, x and y cannot both be odd. If they were both odd, we could write $x = 2m + 1$ and $y = 2n + 1$, where m and n are properly chosen integers. But then we would have

$$\begin{aligned} z^2 = x^2 + y^2 &= (2m + 1)^2 + (2n + 1)^2 \\ &= 2(2m^2 + 2n^2 + 2m + 2n + 1). \end{aligned}$$

Since the second factor in this last expression is odd, we see that z^2 would be divisible by 2 but not by 4, and this is clearly impossible. It follows that x and y cannot both be odd. We have therefore proved that one of the integers x and y must be even and the other odd. It is trivial that (a, b, c) is a primitive Pythagorean triple if and only if (b, a, c) is also, and there will be no real loss of generality if we now limit ourselves to the study of primitive Pythagorean triples (x, y, z) in which x is even, and therefore y is odd.

We are now ready to prove the following theorem.

4.26 Theorem. *If (x, y, z) is a primitive Pythagorean triple in which x is even, then*

4.27 $$x = 2uv, \quad y = u^2 - v^2, \quad z = u^2 + v^2,$$

where u and v are positive integers satisfying the following three conditions:

(*i*)   *u and v are relatively prime.*

(*ii*)   *u > v.*

(*iii*) *One of u, v is even and the other is odd.*

     Conversely, if u and v are any positive integers satisfying these three conditions and x, y, and z are determined by Formulas 4.27, then (x , y , z) is a primitive Pythagorean triple in which x is even.

To prove the first part of the theorem, let (x , y , z) be a primitive Pythagorean triple in which x is even. We have proved that no two of x, y, and z can be even; hence y and z are both odd. This implies that $z + y$ and $z - y$ are both even; that is, that there exist positive integers r and s such that

4.28 $$x + y = 2r, \cdot\ z - y = 2s.$$

From these, it is easy to verify that

4.29 $$z = r + s, \quad y = r - s.$$

Now r and s must be relatively prime since any common factor of r and s would be a common factor of the relatively prime integers z and y. Moreover, since

$$x^2 = z^2 - y^2 = (z + y)(z - y),$$

it follows from Equations 4.28 that

4.30 $$x^2 = 4rs.$$

Since x is even, $x = 2t$ for some integer t, and the preceding equation shows that

4.31 $$t^2 = rs.$$

Since r and s are relatively prime, Exercise 7 of the preceding set implies that both r and s are perfect squares. That is, there exist positive integers u and v such that

4.32 $$r = u^2, \quad s = v^2.$$

Then Equations 4.30 and 4.29 show that

4.33 $$x = 2uv, \quad y = u^2 - v^2, \quad z = u^2 + v^2,$$

and Formulas 4.27 are satisfied. There remains only to prove that u and v have the required properties. Since r and s are relatively prime, it follows from 4.32 that u and v are relatively prime. Next, we see that $u > v$ since $y > 0$. We already know that u and v cannot both be even inasmuch as they are relatively prime. Finally, from 4.33 it follows that they cannot both be odd since otherwise y (and z also) would be even, whereas we know that it is odd. This completes the proof of the first part of the theorem.

To prove the second part, suppose that u and v are any positive integers satisfying conditions (i), (ii), and (iii); and let x, y, and z be defined by Formulas 4.27. Clearly x, y, and z are all positive, and it is easy to verify that

$$(2uv)^2 + (u^2 - v^2)^2 = (u^2 + v^2)^2,$$

and hence that (x, y, z) is a Pythagorean triple. We shall prove that it is necessarily primitive by showing that y and z are relatively prime. By condition (iii), $u^2 - v^2$ and $u^2 + v^2$ are both odd, that is, y and z are both odd. If y and z were not relatively prime, they would have a common prime factor $p \neq 2$. But since $z + y = 2u^2$ and $z - y = 2v^2$, it would follow that p is also a common factor of u and v. However, it is given that u and v are relatively prime, and therefore y and z can have no common prime factor. Hence, (x, y, z) is a primitive Pythagorean triple. It is obvious that x is even, and the proof is therefore complete.

It follows from the theorem that there are infinitely many primitive Pythagorean triples. The triple $(4, 3, 5)$ is obtained by setting $u = 2$, $v = 1$ in 4.27; the triple $(12, 5, 13)$ by choosing $u = 3$, $v = 2$; the triple $(8, 15, 17)$ by choosing $u = 4$, $v = 1$; and so on.

4.7 THE RING OF INTEGERS MODULO N

In this section we shall make use of the concepts of equivalence relation and equivalence set, which were defined in Chapter 1. First, we make the following definition.

4.34 Definition. Let n be a fixed integer greater than 1. If a and b are integers such that $a - b$ is divisible by n, we say that "a is congruent to b modulo n," and indicate this by writing $a \equiv b \pmod{n}$.

As an illustration of the use of this notation, let $n = 5$. Then we have $18 \equiv 3 \pmod 5$ since $18 - 3$ is divisible by 5. In like manner, $-2 \equiv 8 \pmod 5$, $4 \equiv 4 \pmod 5$, $1342 \equiv 2 \pmod 5$, and so on.

We leave it to the reader to verify that congruence modulo n is an equivalence relation on the set **Z** of all integers. By this we mean, of course, that the three properties of Definition 1.12 of an equivalence relation are satisfied. We may emphasize that throughout this section n will always be a positive integer greater than 1.

Now that we have an equivalence relation on the set **Z**, we can consider equivalence sets as introduced in Definition 1.13. We may point out that, relative to the equivalence relation of congruence modulo n, an equivalence set $[k]$ is defined as follows:

$$[k] = \{x \mid x \in \mathbf{Z}, x \equiv k \ (\text{mod } n)\}.$$

For convenience, we shall refer to $[k]$ as an "equivalence set modulo n." If $[k]$ and $[l]$ are equivalence sets modulo n, then 1.15(i) shows that $[k] = [l]$ if and only if $k \equiv l$ (mod n).

Next, let us observe that if $a \in \mathbf{Z}$ and r is the remainder in the division of a by n, then necessarily $a \equiv r$ (mod n). This follows from the observation that if $a = qn + r$, then $a - r = qn$ and hence $a \equiv r$ (mod n). Since we have $0 \leq r < n$, it follows that every integer is congruent modulo n to some one of the n integers $0, 1, 2, \cdots, n - 1$. Moreover, since each of these integers is less than n, no two of them can be congruent to each other modulo n. Since $[k] = [l]$ if and only if $k \equiv l$ (mod n), we have shown that there are precisely n different equivalence sets modulo n, namely, the sets $[0], [1], [2], \cdots, [n - 1]$.

As an example, let us take $n = 5$. It is easy to verify that the five equivalence sets modulo 5 are the following:

4.35
$$\begin{aligned}
[0] &= \{\cdots, -15, -10, -5, 0, 5, 10, 15, \cdots\}, \\
[1] &= \{\cdots, -14, -9, -4, 1, 6, 11, 16, \cdots\}, \\
[2] &= \{\cdots, -13, -8, -3, 2, 7, 12, 17, \cdots\}, \\
[3] &= \{\cdots, -12, -7, -2, 3, 8, 13, 18, \cdots\}, \\
[4] &= \{\cdots, -11, -6, -1, 4, 9, 14, 19, \cdots\}.
\end{aligned}$$

It follows easily from 1.15(i) that if $a \in [2]$, then necessarily $[a] = [2]$. Hence, $[2] = [-3] = [17]$, and so on. In view of the observation made above, we see that $[2]$ consists of all those integers a such that the remainder in the division of a by 5 is 2. Otherwise expressed, the equivalence set $[2]$ consists of the set of all integers of the form $5q + 2$, $q \in \mathbf{Z}$. Similar remarks hold for the other equivalence sets modulo 5, as well as for equivalence sets modulo n.

Still considering the special case of congruence modulo 5, let us give a description of the procedure, which we shall justify in detail below, by which we propose to construct a new ring. Let $U = \{[0], [1], [2], [3], [4]\}$, and hence an element of the set U is just one of the equivalence sets 4.35. We propose to make U into a ring by suitable definitions of addition and multiplication of its elements. What shall we mean, for example, by [2] + [4]? By examining 4.35 it appears that the sum of an element of [2] and an element of [4] always gives an element of [6]. Hence, it is natural to define [2] + [4] = [6]. Of course, [6] = [1], so we could equally well say that [2] + [4] = [1]. Similarly, the product of an element of [2] and an element of [4] is always an element of [8], and we therefore define [2] · [4] = [8]. Again, since [8] = [3], this is the same as saying that [2] · [4] = [3]. In a similar way we could define the sum or the product of any two elements of U, always obtaining an element of U. The importance of all this is that with respect to these operations of addition and multiplication on U, it can be shown that U is a ring. This ring we shall call the "ring of integers modulo 5," and denote it by $\mathbf{Z}_5$. The ring $\mathbf{Z}_5$ therefore has five elements, each element being one of the equivalence sets 4.35.

We now proceed to justify these statements, and to generalize them to the case of congruence modulo n. The following properties of congruence modulo n are fundamental for our purpose.

4.36   Theorem.   *If* $a \equiv b$ *(mod* n) *and* $c \equiv d$ *(mod* n), *then*

(i) $$a + c \equiv b + d \ (mod \ n),$$

and

(ii) $$ac \equiv bd \ (mod \ n).$$

To prove these properties, we observe that $a \equiv b$ (mod n) means that there is an integer k such that $a = b + kn$. Similarly, we have $c = d + ln$ for some integer l. It follows that

$$a + c = b + d + (k + l)n;$$

that is, that $a + c \equiv b + d$ (mod n), and (i) is established. The second part follows easily by observing that

$$ac = (b + kn)(d + ln)$$
$$= bd + (bl + kd + kln)n,$$

and hence $ac \equiv bd$ (mod n), as required.

For the moment, let us denote by T the set of all equivalence sets modulo n. We proceed to define operations of addition and multiplication on T as follows. If $[r], [s] \in T$, we define

4.37 $$[r] + [s] = [r + s],$$

and

4.38
$$[r] \cdot [s] = [rs].$$

Now in order to show that these, in fact, do define addition and multiplication on the set T, we must show that the sum and product of the equivalence sets $[r]$ and $[s]$ do not depend upon the particular *notation* used to designate these sets, but only upon the sets themselves. This is sometimes expressed by saying that we must show that addition and multiplication are *well-defined* by 4.37 and 4.38. To clarify this statement, for the moment let us again consider the case in which $n = 5$. Then, by 4.37, we have that $[6] + [2] = [8]$ and that $[1] + [-3] = [-2]$. So far, the fact that $n = 5$ has played no role. But now, using this value of n, we may observe that $[6] = [1]$ and that $[2] = [-3]$, so we would certainly want to have $[6] + [2] = [1] + [-3]$. Since, in fact, $[8] = [-2]$, we see that this is indeed the case. The fact that a similar result always holds is what we mean by saying that addition of equivalence sets is well-defined. Now let n be arbitrary and let us show that the preceding theorem gives us exactly the information which we need at this point. Suppose that x, $r \in \mathbf{Z}$ such that $[x] = [r]$, and that y, $s \in \mathbf{Z}$ such that $[y] = [s]$. These imply that $x \equiv r \pmod{n}$ and that $y \equiv s \pmod{n}$. The theorem then asserts that $x + y \equiv r + s \pmod{n}$ and that $xy \equiv rs \pmod{n}$, that is, that $[x + y] = [r + s]$ and that $[xy] = [rs]$. Hence, addition and multiplication of elements of T are indeed well-defined by 4.37 and 4.38.

It is now quite easy to establish the following result.

4.39 Theorem. *With respect to the definitions 4.37 and 4.38 of addition and multiplication, the set of all equivalence sets of* **Z** *modulo n is a commutative ring with unity. This ring is called "the ring of integers modulo n," and denoted by* $\mathbf{Z}_n$.

Let us prove, for example, the associative law of addition for elements of $\mathbf{Z}_n$. If $[r]$, $[s]$, and $[t]$ are elements of $\mathbf{Z}_n$, we wish therefore to prove that

4.40
$$([r] + [s]) + [t] = [r] + ([s] + [t]).$$

Now, by 4.37, $[r] + [s] = [r + s]$, and again applying 4.37, we see that the left side of 4.40 is the element $[(r + s) + t]$ of $\mathbf{Z}_n$. A similar calculation shows that the right side of 4.40 is equal to $[r + (s + t)]$. However, by the associative law of addition *for the integers*, we know that $(r + s) + t = r + (s + t)$, and it follows that 4.40 must hold.

In a similar way, each of the other properties of $\mathbf{Z}_n$ which need to be verified in order to establish the theorem follows from the corresponding property of the ring **Z**. The proofs of these will be left as exercises. In particular, it is almost obvious that [0] is the zero of the ring $\mathbf{Z}_n$, and that [1] is its unity.

As an illustration, let us again consider the special case in which $n = 5$. As pointed out above, the five elements of this ring are [0], [1], [2], [3], and [4]. The reader may verify the following addition and multiplication tables for this ring. For convenience, we have omitted the brackets and written "k" in place of "$[k]$." This is often done when the context makes the meaning clear.

(+)	0	1	2	3	4
0	0	1	2	3	4
1	1	2	3	4	0
2	2	3	4	0	1
3	3	4	0	1	2
4	4	0	1	2	3

(·)	0	1	2	3	4
0	0	0	0	0	0
1	0	1	2	3	4
2	0	2	4	1	3
3	0	3	1	4	2
4	0	4	3	2	1

THE RING $\mathbf{Z}_5$

By examining the multiplication table for this ring we see that this ring has no nonzero divisors of zero, and hence that the ring is an integral domain. The following theorem tells us for just what integers n the ring $\mathbf{Z}_n$ is an integral domain.

4.41 Theorem. *The ring $\mathbf{Z}_n$ is an integral domain if and only if n is a prime.*

First, suppose that n is a prime p, and that $[r]$ and $[s]$ are elements of $\mathbf{Z}_p$ such that $[r] \cdot [s] = [0]$. Then $rs \equiv 0 \pmod{p}$, which implies that rs is divisible by p. Now since p is a prime, it follows that r is divisible by p or s is divisible by p, that is, that $r \equiv 0 \pmod{p}$ or $s \equiv 0 \pmod{p}$. Hence, $[r] = [0]$ or $[s] = [0]$, and $\mathbf{Z}_p$ is an integral domain.

Now, suppose that n is not prime. It follows that there exist integers n_1 and n_2 such that $n = n_1 n_2$, $1 < n_1 < n$, $1 < n_2 < n$. Hence, in $\mathbf{Z}_n$, we have $[n_1] \cdot [n_2] = [0]$, with $[n_1] \neq [0]$ and $[n_2] \neq [0]$. This shows that the ring $\mathbf{Z}_n$ is not an integral domain since it does have nonzero divisors of zero.

Although we have not as yet mentioned this important fact, let us now point out that the definitions of addition and multiplication of equivalence sets modulo n show that *the ring $\mathbf{Z}_n$ is a homomorphic image of the ring* **Z**. More precisely, the mapping $\theta: \mathbf{Z} \to \mathbf{Z}_n$ defined by $r\theta = [r]$, $r \in \mathbf{Z}$, is a homomorphic mapping of **Z** onto $\mathbf{Z}_n$. Indeed, it is this fact which assures us that in the proof of Theorem 4.39 each of the ring properties in $\mathbf{Z}_n$ is a consequence of the corresponding property in the ring $\mathbf{Z}$. (See Exercise 12 below.)

EXERCISES

1. Prove that congruence modulo n is an equivalence relation on the set $\mathbf{Z}$.

2. If $a \equiv b$ (mod n), prove by induction that $a^m \equiv b^m$ (mod n) for every positive integer m.

3. Complete the proof of Theorem 4.39.

4. Let S be the set of all positive integers n such that $n > 1$. If a, $b \in S$, let us define $a \sim b$ to mean that a and b have the same number of positive prime factors (distinct or identical). Show that "$\sim$" is an equivalence relation defined on S. If $[a]$ is the equivalence set (relative to this equivalence relation) which contains the integer a, and we set $[a] + [b] = [a + b]$, verify that we do *not* have a well-defined addition of equivalence sets.

5. Make addition and multiplication tables for each of the following rings: $\mathbf{Z}_2$, $\mathbf{Z}_3$, $\mathbf{Z}_4$, $\mathbf{Z}_6$, and $\mathbf{Z}_7$. By examining the multiplication tables, determine which of these rings are integral domains and compare with Theorem 4.41.

6. Verify that the ring $\mathbf{Z}_2$ is isomorphic to the ring of Example 5 of Section 2.3.

7. Determine whether the ring $\mathbf{Z}_4$ is isomorphic to either of the rings of Examples 6 and 7 of Section 2.3.

8. Verify that the elements $[0]$, $[3]$, $[6]$, and $[9]$ of the ring $\mathbf{Z}_{12}$ are the elements of a subring of $\mathbf{Z}_{12}$. Find an isomorphic mapping of $\mathbf{Z}_4$ onto this subring.

9. Is the integral domain $\mathbf{Z}_p$ (p a prime) an ordered integral domain? Why?

10. Characterize those integers a such that the element $[a]$ of $\mathbf{Z}_n$ is a divisor of zero.

11. Prove that the nonzero element $[a]$ of the ring $\mathbf{Z}_n$ has a multiplicative inverse in $\mathbf{Z}_n$ if and only if a and n are relatively prime.

12. Let R be a ring and S a set on which operations of addition and multiplication are defined. If there exists a mapping θ of R onto S which preserves the operations of addition and multiplication, prove that S is a ring with respect to the operations of addition and multiplication defined on S. (This fact is often expressed by saying that "a homomorphic image of a ring is a ring.")

13. (i) If $n = 2k$, where k is a positive odd integer, verify that $k^2 \equiv k$ (mod n).
    (ii) If n is as in the preceding, prove that the ring $\mathbf{Z}_n$ contains a subring which is isomorphic to $\mathbf{Z}_2$. (A more general result is asked for in Exercise 15 below.)

14. Let m and n be positive integers greater than one, and let us denote elements of $\mathbf{Z}_{mn}$ and of $\mathbf{Z}_n$ by subscripts mn and n, respectively. Verify that the mapping $\theta\colon \mathbf{Z}_{mn} \to \mathbf{Z}_n$ defined by $[i]_{mn}\theta = [i]_n$, $i \in \mathbf{Z}$, is well-defined (that is, that it actually defines a mapping of $\mathbf{Z}_{mn}$ into $\mathbf{Z}_n$) and that it is a homomorphic mapping of $\mathbf{Z}_{mn}$ onto $\mathbf{Z}_n$.

15. If m and n are relatively prime positive integers greater than one, prove that the ring $\mathbf{Z}_{mn}$ has a subring which is isomorphic to the ring $\mathbf{Z}_n$. (Hint: If $am + bn = 1$, show that the mapping ϕ defined by $[iam]_{mn}\phi = [i]_n$, $i \in \mathbf{Z}$, is well-defined and is the desired isomorphism.)

NOTES AND REFERENCES

This chapter has given a very brief introduction to that branch of mathematics usually called *The Theory of Numbers*. The word "numbers" in this connection is usually understood to mean "integers."

There are many books on this subject. See, e.g., references [39] through [44] of the bibliography. Several of these books, in particular [43], include some of the interesting history of this subject.

FIELDS AND THE RATIONAL NUMBERS

The ring **Z** of integers has the property, which is not true of the natural numbers (positive integers) alone, that every equation of the form $a + x = b$, where $a, b \in \mathbf{Z}$, has a solution x in **Z**. In fact, one of the principal reasons for the introduction of the negative integers and zero is to assure us that every such equation is solvable. However, in **Z**, an equation of the form $ax = b$ is solvable if and only if a is a divisor of b. Clearly, in order that an equation of this form, where $a, b \in \mathbf{Z}$ and $a \neq 0$, always have a solution we need to have available the rational numbers as well as the integers. Later on in this chapter we shall show how to extend the ring **Z** of integers to the larger system of rational numbers. In this process we shall not use any previous knowledge of the rational number system, except perhaps to motivate the procedure used, but shall carry out the construction using only the properties of the integers which have already been given. Before presenting this construction we shall introduce and discuss the important concept of a *field*.

In a final optional section we shall briefly indicate how the ring of integers can be constructed from the system of natural numbers. This material is presented here because the method closely parallels that by which the rational numbers are constructed from the integers.

5.1 FIELDS

Let us make the following definition.

5.1 Definition. A commutative ring F with more than one element and having a unity is said to be a *field* if every nonzero element of F has a multiplicative inverse in F.

In view of Theorem 2.9, we know that every nonzero element of a field has a *unique* multiplicative inverse. As indicated in Section 2.5, we may denote the multiplicative inverse of a nonzero element r of a field F by r^{-1}. If 1 is the unity of F, r^{-1} is therefore the unique element of F such that

5.2 $$r \cdot r^{-1} = r^{-1} \cdot r = 1.$$

However, the commutative law of multiplication is required to hold in a field, and we shall henceforth use it without explicit mention. In particular, we may consider that r^{-1} is defined by the single equation $r \cdot r^{-1} = 1$.

We shall now prove the following result.

5.3 Theorem. *A field is necessarily an integral domain.*

Suppose that r and s are elements of a field F such that $rs = 0$. If $r \neq 0$, r has a multiplicative inverse r^{-1} in F and it follows that

$$r^{-1}(rs) = (r^{-1}r)s = 1 \cdot s = s.$$

But also,

$$r^{-1}(rs) = r^{-1} \cdot 0 = 0.$$

Hence $s = 0$, and we have shown that $r = 0$ or $s = 0$. This proves that F has no nonzero divisors of zero and F therefore satisfies Definition 3.3 of an integral domain.

Although in the definition of a field we only required the existence of the multiplicative inverse of each nonzero element r, that is, the solvability of each equation of the form $rx = 1$, we can easily establish the following more general result.

5.4 Theorem. *If r and s are elements of a field F and $r \neq 0$, there exists a unique element y of F such that $ry = s$. Moreover, $y = r^{-1} \cdot s$.*

It is clear that $r^{-1} \cdot s$ *is* a solution of this equation since

$$r(r^{-1} \cdot s) = (r \cdot r^{-1})s = 1 \cdot s = s.$$

To obtain the *uniqueness* of the solution, suppose that $ry_1 = s$ and that $ry_2 = s$. Then $ry_1 = ry_2$ and, since $r \neq 0$, the cancellation law of multiplication shows that $y_1 = y_2$.

Let us now give a few examples of fields. It is to be understood that the usual definitions of addition and multiplication are implied.

EXAMPLE 1. The set of all rational numbers; that is, all numbers of the form a/b, where $a, b \in \mathbf{Z}$ with $b \neq 0$.

EXAMPLE 2. The set of all real numbers of the form $x + y\sqrt{2}$, where x and y are rational numbers. What is the multiplicative inverse of each nonzero element?

EXAMPLE 3. The set of all real numbers of the form $u + v\sqrt{3}$, where u and v are elements of the field of the preceding example. It is true that every nonzero element has a multiplicative inverse in this set, but we shall not here write out a proof of this fact.

The following theorem gives some other examples of fields of quite a different type.

5.5 Theorem. *If p is a prime, the ring $\mathbf{Z}_p$ of integers modulo p is a field.*

This theorem is implied by the result of Exercise 11 of the preceding set of exercises. However, we now give a detailed proof of this important theorem.

We already know that $\mathbf{Z}_p$ is a commutative ring with unity and, using the notation of Section 4.7, the unity is [1]. Let [r] be any nonzero element of $\mathbf{Z}_p$. In order to show that we have a field, we need to show that there exists an element [x] of $\mathbf{Z}_p$ such that $[r] \cdot [x] = [1]$. The fact that $[r] \neq [0]$ implies that $r \not\equiv 0 \pmod{p}$, that is, that r is not divisible by p. Since p is a prime, it follows that r and p are relatively prime and Theorem 4.12 then assures us that there exist integers x, y such that $rx + py = 1$. This implies that $rx \equiv 1 \pmod{p}$, and hence that $[r] \cdot [x] = [1]$, as required.

We may remark that if n is not prime, we know by Theorem 4.41 that the ring $\mathbf{Z}_n$ is not even an integral domain, and certainly then is not a field.

A field $\mathbf{Z}_p$ differs from the usual fields of elementary algebra in that it has only a finite number of elements. However, in this as in any field we can always perform the so-called rational operations of addition, multiplication, subtraction, and division (except by zero). We are here using the familiar word "subtraction" to mean addition of additive inverse, and "division" to mean multiplication by the multiplicative inverse. We may emphasize that division by zero is not defined in any field F since $0 \cdot x \neq 1$ for every x in F, and therefore 0 cannot have a multiplicative inverse.

We have required that a field contain at least two elements, and we may now observe that there does exist a field having exactly two elements, namely, the field $\mathbf{Z}_2$.

In view of Theorems 4.41 and 5.5, we know that if the ring $\mathbf{Z}_n$ is an integral domain, it is actually a field. On the other hand, the ring $\mathbf{Z}$ of integers is an integral domain which is not a field. In this connection, the following theorem may be of some interest.

5.6   Theorem.   *An integral domain S with a finite number of elements is necessarily a field.*

PROOF: Suppose that S has exactly n distinct elements a_1, $a_2, \cdots, a_n$ and, for later convenience, let us agree that a_1 is the unity of S. Now suppose that a_k is an arbitrary nonzero element of S and let us show that it has a multiplicative inverse in S. Consider the set $A = \{a_k a_1, a_k a_2, \cdots, a_k a_n\}$ consisting of the product of the n elements of S by the element a_k. Since $a_k \neq 0$, the cancellation law of multiplication shows that $a_k a_i = a_k a_j$ only if $a_i = a_j$. Hence no two of the indicated elements of A can be equal. That is, the elements of A are n distinct elements of S and therefore are *all* the elements of S. Since one of them is the unity a_1, there must exist some element a_l of S such that $a_k a_l = a_1$, and a_l is the multiplicative inverse of a_k. This argument shows that every nonzero element of S has a multiplicative inverse in S and therefore that S is a field.

Incidentally, the proof of this theorem furnishes an alternate proof of Theorem 5.5 since we already know by Theorem 4.41 that $\mathbf{Z}_p$ is an integral domain (with a finite number of elements) if p is a prime.

EXERCISES

1. Find the multiplicative inverse of each nonzero element of each of the following fields: $\mathbf{Z}_5$, $\mathbf{Z}_7$, $\mathbf{Z}_{11}$, $\mathbf{Z}_{13}$, $\mathbf{Z}_{17}$.

2. Find the multiplicative inverse of each of the following elements of the field $\mathbf{Z}_{1847}$: [12], [35], [416], [800].

3. Show that there exists a finite field which is not isomorphic to $\mathbf{Z}_p$ for any prime p. [Hint: Consider Example 7 of Section 2.3.]

4. Determine at exactly what point the proof of Theorem 5.6 makes use of the assumption that S has a finite number of elements.

[Hint: Try to apply the proof to the integral domain **Z** and see where it breaks down.]

5. Prove: If R is a commutative ring with more than one element and with the property that for a, $b \in R$, $a \neq 0$, there exists $x \in R$ such that $ax = b$, then R is a field.

6. Let P be the set of all positive real numbers, and q a fixed positive real number not equal to 1. If a, $b \in P$, we define operations of addition "$\oplus$" and multiplication "$\odot$" on P as follows:

$$a \oplus b = ab \text{ (ordinary multiplication)}, \quad a \odot b = a^{\log_q b}.$$

Assuming as known all the familiar elementary properties of logarithms, prove that P is a field with respect to these definitions of addition and multiplication.

5.2 THE CHARACTERISTIC

Although we are now primarily interested in fields, the concept to be introduced in this section applies to any ring and we therefore give the definition in its general form. We recall that if a is an element of a ring and n is a positive integer, we have given in Section 2.6 a recursive definition of na. We now make the following definition.

5.7 Definition.   Let R be a ring. If there exists a positive integer n such that $na = 0$ for every element a of R, the smallest such positive integer n is called the *characteristic* of R. If no such positive integer exists, R is said to have *characteristic zero*.

All the familiar number systems of elementary algebra certainly have characteristic zero. However, let us consider, for example, the ring $\mathbf{Z}_4$ of integers modulo 4. If $[r]$ is any element of this ring, then $2[r] = [r] + [r] = [2r]$ and, generally, if k is a positive integer, $k[r] = [kr]$. The smallest positive integer k such that $[kr] = [0]$ for every element $[r]$ of $\mathbf{Z}_4$ is clearly 4, so $\mathbf{Z}_4$ has characteristic 4. In general, the ring $\mathbf{Z}_n$ has characteristic n.

The definition of the characteristic of a ring makes an assertion about *every* element of the ring. However, in an important special case, the following theorem shows that the characteristic is determined by some one particular element.

5.8 Theorem.   *Let R be a ring ring with a unity e. If there exists a positive integer n such that $ne = 0$, then the smallest such positive integer is the characteristic of R. If no such positive integer exists, then R has characteristic zero.*

PROOF: If n is the smallest positive integer such that $ne = 0$, the characteristic of R certainly cannot be a positive integer less than n. Moreover, if $a \in R$, then

$$na = (na)e = (ne)a = 0a = 0,$$

so that $na = 0$ for every element a of R; hence R has characteristic n. The last sentence of the theorem is an immediate consequence of the definition of characteristic zero.

We know that the ring $\mathbf{Z}_n$ is a field if and only if n is a prime. Hence the characteristic of every field that has been mentioned so far is either zero or a prime. In fact, we shall now prove that this is always true for every integral domain and certainly then for every field.

5.9 Theorem. *Every integral domain D has characteristic zero or a prime.*

To prove this theorem, suppose that D has characteristic $n > 0$, and that n is *not* a prime. Then $n = n_1 n_2$, where $1 < n_1 < n$, and $1 < n_2 < n$. If e is the unity of D, we have $ne = 0$ and therefore $(n_1 n_2)e = 0$. However, this implies that $(n_1 e)(n_2 e) = 0$ and, by the definition of an integral domain, it follows that $n_1 e = 0$ or $n_2 e = 0$. But if $n_1 e = 0$, the preceding theorem shows that D cannot have characteristic $n > n_1$, hence $n_1 e \neq 0$. Similarly, $n_2 e \neq 0$, and we have a contradiction of the assumption that n is not a prime. The proof is therefore complete.

We next consider the following result.

5.10 Theorem. *An integral domain with characteristic zero has a subring which is isomorphic to $\mathbf{Z}$. An integral domain with characteristic a prime p has a subring which is isomorphic to $\mathbf{Z}_p$.*

We shall present some of the steps in the proof of this theorem and leave some of the details to the reader.

Let D be an integral domain with unity e, and let us set

$$\mathbf{Z}e = \{ne \mid n \in \mathbf{Z}\}.$$

Then $\mathbf{Z}e$ is a subring of D and it is this subring which we consider.

First, suppose that D has characteristic zero and let $\theta: \mathbf{Z} \to \mathbf{Z}e$ be the mapping defined by $n\theta = ne$, $n \in \mathbf{Z}$. Clearly, θ is an onto mapping, so let us verify that it is a one-one mapping. If $n_1 e = n_2 e$ with $n_1, n_2 \in \mathbf{Z}$, the notation can be so chosen that $n_1 \geq n_2$. Then $(n_1 - n_2)e = 0$ and, by Theorem 5.8, we cannot have $n_1 - n_2 > 0$ since this would violate the assumption that D has characteristic zero. Accordingly, we conclude that $n_1 = n_2$ and θ is indeed a one-one mapping. It is then easily verified that addition and multiplication are preserved under the mapping θ, and hence that θ is an isomorphism of $\mathbf{Z}$ onto $\mathbf{Z}e$.

Next, suppose that D has characteristic p and let us, as usual, denote the equivalence set modulo p which contains the integer n by $[n]$. Let $\phi: \mathbf{Z}_p \to \mathbf{Z}e$ be the mapping defined by $[n]\phi = ne$, $n \in \mathbf{Z}$. We leave it to the reader to verify that this mapping is well-defined. However, let us show that it is a one-one mapping. Suppose that $n_1, n_2 \in \mathbf{Z}$ such that $n_1 e = n_2 e$, or $(n_1 - n_2)e = 0$. By the Division Algorithm,

$$n_1 - n_2 = qp + r, \qquad\qquad 0 \leq r < p.$$

Thus

$$(n_1 - n_2)e = (qp + r)e = qpe + re = re.$$

This shows that $re = 0$ and, by Theorem 5.8, it cannot be true that r is a positive integer less than p. Hence we must have $r = 0$ and therefore $n_1 - n_2 = qp$. It follows that $[n_1] = [n_2]$ and ϕ is thus a one-one mapping. We leave it to the reader to verify that ϕ is the desired isomorphism of $\mathbf{Z}_p$ onto the subring $\mathbf{Z}e$ of D.

The literature on the theory of fields is quite extensive. In much of this work the concept of the characteristic of a field plays an essential role. It frequently happens, for example, that although a theorem may be true for every field, different proofs have to be given for the case in which the characteristic is zero and that in which it is a prime. Later on in this book we shall present additional examples of fields.

5.3 SOME FAMILIAR NOTATION

Let F be a field with unity 1, and t a nonzero element of F. We have introduced the symbol t^{-1} to designate the multiplicative inverse of t, and have found that if $s \in F$, the unique element x of F such that $tx = s$ is given by $x = t^{-1}s$. In accordance with familiar usage, we shall also designate this element $t^{-1}s$ by $\dfrac{s}{t}$ or by s/t. In particular, we have $t^{-1} = 1/t$.

Suppose, now, that v is also a nonzero element of F. Since $(tv)\,(v^{-1}t^{-1}) = 1$, the multiplicative inverse of tv is $v^{-1}t^{-1}$, that is,

5.11
$$(tv)^{-1} = v^{-1}t^{-1}.$$

It is now easy to see that

5.12
$$\frac{sv}{tv} = \frac{s}{t}.$$

This follows by the following calculation, making use of 5.11:

$$\frac{sv}{tv} = (tv)^{-1}(sv) = v^{-1}t^{-1}sv = t^{-1}s = \frac{s}{t}.$$

As a generalization of 5.12, let s and u be arbitrary elements of F, and t and v arbitrary nonzero elements of F. Then we assert that

5.13
$$\frac{s}{t} = \frac{u}{v} \quad \text{if and only if} \quad sv = tu.$$

Suppose, first, that $s/t = u/v$, that is, that $t^{-1}s = v^{-1}u$. Multiplication by tv yields $sv = tu$. Conversely, if $sv = tu$, multiplication by $t^{-1}v^{-1}$ shows that $t^{-1}s = v^{-1}u$ or, otherwise expressed, that $s/t = u/v$.

The following are also easy to establish and will be left as exercises:

5.14

(i)
$$\frac{s}{t} + \frac{u}{v} = \frac{sv + tu}{tv},$$

(ii)
$$\frac{s}{t} \cdot \frac{u}{v} = \frac{su}{tv}.$$

Now a few remarks about exponents. If t is a nonzero element of F, we have a definition of t^{-1}; and if n is any positive integer, we now define t^{-n} to be $(t^{-1})^n$; also we define $t^0 = 1$. Under these definitions, the following laws of exponents hold for every choice of m and n as arbitrary integers (positive, negative, or zero), it being understood that t and v are arbitrary nonzero elements of F:

5.15
$$t^m \cdot t^n = t^{m+n},$$
$$\frac{t^m}{t^n} = t^{m-n},$$
$$(t^m)^n = t^{mn},$$
$$(tv)^m = t^m \cdot v^m,$$
$$\left(\frac{t}{v}\right)^m = \frac{t^m}{v^m}.$$

Of course, these are generalizations of the laws 2.26, 2.27, which hold for a commutative ring. Complete proofs of 5.15 can be given by mathematical induction.

EXERCISES

1. Let R be a ring with a finite number of elements, and r a nonzero element of R.

   (i) Show that there must exist a positive integer m such that $mr = 0$.

   (ii) Show that R cannot have characteristic zero.

2. Let a be a fixed nonzero element of an integral domain D such that $ma = 0$ for some positive integer m. Prove that the smallest such positive integer is the characteristic of D (that is, it is independent of the particular nonzero element a which is chosen). Show, by an example, that this result is not necessarily true for a *ring*.

3. Given the characteristics of rings R and S, what can you say about the characteristic of the direct sum $R \oplus S$?

4. Prove 5.14(i), (ii).

5. If s, t, u, and v are elements of a field F, prove (without using the laws of exponents) each of the following in which it is assumed that the necessary elements are different from zero:

   (i) $(t^{-1})^{-1} = t,$

   (ii) $(-t)^{-1} = -(t^{-1}),$

   (iii) $\left(\dfrac{s}{t}\right)^{-1} = \dfrac{t}{s},$

   (iv) $\dfrac{\dfrac{s}{t}}{\dfrac{u}{v}} = \dfrac{vs}{ut},$

   (v) $-\dfrac{s}{t} = \dfrac{(-s)}{t} = \dfrac{s}{(-t)},$

   (vi) $\dfrac{s}{t} + \dfrac{u}{t} = \dfrac{s + u}{t},$

   (vii) $\dfrac{s}{t} - \dfrac{u}{v} = \dfrac{sv - tu}{tv}.$

6. Let c and d be distinct elements of a field F. If new operations of addition and multiplication are defined on F as follows:

$$x \oplus y = x + y - c, \quad x \odot y = c + \frac{(x - c)(y - c)}{d - c},$$

   prove that one obtains a field F'. What are the zero and the unity of F'?

7. If F and F' are as in the preceding exercise, prove that the mapping $\theta: F \rightarrow F'$ defined by $x\theta = (d - c)x + c,\ x \in F$, is an isomorphism of F onto F'.

8. If a and b are elements of a commutative ring with characteristic the prime p, prove that $(a + b)^p = a^p + b^p$. Then generalize this result by proving that for every positive integer n, $(a + b)^{p^n} = a^{p^n} + b^{p^n}$.

5.4   THE FIELD OF RATIONAL NUMBERS

We now change our point of view as follows. Instead of studying properties of a given field, let us see how we can start with the integral domain $\mathbf{Z}$ of the integers and *construct* a field which contains $\mathbf{Z}$. This is our first example of an important algebraic problem which may be stated in a general way as follows. Given an algebraic system U which does not have some specified property, to construct a larger system V which contains U and which does have the property in question. Naturally, this is not always possible, but it is in a number of interesting cases. At present, we start with the integral domain $\mathbf{Z}$ in which not every nonzero element has a multiplicative inverse, and shall construct a larger system—the field of rational numbers—which contains $\mathbf{Z}$ and in which every nonzero element necessarily has a multiplicative inverse. In this construction, our previous knowledge of the rational numbers will certainly be useful in suggesting procedure, but will be used in no other way.

Let S denote the set of all ordered pairs $(a\,,b)$, where $a, b \in \mathbf{Z}$ and $b \neq 0$, that is,

$$S = \{(a\,,b)|a\,,b \in \mathbf{Z}, b \neq 0\}.$$

What we are going to do will be *suggested* by thinking of $(a\,,b)$ as the familiar a/b, but we use an unfamiliar notation in order to clarify the logical procedure and to avoid using any property until we have actually proved it. If $(a\,,b)$ and $(c\,,d)$ are elements of S, we define $(a\,,b) \sim (c\,,d)$ to mean that $ad = bc$. Actually, "$\sim$" is an equivalence relation defined on S. The reflexive and symmetric properties are obviously true, and we now prove the transitive property. Suppose that $(a\,,b) \sim (c\,,d)$ and $(c\,,d) \sim (e\,,f)$, and let us show that $(a\,,b) \sim (e\,,f)$. Since $(a\,,b) \sim (c\,,d)$, we have $ad = bc$; and, similarly, we have $cf = de$. Multiplication of these equations by f and by b, respectively, yields $adf = bcf$ and $bcf = bde$. Hence $adf = bde$ and, since $d \neq 0$, it follows that $af = be$, that is, that $(a\,,b) \sim (e\,,f)$.

Now that we have an equivalence relation "$\sim$" defined on S, we follow a procedure somewhat like that previously used in obtaining the ring of integers modulo n. That is, we shall consider equivalence sets relative to "$\sim$," and give appropriate definitions of addition and multiplication of these sets.

If $(a, b) \in S$, according to our previous usage the equivalence set containing (a, b) would be designated by $[(a, b)]$. However, we shall now use the simpler notation $[a, b]$ to designate this equivalence set. In the sequel it is important to keep in mind that $[a, b] = [a_1, b_1]$ if and only if $(a, b) \sim (a_1, b_1)$, that is, if and only if $ab_1 = ba_1$. Of course, this is just the general property 1.15(i) of equivalence sets as applied in this particular case. The equivalence set $[a, b]$ may therefore be expressed as follows:

5.16 $$[a, b] = \{(x, y) | (x, y) \in S, xb = ya\}.$$

We now define addition and multiplication of equivalence sets as follows:

5.17 $$[a, b] + [c, d] = [ad + bc, bd],$$

and

5.18 $$[a, b] \cdot [c, d] = [ac, bd].$$

First, we observe that since (a, b) and (c, d) are elements of S, we have $b \neq 0$ and $d \neq 0$. Hence, $bd \neq 0$, so that in fact $(ad + bc, bd)$ and (ac, bd) are elements of S and the right sides of 5.17 and 5.18 are equivalence sets.

Now, just as in the case of integers modulo n, we must show that addition and multiplication of equivalence sets are well-defined by 5.17 and 5.18. Suppose, then, that

5.19 $$[a, b] = [a_1, b_1] \quad \text{and} \quad [c, d] = [c_1, d_1].$$

In order to show that addition of equivalence sets is well-defined by 5.17 we must show that necessarily

$$[a, b] + [c, d] = [a_1, b_1] + [c_1, d_1];$$

that is, that

5.20 $$[ad + bc, bd] = [a_1 d_1 + b_1 c_1, b_1 d_1].$$

From 5.19, we have that $ab_1 = ba_1$, and that $cd_1 = dc_1$. If we multiply the first of these equations by dd_1, the second by bb_1, and add the corresponding members, it follows that

$$(ad + bc)b_1d_1 = bd(a_1d_1 + b_1c_1).$$

However, this implies 5.20, and therefore addition of equivalence sets is well-defined by 5.17. The proof that multiplication is well-defined by 5.18 will be left as an exercise.

We may now state the following theorem.

5.21   Theorem.   *Let* $\mathbf{Q}$ *denote the set of all equivalence sets of* S *relative to the equivalence relation "* $\sim$ *." Then with respect to the operations of addition and multiplication on* $\mathbf{Q}$ *defined by 5.17 and 5.18,* $\mathbf{Q}$ *is a field. Moreover, the set of all elements of* $\mathbf{Q}$ *of the form* $[a, 1]$, $a \in \mathbf{Z}$, *is a subring* $\mathbf{Z}'$ *of* $\mathbf{Q}$; *and the mapping* $\theta: \mathbf{Z} \to \mathbf{Z}'$ *defined by*

$$a\theta = [a, 1], \qquad\qquad a \in \mathbf{Z},$$

is an isomorphism of $\mathbf{Z}$ *onto* $\mathbf{Z}'$.

The commutative laws of addition and multiplication, as well as the associative law of multiplication, are almost obvious, and we omit the details. The associative law of addition may be verified by the following straightforward calculation. Let $[a, b]$, $[c, d]$, and $[e, f]$ be elements of $\mathbf{Q}$. Then

$$([a, b] + [c, d]) + [e, f] = [ad + bc, bd] + [e, f]$$
$$= [adf + bcf + bde, bdf],$$

and

$$[a, b] + ([c, d] + [e, f]) = [a, b] + [cf + de, df]$$
$$= [adf + bcf + bde, bdf],$$

and we therefore have

$$([a, b] + [c, d]) + [e, f] = [a, b] + ([c, d] + [e, f]).$$

Since $[0, 1] + [a, b] = [a, b]$, and $[1, 1] \cdot [a, b] = [a, b]$, it follows that $[0, 1]$ is the zero and $[1, 1]$ the unity of $\mathbf{Q}$. However, if d is a nonzero integer, we have $[d, d] = [1, 1]$ and, similarly, $[0, 1] = [0, d]$. Hence the unity is $[d, d]$ and the zero is $[0, d]$ for *any* nonzero integer d. We may also observe that $[a, b] = [0, 1]$ if and only if $a = 0$, and to say, therefore, that $[a, b]$ is a nonzero element of $\mathbf{Q}$ is to say that $a \neq 0$. Since $[a, b] + [-a, b] = [0, b^2]$, and $[0, b^2]$ is the zero of $\mathbf{Q}$, it follows that the additive inverse of $[a, b]$ is $[-a, b]$, that is, we have $-[a, b] = [-a, b]$, and each element of $\mathbf{Q}$ has an additive inverse.

One of the distributive laws is a consequence of the following calculations in which, at one point, we make use of the fact that $[b, b]$ is the unity of $\mathbf{Q}$:

$$[a, b]([c, d] + [e, f]) = [a, b] \cdot [cf + de, df]$$
$$= [acf + ade, bdf],$$

$$[a, b] \cdot [c, d] + [a, b] \cdot [e, f] = [ac, bd] + [ae, bf]$$
$$= [acbf + bdae, b^2df]$$
$$= [acf + ade, bdf] \cdot [b, b]$$
$$= [acf + ade, bdf].$$

The other distributive law is an immediate consequence of this one since multiplication is commutative.

Up to this point we have proved that $\mathbf{Q}$ is a commutative ring with unity. To prove that $\mathbf{Q}$ is a field, there remains only to show that every nonzero element of $\mathbf{Q}$ has a multiplicative inverse in $\mathbf{Q}$. If $[a, b]$ is a nonzero element of $\mathbf{Q}$, then $a \neq 0$ as well as $b \neq 0$, and it is clear that $[b, a] \in \mathbf{Q}$. Moreover,

$$[a, b] \cdot [b, a] = [ab, ab] = [1, 1],$$

and the multiplicative inverse of $[a, b]$ is $[b, a]$. That is, if $[a, b]$ is a nonzero element of $\mathbf{Q}$, then $[a, b]^{-1} = [b, a]$. This completes the proof that $\mathbf{Q}$ is a field.

Now let $\mathbf{Z}'$ be the set of elements of $\mathbf{Q}$ of the form $[a, 1]$, $a \in \mathbf{Z}$, and consider the mapping $\theta: \mathbf{Z} \to \mathbf{Z}'$ defined by $a\theta = [a, 1]$, $a \in \mathbf{Z}$. This is clearly an onto mapping and it is also a one-one mapping since $[a, 1] = [b, 1]$ implies that $a = b$. Moreover, for $a, b \in \mathbf{Z}$, we have

$$(a + b)\theta = [a + b, 1] = [a, 1] + [b, 1] = a\theta + b\theta,$$

and

$$(ab)\theta = [ab, 1] = [a, 1] \cdot [b, 1] = (a\theta)(b\theta).$$

Thus θ is an isomorphism of $\mathbf{Z}$ onto $\mathbf{Z}'$, and the theorem is established.

Since the subring $\mathbf{Z}'$ of $\mathbf{Q}$ is isomorphic to $\mathbf{Z}$, we shall henceforth find it convenient to identify $\mathbf{Z}'$ with $\mathbf{Z}$ and, as a matter of notation, write simply a to designate the element $[a, 1]$ of $\mathbf{Q}$. We may then consider that the field $\mathbf{Q}$ actually contains the ring $\mathbf{Z}$ of integers.

As a further simplification of notation, let us observe that

$$[a , b] = [a , 1] \cdot [1 , b] = [a , 1] \cdot [b , 1]^{-1},$$

and hence we are justified in writing $a \cdot b^{-1}$ or a/b for the element $[a , b]$ of $\mathbf{Q}$. Now that we have justified our familiar notation, we shall henceforth call an element of $\mathbf{Q}$ a *rational number* and the field $\mathbf{Q}$ the *field of rational numbers*. All of the notation of the preceding section naturally applies to the field $\mathbf{Q}$. Throughout the rest of this book, $\mathbf{Q}$ will consistently be used to designate the field of rational numbers.

In the notation which we have finally introduced, the field $\mathbf{Q}$ consists of all numbers of the form a/b, where a and b are integers with $b \neq 0$, addition and multiplication being defined in the usual way (5.17 , 5.18).

Let us emphasize the meaning of the notation we have introduced by considering, for example, the rational number $1/2$. We are writing $1/2$ for the equivalence set $[1 , 2]$ used above. Now $[1 , 2] = [c , d]$ if and only if $d = 2c$, so we see that $1/2$ represents the equivalence set consisting of all ordered pairs of the form $(c , 2c)$, where c is a nonzero integer. Moreover, for example, $1/2 = 3/6$ simply because, by our definition of equivalence, $(1 , 2) \sim (3 , 6)$ and therefore $[1 , 2] = [3 , 6]$.

Since $(-a)/b = a/(-b)$, we see that every rational number can be written in the form c/d, where $d > 0$. Moreover, if the integers c and d have a common nonzero factor k, so that $c = c_1 k$ and $d = d_1 k$, then $c/d = c_1/d_1$. It follows that every rational number r can be written uniquely in the form a/b, where a and b are relatively prime integers with $b > 0$. If r is expressed in this form, it is sometimes said that r is expressed *in lowest terms*.

Before proceeding to establish a few properties of the field $\mathbf{Q}$ of rational numbers, let us point out that in the above construction of the field $\mathbf{Q}$, the *only* properties of the integers which were used are those that imply that $\mathbf{Z}$ is an integral domain. Accordingly, by exactly the same construction we could start with an arbitrary integral domain D and obtain the *field of quotients* of D whose elements are expressible in the form ab^{-1}, where $a, b \in D$ with $b \neq 0$. In this terminology, the field $\mathbf{Q}$ of rational numbers is the field of quotients of $\mathbf{Z}$.

5.5   A FEW PROPERTIES OF THE FIELD OF RATIONAL NUMBERS

We have defined in Section 3.2 what we mean by an ordered integral domain. Since a field is necessarily an integral domain, by an *ordered field* we shall naturally mean a field which is an ordered integral domain. We shall now prove the following result.

5.22   Theorem.   *Let $\mathbf{Q}^+$ denote the set of all rational numbers a/b, where a and b are integers such that $ab > 0$. Then $\mathbf{Q}^+$ has the Properties 3.4 which define an ordered integral domain, and therefore the field $\mathbf{Q}$ is an ordered field whose positive elements are the elements of $\mathbf{Q}^+$.*

We may point out that when we write $ab > 0$, we mean that ab is a positive *integer* and we are only making use of the fact that $\mathbf{Z}$ is an ordered integral domain.

First, we need to show that the definition of an element of $\mathbf{Q}^+$ does not depend upon the particular representation of a rational number. That is, we need to show that if $a/b = c/d$ and $ab > 0$, then also $cd > 0$. This follows from the observation that $a/b = c/d$ means that $ad = bc$, and $ab > 0$ implies that either a and b are both positive or they are both negative. The same must therefore be true of c and d; hence also $cd > 0$.

Now let us show (3.4(i)) that the set $\mathbf{Q}^+$ is closed under addition. Let a/b and c/d be elements of $\mathbf{Q}^+$, and therefore $ab > 0$ and $cd > 0$. Then

$$\frac{a}{b} + \frac{c}{d} = \frac{ad + bc}{bd},$$

and we wish to show that

$$(ad + bc)bd = abd^2 + cdb^2 > 0.$$

However, this inequality follows easily from the following known inequalities: $ab > 0$, $cd > 0$, $b^2 > 0$, and $d^2 > 0$.

It is trivial that $\mathbf{Q}^+$ is closed under multiplication (3.4(ii)). Moreover, if a/b is a nonzero rational number, then either $ab > 0$ or $ab < 0$. It follows that for every rational number a/b, exactly one of the following holds (3.4(iii)):

$$\frac{a}{b} = 0, \quad \frac{a}{b} > 0, \quad -\frac{a}{b} > 0.$$

Hence $\mathbf{Q}^+$ has the three required properties, and the field $\mathbf{Q}$ of rational numbers is ordered.

It will be observed that what we have done is to make use of the known ordering of the integers to establish an ordering of the rational numbers. Inasmuch as we have identified the integer a with the rational number $a/1$, it is clear that a is a positive integer if and only if a is a positive rational number. In other words, our ordering of the rational numbers is an *extension* of the previous ordering of the integers.

In view of Theorem 5.22, we can introduce inequalities involving rational numbers in the usual way. That is, if $r, s \in \mathbf{Q}$, we write $r > s$

(or $s < r$) to mean that $r - s \in \mathbf{Q}^+$, and so on. We now have available all the usual properties (3.6) of inequalities for rational numbers. In the future we shall make use of these properties without specific reference.

The following is a significant property of the rational numbers.

5.23 Theorem. *Between any two distinct rational numbers there is another rational number.*

Suppose that $r, s \in \mathbf{Q}$ with $r < s$. The theorem will be established by showing that

$$r < \frac{r + s}{2} < s,$$

and hence that $(r + s)/2$ is a rational number between r and s. Since $r < s$, we have $r + r < r + s$, or $2r < r + s$. Now multiplying this last inequality by the positive rational number $1/2$, we see that $r < (r + s)/2$. In a similar manner, it can be shown that $(r + s)/2 < s$, and we omit the details.

The property of the rational numbers stated in the preceding theorem is often expressed by saying that the rational numbers are *dense*. We shall now prove in the following theorem another simple, but important, property of the rational numbers.

5.24 Theorem. (Archimedean Property)

If r and s are any positive rational numbers, there exists a positive integer n such that $nr > s$.

Let $r = a/b$, $s = c/d$, where a, b, c, and d are positive integers. If n is a positive integer, then $n(a/b) > c/d$ if and only if $n(ad) > bc$. We now assert that this last inequality is necessarily satisfied if we choose $n = 2bc$. For $ad \geq 1$, and therefore $2ad > 1$. Multiplying this inequality by the positive integer bc shows that $2adbc > bc$. Hence, $n = 2bc$ certainly satisfies our requirement. Of course, we do not mean to imply that this is necessarily the smallest possible choice of n.

5.6 SUBFIELDS AND EXTENSIONS

Let us make the following convenient definition.

5.25 Definition. A subring F' of a field F which is itself a field is called a *subfield* of F. If F' is a subfield of F, F is frequently called an *extension* of F'.

Although we are here primarily interested in fields, we shall first prove the following fairly general result (cf. Exercise 14 of Section 2.5).

5.26 Theorem. *Let D be an integral domain with unity e, and suppose that R is a subring of D having more than one element. Then, if R has a unity, $e \in R$ and e is the unity of R.*

PROOF: Let f be the unity of R and let us prove that $f = e$. Clearly,

$$f(fe - e) = f^2e - fe = fe - fe = 0.$$

However, $f \neq 0$ since R has more than one element, and therefore f is not a divisor of zero in the integral domain D. Hence we must have $fe - e = 0$, or $fe = e$. But e is the unity of D and $f \in D$, so $fe = f$ and we conclude that $f = e$, as we wished to show.

Since a field F is an integral domain and a subfield of F necessarily has a unity and has more than one element, we have the following special case of the result just obtained.

5.27 Corollary. *The unity of a field F is also the unity of each subfield of F.*

We may point out that this corollary and Theorem 5.8 show that a field and all of its subfields have the same characteristic.

Since $\mathbf{Z}_p$ is a field for each prime p, the first statement of the following theorem has already been established as a part of Theorem 5.10.

5.28 Theorem. *A field of characteristic p contains a subfield which is isomorphic to the field $\mathbf{Z}_p$. A field of characteristic zero contains a subfield which is isomorphic to the field $\mathbf{Q}$.*

To prove the second statement of the theorem, let F be a field of characteristic zero and with e as unity. We already know by Theorem 5.10 that the subring $\mathbf{Z}e$ of F is isomorphic to $\mathbf{Z}$. It is perhaps then not surprising that F contains a subfield which is isomorphic to the field $\mathbf{Q}$ of quotients of $\mathbf{Z}$. However, we shall present some of the steps in the proof of this fact.

Since F has characteristic zero, if n is a nonzero integer, $ne \neq 0$ and therefore ne has a multiplicative inverse $(ne)^{-1}$ in F. Let $\mathbf{Q}'$ be the set of all elements of F expressible in the form $(me)(ne)^{-1}$, where $m, n \in \mathbf{Z}$ with $n \neq 0$. We leave it to the reader to verify that $\mathbf{Q}'$ is a subfield of F. (Of course, it is the field of quotients of the integral domain $\mathbf{Z}e$.) We proceed to show that there exists an isomorphism of **Q** onto **Q′**. To this end, we start by defining a mapping $\alpha \colon \mathbf{Q} \to \mathbf{Q}'$ as follows:

$$(mn^{-1})\alpha = (me)(ne)^{-1}, \quad m, n \in \mathbf{Z}, n \neq 0.$$

Since elements of **Q** are not uniquely expressible in the form mn^{-1}, we must first show that α is in fact a well-defined mapping of **Q** into **Q′**. Suppose that $m, n, k,$ and l are integers with $n \neq 0$ and $l \neq 0$ such that in **Q**, $mn^{-1} = kl^{-1}$. Then $ml = nk$ and therefore in **Q′**, $(me)(le) = (ne)(ke)$. It follows that $(me)(ne)^{-1} = (ke)(le)^{-1}$ and the mapping α is indeed well-defined. To verify that it is a one-one mapping, suppose that $(mn^{-1})\alpha = (kl^{-1})\alpha$, that is, that $(me)(ne)^{-1} = (ke)(le)^{-1}$. From this equation it follows that $(ml - nk)e = 0$. Then, since F has characteristic zero, we must have $ml - nk = 0$ or $mn^{-1} = kl^{-1}$. Thus α is a one-one mapping. It is clearly an onto mapping and we leave as an exercise the verification that the operations of addition and multiplication are preserved, and hence that α is the desired isomorphism.

In view of this theorem, we may observe that if we do not consider isomorphic fields as "different," *every* field is an extension of the rational field **Q** or of one of the fields $\mathbf{Z}_p$ for some prime p. The study of extensions of a given field is an important part of the general theory of fields, and we shall return to a further consideration of this topic in Chapter 13.

EXERCISES

1. Prove that multiplication of equivalence sets is well-defined by 5.18.

2. Go through the proof of Theorem 5.21 and verify that all the steps can be carried out with an arbitrary integral domain D in place of **Z**, thus obtaining the field of quotients of D. In this construction, why cannot an arbitrary commutative ring be used in place of **Z**?

3. Complete the proof of Theorem 5.23, and state what properties of inequalities have been used.

4. If u and v are positive rational numbers with $u < v$, show that $1/u > 1/v$.

5. If $r, s \in \mathbf{Q}$ with $r < s$, and $u, v \in \mathbf{Q}^+$, show that

$$r < \frac{ur + vs}{u + v} < s.$$

6. If $r, s \in \mathbf{Q}$ with $r < s$, and n is an arbitrary positive integer, show that there exist rational numbers $t_1, t_2, \cdots, t_n$ such that

$$r < t_1 < t_2 < \cdots < t_n < s.$$

7. Prove that addition and multiplication are preserved under the mapping α defined in the proof of Theorem 5.28.

8. Prove that a subring R (with more than one element) of a field F is a subfield of F if and only if the multiplicative inverse in F of each nonzero element of R is an element of R.

9. Let D and D' be integral domains with respective fields of quotients F and F'. If $\theta: D \to D'$ is an isomorphism of D onto D', prove that the mapping $\alpha: F \to F'$ defined by

$$(ab^{-1})\alpha = (a\theta)(b\theta)^{-1}, \qquad a, b \in D, b \neq 0,$$

is well-defined and is an isomorphism of F onto F'.

5.7 CONSTRUCTION OF THE INTEGERS FROM THE NATURAL NUMBERS (OPTIONAL)

We indicated in Section 3.5 how all the familiar properties of the natural numbers, that is, the positive integers, can be obtained from a few simple axioms. Let N be the system of all natural numbers. In this system we have operations of addition and multiplication, and all the properties of an integral domain hold except that there is no zero, and elements do not have additive inverses. In this section we shall outline a procedure by which we can start with N and *construct* the ring $\mathbf{Z}$ of all integers. The method closely parallels that by which we have constructed the rational numbers from the ring of integers. We may emphasize that we now assume as known only the properties of the natural numbers.

Let T be the set of all ordered pairs (a, b) of elements of N. Our procedure will be *suggested* by thinking of (a, b) as meaning $a - b$, but we must so formulate our statements that only natural numbers are involved. If (a, b) and (c, d) are elements of T, we shall write $(a, b) \sim (c, d)$ to mean that $a + d = b + c$. It is easy to verify that "$\sim$" is an equivalence relation on T. One way to characterize the equivalence set $[a, b]$ which contains (a, b) is as follows:

$$[a, b] = \{(x, y) \mid x, y \in N, x + b = y + a\}.$$

Now let $\mathbf{Z}$ be the set of all such equivalence sets, and let us make the following definitions:

5.29 $[a , b] + [c , d] = [a + c , b + d],$

and

5.30 $[a , b] \cdot [c , d] = [ac + bd , ad + bc].$

It can be shown that addition and multiplication are well-defined, and hence that we have operations of addition and multiplication defined on **Z**. The following theorem can now be established.

5.31   Theorem. *With respect to the Definitions 5.29 and 5.30 of addition and multiplication, **Z** is an integral domain and, by a suitable change of notation, we may consider that **Z** contains the set N of natural numbers. If we now define the set **Z**$^+$ of positive elements of **Z** to be the set N, then **Z** is an ordered integral domain in which the set of positive elements is well-ordered.*

We shall make a few remarks about the proof of this theorem, but shall not write out all the details. The zero of **Z** is $[c , c]$ for an arbitrary natural number c. The additive inverse of $[a , b]$ is $[b , a]$, that is, $-[a , b] = [b , a]$.

Let N' be the set of all elements of **Z** of the form $[x + 1 , 1]$, $x \in N$. Then the mapping $\theta \colon N \to N'$ defined by

$$x\theta = [x + 1 , 1] \qquad\qquad x \in N,$$

is a one-one mapping of N onto N' and, moreover, addition and multiplication are preserved under this mapping. Hence, as a matter of notation, let us identify N' with N; that is, let us write x in place of $[x + 1 , 1]$ so that **Z** now actually contains N. If $[a , b] \in$ **Z** it is easy to verify that

$$\begin{aligned}
[a , b] &= [a + 1 , 1] + [1 , b + 1] \\
&= [a + 1 , 1] - [b + 1 , 1] \\
&= a - b.
\end{aligned}$$

We have therefore justified writing $a - b$ in place of $[a , b]$.

If $c, d \in N$, we defined $c > d$ in Section 3.5 to mean that there exists a natural number e such that $c = d + e$. Since $[a , b] = a - b$, we see that $[a , b]$ is an element of N if $a > b$, and that $-[a , b]$ is an element of N if $b > a$. The elements of **Z** therefore consist of the natural numbers, the additive inverses of the natural numbers, and zero. Of course, the integral domain **Z** is called the *ring of integers*.

If we set **Z**$^+ = N$, then **Z**$^+$ has the properties (3.4) which make **Z** an ordered integral domain. Finally, then, since the set N is well-ordered, we have that **Z** is an ordered integral domain in which the set of positive elements is well-ordered. Our viewpoint in this book has been to *assume* that the ring of integers has all the properties implied in this statement. However, we have now indicated how this result can be proved by starting only with the Peano Axioms for the natural numbers.

REAL AND COMPLEX NUMBERS

In the preceding chapter we gave a detailed construction of the field of rational numbers, starting with the integral domain of integers. In this chapter we shall be concerned with extensions of the field of rational numbers to the field of real numbers and of the field of real numbers to the field of complex numbers. There are different methods of carrying out the first of these extensions but any one of them involves rather long and detailed calculations. Accordingly, instead of presenting the details, we shall merely state the existence of a certain extension of the field of rational numbers which we shall call the field of real numbers, and briefly discuss a few properties of this field. It is quite easy to construct the field of complex numbers from the field of real numbers and we shall carry out this construction and establish a number of fundamental properties of the complex numbers.

6.1   THE FIELD OF REAL NUMBERS

The rational numbers are sufficient for use in all simple applications of mathematics to physical problems. For example, measurements are usually given to a certain number of decimal places, and any finite decimal is a rational number. However, from a theoretical point of view, the system of rational numbers is entirely inadequate. The Pythagoreans made this discovery about 500 B.C. and were profoundly shocked by it. Consider, for example, an isosceles right triangle whose legs are 1 unit in length. Then, by the Pythagorean theorem, the hypotenuse has length $\sqrt{2}$; and from this geometrical consideration it appears that there must exist a "number" $\sqrt{2}$, although we have shown in Section 4.5 that it cannot be a rational number.

The inherent difficulty in extending the field of rational numbers to the field of real numbers is perhaps indicated by the fact that a satisfactory theory of the real numbers was not obtained until the latter half of the 19th century. Although other men also made contributions to the theory, it is usually attributed to the German mathematicians Dedekind (1831–1916) and Cantor (1845–1918). We shall not present here the work of either of these men but shall presently state without proof the fundamental theorem which each of them essentially proved and by quite different methods. In order to do this, we must first make a few preliminary definitions.

So far, the only ordered field which we have studied is the field **Q** of rational numbers. However, for the moment, suppose that F is an arbitrary ordered field and let us make the following definition.

6.1   Definition.   Let S be a set of elements of an ordered field F. If there exists an element b of F such that $x \leq b$ for every element x of S, then b is called an *upper bound* of the set S in F.

As an example, the set $S_1 = \{1/2\,,\,1\,,\,2\}$ of elements of **Q** has an upper bound 2. Also, $5/2$ is an upper bound of this set, as is 117, and so on. Thus, if a set has an upper bound, it has many upper bounds. Clearly, the set $\mathbf{Z}^+$ of all positive integers does not have an upper bound in **Q**. As another example, consider the set

$$S_2 = \{a \mid a \in \mathbf{Q}\,,\,a > 0\,,\,a^2 < 2\}.$$

Then S_2 has upper bounds in **Q**, one of them being 3.

6.2   Definition.   Let S be a set of elements of an ordered field F. If there exists an upper bound c of S in F such that no smaller element of F is an upper bound of S, then c is called the *least upper bound* (l.u.b.) of S in F.

It follows from this definition that if a set S has a l.u.b., it is unique. Moreover, if c is the l.u.b. of the set S in F and $d \in F$ such that $d < c$, then there must exist an element s of S such that $s > d$ since, otherwise, d would be an upper bound of S less than the least upper bound.

For the set S_1 exhibited above, the element 2 of S_1 is clearly the l.u.b. of S_1 in **Q**. However, for the set S_2 the situation is not quite so obvious. Although we shall not give the details, it is true and should perhaps not be surprising that there exists no rational number which is the l.u.b. of the set S_2. That is, if $c \in \mathbf{Q}$ is an upper bound of S_2, there exists $d \in \mathbf{Q}$ such that $d < c$ is also an upper bound of S_2. Therefore S_2 has no l.u.b. in **Q**. Thus we have an example of a set of elements of **Q** which has upper bounds in **Q** but no l.u.b. in **Q**. In the field of real numbers, whose existence is asserted in the next theorem, this situation cannot arise. In fact, it is the existence of an ordered field with this property which may be considered to be the principal contribution of Dedekind and Cantor to the subject. Let us state this result as the following theorem.

6.3   Theorem.   *There exists a field* **R,** *called the field of real numbers with the following properties:*

(*i*)   **R** *is an extension of the field* **Q** *of rational numbers. Moreover,* **R** *is an ordered field and* **Q**$^+$ $\subset$ **R**$^+$.

(*ii*)   *If S is a nonempty set of elements of* **R** *which has an upper bound in* **R,** *it has a l.u.b. in* **R.**

The elements of **R** are called *real numbers*. An element of **R** which is not an element of **Q** is called an *irrational* number. Considered as elements of **R,** the set S_2 defined above has a l.u.b. (by 6.3(ii)) and this l.u.b. we may *define* to be the number $\sqrt{2}$. Clearly, $\sqrt{2}$ is an irrational number and it is the fact that this number is not an element of **Q** which prevents S_2 from having a l.u.b. *in the field* **Q.**

The fact that **Q**$^+$ $\subset$ **R**$^+$ is sometimes expressed by saying that the ordering of **R** is an extension of the ordering of **Q.** That is, a rational number is a positive rational number if and only if, considered as a real number, it is a positive real number. A similar situation arose when we passed from the integers to the rational numbers.

6.2   SOME PROPERTIES OF THE FIELD OF REAL NUMBERS

In this section we shall prove two fundamental properties of real numbers and state one additional property without proof. Of course, our proofs will be based on the assumed properties (i) and (ii) of Theorem 6.3.

Throughout the rest of this book we shall continue to denote the field of real numbers by **R** and the set of positive real numbers by **R**$^+$.

6.4   Theorem.   (Archimedean Property)

If a, b $\in$ **R**$^+$, *there exists a positive integer n such that na > b.*

PROOF: Let us assume that $ka \leq b$ for every positive integer k, and seek a contradiction. Another way of stating this assumption is to assert that b is an upper bound of the set $S = \{ka \mid k \in \mathbf{Z}^+\}$. Since this set has an upper bound, by 6.3(ii) it has a l.u.b., say c. Now $c - a < c$ and therefore $c - a$ is not an upper bound of the set S. This implies that there exists an element la of S, $l \in \mathbf{Z}^+$, such that $la > c - a$. It follows that $(l + 1)a > c$ and since $(l + 1)a \in S$, we have a contradiction of the fact that c is the l.u.b. of the set S. The proof is therefore complete.

It was shown in Section 5.5 that between any two distinct rational numbers there is another rational number. A generalization of this result is given in the following theorem.

6.5 Theorem. *If a, $b \in \mathbf{R}$ with $a < b$, there exists a rational number m/n (m, $n \in \mathbf{Z}$) such that*

$$a < \frac{m}{n} < b.$$

PROOF: For simplicity, we shall assume that $a > 0$ and leave the rest of the proof as an exercise.

Since $b - a > 0$, by the preceding theorem there exists $n \in \mathbf{Z}^+$ such that $n(b - a) > 1$. Let n be some such fixed integer. Again applying the preceding theorem to the real numbers 1 and na, there exists $m \in \mathbf{Z}^+$ such that $m > na$, and let m be the *least* positive integer with this property. Now $m > na$ implies that $a < m/n$ and we proceed to complete the proof by showing that also $m/n < b$ or, equivalently, that $m < nb$. Suppose that $m \geq nb$. Since $n(b - a) > 1$, we have $m \geq nb > na + 1$. Thus $m > 1$ and $(m - 1) \in \mathbf{Z}^+$ such that $(m - 1) > na$. Since $m - 1 < m$, this violates our choice of m as the least positive integer which is greater than na. Our assumption that $m \geq nb$ has led to a contradiction, and we conclude that $m < nb$. This completes the proof.

In particular, this theorem tells us that between any two irrational numbers there is a rational number. It is also true that between any two rational numbers there is an irrational number. (See Exercise 2 below.) Thus the rational and irrational numbers are very closely intertwined.

Although it is true that all the properties of the real numbers can be established using only the properties (i) and (ii) of Theorem 6.3, we shall give no further proofs in this book. However, let us conclude this brief discussion of the real numbers by stating without proof the following familiar and important result.

6.6 Theorem. *For each positive real number a and each positive integer n, there exists exactly one positive real number x such that $x^n = a$.*

The real number x whose existence is asserted by this theorem may be called the *principal nth root of a* and designated by the familiar notation $a^{1/n}$ or by $\sqrt[n]{a}$.

EXERCISES

1. Define lower bound and greatest lower bound of a set of elements of an ordered field. Prove that if a nonempty set of elements of **R** has a lower bound, it has a greatest lower bound in **R**. [Hint: Consider the additive inverses of elements of the set.]

2. Prove that if $a, b \in$ **R** with $a < b$, then

$$a < a + \frac{b - a}{\sqrt{2}} < b.$$

   Hence prove that between any two distinct rational numbers there is an irrational number.

3. Complete the proof of Theorem 6.5 by showing that the stated result holds also for the case in which $a \leq 0$.

4. Let S_1 and S_2 be nonempty sets of real numbers having, respectively, b_1 and b_2 as least upper bounds. If $S_3 = \{s_1 + s_2 \mid s_1 \in S_1, s_2 \in S_2\}$, prove that $b_1 + b_2$ is the least upper bound of the set S_3.

6.3 THE FIELD OF COMPLEX NUMBERS

In order to construct the field of complex numbers, we begin by considering ordered pairs (a, b) of *real* numbers. Our definitions of addition and multiplication will be motivated by the formal properties of expressions of the form $a + bi$, where $i^2 = -1$. However, we are not justified in assuming that there *is* a "number" whose square is -1 until we have constructed a field which has an element with this property. Accordingly, as in the case of the construction of the rational numbers, we begin with an unfamiliar notation in order to avoid using any property until we have established it. We may remind the reader that the equal sign is being used in the sense of identity, that is, $(a, b) = (c, d)$ means that $a = c$ and $b = d$.

   We proceed to prove the following theorem, which establishes the existence of the field we shall presently call the field of complex numbers.

6.7 Theorem. *Let* **C** *be the set of all ordered pairs (a, b) of elements of the field* **R** *of real numbers, and let us define operations of addition and multiplication on* **C** *as follows:*

6.8 $$(a, b) + (c, d) = (a + c, b + d),$$

and

6.9 $$(a, b)(c, d) = (ac - bd, ad + bc).$$

Then **C** *is a field with respect to these definitions of addition and multiplication. Moreover, the set of all elements of* **C** *of the form* $(a, 0)$, $a \in$ **R,** *is a subfield of* **C** *which is isomorphic to the field* **R.**

The required properties of addition are almost obvious. From 6.8, it follows that addition is commutative and associative, that $(0, 0)$ is the zero of **C,** and that the additive inverse of (a, b) is $(-a, -b)$.

The associative law of multiplication is a consequence of the following straightforward calculations:

$$((a, b)(c, d))(e, f) = (ac - bd, ad + bc)(e, f)$$
$$= (ace - bde - adf - bcf, acf - bdf + ade + bce),$$

$$(a, b)((c, d)(e, f)) = (a, b)(ce - df, cf + de)$$
$$= (ace - adf - bcf - bde, acf + ade + bce - bdf),$$

and these turn out to be equal elements of **C.**

Next, let us verify one of the distributive laws as follows:

$$(a, b)((c, d) + (e, f)) = (a, b)(c + e, d + f)$$
$$= (ac + ae - bd - bf, ad + af + bc + be),$$

$$(a, b)(c, d) + (a, b)(e, f) = (ac - bd, ad + bc) + (ae - bf, af + be)$$
$$= (ac - bd + ae - bf, ad + bc + af + be),$$

and again we have equal elements of **C.** The other distributive law follows from this one as soon as we show that multiplication is commutative, and the commutativity of multiplication follows easily from 6.9. For, by interchanging (a, b) and (c, d) in 6.9, we see that

$$(c, d)(a, b) = (ca - db, cb + da),$$

and the right side of this equation is equal to the right side of 6.9. Hence,

$$(a, b)(c, d) = (c, d)(a, b).$$

We have now proved that **C** is a commutative ring, and it is easily verified that it has the unity $(1, 0)$. To show that **C** is a field, we need only show that each nonzero element (a, b) of **C** has a multiplicative inverse in **C.** Since the zero is $(0, 0)$, to say that (a, b) is not the zero of

C is to say that a and b are not both equal to zero. Since a is an element of the ordered field **R**, we know that if $a \neq 0$, then $a^2 > 0$. Similarly, if $b \neq 0$, we have $b^2 > 0$. It follows that if (a, b) is not the zero of **C**, then necessarily $a^2 + b^2 > 0$ and, in particular, $a^2 + b^2 \neq 0$. Hence,

$$\left(\frac{a}{a^2 + b^2}, \frac{-b}{a^2 + b^2} \right)$$

is an element of **C** and it may be verified by direct calculation (using 6.9) that

$$(a, b) \left(\frac{a}{a^2 + b^2}, \frac{-b}{a^2 + b^2} \right) = (1, 0).$$

We have therefore shown that every nonzero element of **C** has a multiplicative inverse in **C**, and hence we have proved that **C** is a field.

To complete the proof of the theorem, let **R'** be the set of all elements of **C** of the form $(a, 0)$, $a \in$ **R**. Then the mapping $\theta : $ **R'** $\rightarrow$ **R** defined by $(a, 0)\theta = a$, $a \in$ **R**, is a one-one mapping of **R'** onto **R**. Moreover,

$$[(a, 0) + (b, 0)]\theta = (a + b, 0)\theta = a + b = (a, 0)\theta + (b, 0)\theta,$$

and

$$[(a, 0)(b, 0)]\theta = (ab, 0)\theta = ab = [(a, 0)\theta][(b, 0)\theta].$$

Hence, the operations of addition and multiplication are preserved under this mapping, and the mapping therefore defines an isomorphism of **R'** onto **R**. This completes the proof of the theorem.

An element of the field which we have constructed is called a *complex number*, and **C** is called the *field of complex numbers*.

We shall henceforth adopt a more familiar notation by identifying **R'** with **R**, that is, we shall write a in place of $(a, 0)$, and consider that the field **C** of complex numbers actually contains the field **R** of real numbers. Also, for simplicity of notation, as well as for historical reasons, we shall use the symbol i to designate the particular element $(0, 1)$ of **C**. Since $(0, 1)^2 = (-1, 0)$, in our new notation we have $i^2 = -1$. Now it is easily verified that

$$(a, 0) + (b, 0)(0, 1) = (a, b)$$

and, using the notation we have introduced, it follows that $a + bi = (a, b)$. Accordingly, in the future we shall write $a + bi$ in place of (a, b).

In this notation, the product 6.9 of two elements of **C** may be expressed in the following form:

6.10 $$(a + bi)(c + di) = ac - bd + (ad + bc)i.$$

Of course, the right side of 6.10 may be obtained from the left by multiplying out with the aid of the usual distributive, associative, and commutative laws, and replacing i^2 by -1.

We have now extended the field of real numbers to the field of complex numbers. It should be pointed out, however, that one familiar property of the field of rational numbers and of the field of real numbers does not carry over to the field of complex numbers.

6.11   Theorem.   *The field* **C** *of complex numbers is not an ordered field.*

By this statement we mean that there does not exist any set **C**$^+$ of elements of **C** having the properties (3.4) required for **C** to be an ordered field. This fact is a consequence of the following observations. If **C** were ordered, 3.6(v) would show that the square of every nonzero element would be positive; in particular, both i^2 and 1 would be positive. Then -1 would be negative, and we have a contradiction since $i^2 = -1$.

The fact that **C** is not ordered means that inequalities cannot be used between complex numbers. In other words, it is meaningless to speak of one complex number as being greater or less than another.

Throughout the rest of this book we shall continue to denote the field of complex numbers by **C**.

6.4   THE CONJUGATE OF A COMPLEX NUMBER

Let us make the following definition.

6.12   Definition.   If $u = a + bi \in$ **C**, we define the *conjugate* of u to be the element u^* of **C** given by: $u^* = a - bi$.†

As examples, we have $(1 + 7i)^* = 1 - 7i$, $(2 - 2i)^* = 2 + 2i$, $4^* = 4$, and so on.

Now the mapping $\alpha \colon$ **C** $\to$ **C** defined by $u\alpha = u^*$, $u \in$ **C**, is a one-one mapping of **C** onto **C**. We proceed to show that the operations of addition and multiplication are preserved under this mapping. Let $u = a + bi$ and $v = c + di$ be elements of **C**. Then

---

† Historically, the usual notation for the conjugate of a complex number z is $\bar{z}$ instead of z^*. The present notation has been adopted only because it makes it easier to print such expressions as the conjugate of the sum of two or more complex numbers.

$$(u + v)\alpha = (u + v)^* = [(a + c) + (b + d)i]^* = a + c - (b + d)i$$
$$= (a - bi) + (c - di) = u^* + v^* = u\alpha + v\alpha,$$

and

$$(uv)\alpha = (uv)^* = [ac - bd + (ad + bc)i]^* = ac - bd - (ad + bc)i$$
$$= (a - bi)(c - di) = u^*v^* = (u\alpha)(v\alpha).$$

Since the operations of addition and multiplication are preserved under the mapping α, it follows that this is an isomorphism of the field $\mathbf{C}$ onto itself. Such an isomorphism is frequently called an *automorphism*.

In working with complex numbers, the concept of conjugate plays an important role. A number of simple, but significant, properties are presented in Exercise 2 below.

EXERCISES

1. Find the multiplicative inverse of the nonzero element (a, b) of $\mathbf{C}$ by assuming that r and s are real numbers such that (a, b) $(r, s) = (1, 0)$, and solving for r and s.

2. Prove each of the following:

   (i) If $u \in \mathbf{C}$, then $uu^* \in \mathbf{R}$ and $u + u^* \in \mathbf{R}$; moreover, if $u \neq 0$, then $uu^* > 0$.

   (ii) If $u \in \mathbf{C}$, then $(u^*)^* = u$.

   (iii) If $u \in \mathbf{C}$ and $u \neq 0$, then $(u^{-1})^* = (u^*)^{-1}$.

   (iv) If $u \in \mathbf{C}$, then $u = u^*$ if and only if $u \in \mathbf{R}$.

   (v) If $u \in \mathbf{C}$ and n is a positive integer, then $(u^n)^* = (u^*)^n$.

3. If $\alpha: \mathbf{C} \to \mathbf{C}$ is the isomorphism defined above, part (iv) of the preceding exercise shows that $u\alpha = u$ if and only if $u \in \mathbf{R}$. Prove that if $\phi: \mathbf{C} \to \mathbf{C}$ is an isomorphism of $\mathbf{C}$ onto $\mathbf{C}$ with the property that $a\phi = a$ for every $a \in \mathbf{R}$, then $\phi = \alpha$ or ϕ is the identity mapping on $\mathbf{C}$. [Hint: Consider the possibilities for $i\phi$.]

4. Let S be an arbitrary ring and T the set of all ordered pairs (a, b) of elements of S. If addition and multiplication are defined by 6.8 and 6.9, respectively, verify each of the following:

   (i) T is a ring,

   (ii) T is a commutative ring if and only if S is a commutative ring,

   (iii) T has a unity if and only if S has a unity.

5. In the notation of the preceding exercise, let S be the ring $\mathbf{Z}_2$ of integers modulo 2. Exhibit addition and multiplication tables for the corresponding ring T. Is T a field in this case? Is it an integral domain? Is it isomorphic to any of the rings with four elements given in Chapter 2?

6.5 GEOMETRIC REPRESENTATION AND TRIGONOMETRIC FORM

It is implicit in our construction of the complex numbers that the mapping $a + bi \to (a, b)$ is a one-one mapping of the set $\mathbf{C}$ of all complex numbers onto the set of all ordered pairs of real numbers. Now in ordinary plane analytic geometry we represent points in the plane by their coordinates, that is, by ordered pairs of real numbers. Accordingly, we may represent a point in the plane by a single complex number. In other words, we shall sometimes find it convenient to associate with the complex number $a + bi$ the point with rectangular coordinates (a, b), and to say that this point has *coordinate* $a + bi$. A number of examples are given in Figure 9. It will be observed that a real number, that is, a complex number of the form $a + 0i$, is the coordinate of a point on the x-axis. A number of the form $0 + bi$, sometimes called a *pure imaginary*, is the coordinate of a point on the y-axis. We may also observe that a complex number $a + bi$ and its conjugate $a - bi$ are coordinates of points that are symmetrically located with respect to the x-axis.

Instead of specifying points in a plane by means of rectangular coordinates, we may of course use polar coordinates. If P is the point with nonzero coordinate $a + bi$, the distance of P from the origin O of coordinates is the positive real number $r = \sqrt{a^2 + b^2}$. If θ is an angle

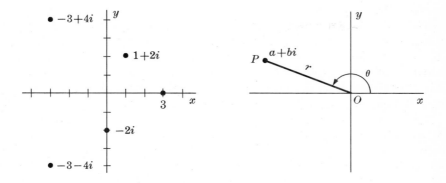

Figure 9   **Figure 10**

in standard position with terminal side OP, as in Figure 10, then by the definition of the trigonometric functions we have

$$a = r \cos \theta, \quad b = r \sin \theta.$$

It follows that the complex number $a + bi$ can be expressed in the form

6.13 $$a + bi = r(\cos \theta + i \sin \theta).$$

We have been assuming that $a + bi \neq 0$. If $a + bi = 0$, then $r = 0$ in 6.13, and θ may be a completely arbitrary angle.

We now introduce some appropriate terms in the following definition.

6.14 Definition. The expression on the right side of 6.13 is called the *trigonometric form* of the complex number $a + bi$. The nonnegative real number $r = \sqrt{a^2 + b^2}$ is called the *absolute value* of the complex number $a + bi$, and may be designated by $|a + bi|$. The angle θ occurring in 6.13 is called *an angle of $a + bi$*.

Clearly, the nonnegative real number r occurring in the trigonometric form of $a + bi$ is uniquely determined. However, the angle θ is not unique, but if $r \neq 0$ and θ_1 and θ_2 are any two possible angles of $a + bi$, then elementary properties of the sine and cosine functions show that $\theta_1 = \theta_2 + n \cdot 360°$ for some integer n.

As a consequence of these observations, let us point out that if r and s are positive real numbers and we know that

$$r(\cos \theta + i \sin \theta) = s(\cos \phi + i \sin \phi),$$

then necessarily $r = s$ and $\theta = \phi + n \cdot 360°$ for some integer n.

We have previously defined (3.7) absolute values for an ordered integral domain, and we know that the field of complex numbers is not ordered. However, the present definition of absolute value is an extension of the concept for real numbers. For if a is a real number, we may consider it to be the complex number $a + 0i$ and, by 6.14, we have $|a| = \sqrt{a^2}$. But if c is a positive real number, by $\sqrt{c}$ we mean the *positive* square root of c. It follows that $\sqrt{a^2} = a$ if $a \geq 0$, whereas $\sqrt{a^2} = -a$ if $a < 0$. Hence, for a *real* number a, the present meaning of $|a|$ coincides with its meaning according to Definition 3.7.

Let us now illustrate the trigonometric form of a complex number by some examples. First, let us consider the number $-2 + 2i$. As indicated in Figure 11, $|-2 + 2i| = 2\sqrt{2}$, and an angle of $-2 + 2i$ is $135°$. Hence, 6.13 takes the form

$$-2 + 2i = 2\sqrt{2}(\cos 135° + i \sin 135°),$$

which is easily verified by direct calculation. Other examples, which the reader may check, are the following:

$$1 + \sqrt{3i} = 2(\cos 60° + i \sin 60°),$$
$$4 = 4(\cos 0° + i \sin 0°),$$
$$-i = 1(\cos 270° + i \sin 270°),$$
$$-2(\cos 40° + i \sin 40°) = 2(\cos 220° + i \sin 220°).$$

It is only in special cases that we can find in degrees an angle of a given complex number. Naturally, an approximation may be obtained by use of trigonometric tables, or an angle may be merely indicated as in the following example. Let us attempt to express $1 + 3i$ in trigonometric form. Clearly, $|1 + 3i| = \sqrt{10}$, but we cannot exactly express its angle in degrees. However, if θ_1 is the positive acute angle such that $\tan \theta_1 = 3$, as indicated in Figure 12, we may write

$$1 + 3i = \sqrt{10}(\cos \theta_1 + i \sin \theta_1)$$

as the trigonometric form of $1 + 3i$.

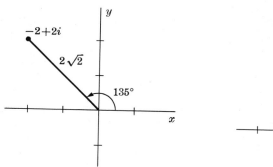

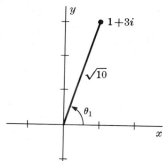

Figure 11

Figure 12

The fact that every complex number can be expressed in trigonometric form is of considerable significance largely because of the following remarkable theorem.

6.15 Theorem. *If u and v are complex numbers such that in trigonometric form,*

$$u = r(\cos \theta + i \sin \theta),$$

and

$$v = s(\cos \phi + i \sin \phi),$$

then the trigonometric form of uv is given by

6.16 $$uv = rs(\cos (\theta + \phi) + i \sin (\theta + \phi)).$$

Otherwise expressed, $|uv| = |u| \cdot |v|$, and an angle of uv is the sum of an angle of u and an angle of v.

To establish this result we need only multiply together the trigonometric forms of u and v and then use the simple addition formulas of trigonometry. Thus we have

$$uv = rs(\cos \theta + i \sin \theta)(\cos \phi + i \sin \phi)$$
$$= rs[(\cos \theta \cos \phi - \sin \theta \sin \phi) + i(\cos \theta \sin \phi + \sin \theta \cos \phi)]$$
$$= rs[\cos (\theta + \phi) + i \sin (\theta + \phi)],$$

and the desired result follows immediately.

The special case of the preceding theorem in which $u = v$ shows at once that

$$u^2 = r^2(\cos 2\theta + i \sin 2\theta).$$

The following generalization of this result is of great importance.

6.17 De Moivre's Theorem. *If n is an arbitrary positive integer and*

$$u = r(\cos \theta + i \sin \theta),$$

then

6.18 $$u^n = r^n(\cos n\theta + i \sin n\theta).$$

For $n = 3$, we use Theorem 6.15 and the case in which $n = 2$ which has just been established as follows:

$$u^3 = u^2 \cdot u = [r^2(\cos 2\theta + i \sin 2\theta)][r(\cos \theta + i \sin \theta)]$$
$$= r^3(\cos 3\theta + i \sin 3\theta).$$

A general proof along these lines can be easily given by induction.

One application of this theorem will be given in the next section. However, let us point out here how certain trigonometric identities can be obtained in an easy way by use of this theorem. By letting $r = 1$ and, as an example, taking $n = 3$, we see that

$$(\cos \theta + i \sin \theta)^3 = \cos 3\theta + i \sin 3\theta.$$

However, by actually multiplying out the left side, we find that

$$(\cos \theta + i \sin \theta)^3 = \cos^3 \theta - 3 \cos \theta \sin^2 \theta + i(3 \cos^2 \theta \sin \theta - \sin^3 \theta),$$

and it follows that

$$\cos 3\theta + i \sin 3\theta = \cos^3 \theta - 3 \cos \theta \sin^2 \theta + i(3 \cos^2 \theta \sin \theta - \sin^3 \theta).$$

From this equation we get at once the two following trigonometric identities:

$$\cos 3\theta = \cos^3 \theta - 3 \cos \theta \sin^2 \theta,$$

and

$$\sin 3\theta = 3 \cos^2 \theta \sin \theta - \sin^3 \theta.$$

EXERCISES

1. Express each of the following complex numbers in trigonometric form and indicate the points in a coordinate plane that have these numbers as coordinates:

   (a) $-1 - i$, (b) $-\sqrt{3} + i$,
   (c) $\sqrt{3} + i$, (d) $-1 + \sqrt{3}i$,
   (e) -4, (f) $3 - 2i$,
   (g) $2 - 2i$, (h) $\cos 26° - i \sin 26°$.

2. Express each of the following complex numbers in the form $a + bi$:

   (a) $4(\cos 45° + i \sin 45°)$,
   (b) $2(\cos 120° + i \sin 120°)$,
   (c) $3(\cos 180° + i \sin 180°)$,
   (d) $3(\cos 270° + i \sin 270°)$,
   (e) $(1/2)(\cos 300° + i \sin 300°)$,
   (f) $12(\cos 0° + i \sin 0°)$,
   (g) $11(\cos 90° + i \sin 90°)$,
   (h) $(\cos 117° + i \sin 117°)(\cos 123° + i \sin 123°)$.

3. Use De Moivre's Theorem to compute each of the following, and then express your answers in algebraic form by evaluating the necessary trigonometric functions:

   (a) $(-1 - i)^5$, (b) $(\sqrt{3} - i)^8$,

   (c) $(-i)^{12}$, (d) $\left(\dfrac{1}{\sqrt{2}} + \dfrac{i}{\sqrt{2}} \right)^{100}$,

   (e) $\left(-\dfrac{1}{2} - \dfrac{\sqrt{3}i}{2} \right)^6$, (f) $(-1 + i)^{10}$,

   (g) $(1 - \sqrt{3}i)^{11}$, (h) $(\cos 18° + i \sin 18°)^{10}$.

4. Verify that the points with coordinates

$$(\cos 60° + i \sin 60°)^n, \quad (n = 1, 2, 3, 4, 5, 6),$$

   are the vertices of a regular hexagon inscribed in a circle of radius 1.

5. If u^* is the conjugate of the complex number u, verify each of the following:

   (a) $|u^*| = |u|$,
   (b) $uu^* = |u|^2$,

   (c) $u^{-1} = \dfrac{u^*}{|u|^2}$, if $u \neq 0$.

6. Show that if $u \neq 0$, De Moivre's Theorem also holds for every *negative* integer n.

7. Let u, $v \in \mathbf{C}$, and let P and Q be the points in a coordinate plane having respective coordinates u and v. Let R be the point with coordinate $u + v$. If O is the origin, show that OR is a diagonal of the parallelogram having OP and OQ as adjacent sides.

8. Show that if u, $v \in \mathbf{C}$, then $|u + v| \leq |u| + |v|$.

9. Use De Moivre's Theorem to find trigonometric identities for $\cos 4\theta$ and $\sin 4\theta$.

10. If $u = a + bi$, we have defined $|u| = \sqrt{a^2 + b^2}$. Use this definition to prove directly that if u, $v \in \mathbf{C}$, then $|uv| = |u| \cdot |v|$.

11. If u, $v \in \mathbf{C}$ with $v \neq 0$, prove that $\left| \dfrac{u}{v} \right| = \dfrac{|u|}{|v|}$.

6.6   THE NTH ROOTS OF A COMPLEX NUMBER

In this section we give an important application of the use of the trigonometric form of a complex number. First, we give the following familiar definition.

6.19   Definition.   Let n be a positive integer greater than 1. If u, $v \in \mathbf{C}$ such that $v^n = u$, we say that v is an *n*th root of u.

We shall now prove the following theorem.

6.20   Theorem.   *If n is a positive integer greater than* 1, *and*

$$u = r(\cos \theta + i \sin \theta)$$

is a nonzero complex number in trigonometric form, there exist exactly n nth roots of u, namely,

6.21
$$r^{1/n} \left(\cos \frac{\theta + k \cdot 360°}{n} + i \sin \frac{\theta + k \cdot 360°}{n} \right),$$
$$(k = 0, 1, \cdots, n - 1).$$

Here $r^{1/n}$ represents the principal *n*th root of the positive real number r; that is, the positive real *n*th root of r whose existence is asserted in Theorem 6.6.

Suppose that $v = s(\cos \phi + i \sin \phi)$ is an *n*th root of u. Then $v^n = u$ and De Moivre's Theorem assures us that

$$s^n(\cos n\phi + i \sin n\phi) = r(\cos \theta + i \sin \theta).$$

It follows that the absolute values of the two members of this equation are equal, and an angle of one must be equal to an angle of the other. Hence, $s^n = r$, so that $s = r^{1/n}$. Moreover, $n\phi = \theta + k \cdot 360°$ for some integer k, and it follows that $\phi = (\theta + k \cdot 360°)/n$. We have therefore shown that every nth root v of u must be of the form

6.22 $$v = r^{1/n} \left(\cos \frac{\theta + k \cdot 360°}{n} + i \sin \frac{\theta + k \cdot 360°}{n} \right)$$

for some integer k. Conversely, it is readily verified by De Moivre's Theorem that if v is given by 6.22, then $v^n = u$ for *every* choice of the integer k. The number of distinct nth roots of u is therefore the number of ways in which the integer k can be chosen in 6.22 so as to give distinct values of v. The angles obtained by letting k take the values, 0, 1, $\cdots$, $n - 1$ have distinct terminal sides, and this fact makes it almost obvious that these n values of k yield distinct values of v. Moreover, if t is an arbitrary integer, the Division Algorithm asserts that there exist integers q and r with $0 \leq r < n$ such that $t = qn + r$, and therefore

$$\frac{\theta + t \cdot 360°}{n} = \frac{\theta + r \cdot 360°}{n} + q \cdot 360°.$$

It is then clear that the angle $(\theta + t \cdot 360°)/n$ has the same terminal side as the angle $(\theta + r \cdot 360°)/n$. Since $0 \leq r < n$, we see that all possible different values of v are obtained if in 6.22 we let k take the values 0, 1, $\cdots$, $n - 1$. This completes the proof of the theorem.

As an example of the use of this theorem, let us find the fifth roots of the complex number $-2 + 2i$. First, we express this number in trigonometric form as follows:

$$-2 + 2i = 2^{3/2}(\cos 135° + i \sin 135°).$$

In the notation of the theorem, we have $r = 2^{3/2}$, $\theta = 135°$, and $n = 5$. Accordingly, the fifth roots of $-2 + 2i$ are the following:

$$2^{3/10}(\cos 27° + i \sin 27°),$$
$$2^{3/10}(\cos 99° + i \sin 99°),$$
$$2^{3/10}(\cos 171° + i \sin 171°),$$
$$2^{3/10}(\cos 243° + i \sin 243°),$$
$$2^{3/10}(\cos 315° + i \sin 315°).$$

An interesting special case of Theorem 6.20 arises if we choose $u = 1$; hence $r = 1$ and $\theta = 0°$. We state this case as follows.

6.23 Corollary. *The distinct nth roots of 1 are the complex numbers*

6.24 $\cos \dfrac{k \cdot 360°}{n} + i \sin \dfrac{k \cdot 360°}{n}$, $(k = 0, 1, \cdots, n - 1)$.

By De Moivre's Theorem, we have

$$\left(\cos \frac{360°}{n} + i \sin \frac{360°}{n}\right)^k = \cos \frac{k \cdot 360°}{n} + i \sin \frac{k \cdot 360°}{n}.$$

Hence, the n distinct nth roots of 1, as given in 6.24, may all be expressed as powers of a certain nth root of 1. We have then the following alternate form of the preceding corollary.

6.25   Corollary.   *Let us set*

6.26 $w = \cos \dfrac{360°}{n} + i \sin \dfrac{360°}{n}$,

so that w is the nth root of 1 having the smallest positive angle. Then the nth roots of 1 are the numbers

6.27 $w, w^2, w^3, \cdots, w^n = 1$.

Since all nth roots of 1 have absolute value 1, they are coordinates of points on the circle with radius 1 and center the origin. Moreover, it is clear from 6.24 that they are the vertices of a regular polygon of n sides inscribed in this circle, with one vertex at the real number 1. This fact is of considerable importance in the study of the constructability of regular polygons with ruler and compass.

EXERCISES

1.   Find the cube roots of 1 and express the answers in algebraic form. Draw a figure showing that these numbers are the coordinates of the vertices of a regular polygon of three sides (equilateral triangle).

2.   Do the corresponding thing for the fourth roots of 1.

3.   Do the corresponding thing for the eighth roots of 1.

4.   Show that the sixth roots of 1 are the cube roots of 1 and their negatives.

5. Find the required roots and express the answers in algebraic form:

    (a) The cube roots of $-2 + 2i$.
    (b) The cube roots of $-8i$.
    (c) The fourth roots of -4.
    (d) The sixth roots of $-i$.
    (e) The fourth roots of $-1 - \sqrt{3}i$.
    (f) The square roots of $-1 + \sqrt{3}i$.

6. In each of the following, express the required roots in trigonometric form:

    (a) The fifth roots of 1.
    (b) The fourth roots of $-1 + i$.
    (c) The fourth roots of $\dfrac{1}{2} + \dfrac{\sqrt{3}i}{2}$.
    (d) The sixth roots of $1 - i$.
    (e) The square roots of $1 + 2i$.
    (f) The fourth roots of $16(\cos 12° + i \sin 12°)$.

7. Show that if v is any one of the nth roots of the nonzero complex number u, and w is given by 6.26, then $v, wv, w^2v, \cdots, w^{n-1}v$ are all the nth roots of u.

8. Show that the multiplicative inverse of an nth root of 1 is also an nth root of 1.

9. If $t \in \mathbf{C}$ such that $t^n = 1$ but $t^m \neq 1$ for $0 < m < n$, t is called a *primitive* nth root of 1. Show each of the following:

    (i) The number w, defined in 6.26, is a primitive nth root of 1.
    (ii) If t is a primitive nth root of 1, then $1, t, t^2, \cdots, t^{n-1}$ are distinct and are all of the nth roots of 1.
    (iii) If t is a primitive nth root of 1, then t^l is also a primitive nth root of 1 if and only if l and n are relatively prime.

NOTES AND REFERENCES

Proofs of the fundamental theorem (6.3) on the field of real numbers may be found in many texts on analysis as well as on algebra. A classic presentation of Dedekind's method is found in Landau [47]. This book starts with the Peano axioms for the natural numbers and develops in full detail the field of real numbers and the field of complex numbers.

For the details of Cantor's method, see, for example, Dubisch [4].

GROUPS

In all the algebraic systems studied so far we have always had two operations, namely, addition and multiplication. Later on we shall continue the study of these systems and, in particular, shall give many additional examples of rings and fields. However, we now proceed to study an important class of systems in which there is only one operation. As soon as the definition of a *group* is given in the next section it will be apparent that we already have many examples of groups from previous chapters, although we have not used this terminology. The theory of groups is an important part of modern algebra, and many books have been written on the subject. In this chapter we shall present only a few of the most fundamental properties of groups and give a number of examples that may serve to suggest the wide range of applications of the theory. The study of group theory will be continued in the following two chapters, and references for further reading will be given at the end of each chapter.

7.1 DEFINITION AND SIMPLE PROPERTIES

Let "∘" be a binary operation defined on a nonempty set G. We recall that this statement only means that if (a, b) is any ordered pair of elements of G, then $a \circ b$ is a uniquely determined element of G. As a matter of fact, it is customary to call this operation either "addition" or "multiplication," and to use the familiar notation that is associated with these words. However, we shall first give the definition of a group, using the symbol "∘" for the operation.

7.1 Definition. A nonempty set G on which there is defined a binary operation "∘" is called a *group* (with respect to this operation) provided the following properties are satisfied:

(i)   If $a, b, c \in G$, then $(a \circ b) \circ c = a \circ (b \circ c)$ (*associative law*).
(ii) There exists an element e of G such that $e \circ a = a \circ e = a$ for every
      element a of G (*existence of an identity*).
(iii) If $a \in G$, there exists an element x of G such that $a \circ x = x \circ a = e$
                                  (*existence of inverses*).

In Section 1.5 we called an element e, whose existence is asserted in (ii), an identity for the operation "$\circ$". However, we shall now call it an identity of the group. As suggested by the indicated name of the third property, as well as by previous use of the term, the element x whose existence is asserted in (iii) is called an *inverse* of the element a. Note that in a group *every* element has an inverse. As a matter of fact, it is quite easy to prove that in a group the identity is unique and also that every element has a unique inverse.

In order to give an example of a group, it is necessary to specify the elements of the set and to define an operation on this set in such a way that the three properties stated above are satisfied. We now give several examples of groups.

EXAMPLE 1.   The set **Z** of all integers, with the operation "$\circ$" taken as the usual operation $(+)$ of addition. The first property then merely states that

$$(a + b) + c = a + (b + c),$$

and this is just the associative law of addition for the integers. In this case, the identity of the group is the zero integer since $0 + a = a + 0 = a$ for $a \in Z$. The inverse of the element a is the element $-a$ since $a + (-a) = -a + a = 0$, and in the present notation this is just what is required in the statement of the third property. We have therefore verified all three properties, and hence we have a group. This group may be called the *additive group of the integers*.

This example can easily be generalized as follows. Let S be the set of all elements of any *ring*, and let the operation "$\circ$" be taken as the operation of addition already defined in the ring. Then the three properties of a group are precisely the properties P_2, P_3, and P_4 of Section 2.2 required of addition in the ring. Hence, S must be a group relative to the operation of addition. We shall refer to this group as the *additive group of the ring S*.

EXAMPLE 2.   The set T of all nonzero rational numbers, with the operation "$\circ$" taken as the familiar operation of multiplication of rational numbers. Since the product of two nonzero rational numbers is also a nonzero rational number, the set T is closed under multiplication, that is, multiplication is an operation defined on T. If a, b, $c \in T$, then $(ab)c = a(bc)$ by the associative law of multiplication for rational numbers, and this is just 7.1(i) in this case. Moreover, the identity is the rational number 1, and the inverse of an element a of T is the rational number a^{-1}. Hence, T is a group with respect to the operation of multiplication. We may emphasize that in a group *every* element must have an inverse, and this explains why the set of *all* rational numbers would not be a group with respect to multiplication.

This example can also be generalized as follows. If F is an arbitrary *field*, the set of all nonzero elements of F is a group with respect to the operation of multiplication in the field. This group we shall call the *multiplicative group of the field F*. We emphasize again that there is exactly one element of F, the zero, which is not an element of the multiplicative group of F.

EXAMPLE 3.   The set $\mathbf{R}^+$ of all *positive* real numbers with multiplication as the operation. Properties (ii) and (iii) are satisfied because $1 \in \mathbf{R}^+$ and if $a \in \mathbf{R}^+$, then also $a^{-1} \in \mathbf{R}^+$.

In like manner, $\mathbf{Q}^+$ is a group with respect to the operation of multiplication. More generally, if F is any *ordered* field, then F^+ is a group with respect to the operation of multiplication.

EXAMPLE 4.   The set $\{1 , -1 , i , -i\}$ consisting of these four complex numbers, with the operation of multiplication of complex numbers. It is easy to verify that the set is closed under multiplication and, of course, the number 1 is the identity. Moreover, 1 and -1 are their own inverses, and i and $-i$ are inverses of each other. The associative law clearly holds since it holds for multiplication of complex numbers in general.

EXAMPLE 5.   The set L of all complex numbers z with $|z| = 1$, again with respect to the operation of multiplication. Since, by Theorem 6.15, we have $|uv| = |u| \cdot |v|$, it follows that if $u \in L$ and $v \in L$, then $uv \in L$, and L is therefore closed under multiplication. Moreover, if $|u| = 1$, it is easy to verify that $|u^{-1}| = 1$. Hence, if $u \in L$, then also $u^{-1} \in L$ and each element of L has an inverse in L. The other properties are obviously satisfied, and therefore L is a group.

EXAMPLE 6.   Let H be the set $\{p , q , r\}$ with an operation, which we shall consider as multiplication, defined by the following table.

$(\cdot)$	p	q	r
p	p	q	r
q	q	r	p
r	r	p	q

Clearly, p is the identity of H. Moreover, p is its own inverse, and q and r are inverses of each other. The associative law is also satisfied, although it would be tedious to verify it from the table.

EXAMPLE 7. Let G be the set $\{e, a, b, c\}$ with an operation of multiplication defined by the following table.

$(\cdot)$	e	a	b	c
e	e	a	b	c
a	a	e	c	b
b	b	c	e	a
c	c	b	a	e

The associative law holds, although we shall not verify it; and e is the identity. In this group, each element is its own inverse.

All of these examples have an additional property not required by the definition of a group. That is, they are abelian groups according to the following definition.

7.2 Definition. If in a group G with operation "$\circ$", $a \circ b = b \circ a$ for all a, $b \in G$, G is said to be an *abelian group* (or a commutative group).

The term "abelian group" is most commonly used for this concept. The name is derived from Niels Henrik Abel (1802–1829), a famous Norwegian mathematician whose fundamental work furnished an inspiration for many later mathematicians.

All the above examples are examples of abelian groups. In the following section we shall introduce some very important nonabelian groups.

As in the examples, we shall always call the operation in a group either addition or multiplication, and shall use the usual notation associated with these names. We shall never use addition as the operation in a nonabelian group. That is, whenever addition is used as the operation, we shall always assume, whether or not it is explicitly mentioned, that the group is abelian. It follows that in such a group *all* the properties of addition in a ring are satisfied. The identity will be denoted by 0 and called "zero"; the inverse of an element a will be denoted by $-a$; we shall write $b - a$ for $b + (-a)$, and so on.

When the operation in a group is called multiplication, the group may be either abelian or nonabelian. Accordingly, when we come to prove a property of arbitrary groups, we shall think of the operation as multiplication, and use the implied notation. In particular, the inverse of an element a will then be denoted by a^{-1}. We shall usually let e be the

identity of the group, and reserve the symbol "1" for the smallest positive integer.

Perhaps we should emphasize that an operation indicated by writing elements in juxtaposition and called multiplication need not be
"ordinary" multiplication (of numbers, for example). It is just an operation having *only* the properties required in the definition of a group.

Now let G be an arbitrary group with operation multiplication. The
following properties can be easily proved using only trivial modifications of proofs that we have already met in our study of rings and fields.
We may emphasize that here multiplication need not be commutative.
The first two of these properties have already been stated in the preceding section.

7.3   Theorem.   *The following hold in every group G:*

   (i) *The identity of G is unique.*

   (ii) *If $a \in G$, a has a unique inverse a^{-1}.*

   (iii) *If a, b, $c \in G$ such that $ab = ac$, then $b = c$.*

   (iv) *If a, b, $c \in G$ such that $ba = ca$, then $b = c$.*

   (v) *If a, $b \in G$, there exists a unique element x of G such that $ax = b$*
         and a unique element y of G such that $ya = b$. In fact, $x = a^{-1}b$
         and $y = ba^{-1}$.

   (vi) *The inverse of a product is the product of the inverses in the reverse*
         order, that is, if a, $b \in G$, then $(ab)^{-1} = b^{-1}a^{-1}$.

Properties (iii) and (iv) are naturally called the *cancellation laws*.
The proofs of the various parts of 7.3 will be assigned as an exercise
below.

Just as in the case of multiplication in a ring, the generalized associative law holds and we can write products without use of parentheses
to indicate association.

If $a \in G$, we define $a^0 = e$, where e is the identity of the group.
Then, just as though a were a nonzero element of a field, we can define
a^n for *every* integer n. Moreover, for all choices of integers m and n, the
following laws of exponents hold:

$$a^m \cdot a^n = a^{m+n},$$
$$(a^m)^n = a^{mn}.$$

For an *abelian* group, we also have $(ab)^n = a^n \cdot b^n$, but this is not true in
general.

In those cases in which we use addition as the operation, we make
use of multiples in place of powers; that is, na takes the place of a^n.
Such a group is always assumed to be abelian and we have the following
analogues of the above laws of exponents:

$$ma + na = (m + n)a,$$
$$n(ma) = (nm)a,$$
$$n(a + b) = na + nb.$$

These are properties that are already familiar as properties of addition in any ring.

A set H of elements of a group G is naturally called a *subgroup* of G if H is itself a group with respect to the operation already defined on G. If e is the identity of G, then G certainly has the two so-called *trivial* subgroups $\{e\}$ and G. Any other subgroup is called a *proper* subgroup.

The following theorem, whose proof will be required in Exercise 3 below, is often useful in determining subgroups of a given group.

7.4   Theorem.   (a) *A nonempty subset K of a group G is a subgroup of G if and only if the following two conditions are satisfied:*

(i)   *If $a, b \in K$, then $ab \in K$.*

(ii)   *If $a \in K$, then $a^{-1} \in K$.*

(b) *If K has a finite number of elements, condition (ii) is implied by condition (i).*

In view of this theorem, we see therefore that a nonempty set of elements of a group G having a finite number of elements is a subgroup of G if and only if the set is closed under the operation on G. However, for infinite groups condition (ii) is not a consequence of condition (i). As an example, the set of all positive integers is a nonempty subset of the additive group of the integers which satisfies condition (i) but not condition (ii).

We conclude this section by introducing one additional concept which is analogous to the concept of direct sum of rings. Suppose that G and H are groups and let us first assume that they are abelian groups and that the operation in each of these groups is written as addition. On the Cartesian product set $G \times H$ we define an operation of addition as follows:

$$(g_1, h_1) + (g_2, h_2) = (g_1 + g_2, h_1 + h_2), \qquad g_1, g_2 \in G; h_1, h_2 \in H.$$

It is easy to verify that we obtain in this way an abelian group. This group is called the *direct sum* of G and H and usually denoted by $G \oplus H$.

In a similar manner, if G and H are completely arbitrary groups with the operation in both groups written as multiplication, we may modify the above procedure in the obvious way by defining multiplication on the product set $G \times H$ as follows:

$$(g_1, h_1)(g_2, h_2) = (g_1 g_2, h_1 h_2), \qquad g_1, g_2 \in G; h_1, h_2 \in H.$$

The group obtained in this way is called the *direct product* of the groups G and H, and it is customary to denote it by the same notation $G \times H$ as used for the Cartesian product of the *sets* G and H.

We have defined the direct sum (or the direct product) of *two* groups. We leave it to the reader to give a corresponding definition of the direct sum (or the direct product) of any finite number of groups.

EXERCISES

1. Prove Theorem 7.3(i)–(vi).

2. Which of the following are groups with respect to the indicated operation?

   (a) The set $\{1, 3, 7, 9\}$ of elements of $\mathbf{Z}_{10}$, with operation multiplication.

   (b) The set $\{0, 2, 4, 6, 8\}$ of elements of $\mathbf{Z}_{10}$, with operation addition.

   (c) The set $\{1, 3, 9\}$ of elements of $\mathbf{Z}_{10}$, with operation multiplication.

   (d) The set of all rational numbers x such that $0 < x \leq 1$, with operation multiplication.

   (e) The set of all positive irrational real numbers with operation multiplication.

   (f) The set of all integers with operation "$\circ$" defined as follows: $a \circ b = a + b + 1$.

   (g) The set of all integers with operation "$\circ$" defined as follows: $a \circ b = a - b$.

   (h) The set of all rational numbers, other than 1, with operation "$\circ$" defined as follows: $a \circ b = a + b - ab$.

   (i) The set of complex numbers that are nth roots of unity, where n is a fixed positive integer, with operation multiplication.

3. Prove Theorem 7.4. [Hint for part (b): Adapt the proof of Theorem 5.6.]

4. If H_1 and H_2 are subgroups of a group G, prove that $H_1 \cap H_2$ is a subgroup of G. Generalize this result by proving that the intersection of any number of subgroups of G is a subgroup of G.

5. Find all subgroups of each of the following groups:

   (a) The additive group of the ring $\mathbf{Z}_{12}$.
   (b) The additive group of the ring $\mathbf{Z}_5$.
   (c) The multiplicative group of the field $\mathbf{Z}_7$.
   (d) The multiplicative group of the field $\mathbf{Z}_{11}$.

6. Show that the set of all elements of the ring $\mathbf{Z}_n$ of the form $[k]$, where k and n are relatively prime, is a group with respect to the operation of multiplication.

7. Prove that $(ab)^2 = a^2b^2$ for all choices of a and b as elements of a group G if and only if G is abelian.

8. Let a be a fixed element of a group G. Prove that the set $\{x \mid x \in G, ax = xa\}$ is a subgroup of G.

9. If R is a ring with unity, prove that the set of all elements of R which have multiplicative inverses in R is a group G with respect to the operation of multiplication as defined in the ring R. Verify that the result of Exercise 6 above is a special case of this result.

10. If $R = \mathbf{Z}_4 \oplus \mathbf{Z}$, verify that the group G obtained by the method of the preceding exercise has four elements, and write out a multiplication table for this group.

11. Let G be the set of all ordered pairs (a, b) of real numbers with $a \neq 0$, and on this set let us define an operation of multiplication as follows:

$$(a, b)(c, d) = (ac, bc + d).$$

   Verify that G is a nonabelian group.

7.2   GROUPS OF PERMUTATIONS

In the following we shall tacitly assume that the set A is a nonempty set. Let us begin by introducing a convenient definition.

7.5   Definition.   A one-one mapping of a set A onto itself is called a *permutation* of A.

Now if α and β are permutations of A, in a familiar way the product mapping $\alpha\beta$ is defined as follows:

7.6 $$a(\alpha\beta) = (a\alpha)\beta, \qquad\qquad a \in A.$$

Moreover, it is easy to verify that $\alpha\beta$ is also a one-one mapping of A onto A, that is, it is a permutation of A.

The significance of the concept of permutation in connection with the study of groups is suggested by the following result.

7.7   Theorem.   *The set S of all permutations of a set A is a group with respect to the multiplication defined by 7.6.*

We have already observed that if $\alpha, \beta \in S$, then $\alpha\beta \in S$, so we have an operation of multiplication defined on the set S. We proved in 1.9 that the associative law always holds for products of mappings whenever the products are defined. If we now denote the identity mapping on A by ϵ, it is clear that ϵ is an element of S and is the required identity for the group. Finally, as pointed out following the proof of Theorem 1.11, each permutation α has an inverse mapping α^{-1} with the property that it also is a permutation of A and $\alpha\alpha^{-1} = \alpha^{-1}\alpha = \epsilon$. Thus, all of the defining properties of a group are satisfied, and this completes the proof of the theorem. The group S is naturally called the *group of all permutations of the set A*.

So far, the set A has been a completely arbitrary set. However, we are now primarily interested in the case in which A is restricted to have a finite number of elements. Accordingly, we make the following definition.

7.8   Definition.   Let n be a positive integer. The group of all permutations of a set with n elements is called the *symmetric group* on n symbols, and may be designated by S_n.

Let us now consider an example in which $A = \{1, 2, 3\}$ a set with three elements. Then the symmetric group S_3, consisting of all permutations of A, contains the six elements $\alpha_1, \alpha_2, \alpha_3, \alpha_4, \alpha_5, \alpha_6$, as follows:

7.9
$$
\begin{aligned}
1\alpha_1 &= 1, & 2\alpha_1 &= 2, & 3\alpha_1 &= 3, \\
1\alpha_2 &= 2, & 2\alpha_2 &= 1, & 3\alpha_2 &= 3, \\
1\alpha_3 &= 3, & 2\alpha_3 &= 2, & 3\alpha_3 &= 1, \\
1\alpha_4 &= 1, & 2\alpha_4 &= 3, & 3\alpha_4 &= 2, \\
1\alpha_5 &= 2, & 2\alpha_5 &= 3, & 3\alpha_5 &= 1, \\
1\alpha_6 &= 3, & 2\alpha_6 &= 1, & 3\alpha_6 &= 2.
\end{aligned}
$$

The product of two of these permutations may, of course, be computed by using the definition of product of mappings. For example, let us compute $\alpha_2\alpha_5$. We have

$$
\begin{aligned}
1(\alpha_2\alpha_5) &= (1\alpha_2)\alpha_5 = 2\alpha_5 = 3, \\
2(\alpha_2\alpha_5) &= (2\alpha_2)\alpha_5 = 1\alpha_5 = 2, \\
3(\alpha_2\alpha_5) &= (3\alpha_2)\alpha_5 = 3\alpha_5 = 1.
\end{aligned}
$$

Hence, $\alpha_2\alpha_5 = \alpha_3$ since under the mapping $\alpha_2\alpha_5$ each element of A has the same image as under the mapping α_3. In like manner we can compute all products and obtain the following multiplication table for the group S_3.

7.10

	α_1	α_2	α_3	α_4	α_5	α_6
α_1	α_1	α_2	α_3	α_4	α_5	α_6
α_2	α_2	α_1	α_5	α_6	α_3	α_4
α_3	α_3	α_6	α_1	α_5	α_4	α_2
α_4	α_4	α_5	α_6	α_1	α_2	α_3
α_5	α_5	α_4	α_2	α_3	α_6	α_1
α_6	α_6	α_3	α_4	α_2	α_1	α_5

It is clear that α_1 is the identity of this group, and from the table one can easily find the inverse of each element. The group S_3 is not an abelian group since, for example, $\alpha_2\alpha_5 = \alpha_3$, whereas $\alpha_5\alpha_2 = \alpha_4$.

Before leaving this example, let us mention still another way of exhibiting the individual permutations of this group. For example, let us consider the element α_2 of S_3, as defined in 7.9. It is sometimes convenient to write

7.11
$$\alpha_2 = \begin{pmatrix} 1 & 2 & 3 \\ 2 & 1 & 3 \end{pmatrix}$$

to express the fact that under the mapping α_2 the image of 1 is 2, the image of 2 is 1, and the image of 3 is 3. According to this notation, we merely write the elements of the set A (in any order) in the top row, and under each element of A we write its image under the mapping α_2. In like manner, we see that

$$\alpha_5 = \begin{pmatrix} 1 & 2 & 3 \\ 2 & 3 & 1 \end{pmatrix}.$$

Then to compute the product $\alpha_2\alpha_5$ we observe that under this product 1 maps into 2 and then 2 maps into 3; hence 1 maps into 3. In like manner, 2 maps into 2 and 3 into 1. Hence, we may write

$$\begin{pmatrix} 1 & 2 & 3 \\ 2 & 1 & 3 \end{pmatrix}\begin{pmatrix} 1 & 2 & 3 \\ 2 & 3 & 1 \end{pmatrix} = \begin{pmatrix} 1 & 2 & 3 \\ 3 & 2 & 1 \end{pmatrix} = \alpha_3,$$

and we have again verified that $\alpha_2\alpha_5 = \alpha_3$.

We can use a notation similar to 7.11 to denote a permutation of any finite set. In general, if $\{i_1, i_2, \cdots, i_n\}$ is an arrangement of the integers $1, 2, \cdots, n$; by

$$\begin{pmatrix} 1 & 2 & 3 \cdots n \\ i_1 & i_2 & i_3 \cdots i_n \end{pmatrix}$$

we mean the permutation α of the set $A = \{1, 2, \cdots, n\}$ such that $1\alpha = i_1, 2\alpha = i_2, \cdots, n\alpha = i_n$. We shall use this notation whenever it seems convenient to do so.

We found above that S_3 has six elements. Let us now determine the number of elements in the symmetric group S_n, that is, the number of permutations of a set $A = \{1, 2, \cdots, n\}$ with n elements. Clearly, the image of 1 may be any element of A, and hence there are n choices for the image of 1. After an image of 1 is selected, there are then $n - 1$ choices for the image of 2, and so on. It follows that there are $n(n - 1)$ $(n - 2) \cdots 2 \cdot 1$ different permutations of A. This number is usually denoted by $n!$ and called "n factorial." We have therefore shown that S_n has $n!$ elements.

Any group whose elements are permutations is naturally called a *permutation group* or a *group of permutations*. Any subgroup of a symmetric group S_n is certainly a permutation group. For example, from the table 7.10 and Theorem 7.4 it follows that $\{\alpha_1, \alpha_5, \alpha_6\}$ is a subgroup of S_3, and this is therefore an example of a permutation group which is not a symmetric group since it is not the group of *all* permutations of any set.

We conclude this section with a brief indication of how one can construct some interesting permutation groups by use of properties of symmetry of certain geometric figures. As an example, let us consider a square and study all rigid motions of the square into itself. That is, if the square is thought of as being made of some rigid material, such as cardboard, we consider motions such that the figure will look the same after the motion as before. In this, as well as in all other examples we shall consider, the rigid motions will consist of rotations either in the plane or in space. Each rigid motion of the square can be used in an almost obvious way to define a permutation of the vertices of the square. Let us designate the vertices of the square by 1, 2, 3, and 4. Moreover, let E, F, G, and H be the midpoints of the sides, as indicated in Figure 13; and let O be the center of the square. A rotation, in the plane of the square, through an angle of 90° about point O would place the vertices in the position shown in Figure 14. We may interpret the result of this rotation as mapping 1 into 2, 2 into 3, 3 into 4, and 4 into 1; that is, as effecting the permutation

$$\alpha = \begin{pmatrix} 1 & 2 & 3 & 4 \\ 2 & 3 & 4 & 1 \end{pmatrix}$$

of the set $\{1, 2, 3, 4\}$ whose elements denote the vertices. A similar rotation through an angle of 180° or 270° leads to the respective permutations

$$\alpha^2 = \begin{pmatrix} 1 & 2 & 3 & 4 \\ 3 & 4 & 1 & 2 \end{pmatrix} \quad \text{or} \quad \alpha^3 = \begin{pmatrix} 1 & 2 & 3 & 4 \\ 4 & 1 & 2 & 3 \end{pmatrix}.$$

Clearly, $\alpha^4 = \epsilon$, the identity permutation. We also have other rigid motions consisting of rotations in space about a line of symmetry of

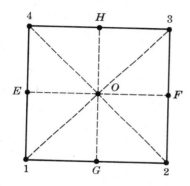

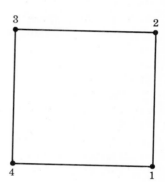

Figure 13

                                                                    Figure 14

the square. Let β be the permutation which arises from a rotation through an angle of 180° about the line EF, and γ the permutation which arises from a similar rotation about GH. Then we see that

$$\beta = \begin{pmatrix} 1 & 2 & 3 & 4 \\ 4 & 3 & 2 & 1 \end{pmatrix} \quad \text{and} \quad \gamma = \begin{pmatrix} 1 & 2 & 3 & 4 \\ 2 & 1 & 4 & 3 \end{pmatrix}.$$

There remain two other permutations arising from rotations through 180° about the diagonals of the square. These are

$$\delta = \begin{pmatrix} 1 & 2 & 3 & 4 \\ 1 & 4 & 3 & 2 \end{pmatrix} \quad \text{and} \quad \sigma = \begin{pmatrix} 1 & 2 & 3 & 4 \\ 3 & 2 & 1 & 4 \end{pmatrix}.$$

The set $\{\epsilon, \alpha, \alpha^2, \alpha^3, \beta, \gamma, \delta, \sigma\}$ of permutations obtained in this way is closed under multiplication, as is easily verified by the multiplication table given below.

	ϵ	α	α^2	α^3	β	γ	δ	σ
ϵ	ϵ	α	α^2	α^3	β	γ	δ	σ
α	α	α^2	α^3	ϵ	σ	δ	β	γ
α^2	α^2	α^3	ϵ	α	γ	β	σ	δ
α^3	α^3	ϵ	α	α^2	δ	σ	γ	β
β	β	δ	γ	σ	ϵ	α^2	α	α^3
γ	γ	σ	β	δ	α^2	ϵ	α^3	α
δ	δ	γ	σ	β	α^3	α	ϵ	α^2
σ	σ	β	δ	γ	α	α^3	α^2	ϵ

7.12

Moreover, it is evident that each permutation of this set has an inverse in this set, and we therefore have a group of permutations. This particular group with eight elements is called the *octic group*. Since we obtained this group by a consideration of the rigid motions of a square, we may also say that it is the group of rigid motions of a square.

In a similar way we may construct the group of rigid motions of other geometric figures. We observe that by this process we must actually obtain a *group* of permutations. In the first place, a rigid motion followed by another rigid motion is itself a rigid motion, and hence the set we obtain must be closed under multiplication. Since, also, each rigid motion can be reversed by another rigid motion, the inverse of each permutation in the set will also be in the set. The fact that we obtain a group of permutations then follows from Theorem 7.4.

EXERCISES

1. In the following, α and β are the given permutations of the set $A = \{1, 2, 3, 4, 5\}$. Compute, in each case, $\alpha\beta$, $\beta\alpha$, α^2, and β^2.

   (a) $1\alpha = 2$, $2\alpha = 1$, $3\alpha = 3$, $4\alpha = 5$, $5\alpha = 4$;
   $1\beta = 1$, $2\beta = 4$, $3\beta = 2$, $4\beta = 3$, $5\beta = 5$.

   (b) $1\alpha = 4$, $2\alpha = 3$, $3\alpha = 5$, $4\alpha = 1$, $5\alpha = 2$;
   $1\beta = 2$, $2\beta = 3$, $3\beta = 1$, $4\beta = 4$, $5\beta = 5$.

   (c) $1\alpha = 2$, $2\alpha = 1$, $3\alpha = 4$, $4\alpha = 5$, $5\alpha = 3$;
   $1\beta = 2$, $2\beta = 3$, $3\beta = 4$, $4\beta = 5$, $5\beta = 1$.

   (d) $\alpha = \begin{pmatrix} 1 & 2 & 3 & 4 & 5 \\ 5 & 4 & 3 & 1 & 2 \end{pmatrix}$, $\beta = \begin{pmatrix} 1 & 2 & 3 & 4 & 5 \\ 3 & 2 & 1 & 5 & 4 \end{pmatrix}$.

   (e) $\alpha = \begin{pmatrix} 1 & 2 & 3 & 4 & 5 \\ 1 & 3 & 2 & 5 & 4 \end{pmatrix}$, $\beta = \begin{pmatrix} 1 & 2 & 3 & 4 & 5 \\ 2 & 3 & 1 & 4 & 5 \end{pmatrix}$.

   (f) $\alpha = \begin{pmatrix} 1 & 2 & 3 & 4 & 5 \\ 5 & 4 & 3 & 2 & 1 \end{pmatrix}$, $\beta = \begin{pmatrix} 1 & 2 & 3 & 4 & 5 \\ 5 & 4 & 2 & 1 & 3 \end{pmatrix}$.

2. Verify the entry in the table 7.12 giving each of the following products: $\alpha^2\sigma$, $\beta\gamma$, $\gamma\beta$, $\alpha^3\gamma$, $\delta\sigma$.

3. Find all subgroups of the symmetric group S_3.

4. Find all subgroups of the octic group (7.12).

5. Show that the group of rigid motions of an equilateral triangle is the symmetric group S_3.

6. Find the group of rigid motions of a rectangle that is not a square. Make a multiplication table for this group and show that it is a subgroup of the octic group.

7. How many elements are there in the group of rigid motions of a regular pentagon? A regular hexagon?

7.3   HOMOMORPHISMS AND ISOMORPHISMS

The concept of a group homomorphism is essentially the same as that of a ring homomorphism except that we now have only one operation instead of two. However, the operations may be written differently in the two groups, so we shall state the definition in the following general way.

7.13   Definition.   Let G be a group with operation "$\circ$" and H a group with operation "$\square$". A mapping $\theta: G \to H$ of G into H is called a *homomorphism* if and only if for $a, b \in G$, we have

7.14 $$(a \circ b)\theta = (a\theta) \,\square\, (b\theta).$$

If there exists a homomorphism of G onto H, we may say that G is *homomorphic* to H or that H is a *homomorphic image* of G.

Again, the special case of a homomorphism in which the mapping is one-one is of such importance that we introduce as follows the terminology which has already been used for rings.

7.15   Definition.   A homomorphism which is a one-one mapping is called an *isomorphism*. If there exists an isomorphism of G onto H, we may say that G is *isomorphic to* H or that H is an *isomorphic image* of G.

Of course, just as with rings, if θ is an isomorphism of G onto H, then θ^{-1} is an isomorphism of H onto G, and we may say that G and H are isomorphic. We may write $G \cong H$ to indicate that G is isomorphic to H.

The operations "∘" and "□" appearing in Definition 7.13 will be considered to be either addition or multiplication, but the new feature here is that one of them may be written as addition and the other as multiplication. In any case, we may for convenience indicate that condition 7.14 holds by saying that *the group operation is preserved under the mapping θ.*

Let us now illustrate these concepts by a few illustrative examples.

EXAMPLE 1.   Let G be the additive group of the ring $\mathbf{Z}_4$, and H the multiplicative group of the field $\mathbf{Z}_5$. For convenience, let us designate the elements of G by 0, 1, 2, 3; and the elements of H by 1*, 2*, 3*, 4*. Now let $\theta: G \to H$ be the one-one mapping of G onto H defined as follows:

$$0\theta = 1^*, \quad 1\theta = 2^*, \quad 2\theta = 4^*, \quad 3\theta = 3^*.$$

We assert that the group operation is then preserved under the mapping θ. For example, we have

$$(2 + 3)\theta = 1\theta = 2^* = 4^* \cdot 3^* = (2\theta)(3\theta).$$

The reader may verify that in every case a sum of elements of G has as image the product of the corresponding images in H. Hence θ is an isomorphism of G onto H.

EXAMPLE 2.   Let $\mathbf{R}^+$ be the group of all positive real numbers with operation multiplication (Example 3 of Section 7.1), and let L be the additive group of the field of all real numbers. If $\phi: \mathbf{R}^+ \to L$ is defined by

$$x\phi = \log_{10} x, \qquad\qquad x \in \mathbf{R}^+,$$

it is known that ϕ is a one-one mapping of $\mathbf{R}^+$ onto L and, moreover, one of the familiar laws of logarithms assures us that

$$(xy)\phi = \log_{10} xy = \log_{10} x + \log_{10} y, \qquad x, y \in \mathbf{R}^+.$$

This shows that the group operation is preserved under the mapping ϕ, and ϕ is therefore an isomorphism of $\mathbf{R}^+$ onto. L It is this fact that is of central importance in the theory of logarithms. Of course, in place of 10 we could use as a base any fixed element of $\mathbf{R}^+$ other than 1.

EXAMPLE 3.   Let S_3 be the symmetric group on three symbols, with multiplication table given by 7.10; and let H be the group consisting of the set $\{1, -1, i, -i\}$ of complex numbers with operation multiplication. Let $\theta: S_3 \to H$ be defined as follows:

$$\alpha_1\theta = 1, \quad \alpha_2\theta = -1, \quad \alpha_3\theta = -1, \quad \alpha_4\theta = -1, \quad \alpha_5\theta = 1, \quad \alpha_6\theta = 1.$$

It may be verified that the group operation is preserved under this mapping. As an example, we have

$$(\alpha_2\alpha_4)\theta \;=\; \alpha_6\theta \;=\; 1 \;=\; (-1)(-1) \;=\; (\alpha_2\theta)(\alpha_4\theta).$$

Thus θ is a homomorphism of S_3 into H. However, θ is clearly not an onto mapping, so we cannot say that H is a homomorphic image of S_3. However, if we let $H' = \{1\,,\,-1\}$, then H' is a subgroup of H and θ does define a mapping of S_3 onto H', and hence H' is a homomorphic image of S_3.

EXAMPLE 4.   Let G and H be arbitrary groups with operation multiplication. Then the mapping $\theta\colon G \times H \to G$ defined by $(g\,,\,h)\theta = g$ (that is, the projection of the set $G \times H$ onto G) is clearly a homomorphism of the direct product $G \times H$ onto G. Similarly, there exists a homomorphism of $G \times H$ onto H. Thus, both of the groups G and H are homomorphic images of the direct product $G \times H$.

We may point out that there always exists a (trivial) homomorphism of an arbitrary group G into an arbitrary group H in which every element of G maps into the identity of H.

Some fundamental properties of homomorphisms of groups are stated in the following theorem (cf. Theorem 2.32) in which we shall consider the operations in both groups to be multiplication.

7.16   Theorem.   *Let $\theta\colon G \to H$ be a homomorphism of the group G into the group H. Then each of the following is true:*

(*i*)   *If e is the identity of G, then $e\theta$ is the identity of H.*

(*ii*)   *If $a \in G$, then $(a^{-1})\theta = (a\theta)^{-1}$.*

(*iii*)   *If G is abelian and θ is an onto mapping, then H is abelian.*

We leave the proof of this theorem as an exercise.

The reader may sometimes have to make a suitable modification in notation. For example, if the operation in G is multiplication and that in H is addition, property (ii) of the preceding theorem should be interpreted as stating that $(a^{-1})\theta = -(a\theta)$, since $-(a\theta)$ is the inverse of $a\theta$ in H.

The concept introduced in the following definition plays an important role in the study of homomorphisms of groups.

7.17   Definition.   Let $\theta\colon G \to H$ be a homomorphism of the group G into the group H. The set of all elements of G which map into the identity of H is called the *kernel* of the homomorphism θ, and may be denoted by ker θ.

In Example 3 above, ker $\theta = \{\alpha_1, \alpha_5, \alpha_6\}$. It may be verified that in this case ker θ is actually a subgroup of S_3. The next theorem will show that this fact is no accident.

7.18   Theorem. *If $\theta: G \to H$ is a homomorphism, then ker θ is a subgroup of G. Moreover, if e is the identity of G, ker $\theta = \{e\}$ if and only if θ is an isomorphism.*

PROOF: Let $K = $ ker θ. By Theorem 7.16(i), the identity of H is $e\theta$. If $a, b \in K$, then $(ab)\theta = (a\theta)(b\theta) = (e\theta)(e\theta) = e\theta$, and thus K is closed with respect to multiplication. Moreover, if $a \in K$, by Theorem 7.19(ii) we have that $(a^{-1}\theta) = (a\theta)^{-1} = (e\theta)^{-1} = e\theta$, and hence $a^{-1} \in K$. Theorem 7.4 then shows that K is a subgroup of G. To prove the second statement of the theorem, suppose first that θ is an isomorphism. Since $e \in$ ker θ, and the mapping is one-one, this assures us that no other element of G has as image the identity $e\theta$ of H, and it follows that ker $\theta = \{e\}$. Conversely, let us assume that θ is a homomorphism of G into H such that ker $\theta = \{e\}$. Suppose that $a, b \in G$ such that $a\theta = b\theta$. It follows that

$$(ab^{-1})\theta = (a\theta)(b^{-1}\theta) = (a\theta)(b\theta)^{-1} = e\theta,$$

and hence that $ab^{-1} \in K$. Thus, $ab^{-1} = e$ and $a = b$. This shows that θ is a one-one mapping and is therefore an isomorphism. This completes the proof of the theorem.

The result just established is often useful in the following way. To show that a mapping of a group G into a group H is an isomorphism, we may first show that it is a homomorphism and then verify that its kernel consists of the identity only.

We conclude this section by proving a theorem which is due to the famous English mathematician, Arthur Cayley (1821–1895).

7.19   Theorem. *Every group G is isomorphic to a group of permutations.*

PROOF: In order to prove this result we need first of all to determine the *set* some of whose permutations we shall associate with the elements of the given group G. We make what is perhaps the most obvious choice, namely, the set of elements of G itself. Moreover, we shall let G denote both the group and the set of its elements as it suits our convenience. Actually, the desired permutations will be obtained by multiplication by the elements of the group. More precisely, let us first observe that if $a \in G$, then

$$\{xa \mid x \in G\} = G.$$

Therefore the mapping $\theta_a: G \to G$ defined by $x\theta_a = xa$, $x \in G$, is a mapping of G onto G and it is clearly also a one-one mapping; hence

θ_a is a permutation of the set G associated with the element a of the group G.

Now let us set

$$H = \{\theta_a \mid a \in G\},$$

that is, H is the set of all permutations of the type introduced above. Since for $x \in G$, we have

$$x(\theta_a \cdot \theta_b) = (x\theta_a)\theta_b = (x\theta_a)b = xab,$$

we see that

7.20 $$\theta_a \cdot \theta_b = \theta_{ab},$$

and H is therefore closed with respect to multiplication. Moreover, H has identity θ_e, where e is the identity of G; and 7.20 shows that $\theta_{a^{-1}}$ is the inverse of θ_a. Hence H is a subgroup of the group of all permutations of the set G.

We now assert that the mapping $\alpha: G \to H$ defined by $a\alpha = \theta_a$, $a \in G$, is an isomorphism of G onto H. It is clearly an onto mapping. Moreover, it is a homomorphism since by 7.20,

$$(ab)\alpha = \theta_{ab} = \theta_a \cdot \theta_b = (a\alpha)(b\alpha).$$

There remains only to prove that α is a one-one mapping. However, if $\theta_a = \theta_b$, it follows that $xa = xb$ for every element x of G, and clearly we must have $a = b$. Thus α is indeed a one-one mapping, and this completes the proof.

In view of this theorem, in order to prove a theorem for arbitrary groups it is sufficient to prove it for groups of permutations. Although the subject of group theory is sometimes approached through the study of permutation groups, we shall not limit ourselves to this point of view.

EXERCISES

1. Verify that there exists an isomorphism of the additive group of the ring $\mathbf{Z}_6$ onto the multiplicative group of the field $\mathbf{Z}_7$ such that the image of the element 1 of the first group is the element 3* of the second group.

2. What familiar properties of logarithms follow from Theorem 7.16 as applied to the isomorphism given in Example 2 above?

3. Prove that a group G is abelian if and only if the mapping $\theta : G \to G$ defined by $a\theta = a^{-1}$, $a \in G$, is an isomorphism

4. If G is the additive group of the ring $\mathbf{Z}_{15}$ and H is the additive group of the ring $\mathbf{Z}_5$, find a homomorphism of G onto H.

5. Show that two groups are necessarily isomorphic if each of them has exactly two elements. Show that the same conclusion holds if each has exactly three elements.

6. Find two groups, each with exactly four elements, which are not isomorphic. Do the same thing, with "four" replaced by "six."

7. If G is the multiplicative group of the field $\mathbf{Z}_5$, use the method of proof of Theorem 7.19 to find a group of permutations which is isomorphic to G.

8. If $\theta : G \to H$ and $\phi : H \to K$ are group homomorphisms, show that $\theta\phi$ also is a homomorphism.

9. The subgroup $\{\epsilon, \alpha^2, \beta, \gamma\}$ of the octic group (7.12) is sometimes called the *four-group*. Verify that the four-group is isomorphic to the additive group of the ring $\mathbf{Z}_2 \oplus \mathbf{Z}_2$, and also to the group of Example 7 of Section 7.1.

10. If $\theta : G \to H$ is a homomorphism of G into H and $a \in G$, prove that $a^k\theta = (a\theta)^k$ for *every* integer k.

11. Verify that the group G of Exercise 11 at the end of Section 7.1 has a subgroup which is isomorphic to the multiplicative group of the field of real numbers.

12. For each ordered pair (a, b) of real numbers with $a \neq 0$, let $\alpha_{a,b} : \mathbf{R} \to \mathbf{R}$ be the mapping of the field $\mathbf{R}$ into the field $\mathbf{R}$ defined by $x\alpha_{a,b} = ax + b$, $x \in \mathbf{R}$. Prove that the set H of all such mappings $\alpha_{a,b}$ is a group of permutations of $\mathbf{R}$, and that H is isomorphic to the group G mentioned in the preceding exercise.

13. Determine the set L of all elements $\alpha_{a,b}$ of the group H of the preceding exercise such that $\alpha_{a,b}\alpha_{1,2} = \alpha_{1,2}\alpha_{a,b}$. How do you know without detailed calculation that L is a subgroup of H? Verify that the group L is isomorphic to the additive group of the field $\mathbf{R}$.

14. Let G be a group and H merely a *set* on which a binary operation is defined. If there exists a mapping $\theta : G \to H$ of G *onto* H which preserves the operation, prove that H is a group with respect to the given operation and that θ is a homomorphism of the group G onto the group H. [This fact is usually expressed by saying that a homomorphic image of a group is a group.]

7.4 CYCLIC GROUPS

If a is an element of an arbitrary group G, then since G is closed with respect to the operation (which we will consider to be multiplication), we see that $a^k \in G$ for every positive integer k. Moreover, a^0 is the identity e of G by definition, and a^{-k} is the inverse of a^k. It follows easily that the set $\{a^k \mid k \in \mathbf{Z}\}$ is a subgroup of G. We are particularly interested in the case in which this subgroup turns out to be all of G. Accordingly, let us make the following definition.

7.21   Definition. If the group G contains an element a such that $G = \{a^k \mid k \in \mathbf{Z}\}$, we say that G is a *cyclic group* and that G is *generated by* a or that a is a *generator of* G.

Since $a^i \cdot a^j = a^j \cdot a^i$ for $i, j \in \mathbf{Z}$, we see that a cyclic group is necessarily abelian.

Whether or not a group G is cyclic, if $a \in G$, the subgroup $\{a^k \mid k \in \mathbf{Z}\}$ of G is a cyclic group which we naturally call the *subgroup of G generated by* a.

Let us now give some examples of cyclic groups.

EXAMPLE 1.   The multiplicative group of the field $\mathbf{Z}_5$. Let us write the elements as 1, 2, 3, and 4; and remember that multiplication is to be carried out modulo 5. It is easily verified that $2^1 = 2$, $2^2 = 4$, $2^3 = 3$, $2^4 = 1$; hence each element of the group is of the form 2^k for some integer k. It follows that the group must be cyclic with generator 2. The reader may show that 3 is also a generator of this group. The element 4 generates the cyclic subgroup $\{1, 4\}$.

EXAMPLE 2.   The additive group of the ring $\mathbf{Z}$ of integers. In a ring with addition as the operation, ka is the analogue of a^k used above. The integer 1 is a generator of this group since every element is of the form $k \cdot 1$ for some integer k.

EXAMPLE 3.   The additive group of the ring $\mathbf{Z}_n$ of integers modulo n. This group is generated by the element 1 of $\mathbf{Z}_n$. Of course, it may have other generators as well.

EXAMPLE 4.   The group of all complex numbers that are nth roots of unity, where n is a fixed positive integer, with multiplication as the operation. The fact that this group is cyclic is the content of Corollary 6.25, where it was shown that $w = \cos (360°/n) + i \sin (360°/n)$ is a generator.

EXAMPLE 5.   The subgroup $\{\alpha_1, \alpha_5, \alpha_6\}$ of the symmetric group S_3, whose multiplication table is given in 7.10. It is easily verified that $\alpha_5^2 = \alpha_6$ and $\alpha_5^3 = \alpha_1$; hence α_5 is a generator of this subgroup. As a matter of fact, α_6 is also a generator of this same subgroup. The group S_3 is not a cyclic group. This may be shown by direct calculation or by observing that S_3 is nonabelian whereas a cyclic group must be abelian.

We are now ready to give another definition as follows:

7.22   Definition.

   (i)   If a group G has n elements, where n is a positive integer, G is said to have *finite order* or, more precisely, to have *order n*. If there exists no such positive integer, G is said to have *infinite order*.

   (ii)   The *order of an element a* of a group G is the order of the cyclic subgroup of G generated by a.

In the language here introduced, we may say that the additive group of the integers has infinite order, the symmetric group S_n has order $n!$, the additive group of the ring $\mathbf{Z}_n$ has order n, and the multiplicative group of the field $\mathbf{Z}_p$ has order $p - 1$. All of these, except the first, are groups of finite order.

The next theorem gives an important characterization of the order of an element of a group. In fact, in order to compute the order of a given element it is usually simpler to apply this theorem than to use the definition.

7.23   Theorem.   *An element a of a group G has order n if and only if n is the smallest positive integer such that $a^n = e$, where e is the identity of G. If no such integer exists, a has infinite order.*

As a first step in the proof, we shall prove the following lemma.

7.24   Lemma.   *Let a be an element of the group G, and suppose that $a^n = e$, with n the smallest such positive integer. If $k \in \mathbf{Z}$, then $a^k = e$ if and only if $k \equiv 0 \pmod{n}$. More generally, if $i, j \in \mathbf{Z}$, then $a^i = a^j$ if and only if $i \equiv j \pmod{n}$.*

By the Division Algorithm, we may write any integer k in the form $k = qn + r$, where q and r are integers and $0 \leq r < n$. Then, since $a^n = e$, we have

$$a^k = a^{qn+r} = (a^n)^q \cdot a^r = e^q \cdot a^r = a^r.$$

If $a^k = e$, we see that $a^r = e$, and it follows that $r = 0$ since, otherwise, r would be a positive integer less than n and we have assumed that n is the smallest positive integer such that $a^n = e$. Hence, if $a^k = e$, we have $k = qn$ and $k \equiv 0 \pmod{n}$. Conversely, if $k = qn$, it is apparent that $a^q = (a^n)^q = e^q = e$. This establishes the first part of the lemma. The second part now follows easily. For if $a^i = a^j$, it follows that $a^{i-j} = e$, and by what we have just proved, this is true if and only if $i - j \equiv 0 \pmod{n}$ or $i \equiv j \pmod{n}$.

Let us return to the proof of the theorem, and suppose first that $a^n = e$, with n as the smallest such positive integer. We now assert that the elements

7.25 $$e, a, a^2, \cdots, a^{n-1}$$

are distinct and are all of the elements of the cyclic subgroup of G generated by a. Since no two of the integers $0, 1, 2, \cdots, n - 1$ are congruent modulo n, the preceding lemma shows that the elements 7.25 are distinct. Moreover, since every integer is congruent modulo n to some one of the integers $0, 1, 2, \cdots, n - 1$, it also follows that a^k is equal to one of the elements 7.25, for every integer k. Hence the cyclic subgroup of G generated by a has exactly the n distinct elements 7.25; that is, it has order n and therefore a has order n.

To prove the converse, let us now assume that a has order n. Then not all positive powers of a can be distinct; that is, we must have $a^i = a^j$ for different positive integers i and j. Suppose that $i > j$, and it then follows that $a^{i-j} = e$, with $i - j > 0$. Hence, there exists some positive power of a which is equal to e. Suppose that m is the smallest positive integer such that $a^m = e$. Now, by what we have proved above, a has order m. Since it was given that a has order n, we must have $m = n$. This completes the proof of the first sentence of the theorem.

If there exists no positive integer n such that $a^n = e$, it is easy to show that $a, a^2, a^3, \cdots$ must all be distinct. (Why?) Hence a must have infinite order, and the theorem is established.

Theorem 7.23 makes it easy to determine the order of an element of a given group. For example, let us find the order of the element 3 of the multiplicative group of the ring $\mathbf{Z}_{11}$. By computing the successive powers of 3, we find that $3^2 = 9$, $3^3 = 5$, $3^4 = 4$, $3^5 = 1$. Hence, the element 3 has order five. As another example, let us find the order of the element 10 of the additive group of the ring $\mathbf{Z}_{18}$. By Theorem 7.23, with the proper change of notation, this order will be the least positive integer n such that $n \cdot 10 \equiv 0 \pmod{18}$. It follows easily that $n = 9$, and the element 10 therefore has order 9.

It is not difficult to prove that two cyclic groups are isomorphic if and only if they have the same order. This fact will follow immediately from the following theorem.

7.26   Theorem.

(*i*)   *Every cyclic group of infinite order is isomorphic to the additive group of the ring* **Z** *of integers.*

(*ii*) *Every cyclic group of order n is isomorphic to the additive group of the ring* **Z**$_n$ *of integers modulo n.*

First, let G be an infinite cyclic group with generator a, and let $\theta \colon \mathbf{Z} \to G$ be the mapping of **Z** into G defined by

$$k\theta = a^k, \qquad\qquad\qquad k \in \mathbf{Z}.$$

Then, if $i, j \in \mathbf{Z}$, we have

$$(i + j)\theta = a^{i+j} = a^i \cdot a^j = (i\theta)(j\theta),$$

and hence θ is a homomorphism of the additive group of the integers into the group G. Suppose, now, that $i, j \in \mathbf{Z}$ such that $i\theta = j\theta$, that is, such that $a^i = a^j$. If, for example, $i > j$, then $a^{i-j} = e$, the identity of G. But Theorem 7.23 would then show that a has finite order, whereas we are given that it has infinite order. Hence $i\theta = j\theta$ implies that $i = j$, and θ is a one-one mapping. Finally, every element of G is of the form a^k for some $k \in \mathbf{Z}$ and the mapping θ is therefore an onto mapping. This completes the proof of the first part of the theorem.

Next, let G be a cyclic group of order n with generator a. In order to keep the notation straight, we shall now denote the elements of **Z**$_n$ by $[k]$, $k \in \mathbf{Z}$, and we shall show that the mapping $\theta \colon \mathbf{Z}_n \to G$ defined by

$$[k]\theta = a^k, \qquad\qquad\qquad k \in \mathbf{Z},$$

is the desired isomorphism of the additive group of **Z**$_n$ onto the group G. First, let us show that the mapping is well-defined. In other words, let us show that if $i, j \in \mathbf{Z}$, then $[i] = [j]$ if and only if $a^i = a^j$. However, we know that $[i] = [j]$ if and only if $i \equiv j \pmod{n}$ and, by Theorem 7.23 and Lemma 7.24, we also know that $a^i = a^j$ if and only if $i \equiv j \pmod{n}$. Thus θ is indeed a mapping of **Z**$_n$ into G, and it is clear that it is an onto mapping. Moreover, it is a one-one mapping since we have just observed that $a^i = a^j$ if and only if $[i] = [j]$. Finally, we have

$$([i] + [j])\theta = [i + j]\theta = a^{i+j} = a^i \cdot a^j = ([i]\theta)([j]\theta).$$

Hence the operation is preserved, and θ is the required isomorphism of the additive group of **Z**$_n$ onto the group G. The proof of the theorem is therefore complete.

In Example 1 above, we verified that the multiplicative group of the ring **Z**$_5$ is cyclic with generator 2 (or 3), and clearly its order is 4.

According to the theorem just proved, it must therefore be isomorphic to the additive group of the ring $\mathbf{Z}_4$. In order to distinguish between them, let us designate the elements of $\mathbf{Z}_4$ by [0], [1], [2], [3]; and the nonzero elements of $\mathbf{Z}_5$ by 1, 2, 3, 4. Using the generator 2 of the latter group, the proof just given shows that $[k]\theta = 2^k$, $k \in \mathbf{Z}$, defines an isomorphism of these two groups. Written out in detail, this mapping is as follows:

$$[1]\theta = 2, \quad [2]\theta = 4, \quad [3]\theta = 3, \quad [0]\theta = 1.$$

We can obtain a different isomorphism by using the generator 3 of the multiplicative group of $\mathbf{Z}_5$. This isomorphism ϕ defined by $[k]\phi = 3^k$ yields the following explicit isomorphism:

$$[1]\phi = 3, \quad [2]\phi = 4, \quad [3]\phi = 2, \quad [0]\phi = 1.$$

We have thus exhibited two different isomorphisms of these two groups. Our final theorem about cyclic groups is the following.

7.27 Theorem. *Every subgroup of a cyclic group G is itself a cyclic group.*

Suppose that G is generated by a, and let H be a subgroup of G. Let m be the smallest positive integer such that $a^m \in H$. We shall show that H is a cyclic group generated by a^m. Since $H \subseteq G$, any element of H is of the form a^k for some integer k. By the Division Algorithm, we may write $k = qm + r$, where $0 \le r < m$. Hence,

$$a^k = a^{qm+r} = (a^m)^q \cdot a^r,$$

and from this it follows that

$$a^r = (a^m)^{-q} \cdot a^k.$$

Since $a^m \in H$ and $a^k \in H$, this equation implies also that $a^r \in H$. In view of the choice of m as the smallest positive integer such that $a^m \in H$, and since $r < m$, we must have $r = 0$. We conclude that $k = qm$, and hence that every element a^k of H is of the form $(a^m)^q$ for some integer q. This shows that H is a cyclic group generated by a^m.

As an almost immediate consequence of the *proof* of the preceding theorem, we obtain the following result.

7.28 Corollary. *If a cyclic group G has finite order n and is generated by a, every subgroup H of G is generated by an element of the form a^m, where m is a divisor of n.*

Since Theorem 7.23 shows that $a^n = e$, and $e \in H$, we apply the above argument with $k = n$ and obtain $n = qm$. Hence, m is a divisor of n.

Of course, by a simple change in notation, these results apply equally well to the case in which the operation is addition. As an illustration of the preceding corollary, let us find all subgroups of the additive group of the ring $\mathbf{Z}_{14}$. This is a cyclic group of order 14 generated by the element 1; hence the only subgroups are the cyclic subgroups generated by 1, 2, 7, and 14. The subgroup generated by 14 consists only of the identity 0. The subgroup generated by 2 has order 7 and the subgroup generated by 7 has order 2.

EXERCISES

1. Find the order of each element of the octic group (7.12).

2. Find an element of the symmetric group S_4 of order 4. Similarly, find an element of S_5 of order 5; of S_n of order n.

3. It can be proved that for every prime p, the multiplicative group of the field $\mathbf{Z}_p$ is cyclic. Verify this fact for $p = 7$, 11, and 13.

4. Find all subgroups of the additive group of the ring $\mathbf{Z}_{20}$.

5. Prove: If G is a cyclic group of order n and k is a positive divisor of n, there exists a subgroup of G of order k.

6. If G is a cyclic group of order n with generator a, prove that a^k is also a generator of G if and only if $(k, n) = 1$.

7. Apply the result of the preceding exercise to find all generators of the additive group of the ring $\mathbf{Z}_{30}$.

8. Prove that if $\theta: G \to H$ is a homomorphism of a cyclic group G with generator a onto a group H, then H is a cyclic group with generator $a\theta$, and if a has finite order, the order of $a\theta$ is a divisor of the order of a.

9. Let G and H be cyclic groups of the same order, and let g be an arbitrary generator of G and h an arbitrary generator of H. Show that there exists an isomorphism θ of G onto H such that $g\theta = h$.

10. Determine all isomorphisms of the multiplicative group of the field $\mathbf{Z}_{11}$ onto the additive group of the ring $\mathbf{Z}_{10}$.

11. Apply Theorem 7.27 to determine all subgroups of the additive group of the ring **Z**.

12. If a and b are elements of a group G such that a, b, and ab all have order two, prove each of the following:
    (i) $ab = ba$.
    (ii) The set $\{e, a, b, ab\}$ is a subgroup of G.

13. Prove that if a and b are elements of a group G, then ab and ba have the same order.

14. Prove that if in an abelian group the element a has order k and the element b has order l, and if k and l are relatively prime, then the element ab has order kl. [Hint: If $(ab)^t = e$, raise both sides to the power k and conclude that t must be divisible by l. Similarly, show that t must be divisible by k.]

7.5 COSETS AND LAGRANGE'S THEOREM

Let G be an arbitrary group, and H a subgroup of G. If $a \in G$, we shall designate by aH the *set* of all elements of G of the form ah, where $h \in H$. That is, $aH = \{ah \mid h \in H\}$.

7.29 Definition. If H is a subgroup of the group G and $a \in G$, we call aH a *coset* of H (in G).*

Since $eH = H$, we see that H is itself a coset. Moreover, since $e \in H$, it is clear that $a \in aH$.

The following lemma will be very useful in studying cosets.

7.30 Lemma. *If H is a subgroup of the group G and a, $b \in G$, then each of the following is true:*
    (i) *If $aH \cap bH \neq \varnothing$, then $aH = bH$.*
    (ii) *$aH = bH$ if and only if $a \in bH$.*

PROOF OF (i): Suppose that aH and bH have at least one element in common. Thus, there exist h_1, $h_2 \in H$ such that $ah_1 = bh_2$. Then $a = bh_2 h_1^{-1}$ and any element ah of aH can be expressed in the form $bh_2 h_1^{-1} h$. Since $h_2 h_1^{-1} h \in H$, it follows that $ah \in bH$. We have

---

* More precisely, we have here defined a *left* coset, and one can similarly define a right coset Ha. However, in accordance with the definition just given we shall in this section use the word *coset* to mean *left coset*.

therefore shown that $aH \subseteq bH$. In a similar way we can show that $bH \subseteq aH$, and therefore we conclude that $aH = bH$. One way of stating the property we have just proved is to say that two cosets either coincide or have no element in common.

PROOF OF (ii): Since $a \in aH$ it is obvious that if $aH = bH$, then $a \in bH$. Conversely, suppose that $a \in bH$. Then $a \in aH \cap bH$, and part (i) of the lemma implies at once that $aH = bH$.

In view of this lemma, we see that every element of G is in exactly one coset of H in G, that is, that the distinct cosets of H in G form a partition of G.

As an example of cosets, consider the symmetric group S_3 with multiplication table 7.10. We know that α_1 is the identity of this group, and it is easy to verify that $H = \{\alpha_1, \alpha_2\}$ is a subgroup. By use of the table, we find the following cosets of H in S_3:

$$\alpha_1 H = \{\alpha_1, \alpha_2\}, \quad \alpha_4 H = \{\alpha_4, \alpha_5\},$$
$$\alpha_2 H = \{\alpha_2, \alpha_1\}, \quad \alpha_5 H = \{\alpha_5, \alpha_4\},$$
$$\alpha_3 H = \{\alpha_3, \alpha_6\}, \quad \alpha_6 H = \{\alpha_6, \alpha_3\}.$$

We see, therefore, that there are three different cosets of H in S_3, that every coset contain two elements, and that every element of S_3 is in exactly one of these three cosets. As an illustration of Lemma 7.30(ii), we may observe that $\alpha_6 H = \alpha_3 H$ since $\alpha_6 \in \alpha_3 H$, but that $\alpha_4 H \neq \alpha_3 H$ since $\alpha_4 \notin \alpha_3 H$.

So far we have used multiplication as the operation but, as usual, it is easy to make the necessary modifications if the operation is addition. In this case, a coset is of the form $a + H = \{a + h \mid h \in H\}$. As an example, let G be the additive group of the ring $\mathbf{Z}_{12}$ and H the subgroup $\{[0], [3], [6], [9]\}$. Then it may be verified that the *different* cosets of H in G are the following:

$$[0] + H = \{[0], [3], [6], [9]\},$$
$$[1] + H = \{[1], [4], [7], [10]\},$$
$$[2] + H = \{[2], [5], [8], [11]\}.$$

Let us now make the following definition.

7.31 Definition. If the group G has finite order and H is a subgroup of G, the number of distinct cosets of H in G is called the *index* of H in G.

Although we have been using *coset* to mean *left coset*, we should perhaps point out that Exercise 7 below shows that there are the same number of right cosets as of left cosets of H in G. Accordingly, in the definition just given it does not matter whether we think of left cosets or right cosets.

We shall next prove the following theorem of Lagrange which is of fundamental importance in the study of groups of finite order.

7.32 Theorem. *Suppose that the group G has order n. If H is a subgroup of G of order m and of index k, then n = km. In particular, both the order and the index of H are divisors of the order of G.*

PROOF: We first observe that every coset of H has exactly m elements. For if $a \in G$ and $h_1, h_2 \in H$, then $ah_1 = ah_2$ if and only if $h_1 = h_2$. Hence an arbitrary coset aH has the same number of elements as H, namely, m.

We have already shown that the distinct cosets of H in G form a partition of G. Since there are k distinct cosets and each of them contains m elements, G must contain km elements. This proves that $n = km$, and completes the proof.

There are some interesting consequences of the fact that the order of a subgroup of a finite group is a divisor of the order of the group. First of all, since the order of an element of a group is the order of the cyclic subgroup generated by that element, we have at once the following corollary.

7.33 Corollary. *The order of an element of a group of finite order is a divisor of the order of the group.*

If the order of a group is a prime p, then every element of the group, other than the identity, must have order p. This yields the next result as follows.

7.34 Corollary. *A group of order p, where p is a prime, is a cyclic group. Moreover, every element except the identity is a generator of the group.*

If the group G has order n, and the element a of G has order m, then, by Corollary 7.33, we have $n = mk$ for some integer k. By Theorem 7.23, we know that $a^m = e$, and hence $a^n = (a^m)^k = e^k = e$. We have established the following corollary.

7.35 Corollary. *If a is an element of a group of order n, then $a^n = e$.*

If the integer s is not divisible by the prime p, then $[s]$ is an element of the multiplicative group of the field $\mathbf{Z}_p$. Since this group has order

$p - 1$, the preceding corollary shows that $[s]^{p-1} = [1]$. However, this implies that $[s^{p-1}] = [1]$ and we conclude that $s^{p-1} \equiv 1 \pmod{p}$. We have therefore obtained the following theorem of Fermat.

7.36   Corollary.   *If s is an integer not divisible by the prime p, then $s^{p-1} \equiv 1$ (mod p).*

EXERCISES

1.   Exhibit all cosets of the subgroup $\{\epsilon, \alpha, \alpha^2, \alpha^3\}$ of the octic group (7.12).

2.   Let G be the multiplicative group of the field $\mathbf{Z}_{19}$ and H the cyclic subgroup of G generated by the element $[8]$. Exhibit all of the cosets of H in G.

3.   Exhibit all cosets of the subgroup $\{0, 4, 8, 12, 16\}$ of the additive group of $\mathbf{Z}_{20}$.

4.   Prove that a group of order n has a proper subgroup if and only if n is not a prime.

5.   Prove that if an abelian group G of order 6 contains an element of order 3, G must be a cyclic group.

6.   Let H be a subgroup of a group G. If $a, b \in G$, let $a \sim b$ mean that $b^{-1}a \in H$. Show that $\sim$ is an equivalence relation defined on G. If $[a]$ is the equivalence set which contains a, show that $[a] = aH$ and therefore the cosets of H in G are the equivalence sets relative to this equivalence relation.

7.   Let H be a subgroup of a group G and define a mapping β of the set of left cosets of H into the set of right cosets of H as follows: $(aH)\beta = Ha^{-1}$. Prove that β is a well-defined mapping and that, in fact, it is a one-one mapping of the set of all left cosets of H onto the set of all right cosets of H.

7.6   THE SYMMETRIC GROUP S_n

We now return to a further study of permutations of a finite set $A = \{1, 2, \cdots, n\}$. We have already defined the symmetric group S_n to be the group of all permutations of A. Throughout this section the word *permutation* will mean an element of S_n for some positive integer n, and we shall sometimes find it convenient to refer to the elements of A as "symbols."

We shall first study permutations of the particular type described in the following definition.

7.37   **Definition.**   An element α of S_n is said to be a *cycle of length* k if there exist distinct elements $a_1, a_2, \cdots, a_k (k \geq 1)$ of A such that

$$a_1\alpha = a_2, \quad a_2\alpha = a_3, \quad \cdots, \quad a_{k-1}\alpha = a_k, \quad a_k\alpha = a_1,$$

and $i\alpha = i$ for each element i of A other than $a_1, a_2, \cdots, a_k$. This cycle α may be designated by $(a_1 a_2 \cdots a_k)$.

It will be observed that a cycle of length one is necessarily the identity permutation. It sometimes simplifies statements to consider the identity permutation as a cycle, but we shall usually be interested in cycles of length greater than one.

As an example of a cycle, suppose that β is the element of S_6 defined by

$$1\beta = 3, \quad 3\beta = 2, \quad 2\beta = 5, \quad 5\beta = 6, \quad 6\beta = 1, \quad 4\beta = 4.$$

Then β is a cycle of length 5, and we may write $\beta = (13256)$. In a cycle, such as (13256) the symbols appearing are permuted cyclically; that is, each symbol written down maps into the next one, except that the last maps into the first. A symbol, such as 4 in this example, which is not written down is assumed to map into itself. There are other ways of writing the cycle defined above. For example, $\beta = (32561) = (25613)$, and so on. Also, in another notation introduced in Section 7.3, we have

$$\beta = \begin{pmatrix} 1 & 2 & 3 & 4 & 5 & 6 \\ 3 & 5 & 2 & 4 & 6 & 1 \end{pmatrix}.$$

As further illustrations of all the various notations used, let us consider elements of S_6 and verify that

$$(1345)(146) = \begin{pmatrix} 1 & 2 & 3 & 4 & 5 & 6 \\ 3 & 2 & 6 & 5 & 4 & 1 \end{pmatrix}.$$

In the first factor 1 maps into 3, and in the second factor 3 is unchanged; hence in the product, 1 maps into 3. The symbol 2 does not appear in either factor, hence 2 maps into 2. In the left factor 3 maps into 4, and then in the second factor 4 maps into 6; hence in the product 3 maps into 6. Similarly, the other verifications are easily made.

Now let α be the cycle $(a_1 a_2 \cdots a_k)$ of S_n of length k, and let us consider the powers of α. Under the mapping α^2, we see that a_1 maps into a_3 (if $k \geq 3$), for

$$\alpha_1\alpha^2 = (a_1\alpha)\alpha = a_2\alpha = a_3.$$

Similarly, under the mapping α^3, a_1 maps into a_4 (if $k \geq 4$), and so on. Continuing, we find that $a_1\alpha^k = a_1$. Since we could just as well write $\alpha = (a_2a_3 \cdots a_ka_1)$, a similar argument shows that $a_2\alpha^k = a_2$ and, in general, that $a_i\alpha^k = a_i$ for $i = 1, 2, \cdots, k$. It follows that $\alpha^k = \epsilon$, the identity permutation, and, moreover, k is the smallest power of α which is equal to ϵ. The following result then follows immediately from Theorem 7.23.

7.38   Theorem.   *A cycle of length k has order k.*

Two cycles $(a_1a_2 \cdots a_k)$ and $(b_1b_2 \cdots b_l)$ of S_n are said to be *disjoint* if the sets $\{a_1, a_2, \cdots, a_k\}$ and $\{b_1, b_2, \cdots, b_l\}$ have no elements in common. A set of more than two cycles is said to be disjoint if each pair of them is disjoint. The next result shows why cycles play an important role in the study of permutations.

7.39   Theorem.   *Every element γ of S_n that is not itself a cycle is expressible as a product of disjoint cycles.*

Before considering the proof, let us look at an example. Suppose that

$$\gamma = \begin{pmatrix} 1 & 2 & 3 & 4 & 5 & 6 \\ 3 & 1 & 4 & 2 & 6 & 5 \end{pmatrix},$$

and let us start with any symbol which does not map into itself, for example, the symbol 1. We see that $1\gamma = 3$, $3\gamma = 4$, $4\gamma = 2$, and $2\gamma = 1$. Now take any symbol which has not yet been used and which does not map into itself, for example 5. Then $5\gamma = 6$, and $6\gamma = 5$. It is then almost obvious that $\gamma = (1342)(56)$.

The proof in the general case follows the same pattern as in this example. Since the identity permutation is a cycle (of length 1), we assume that γ is not the identity. Start with any symbol a_1 such that $a_1\gamma \neq a_1$, and suppose that $a_1\gamma = a_2$, $a_2\gamma = a_3$, $a_3\gamma = a_4$, and so on until we come to the point where, say, $a_k\gamma$ equals some one of the symbols $a_1, a_2, \cdots, a_{k-1}$ already used. Then we must have $a_k\gamma = a_1$ since every other one of these symbols is already known to be the image of some symbol under the mapping γ. Thus γ has the same effect on the symbols $a_1, a_2, \cdots, a_k$ as the cycle $(a_1a_2 \cdots a_k)$, and also effects a permutation of the remaining symbols (if any). If b_1 is a symbol other than $a_1, a_2, \cdots, a_k$

and $b_1\gamma \neq b_1$, we proceed as above and obtain a cycle $(b_1b_2 \cdots b_l)$. Now if all symbols that do not map into themselves have been used, we have

$$\gamma = (a_1a_2 \cdots a_k)(b_1b_2 \cdots b_l).$$

If there is another symbol c_1 such that $c_1\gamma \neq c_1$, we can similarly obtain another cycle. Evidently, the process can be continued to obtain the desired result. A complete proof can be given by induction.

EXERCISES

1. In each of the following, γ is an element of S_7. Express it as a product of disjoint cycles.

    (a) $1\gamma = 3, 2\gamma = 4, 3\gamma = 1, 4\gamma = 7, 5\gamma = 5, 6\gamma = 6, 7\gamma = 2$.
    (b) $1\gamma = 5, 2\gamma = 3, 3\gamma = 4, 4\gamma = 7, 5\gamma = 6, 6\gamma = 1, 7\gamma = 2$.
    (c) $\gamma = \begin{pmatrix} 1 & 2 & 3 & 4 & 5 & 6 & 7 \\ 3 & 4 & 1 & 2 & 6 & 7 & 5 \end{pmatrix}$.
    (d) $\gamma = \begin{pmatrix} 1 & 2 & 3 & 4 & 5 & 6 & 7 \\ 2 & 3 & 1 & 5 & 4 & 7 & 6 \end{pmatrix}$.

2. Express each of the following elements of S_7 as a product of disjoint cycles:

    (a) $(123)(16543)$,
    (b) $(213456)(172)$,
    (c) $(4215)(3426)(5671)$,
    (d) $(1234)(124)(3127)(56)$.

The cycles of length 2 are of special interest, and we make the following definition.

7.40 Definition. A cycle of length 2 is called a *transposition*.

A transposition (ij) merely interchanges the symbols i and j, and leaves the other symbols unchanged. Since $(ij)(ij) = \epsilon$, it follows that a *transposition is its own inverse*.

It is quite easy to show that every cycle of length more than 2 can be expressed as a product of transpositions. In fact, this result follows from the observation that

$$(a_1a_2 \cdots a_k) = (a_1a_k)(a_2a_k) \cdots (a_{k-1}a_k),$$

which can be verified by direct calculation. In view of Theorem 7.39, it follows immediately that *every* permutation can be expressed as a product of transpositions. However, it is easy to verify that there is more than one way to express a permutation as such a product. As examples, we see that

$$(1234) = (14)(24)(34) = (32)(12)(14) = (13)(24)(34)(12)(24),$$
$$(123)(14) = (12)(13)(14) = (14)(24)(34) = (14)(24)(34)(23)(23),$$

and so on. Since $(ij)(ij) = \epsilon$, we can insert as many such pairs of identical transpositions as we wish. Clearly, then, a permutation can be expressed as a product of transpositions in many different ways.

The following theorem, of which the first statement has already been proved, is one of the principal theorems about permutations.

7.41   Theorem.   *Every permutation α can be expressed as a product of transpositions. Moreover, if α can be expressed as a product of r transpositions and also as a product of s transpositions, then either r and s are both even or they are both odd.*

Suppose that α is a permutation of the set $A = \{1, 2, \cdots, n\}$. Suppose, further, that

7.42 $\alpha = \beta_1\beta_2 \cdots \beta_r = \gamma_1\gamma_2 \cdots \gamma_s,$

where each β and each γ is a transposition. To establish the theorem, we need to prove that r and s are both even or that they are both odd. There are ways to prove this fact by calculating entirely with permutations, but we proceed to give a well-known proof which is simpler in its details but which involves the introduction of a certain "counting device" which has no inherent connection with the permutations themselves. Let $x_1, x_2, \cdots, x_n$ be independent symbols (or variables, if you wish) and let P denote the polynomial * with integral coefficients defined as follows:

7.43 $$P = \prod_{i<j} (x_i - x_j),$$

it being understood that this stands for the product of all expressions of the form $x_i - x_j$, where i and j take values from 1 to n, with $i < j$. We now define

---

* Logically, this proof should be deferred until after polynomials have been studied in some detail. However, it seems preferable to insert it here with the expectation that it will be convincing, even though use is made of a few simple properties of polynomials which will not be established until later.

7.44
$$P\alpha = \prod_{i<j} (x_{i\alpha} - x_{j\alpha}),$$

that is, $P\alpha$ is the polynomial obtained by performing the permutation α on the *subscripts* of the symbols $x_1, x_2, \cdots, x_n$.

As an illustration of this notation, if $n = 4$, we have

$$P = (x_1 - x_2)(x_1 - x_3)(x_1 - x_4)(x_2 - x_3)(x_2 - x_4)(x_3 - x_4).$$

Moreover, if

$$\alpha = \begin{pmatrix} 1 & 2 & 3 & 4 \\ 4 & 1 & 2 & 3 \end{pmatrix},$$

we find that

$$P\alpha = (x_4 - x_1)(x_4 - x_2)(x_4 - x_3)(x_1 - x_2)(x_1 - x_3)(x_2 - x_3).$$

and it is easily verified that $P\alpha = -P$. In general, it is fairly clear that always $P\alpha = \pm P$, with the sign depending in some way on the permutation α. We next prove the following lemma.

7.45 Lemma. *If $\delta = (kl)$ is a transposition, then $P\delta = -P$.*

Now $k \neq l$, and there is no loss of generality in assuming that $k < l$. Hence, one of the factors in P is $x_k - x_l$ and in $P\delta$ the corresponding factor is $x_l - x_k$; that is, this factor is just changed in sign under the mapping δ on the subscripts. Any factor of P of the form $x_i - x_j$, where neither i nor j is equal to k or l, is clearly unchanged under the mapping δ. All other factors of P can be paired to form products of the form $\pm(x_i - x_k)(x_i - x_l)$, with the sign determined by the relative magnitudes of i, k, and l. But since the effect of δ is just to interchange x_k and x_l, any such product is unchanged. Hence, the only effect of δ is to change the sign of P, and the lemma is established.

The proof of the theorem now follows easily. Since, by 7.42, $P\alpha$ can be computed by performing in turn the r transpositions $\beta_1, \beta_2, \cdots, \beta_r$, and by the lemma each of these merely changes the sign of P, it follows that $P\alpha = (-1)^r P$. In like manner, using the fact that $\alpha = \gamma_1\gamma_2 \cdots \gamma_s$, we see that also $P\alpha = (-1)^s P$. Hence, we must have $(-1)^r P = (-1)^s P$ from which it follows that $(-1)^r = (-1)^s$. This implies that r and s are both even or they are both odd, and the proof is complete.

7.46 Definition. A permutation is called an *even* permutation or an *odd* permutation according as it can be expressed as a product of an even or an odd number of transpositions.

If the permutation α can be expressed as a product of k transpositions, and the permutation β can be expressed as a product of l transpositions, it is obvious that $\alpha\beta$ can be expressed as a product of $k + l$ transpositions. It follows that the product of two even, or of two odd, permutations is an even permutation, whereas the product of an odd permutation and an even permutation is an odd permutation.

Another observation of some importance is the following. Suppose that α is a product of k transpositions, say $\alpha = \alpha_1\alpha_2 \cdots a_k$. Then, since a transposition is its own inverse, it is easy to see that $\alpha^{-1} = \alpha_k\alpha_{k-1} \cdots \alpha_1$. It follows that α^{-1} is an even permutation if and only if α is an even permutation. We shall conclude our study of permutation groups by proving the following theorem.

7.47 Theorem. *The set A_n of all even permutations of the symmetric group S_n is a subgroup of S_n of order $n!/2$.*

The fact that A_n is a subgroup of S_n follows at once from the preceding remarks and Theorem 7.4. This subgroup A_n of S_n is usually called the *alternating group* on n symbols.

Let us now consider the order of A_n. If β is a fixed odd permutation, all the elements of the coset βA_n are odd permutations since the product of an odd permutation by an even permutation is necessarily an odd permutation. We proceed to show that *all* odd permutations of S_n are in the coset βA_n. If γ is an arbitrary odd permutation, we may write $\gamma = \beta(\beta^{-1}\gamma)$, and $\beta^{-1}\gamma$ is an even permutation since β^{-1} and γ are both odd. It follows that $\beta^{-1}\gamma \in A_n$, and hence that $\gamma \in \beta A_n$. We have shown that the coset βA_n consists of *all* the odd permutations, and hence that there are just the two cosets A_n and βA_n of A_n in S_n. Since these cosets have the same number of elements and S_n has order $n!$, it follows that the alternating group A_n has order $n!/2$.

EXERCISES

1. Verify that a cycle of length k is an even or an odd permutation according as k is odd or even, respectively.

2. Prove that every even permutation is a cycle of length three or can be expressed as a product of cycles of length three. [Hint: $(12)(13) = (123)$, and $(12)(34) = (134)(321)$.]

3. Exhibit the elements of the alternating group A_3 and of the alternating group A_4.

4. Let G be a subgroup of the symmetric group S_n, and suppose that G contains at least one odd permutation. By a suitable modification of the proof of Theorem 7.47, prove that the set of all even permutations in G is a subgroup of G, and then prove that G contains the same number of odd permutations as of even permutations.

7.7 NORMAL SUBGROUPS AND QUOTIENT GROUPS

If H is a subgroup of the group G and $a \in G$, the set $aH = \{ah \mid h \in H\}$, which in Section 7.5 was called a coset, we shall for the present call a *left* coset of H in G. Similarly, the set $Ha = \{ha \mid h \in H\}$ is called a *right* coset of H in G. It need not be true that a left coset aH is equal to the right coset Ha. However, we shall be interested in subgroups which do have this property, and we therefore introduce the following definition.

7.48 Definition. A subgroup K of a group G is said to be a *normal* (or *invariant*) subgroup of G if and only if $aK = Ka$ for every element a of G.

We may emphasize that this definition does not state that necessarily $ak = ka$ for each $a \in G$ and $k \in K$; it merely states that the *sets* aK and Ka coincide. In particular, if $a \in G$ and $k \in K$, there must exist an element k_1 of K (not necessarily the same element k) such that $ak = k_1a$.

There is another equivalent way of characterizing a normal subgroup as follows: If we define

$$a^{-1}Ka = \{a^{-1}xa \mid x \in K\},$$

then K is a normal subgroup of G if and only if $a^{-1}Ka = K$ for every $a \in G$.

Clearly, every subgroup of an abelian group is a normal subgroup. As an example of a subgroup which is not normal, consider the symmetric group S_3 with multiplication table 7.10 and the subgroup $H = \{\alpha_1, \alpha_2\}$ of S_3. It may be verified that $\alpha_3 H = \{\alpha_3, \alpha_6\}$, whereas $H\alpha_3 = \{\alpha_3, \alpha_5\}$, and hence that $\alpha_3 H \neq H\alpha_3$, so H is not a normal subgroup of S_3. However, S_3 has as normal subgroup the alternating group $A_3 = \{\alpha_1, \alpha_5, \alpha_6\}$. Instead of verifying this fact by direct calculation, let us prove that for each positive integer $n > 1$, *the alternating group A_n is a normal subgroup of the symmetric group S_n*. If α is an even permutation, then $\alpha \in A_n$ and $\alpha A_n = A_n\alpha = A_n$. If α is an odd permutation, the proof of Theorem 7.47 shows that αA_n is the set of all odd permutations of S_n. A similar argument will show that also $A_n\alpha$ is the set of all odd permutations of S_n. Hence, for every $\alpha \in S_n$ we have $\alpha A_n = A_n\alpha$, and A_n is therefore a normal subgroup of S_n.

Now let G be an arbitrary group and K a normal subgroup of G. Since K is normal, we need not distinguish between left cosets and right cosets; so we shall again simply call them cosets and write them as left cosets. On the set of all cosets of K in G we propose to define an operation of multiplication which will make this set into a group. Accordingly, let us define

7.49 $(aK)(bK) = (ab)K,$ $a, b \in G.$

In order to verify that this does define an operation on the set of all cosets, we need to show that multiplication is well-defined by this equation. That is, we must show that if $aK = a_1K$ and $bK = b_1K$, then $(ab)K = (a_1b_1)K$. By 7.30(ii), this fact can be established by showing that if $a \in a_1K$ and $b \in b_1K$, then $ab \in (a_1b_1)K$. Suppose, then, that $a = a_1k$, and $b = b_1k'$, where $k, k' \in K$. Thus $ab = a_1kb_1k'$ and, since K is a normal subgroup of G, there exists $k'' \in K$ such that $kb_1 = b_1k''$. Hence, $ab = a_1b_1k''k'$ and it follows that $ab \in (a_1b_1)K$, as we wished to show. This proves that 7.49 does indeed define an operation of multiplication on the set of all cosets of K in G, and we proceed to prove the following theorem.

7.50   Theorem.   *Let K be a normal subgroup of the group G. With respect to the multiplication 7.49 of cosets, the set of all cosets of K in G is a group, usually called the* quotient group *of G by K and denoted by G/K. Moreover, the mapping $\theta: G \to G/K$ defined by $a\theta = aK$, $a \in G$, is a homomorphism of G onto G/K, with kernel K.*

PROOF: The associative law in G/K is an almost immediate consequence of the associative law in G, and we leave this part of the proof to the reader. Now, if e is the identity of G, then since by 7.49,

$$(aK)(eK) = (eK)(aK) = aK, \qquad\qquad a \in G,$$

we see that $eK = K$ is the identity of G/K. Finally, 7.49 implies that

$$(aK)(a^{-1}K) = (aa^{-1})K = eK = K$$

and, similarly, $(a^{-1}K)(aK) = K$. Hence $a^{-1}K$ is the inverse of aK, and we have proved that G/K is a group. (Cf. Exercise 14 of Section 7.3.) Furthermore, the definition of the mapping θ shows that it is a mapping of G onto G/K, and the definition of multiplication of coset shows that

$$(ab)\theta = (ab)K = (aK)(bK) = (a\theta)(b\theta), \qquad a, b \in G,$$

and hence that θ is a homomorphism. Finally, since K is the identity of G/K, an element a of G is in ker θ if and only if $aK = K$, that is, if and only if $a \in K$. This completes the proof of the theorem.

We may remark that since the elements of the quotient group G/K are the distinct cosets of K in G, if G has finite order, the order of the group G/K is the index of K in G. In fact, by Theorem 7.32, we see that the order of G/K is a divisor of the order of G. More precisely, if G has finite order, we have

$$\text{order of } G/K = \frac{\text{order of } G}{\text{order of } K}.$$

In the above, we have used multiplication as the operation in G. If G is abelian and the operation is considered to be addition, it is important to keep in mind that a coset is of the form $a + K$, and the multiplication 7.49 of cosets is replaced by addition of cosets defined as follows:

7.51 $$(a + K) + (b + K) = (a + b) + K, \qquad a, b \in G.$$

In this case, the identity of G is called the "zero" as usual, and the zero of the quotient group G/K is the coset K.

We have shown that if K is a normal subgroup of an arbitrary group G, then there exists a homomorphism of G, with kernel K, onto the quotient group G/K. We shall next prove that "essentially" all homomorphisms of G are of this type. More precisely, we shall show that the kernel of every homomorphism of G is a normal subgroup of G and that every homomorphic image of G is isomorphic to a quotient group G/K for some choice of the normal subgroup K. This is the content of the following theorem.

7.52 Fundamental Theorem on Group Homomorphisms. *Let $\phi: G \to H$ be a homomorphism of the group G onto the group H with kernel K. Then K is a normal subgroup of G, and $H \cong G/K$. More precisely, the mapping $\alpha: G/K \to H$ defined by*

7.53 $$(aK)\alpha = a\phi, \qquad a \in G,$$

is an isomorphism of G/K onto H.

PROOF: Let us first show that the kernel K of a homomorphism $\phi: G \to H$ is necessarily a normal subgroup of G. We have already proved in Theorem 7.18 that K must be a subgroup, so there only remains to prove that it is normal. If $a \in G$ and $k \in K$, then

$$(aka^{-1})\phi = (a\phi)(k\phi)(a\phi)^{-1}.$$

But if e is the identity of G, $e\phi$ is the identity of H and $k\phi = e\phi$ by definition of ker ϕ. Thus $(aka^{-1})\phi = e\phi$ and $aka^{-1} \in$ ker $\phi = K$. Hence $aka^{-1} = k_1$ for some element k_1 of K. It follows that $ak = k_1 a$ and this shows that $aK \subseteq Ka$. In like manner, it can be shown that $Ka \subseteq aK$, so that $aK = Ka$ and K is indeed a normal subgroup. Thus we can now speak of the quotient group G/K.

Before proving the rest of the theorem, its meaning may perhaps be clarified by reference to the accompanying diagram. Here ϕ is the given homomorphism of G onto H, $K =$ ker ϕ, and

$\theta \colon G \to G/K$ is the homomorphism of G onto G/K defined by $a\theta = aK$, $a \in G$, as in the preceding theorem. Our present theorem may then be interpreted as stating that $\phi = \theta\alpha$, that is, that $a\phi = (a\theta)\alpha = (aK)\alpha$ for each $a \in G$. Otherwise expressed, an element a of G has the same image in H no matter which of the two paths from G to H is taken.

Let us now show that a mapping α of G/K into H is well-defined by 7.53. That is, we shall show that if $aK = a_1 K$, then $a\phi = a_1\phi$. If $aK = a_1 K$, we have that $a = a_1 k$ for some element k of K. Hence $a\phi = (a_1\phi)(k\phi) = a_1\phi$ since $k \in$ ker ϕ and therefore $k\phi$ is the identity of H. This proves that the mapping α is well-defined.

Next, using the fact that ϕ is a homomorphism, and the definition of multiplication of cosets, we see that for $a, b \in G$,

$$[(aK)(bK)]\alpha = [(ab)K]\alpha = (ab)\phi = (a\phi)(b\phi) = [(aK)\alpha][(bK)\alpha].$$

This shows that α is a homomorphism and it is clearly a mapping onto H. There remains only to prove that it is an isomorphism.

Suppose that $aK \in$ ker α. Hence, if e is the identity of G, and therefore $e\phi$ is the identity of H, we have $(aK)\alpha = e\phi$ or $a\phi = e\phi$. However, this implies that $a \in$ ker $\phi = K$, so $aK \in$ ker α implies that $a \in K$ and therefore that $aK = K$. Since K is the identity of the group G/K, we conclude that ker α consists only of the identity of G/K. By Theorem 7.18 it follows that α is an isomorphism, and the theorem is proved.

EXERCISES

1. If H is a subgroup of a group G and $a \in G$, prove that $aHa^{-1} = \{aha^{-1} \mid h \in H\}$ is a subgroup of G which is isomorphic to H.

2. Prove that the intersection of two or more normal subgroups of a group G is a normal subgroup of G.

3. If G is a group, prove that the set $\{a \mid a \in G,\ ax = xa$ for every $x \in G\}$ is a normal subgroup of G.

4. If e is the identity of G, and H and K are normal subgroups of G with $H \cap K = \{e\}$, prove that $hk = kh$ for any $h \in H,\ k \in K$. [Hint: Show that $h^{-1}k^{-1}hk \in H \cap K$.]

5. Verify that the subgroup $\{\epsilon,\alpha,\alpha^2,\alpha^3\}$ of the octic group (7.12) is a normal subgroup.

6. Prove that if every right coset of a subgroup H in G is also a left coset, then H is necessarily normal. [Hint: If $Ha = bH$, show that $bH = aH$.]

7. Let G be the cyclic group of order 20 generated by an element a, and let H be the subgroup of G generated by a^4. Write out the cosets of H in G and verify that the quotient group G/H is a cyclic group of order 4.

8. It can be shown that the set of elements $K = \{(1),(12)(34),(13)(24),(14)(23)\}$ of the alternating group A_4 on four symbols is a normal subgroup of A_4. Without calculation, explain how you know that the quotient group A_4/K must be cyclic.

9. Prove: If there exist exactly two left cosets (or right cosets) of a subgroup H in a group G, then H is necessarily a normal subgroup of G.

10. Let $\mathbf{Q}$ be the additive group of the field of rational numbers and $\mathbf{Z}$ the additive group of the ring of integers. Show that every element of the quotient group $\mathbf{Q}/\mathbf{Z}$ has finite order. Does the group $\mathbf{Q}/\mathbf{Z}$ have finite order?

11. Let K be a normal subgroup of the group G, and let A be a subgroup of the quotient group G/K. Thus we may consider A to

be a set of cosets of K in G. Prove that the union of these cosets is a subgroup of G.

12. Prove the following generalization of Theorem 7.52: Let $\phi: G \to H$ be a homomorphism of G into H (not necessarily an onto mapping), and let K be a normal subgroup of G contained in ker ϕ. Prove that the mapping $\alpha: G/K \to H$ defined by $aK\alpha = a\phi$ is a well-defined ismomorphism of G/K into H, and that $\theta\alpha = \phi$, where $\theta: G \to G/K$ is defined by $a\theta = aK$.

13. Let H and K be subgroups of a group G, with K a normal subgroup of G. Prove each of the following:

   (i) $H \cap K$ is a normal subgroup of H.

   (ii) If $HK = \{hk \mid h \in H , k \in K\}$, then HK is a subgroup of G.

   (iii) K is a normal subgroup of the group HK.

14. If H and K are as in the preceding exercise, prove each of the following:

   (i)   Every element of the quotient group HK/K is expressible in the form hK, $h \in H$.

   (ii) The mapping $\alpha: H \to HK/K$ defined by $h\alpha = hK$, $h \in H$, is a homomorphism of H onto HK/K, with kernel $H \cap K$.

   (iii) The group $H/(H \cap K)$ is isomorphic to the group HK/K.

7.8 HOMOMORPHISMS AND SUBGROUPS

In this section we shall present a few of the relationships which hold between subgroups of a given group G and subgroups of a homomorphic image of G.

First, suppose that $\theta: G \to H$ is merely a *mapping* of a *set* G into a *set* H. A little later, we shall be primarily interested in the case in which G and H are groups and θ is a homomorphism of G onto H.

We recall that if A is a subset of G, we have introduced the notation $A\theta$ for the set of images of elements of A under the mapping θ. That is

7.54 $$A\theta = \{a\theta \mid a \in A\}.$$

It will now be convenient to introduce a little additional notation. If U is a subset of H, let us denote by $U\theta^{-1}$ the *inverse image* of U, that is, the set of all elements of G whose images under the mapping θ lie in the subset U. Expressed formally,

7.55 $$U\theta^{-1} = \{x \mid x \in G,\ x\theta \in U\}.$$

This use of θ^{-1} should not be confused with the inverse mapping introduced in Section 1.3. Note that as here defined, θ^{-1} is not a mapping of H into G, but it does map *subsets* of H into *subsets* of G, and it is a convenient concept for our present purposes.

The following facts, which we shall number for easy reference, are almost immediate consequences of the definitions. We shall list their proofs as an exercise below.

7.56 *If A is a subset of G, then $A \subseteq (A\theta)\theta^{-1}$.*

7.57 *If A is a subset of G and θ is a one-one mapping, then $A = (A\theta)\theta^{-1}$.*

7.58 *If U is a subset of H, then $(U\theta^{-1})\theta \subseteq U$.*

7.59 *If U is a subset of H and θ is an onto mapping, then $U = (U\theta^{-1})\theta$.*

Using the notation just presented, we now state the following theorem.

7.60 Theorem.   *Let $\theta: G \to H$ be a homomorphism of the group G onto the group H, and let $K = \ker \theta$. Then each of the following is true:*

(i)   *If A is a subgroup (normal subgroup) of G, then $A\theta$ is a subgroup (normal subgroup) of H.*

(ii)   *If A is a subgroup of G which contains K, then $A = (A\theta)\theta^{-1}$.*

(iii) *If U is a subgroup (normal subgroup) of H, then $U\theta^{-1}$ is a subgroup (normal subgroup) of G which contains K.*

In (i) and (iii) it is to be understood that "normal subgroup" may be substituted for "subgroup" both times it appears in the statement.

PROOF OF (i):   Let A be a subgroup of G. To prove that $A\theta$ is a subgroup of H, we need to show that it is closed with respect to multiplication and with respect to taking inverses. Let $a_1\theta$ and $a_2\theta$ be elements of $A\theta$, a_1 and a_2 being elements of A. Then $(a_1\theta)(a_2\theta) = (a_1 a_2)\theta \in A\theta$, since $a_1 a_2 \in A$. Moreover, since A is a subgroup of G and therefore $a_1^{-1} \in A$, $(a_1\theta)^{-1} = a_1^{-1}\theta \in A\theta$. This proves that $A\theta$ is a subgroup of H.

Now suppose that A is a normal subgroup of G. An appropriate way of expressing this fact is to say that $x^{-1}Ax = A$ for each $x \in G$. Consider $h^{-1}(A\theta)h$, where h is an arbitrary element of H. Since θ is an onto mapping, there exists an element a in G such that $a\theta = h$. Then

$$h^{-1}(A\theta)h = (a\theta)^{-1}(A\theta)(a\theta) = (a^{-1}Aa)\theta = A\theta,$$

since $a^{-1}Aa = A$ by normality of A. Thus $h^{-1}(A\theta)h = A\theta$ for each h in H, and therefore $A\theta$ is a normal subgroup of H.

PROOF OF (ii): From 7.56, we know that $A \subseteq (A\theta)\theta^{-1}$. If $c \in (A\theta)\theta^{-1}$, then $c\theta \in A\theta$. Thus, there exists $a \in A$ such that $c\theta = a\theta$. It follows that

$$(ca^{-1})\theta = (c\theta)(a^{-1}\theta) = (c\theta)(a\theta)^{-1} = (c\theta)(c\theta)^{-1},$$

and this is the identity of H. Accordingly, $ca^{-1} \in K = \ker \theta$. Since we are assuming that $K \subseteq A$, we conclude that $ca^{-1} \in A$. Since $a^{-1} \in A$, we see that $c \in A$. This shows that $(A\theta)\theta^{-1} \subseteq A$, completing the proof that $A = (A\theta)\theta^{-1}$.

PROOF OF (iii): Let U be a subgroup of H and suppose that $x, y \in U\theta^{-1}$. This means that $x\theta \in U$ and $y\theta \in U$. Since U is a subgroup of H, $(x\theta)(y\theta) = (xy)\theta \in U$. Accordingly, $xy \in U\theta^{-1}$, and $U\theta^{-1}$ is closed under multiplication. It is also closed under taking inverses. For if $x \in U\theta^{-1}$, then $x\theta \in U$ and $x^{-1}\theta = (x\theta)^{-1} \in U$. In turn, this implies that $x^{-1} \in U\theta^{-1}$. Hence $U\theta^{-1}$ is a subgroup of G, and it clearly contains K since U must contain the identity of H.

   Now suppose that U is a normal subgroup of H, and let us show that $U\theta^{-1}$ is a normal subgroup of G. Let y be an arbitrary element of G. Then, using 7.59 and the fact that U is a normal subgroup of H, we have

$$\begin{aligned}[y^{-1}(U\theta^{-1})y]\theta &= y^{-1}\theta[(U\theta^{-1})\theta]y\theta \\ &= (y\theta)^{-1}U(y\theta) = U.\end{aligned}$$

Therefore $y^{-1}(U\theta^{-1})y \subseteq U\theta^{-1}$. We shall now show inclusion the other way. Let $a \in U\theta^{-1}$, so that $a\theta \in U$. If we set $t = yay^{-1}$, then $a = y^{-1}ty$. But $t\theta = (y\theta)(a\theta)(y\theta)^{-1} \in U$ since $a\theta \in U$ and U is normal. It follows that $t \in U\theta^{-1}$ and therefore $a \in y^{-1}(U\theta)^{-1}y$. This shows that $U\theta^{-1} \subseteq y^{-1}(U\theta^{-1})y$, and we conclude that for every y in G, $y^{-1}(U\theta^{-1})y = U\theta^{-1}$, and $U\theta^{-1}$ is therefore a normal subgroup of G, completing the proof.

We now apply the theorem just established to the following situation. Let K be a normal subgroup of G and let $\theta: G \to G/K$ be the homomorphism defined (as in Theorem 7.50) by $a\theta = aK$, $a \in G$. Then $\ker \theta = K$, and if A is a subgroup of G, $A\theta$ consists of those cosets of K in G which contain an element of A. On the other hand, if U is a subgroup of G/K, $U\theta^{-1}$ consists of all those elements of G appearing in any one of the cosets which make up the subgroup U of G/K. In other words, $U\theta^{-1}$ is the union of those cosets which are elements of the subgroup U of G/K. Accordingly, we have the following immediate consequences of the preceding theorem.

7.61   Corollary.   *Let K be a normal subgroup of the group G. Then*

(*i*)   *If A is a subgroup (normal subgroup) of G, the cosets of K in G which contain an element of A are the elements of a subgroup (normal subgroup) of the quotient group G/K.*

(*ii*)   *If U is a subgroup (normal subgroup) of the quotient group G/K, the union of the cosets appearing as elements of U is a subgroup (normal subgroup) of G.*

Suppose now that G is a finite group. In particular, suppose that the subgroup U of G/K has order r and that the subgroup K of G has order s. Then the subgroup of G whose existence is asserted in part (*ii*) of the preceding corollary has order rs since it consists of elements of G occurring in r different cosets, each of which contains s elements. In particular, we have the following result.

7.62   Corollary.   *If K is a normal subgroup of G of order s and the quotient group G/K contains a subgroup of order r, then the group G contains a subgroup of order rs.*

EXERCISES

1.   Prove 7.56–7.59.

2.   In the notation of Theorem 7.60, prove that the mapping $A \rightarrow A\theta$ defines a one-one mapping of the set of subgroups (normal subgroups) of G which contain K onto the set of all subgroups (normal subgroups) of H.

3.   If K is given as a normal subgroup of G, what conclusions can you draw from the preceding exercise about the subgroups of G which contain K and the subgroups of the quotient group G/K?

4.   Let $\theta: G \rightarrow H$ be a homomorphism of G onto H, and A a normal subgroup of G which contains ker θ. Show that the homomorphic mapping $x \rightarrow (x\theta)(A\theta)$ of G onto $G\theta/A\theta$ has kernel A, and hence conclude that $G/A \cong G\theta/A\theta$.

NOTES AND REFERENCES

There are many books on group theory, a few of which are listed in items 17–25 of the bibliography. In particular, Lederman [22] is quite readable but covers fewer topics than some of the other books mentioned. Hall [20] treats a rather wide range of topics and has an extensive bibliography of books and articles on the subject. Rotman [25] also covers a fairly wide range of topics and has a particularly modern approach to the subject. Fuchs [19] and Kaplansky [21] concentrate on the study of infinite abelian groups.

VIII

FINITE ABELIAN GROUPS

The problem of determining all finite groups is a difficult and, in fact, an unsolved problem. However, in a sense to be made precise later, it is possible to determine all finite *abelian* groups. The purpose of this chapter is to prove the fundamental results in the theory of such groups.

Let G be a finite abelian group. Throughout this chapter we shall use addition as the operation in G. Of course, everything could just as well be stated in terms of multiplication as the operation. Unless otherwise explicitly stated, we shall always assume that the group G under discussion is a nonzero group, that is, that it does not consist of the identity alone.

Let us recall the following essential facts which will be used frequently in the sequel. Since G has finite order, each element a of G has finite order. If a has order n, Lemma 7.24 shows that n is the least positive integer such that $na = 0$. The order of the zero element is one, all other elements have order greater than one. If a has order n and $k \in \mathbf{Z}$, then $ka = 0$ if and only if $n \mid k$.

8.1 DIRECT SUMS OF SUBGROUPS

If $G_1, G_2, \cdots, G_r$ are subgroups of the abelian group G, we define the *sum*

$$G_1 + G_2 + \cdots + G_r$$

of these subgroups to be the set of all elements of G which can be expressed in the form

$$a_1 + a_2 + \cdots + a_r, \qquad a_i \in G_i (i = 1, 2, \cdots, r).$$

This set is seen to be a subgroup of G, and each G_i is contained in this subgroup since the identity 0 of G is an element of each G_i. Actually, this sum is the smallest subgroup of G which contains all the subgroups G_i.

We now make the following definition.

8.1   Definition.   If $G_i (i = 1, 2, \cdots, r)$ are subgroups of the abelian group G, the sum $G_1 + G_2 + \cdots + G_r$ is said to be a *direct sum* if and only if the following condition is satisfied:

(i)   If $a_i \in G_i (i = 1, 2, \cdots, r)$ such that

$$a_1 + a_2 + \cdots + a_r = 0,$$

then each $a_i = 0$.

We shall indicate that a sum $G_1 + G_2 + \cdots + G_r$ is a direct sum by writing it in the form

$$G_1 \oplus G_2 \oplus \cdots \oplus G_r.$$

It is worth pointing out that condition (i) is equivalent to the following condition:

(ii)   If $a_i, b_i \in G(i = 1, 2, \cdots, r)$ such that

$$a_1 + a_2 + \cdots + a_r = b_1 + b_2 + \cdots + b_r,$$

then $a_i = b_i (i = 1, 2, \cdots, r)$.

The equivalence of (i) and (ii) follows readily from the fact that the equation $a_1 + a_2 + \cdots + a_r = b_1 + b_2 + \cdots + b_r$ may be written in the form

$$(a_1 - b_1) + (a_2 - b_2) + \cdots + (a_r - b_r) = 0.$$

We leave the details of the proof of the equivalence of conditions (i) and (ii) as an exercise.

The condition (ii) for a sum $G_1 + G_2 + \cdots + G_r$ to be a direct sum is often expressed by saying that the sum is direct if and only if each element of the sum is *uniquely* expressible in the form

$$a_1 + a_2 + \cdots + a_r, \qquad a_i \in G_i (i = 1, 2, \cdots, r).$$

If G_i has order n_i, we see that in a sum of the type just written there are n_i choices for a_i; and the uniqueness property just mentioned shows that the order of a direct sum $G_1 \oplus G_2 \oplus \cdots \oplus G_r$ is the product $n_1 n_2 \cdots n_r$ of the orders of the respective subgroups G_i.

Since addition is a commutative operation in G, it is clear, for example, that $G_1 \oplus G_2 = G_2 \oplus G_1$. In general, the order in which the subgroups G_i are written in the symbol for their direct sum is immaterial.

As a simple illustration of a general property, suppose that G_1 and G_2 are subgroups of G such that $G = G_1 \oplus G_2$. Now if $G_1 = H_1 \oplus H_2$ and $G_2 = K_1 \oplus K_2$, where H_1 and H_2 are subgroups of G_1, and K_1 and K_2 are subgroups of G_2, then all of H_1, H_2, K_1, K_2 are subgroups of G and

$$G = H_1 \oplus H_2 \oplus K_1 \oplus K_2.$$

It will be clear that a similar result holds for any number of summands. (See Exercise 3 below.) This fact will be useful later on.

REMARK. To avoid any possible confusion, let us point out that if G_1, G_2, $\cdots$, G_r are *any* additively written abelian groups (not necessarily subgroups of a given group), according to Section 7.1 the direct sum of these groups would consist of all ordered r-tuples

$$(a_1, a_2, \cdots, a_r),$$

with $a_i \in G_i$ for $i = 1, 2, \cdots, r$, and with addition defined as follows:

$$(a_1, a_2, \cdots, a_r) + (b_1, b_2, \cdots, b_r)$$
$$= (a_1 + b_1, a_2 + b_2, \cdots, a_r + b_r).$$

Now if the G_i are subgroups of a group G and their sum is direct as defined in 8.1, it is not difficult to prove that the mapping

$$(a_1, a_2, \cdots, a_r) \to a_1 + a_2 + \cdots + a_r$$

is an isomorphism of the direct sum as defined in Section 7.1 onto the direct sum as defined in this section. Prove it! This fact justifies the use of the term *direct sum* in two different situations. Sometimes, the direct sum as defined in 8.1 is called an *internal* direct sum (since all groups G_i are subgroups of a given group G and therefore their direct sum is a subgroup of G), and the direct sum of Section 7.1 is called an *external* direct sum (since the G_i are arbitrary groups, not given as subgroups of some given group).

Now let G be an abelian group of order $n = p_1^{e_1}p_2^{e_2} \cdots p_k^{e_k}$, where the p's are distinct primes, $k \geq 1$, and each $e_i \geq 1$. Thus p_1, p_2, $\cdots p_k$ are the distinct prime divisors of n. Let $G(p_i)$ be the set of all elements of G having order a power of p_i. The order of the identity 0 of G is $1 = p_i^0$ and hence $0 \in G(p_i)$. Actually, $G(p_i)$ is a subgroup of G since one can see as follows that $G(p_i)$ is closed under addition. If $a, b \in G(p_i)$, suppose that a has order $p_i{}^m$ and b has order $p_i{}^n$. If t is the larger of n and m, then $p_i{}^t(a + b) = 0$, and the order of $a + b$ is a divisor of $p_i{}^t$; hence is a power of p_i. It follows that $a + b \in G(p_i)$, and by Theorem 7.4 we see that $G(p_i)$ is a subgroup of G. Our next goal is to prove the following theorem.

8.2   Theorem. *Let G be an abelian group of order n, and let p_1, p_2, $\cdots$ p_k be the distinct prime divisors of n. If $G(p_i)$ is the subgroup of G consisting of all elements having order a power of p_i, then*

8.3 $$G = G(p_1) \oplus G(p_2) \oplus \cdots \oplus G(p_k).$$

Much later in this chapter we shall prove that no one of the subgroups $G(p_i)$ consists of the zero alone. In fact, if $p_i{}^{e_i}$ is the highest power of p_i which divides n, we shall show that $G(p_i)$ has order $p_i{}^{e_i}$.

Before proving Theorem 8.2, let us introduce some lemmas that will be helpful in carrying out the proof. It should be noted that in these lemmas n is temporarily being used to denote the order of an element, not the order of the group.

8.4   Lemma. *Suppose that the element a of an abelian group G has order n. If m is an integer such that $(m , n) = 1$, then $ma = 0$ implies that $a = 0$.*

PROOF: Since $(m , n) = 1$, there exist integers x and y such that $1 = xm + yn$. Hence $a = xma + yna$. We are assuming that $ma = 0$, and $na = 0$ since a has order n. It follows that $a = 0$, as we wished to show.

8.5   Lemma. *If the element a of the abelian group G has order $n = kl$ with $(k , l) = 1$, then there exist elements b and c of G such that $a = b+c$, with b and c having respective orders k and l.*

PROOF: Since $(k , l) = 1$, there exist integers s and t such that $1 = sk + tl$. Thus we have $a = ska + tla$. Let us show that ska has order l. Clearly, $lska = sna = 0$. Moreover, if $z \in \mathbf{Z}$ such that $zska = 0$, then $n \mid zsk$. But $n = kl$, so we conclude that $kl \mid zsk$ or $l \mid zs$. Now the equation $1 = sk + tl$ implies that $(s , l) = 1$ and therefore $l \mid z$. Accordingly, we conclude that ska has order l. Similarly, tla has order k and if we set $b = tla$ and $c = ska$, we have $a = b + c$, b of order k and c of order l. This completes the proof.

We leave as an exercise the proof by induction of the following generalization of the preceding lemma.

8.6 Lemma. *If the element a of the abelian group G has order* $n = n_1 n_2 \cdots n_k$, *where* $(n_i, n_j) = 1$ *for* $i \neq j$, *then a can be expressed in the form*

$$a = b_1 + b_2 + \cdots + b_k,$$

where b_i *has order* n_i $(i = 1, 2, \cdots, k)$.

Let us now return to the proof of Theorem 8.2 and show first that the sum $G(p_1) + G(p_2) + \cdots + G(p_k)$ is a direct sum. To this end, suppose that

8.7
$$a_1 + a_2 + \cdots + a_k = 0 \qquad\qquad a_i \in G(p_i).$$

By definition of direct sum, we need to prove that each $a_i = 0$. For convenience of notation, let us concentrate on proving that $a_1 = 0$. Each a_i has order a power of p_i, so let us assume that a_i has order $p_i{}^{t_i}$ $(i = 1, 2, \cdots, k)$. From Equation 8.7, it now follows that

$$p_2{}^{t_2} p_3{}^{t_3} \cdots p_k{}^{t_k} a_1 = 0.$$

Since this coefficient of a_1 is relatively prime to the order of a_1, it follows from Lemma 8.4 that $a_1 = 0$. Similarly, each $a_i = 0$, and this proves that the sum is direct.

Clearly, $G(p_1) \oplus G(p_2) \oplus \cdots \oplus G(p_k) \subseteq G$, so we only need to obtain inclusion the other way. By Corollary 7.33, every element a of G has order a divisor of the order n of G, and therefore the order of a has no prime divisors except for some or all of the $p_i (i = 1, 2, \cdots, k)$. For convenience of notation only, suppose that the order of a contains only the prime factors $p_1, p_2, \cdots, p_u$, $u \leq k$. By Lemma 8.6, a is expressible as a sum of elements of $G(p_i)$, $i = 1, 2, \cdots, u$. In particular, every element of G is a sum of elements of some or all of the $G(p_i)$, $i = 1, 2, \cdots, k$. We therefore conclude that $G \subseteq G(p_i) \oplus G(p_2) \oplus \cdots \oplus G(p_k)$, and this completes the proof of the theorem.

8.2 CYCLIC SUBGROUPS AND BASES

We shall continue to let G be a finite abelian group. If $a \in G$, let us denote by (a) the cyclic subgroup generated by a. If a has order n, then

$$(a) = \{0, a, 2a, \cdots, (n-1)a\}.$$

8.8 Definition. If $a_1, a_2, \cdots, a_k$ are nonzero elements of G such that the sum $(a_1) + (a_2) + \cdots + (a_k)$ is direct, we say that the elements $a_1, a_2, \cdots, a_k$ are *independent* or form an *independent set*.

Suppose that a_i has order $n_i (i = 1, 2, \cdots, k)$. Then, by definition of direct sum, the $a_i (i = 1, 2, \cdots, k)$ are independent if for integers z_i,

$$z_1 a_1 + z_2 a_2 + \cdots + z_k a_k = 0$$

if and only if $z_i a_i = 0$, that is, if and only if $n_i \mid z_i\ (i = 1, 2, \cdots, k)$.

Observe that a single element a of G is independent if and only if $a \neq 0$. Clearly, any nonempty subset of an independent set is also independent.

8.9   Definition.   The set $\{a_1, a_2, \cdots, a_r\}$ forms a *basis* of the abelian group G if and only if the elements of this set are independent and

$$G = (a_1) \oplus (a_2) \oplus \cdots \oplus (a_r).$$

Otherwise expressed, the group G has a basis if and only if it is expressible as a direct sum of a finite number of cyclic subgroups.

We may remark that if $G = H_1 \oplus H_2$, where H_1 is a subgroup of G having basis $\{b_1, b_2, \cdots b_s\}$ and H_2 is a subgroup of G having basis $\{c_1, c_2, \cdots, c_t\}$; then G has a basis $\{b_1, b_2, \cdots, b_s, c_1, c_2, \cdots, c_t\}$. (See Exercise 6 below.)

One of the principal theorems which we shall eventually prove is the following.

8.10   Theorem.   *Every finite abelian group has a basis, each element of which has order a power of a prime.*

In view of our definitions, an equivalent formulation of this theorem would be the assertion that every finite abelian group can be expressed as the direct sum of cyclic subgroups, each of which has order a power of a prime.

By a generalization of the remark made above, the result of Theorem 8.2 shows that Theorem 8.10 will be true in general when we have established it for each of the groups $G(p_i)$. In the next section we study in some detail a class of groups which will include those of the form $G(p_i)$ as defined in Theorem 8.2.

EXERCISES

1.   Prove the equivalence of conditions (i) and (ii) in connection with Definition 8.1.

2.   Suppose that $G_i (i = 1, 2, \cdots, r)$ are subgroups of the abelian group G such that the sum $G_1 + G_2 + \cdots + G_r$ is direct. If, for

each i, H_i is a subgroup of G_i, prove that the sum $H_1 + H_2 + \cdots + H_r$ is direct.

3. Suppose that $G = G_1 \oplus G_2$, where $G_1 = H_1 \oplus H_2 \oplus H_3$ and $G_2 = K_1 \oplus K_2$. Prove that $G = H_1 \oplus H_2 \oplus H_3 \oplus K_1 \oplus K_2$. Choose an appropriate notation and generalize to an arbitrary finite number of summands.

4. Let G be the additive group of the ring $\mathbf{Z}_{24}$. In the notation of Theorem 8.2, determine the elements of $G(2)$ and of $G(3)$. Verify that these are subgroups of G and that $G = G(2) \oplus G(3)$, thus directly verifying Theorem 8.2 for this particular group.

5. Give an example to show that in a finite nonabelian group the elements which have order a power of some fixed prime need not be a subgroup.

6. Suppose that G_1 and G_2 are subgroups of the abelian group G such that $G = G_1 \oplus G_2$. If $\{a_1, a_2, \cdots, a_r\}$ is a basis of G_1 and $\{b_1, b_2, \cdots, b_s\}$ is a basis of G_2, prove that $\{a_1, a_2, \cdots, a_r, b_1, b_2, \cdots, b_s\}$ is a basis of G. Generalize to direct sums of an arbitrary finite number of subgroups.

7. Illustrate Theorem 8.10 by verifying that for the group G which is the additive group of the ring $\mathbf{Z}_{24}$, a basis of the required kind is $\{3, 8\}$.

8. Prove Lemma 8.6.

9. Prove that a cyclic group of order p^k, where p is a prime and $k \geq 1$, cannot be expressed as a direct sum of two nonzero subgroups. [Hint: Consider the maximal order that an element can have.]

10. If (a) is a cyclic group of order kl with $(k, l) = 1$, prove that there exist elements b and c of (a) of respective orders k and l, such that $(a) = (b) \oplus (c)$.

11. If b and c are elements of an abelian group G with orders k and l respectively, and if $(k, l) = 1$, prove that the sum $(b) + (c)$ is direct and that $(b) \oplus (c)$ is a cyclic subgroup of G of order kl.

8.3 FINITE ABELIAN p–GROUPS

Let us begin with the following definition.

8.11 Definition. Let p be a fixed prime. A group is said to be a *p-group* if the order of each of its elements is a power of p.

We may observe that the identity element (the zero) has order p^0. Every other element of a p–group has order p^m for some positive integer m. Thus a nonzero element a of a p–group has order p^m if and only if $p^m a = 0$, $p^{m-1}a \neq 0$. Moreover, if a has order p^m and the order of an element b of the p–group is less than or equal to the order of a, then $p^m b = 0$.

The main goal of this section is to prove the following special case of Theorem 8.10.

8.12 Lemma.   *A finite abelian p-group has a basis.*

Throughout this section, let p be a fixed prime and G a finite abelian p–group. As a first step in the proof of Lemma 8.12, we collect a few useful facts for easy reference.

Let H be a subgroup of G and suppose that a is an element of G of order p^m. Since $p^m a = 0 \in H$, there exists a smallest positive integer z (necessarily less than or equal to p^m) such that $za \in H$. Throughout this section it will be convenient to have a distinctive name for this positive integer z. We shall call it the *degree of a relative to H*. Thus, the order of a is the degree of a relative to the zero subgroup.

(A) (*i*) *If z is the degree of a relative to H and $n \in \mathbf{Z}$, then $na \in H$ if and only if $z \mid n$. In particular, if z is the degree of a relative to H and $za = 0$, then z is the order of a.*

(*ii*) *If a has order p^m, and z is the degree of a relative to H, then $z \mid p^m$ and therefore the degree of each element of G relative to any subgroup of G is a power of p.*

To prove (*i*), let us use the Division Algorithm to write $n = qz + r$, where $0 \leq r < z$. Thus $na = q(za) + ra$. Now $za \in H$, so if $na \in H$, it follows that $ra \in H$. Since z is the smallest positive integer such that $za \in H$, we conclude that $r = 0$ and therefore $n = qz$. Conversely, if $z \mid n$, it is trivial that $na \in H$. The last statement of (*i*) follows from the observation that the given conditions imply that z and the order of a divide each other.

Part (*ii*) follows from (*i*) by observing that $p^m a = 0 \in H$, and therefore $z \mid p^m$ and z must therefore be a power of p.

(B) *Suppose that H is a subgroup of G and that $a \notin H$. If the order p^m of a is equal to the degree of a relative to H, then the sum $H + (a)$ is direct.*

To see the truth of this statement, suppose that $h + xa = 0$, where $h \in H$ and $x \in \mathbf{Z}$, and let us prove that $h = 0$ and that $xa = 0$. Now

$xa \in H$ and since a has degree p^m relative to H, part (i) of (A) shows that $p^m \mid x$. But this implies that $xa = 0$ since p^m is also the order of a. The equation $h + xa = 0$ then shows that $h = 0$. The sum $H + (a)$ is therefore a direct sum, as we wished to show.

The proof of Lemma 8.12 is carried out by the process of induction. We illustrate the approach by a fairly detailed account of the first two steps in this procedure, and then pass on to the general situation.

Let a_1 be an element of G of maximum order, say p^{m_1}. If it happens that $G = (a_1)$, we have found a basis $\{a_1\}$ of G consisting of the single element a_1. Suppose, then, that $G \neq (a_1)$. Since a_1 has maximum order among the elements of G, we see that $p^{m_1}c = 0$ for *every* element c of G.

Since $G \neq (a_1)$, we proceed to seek an element a_2 of G such that a_1, a_2 are independent and therefore $(a_1) \oplus (a_2) \subseteq G$.

Let b be an element of G of maximum degree, say p^{m_2}, relative to (a_1). Since $p^{m_1}b = 0 \in (a_1)$, it follows that $p^{m_2} \leq p^{m_1}$, that is, $m_2 \leq m_1$. Since b has maximum degree relative to (a_1), we see that $p^{m_2}c \in (a_1)$ for every element c of G. Thus if $c \in G$, there exists $y \in Z$ such that

8.13 $$p^{m_2}c = ya_1.$$

We proceed to show that $p^{m_2} \mid y$. Multiplying the preceding equation by $p^{m_1-m_2}$, we find that $p^{m_1}c = p^{m_1-m_2}ya_1$. But $p^{m_1}c = 0$, and since a_1 has order p^{m_1}, we conclude that $p^{m_1} \mid p^{m_1-m_2}y$, that is, that $p^{m_2} \mid y$. Thus $y = up^{m_2}$, where $u \in \mathbf{Z}$. Now applying what we have just proved to the special case in which c is an element b of maximum degree relative to (a_1), we find from 8.13 that there exists $u \in \mathbf{Z}$ such that

8.14 $$p^{m_2}b = p^{m_2}ua_1.$$

We now set

8.15 $$a_2 = b - ua_1,$$

and observe that if $z \in \mathbf{Z}$, then $za_2 \in (a_1)$ if and only if $zb \in (a_1)$. Thus the degree of a_2 relative to (a_1) is p^{m_2}. Now 8.14 and 8.15 imply that $p^{m_2}a_2 = 0$, and it follows from (A)(i) that the order of a_2 is p^{m_2}. We now know from (B) that the sum $(a_1) + (a_2)$ is a direct sum, and we have $G \supseteq (a_1) \oplus (a_2)$. If $G = (a_1) \oplus (a_2)$, we have exhibited a basis $\{a_1, a_2\}$. Otherwise, we can continue this process. We have just completed the case $k = 2$ of the following induction procedure.

Assume that we have found elements $a_1, a_2, \cdots, a_k$ of G of respective orders $p^{m_1}, p^{m_2}, \cdots, p^{m_k}$ such that all of the following are true:

(i) $m_1 \geq m_2 \geq \cdots \geq m_k$.

(ii) If $c \in G$, there exist integers $y_1, \cdots, y_{k-1}$ such that $p^{m_k}c = y_1 a_1 + \cdots + y_{k-1} a_{k-1}$, and $p^{m_k} \mid y_i (i = 1, 2, \cdots, k - 1)$.

(iii) $a_1, a_2, \cdots, a_k$ are independent.

For convenience, let us set $G_{k-1} = (a_1) \oplus (a_2) \oplus \cdots \oplus (a_{k-1})$ and $G_k = (a_1) \oplus (a_2) \oplus \cdots \oplus (a_k)$. If $G \neq G_k$, we propose to find another element a_{k+1} of G such that all of the above three properties are true with k replaced by $k + 1$.

We may point out that (ii) above states not only that if $c \in G$, then $p^{m_k}c \in G_{k-1}$, but even gives some additional information in that the integers y_i are all divisible by p^{m_k}.

Let b be an element of G of maximum degree, say $p^{m_{k+1}}$, relative to G_k. Thus, if $c \in G$, then $p^{m_{k+1}}c \in G_k$. Observe that since $p^{m_k}b \in G_{k-1} \subseteq G_k$, $p^{m_{k+1}} \leq p^{m_k}$ and $m_k \geq m_{k+1}$, so (i) holds for $k + 1$.

If $c \in G$, since $p^{m_{k+1}}c \in G_k$, there exist integers $z_1, \cdots, z_k$ such that

8.16 $p^{m_{k+1}}c = z_1 a_1 + z_2 a_2 + \cdots + z_k a_k$.

We propose to show that $p^{m_{k+1}} \mid z_i$ for $i = 1, 2, \cdots, k$. By (ii) of our induction hypothesis, there exist integers $y_1, \cdots, y_{k-1}$ such that

8.17 $p^{m_k}c = y_1 a_1 + \cdots + y_{k-1} a_{k-1}$, $p^{m_k} \mid y_i \ (i = 1, 2, \cdots, k)$.

If we multiply 8.16 by $p^{m_k - m_{k-1}}$, we obtain $p^{m_k}c = p^{m_k - m_{k+1}}z_1 a_1 + \cdots + p^{m_k - m_{k+1}}z_k a_k$. By equating the right sides of the two preceding equations, we obtain

$$(p^{m_k - m_{k+1}}z_1 - y_1)a_1 + \cdots + (p^{m_k - m_{k+1}}z_{k-1} - y_{k-1})a_{k-1} + p^{m_k - m_{k+1}}z_k a_k = 0.$$

Since, by assumption, $a_1, a_2, \cdots, a_k$ are independent, for each i the coefficient of a_i in this equation must be divisible by the order of a_i. In particular $p^{m_k} \mid p^{m_k - m_{k+1}}z_k$ and this implies that $p^{m_{k+1}} \mid z_k$. Now for $1 \leq i < k$, we have $p^{m_i} \mid (p^{m_k - m_{k+1}}z_i - y_i)$. But $i < k$ and so $m_i \geq m_k$, and thus

$$p^{m_k} \mid (p^{m_k - m_{k+1}}z_i - y_i).$$

But, as indicated in 8.17, we know that $p^{m_k} \mid y_i$. It follows that $p^{m_k} \mid p^{m_k - m_{k+1}}z_i$ and hence that $p^{m_{k+1}} \mid z_i$. Since this is true for $1 \leq i < k$, and we have already shown that $p^{m_{k+1}} \mid z_k$, we conclude that $p^{m_{k+1}}$ divides every z_i in 8.16. This establishes part (ii) of our induction statement for the case in which k is replaced by $k + 1$.

Now let us apply what we have just proved to the special case in which the element c in 8.16 is chosen to be a particular element b of maximal degree p^{m_k+1} relative to G_k. Thus, since $p^{m_k+1} \mid z_i$, there exist integers $u_1, \cdots, u_k$ such that

8.18 $$p^{m_k+1}b = p^{m_k+1}u_1a_1 + p^{m_k+1}u_2a_2 + \cdots + p^{m_k+1}u_ka_k.$$

We next define

8.19 $$a_{k+1} = b - u_1a_1 - \cdots - u_ka_k,$$

and observe from this equation that a_{k+1} has the same degree relative to G_k as does b, namely, p^{m_k+1}. The last two equations show that $p^{m_k+1}a_{k+1} = 0$ and it follows from (A)(i) that the order of a_{k+1} is p^{m_k+1}. By (B), the sum $G_k + (a_{k+1})$ is direct and it follows that $a_1, a_2, \cdots, a_{k+1}$ are independent. We have shown that if $a_1, a_2, \cdots, a_k$ satisfy the induction hypotheses (i), (ii) and (iii), and if $G \neq (a_1) \oplus \cdots \oplus (a_k)$, there exists an element a_{k+1} such that $a_1, \cdots, a_{k+1}$ satisfy (i), (ii) and (iii), with k replaced by $k + 1$. In particular, $G \supseteq (a_1) \oplus \cdots \oplus (a_{k+1})$. Since G is assumed to be a *finite* p–group, these steps must come to an end, and thus for some positive integer r, there exist elements $a_1, a_2, \cdots, a_r$ such that

8.20 $$G = (a_1) \oplus (a_2) \oplus \cdots \oplus (a_r).$$

This completes the proof of Lemma 8.12 which states that every finite abelian p–group has a basis.

In proving 8.20, we have obtained the basis elements $a_1, a_2, \cdots, a_r$ such that their orders are respectively, $p^{m_1}, p^{m_2}, \cdots, p^{m_r}$ with $m_1 \geq m_2 \geq \cdots \geq m_r \geq 1$. It follows from 8.20 that the order of G is the product of the orders of the cyclic groups (a_i), namely p^t, where $t = m_1 + m_2 + \cdots + m_r$. In particular, this shows that *the order of a finite abelian p–group is a power of p*.

Before returning to the study of arbitrary abelian groups, let us discuss the question of the uniqueness of a basis for a p–group. Clearly, our construction of a basis indicates that a basis is *not* unique since, as a simple example, a_1 might have been chosen to be any element of maximal order. However, we shall prove the following result.

8.21   Theorem.   *Any two bases of a finite abelian p–group have the same number of elements. Moreover, the orders of the elements of one basis coincide, in some arrangement, with the orders of the elements of any other basis.*

In proving this theorem, we shall assume that the p–group G has a basis $\{a_1, a_2, \cdots, a_r\}$, with a_i having order p^{m_i}; and that G also has a basis $\{b_1, b_2, \cdots, b_s\}$, with b_i having order p^{n_i}. Moreover, we assume that the notation is chosen so that $m_1 \geq m_2 \geq \cdots \geq m_r \geq 1$ and $n_1 \geq n_2 \geq \cdots \geq n_s \geq 1$. We proceed to prove that $r = s$ and that $m_i = n_i (i = 1, 2, \cdots, r)$.

It will be convenient to consider subgroups pG and G_p of G, defined as follows:

$$pG = \{px \mid x \in G\},$$

and

$$G_p = \{x \mid x \in G, \ px = 0\}.$$

Thus $pG = \{0\}$ if and only if $G_p = G$.

Making use of the basis $\{a_1, a_2, \cdots, a_r\}$ of G, we leave it to the reader to verify that

8.22 $\{p^{m_1-1}a_1, \ p^{m_2-1}a_2, \cdots, p^{m_r-1}a_r\}$

is a basis of the p–group G_p. Since each of these basis elements has order p and G_p is the direct sum of the cyclic groups generated by these elements, we conclude that G_p has order p^r. In exactly the same way, using the basis $\{b_1, b_2, \cdots, b_s\}$ of G, we see that G_p has order p^s. Hence $p^r = p^s$, and $r = s$. This completes the proof of the first statement of the theorem.

The proof of the second statement is by induction on the order of G, and we therefore assume as an induction hypothesis that the statement is true for all p–groups with order less than the order of G. We now make two cases, in the first of which we do not really need this induction hypothesis.

CASE 1. $pG = \{0\}$. In this case, every nonzero element (in particular, every basis element) of G has order p. Hence, $m_i = n_i = 1 \ (i = 1, 2, \cdots, r)$.

CASE 2. $pG \neq \{0\}$. In this case, pG is a nonzero subgroup of G. Moreover, the order of pG is less than the order of G, since G necessarily has some elements of order p. Why? Using the notation in which the order of a_i is p^{m_i}, not all m_i can equal 1. Suppose that u is a positive integer so chosen that $m_1 \geq m_2 \geq \cdots \geq m_u > m_{u+1} = \cdots = m_r = 1$. It may now be verified that pG has a basis

8.23 $\{pa_1, \cdots, pa_u\}.$

In like manner, make use of the other given basis $\{b_1, \cdots, b_r\}$ of G, if v is the positive integer so chosen that $n_1 \geq n_2 \geq \cdots \geq n_v > n_{v+1} = \cdots = n_r = 1$, we see that pG has a basis

8.24 $$\{pb_1, \cdots, pb_v\}.$$

Thus the p–group pG has bases 8.23 and 8.24. By the first statement of the theorem, already proved, we conclude that $u = v$. Using the fact that the order of pa_i is p^{n_i-1} and the order of pb_i is p^{n_i-1}, the induction hypothesis as applied to the group pG shows that $m_i - 1 = n_i - 1$ for $i = 1, 2, \cdots, u$. Since all other m_i and n_i are equal to 1, we have that $m_i = n_i (i = 1, 2, \cdots, r)$. This concludes the proof of the theorem.

8.4 THE PRINCIPAL THEOREMS FOR FINITE ABELIAN GROUPS

Henceforth, we shall let G be an arbitrary finite abelian group. Let us assume that G has order n with distinct prime factors $p_1, p_2, \cdots, p_k$. Thus

8.25 $$n = p_1^{e_1} p_2^{e_2} \cdots p_k^{e_k},$$

where $e_i > 0$ for all i. If $G(p_i)$ denotes the subgroup of G consisting of all elements of order a power of p_i, we have proved in Theorem 8.2 that

8.26 $$G = G(p_1) \oplus \cdots \oplus G(p_k).$$

Now $G(p_i)$ is a p_i–group and as indicated shortly before the statement of Theorem 8.21, its order is a power of p_i. Moreover, from Equation 8.26, the order n of G must be the product of the orders of the groups $G(p_i)$. In view of the unique factorization of n into a product of primes, we conclude from 8.25 that the order of $G(p_i)$ must be $p_i^{e_i} (i = 1, 2, \cdots, k)$. We have therefore proved the first statement of the following lemma.

8.27 Lemma. *Let G be an abelian group of order n.*

(i) *If p is a prime divisor of n, let p^e be the highest power of p which divides n. Then the subgroup $G(p)$ of G, which consists of all elements with order a power of p, has order p^e. In particular, $G(p) \neq \{0\}$.*

(ii) *If p is a prime divisor of n, then G contains an element of order p.*

The proof of part (ii) follows at once from the observation that if a is a nonzero element of $G(p)$, then a has order p^t for some positive integer t. Hence $p^{t-1}a$ has order p.

The results of the preceding section show that each subgroup $G(p_i)$ occurring in 8.26 has a basis, say, $\{a_{i1}, a_{i2}, \cdots, a_{ir_i}\}$, and clearly each element of this basis has order a power of p_i. Using this information, Equation 8.26 shows that G has a basis

8.28 $\{a_{11}, a_{12}, \cdots, a_{1r_1}\ ;\ a_{21}, a_{22}, \cdots, a_{2r_2}\ ;\ \cdots ; a_{k1}, a_{k2}, \cdots, a_{kr_k}\},$

and each element of this basis has order a power of a prime. This result was stated as Theorem 8.10, one of our principal goals. We have therefore proved part (*i*) of the following fundamental theorem.

8.29   Fundamental Theorem on Finite Abelian Groups.

(*i*)   *Every finite abelian group G has a basis, each element of which has order a power of a prime.*

(*ii*)   *Suppose we have any two bases of a finite abelian group G, with each basis element having order a power of a prime. Then the two bases have the same number of elements and the orders of the elements of one basis are, in some arrangement, the same as the orders of the elements of the other basis.*

To prove part (*ii*) of this theorem, suppose that one basis of G is given by 8.28. If G has order n, given by 8.25, the order of every element of G is a divisor of n and hence the only possible primes a power of which can occur as the order of any (basis) element are $p_1, p_2, \cdots, p_k$. Suppose that in a second basis of G, the elements $b_1, \cdots, b_t$ are those whose orders are a power of p_1. Then the elements of G whose elements are a power of p_1 are precisely the elements of the direct sum

8.30 $(b_1) \oplus \cdots \oplus (b_t).$

It follows that the direct sum 8.30 is equal to $G(p_1)$. Since from 8.28, we also have
8.31 $G(p_1) = (a_{11}) \oplus \cdots \oplus (a_{1r_1}),$

we may apply Theorem 8.21 to the p_1-group $G(p_1)$, and conclude that $t = r_1$, and that the orders of $b_1, \cdots, b_t$ coincide, in some arrangement, with the orders of $a_{11}, \cdots, a_{1r_1}$. Thus the number of basis elements having order a power of p_1 is the same in the two bases, as are also the orders of the elements of the two bases. The same argument applies equally well to each prime p_i, and this completes the proof of the theorem.

Let us next make the following definition.

8.32   **Definition.**   Let G be a finite abelian group. The orders of the elements of a basis (repetitions being allowed), in which each basis element is required to have order a power of a prime, are called the *invariants* (or *elementary divisors*) of G.

Thus, for example, if we say that G has invariants 3, 2^2, 2, 2, it means that G is expressible as a direct sum of cyclic groups of these respective orders. Thus for this group G, we have

$$G \cong C_3 \oplus C_{2^2} \oplus C_2 \oplus C_2,$$

where C_n represents a cyclic group of order n.

The concept of the invariants of an abelian group is important because of the following theorem.

8.33 Theorem. *Two finite abelian groups are isomorphic if and only if they have the same invariants.*

One part of this result follows fairly easily from results obtained above. Suppose that $\theta\colon G \to G'$ is an isomorphism of the finite abelian group G onto the finite abelian group G'. If $\{a_1, a_2, \cdots, a_n\}$ is a basis of G, with each a_i having order a power of a prime, the orders of a_1, a_2, $\cdots$, a_n are then the invariants of G. Now, $\{a_1\theta, a_2\theta, \cdots, a_n\theta\}$ is a basis of G' (see Exercise 5 below), and under the isomorphism θ, a_i and $a_i\theta$ have the same order. Hence G' has the same invariants as G.

Conversely, suppose that G and G' have the same invariants. This means that

$$G \cong D_1 \oplus D_2 \oplus \cdots \oplus D_n$$

and

$$G' \cong E_1 \oplus E_2 \oplus \cdots \oplus E_n$$

where D_i and E_i are cyclic groups of the same order (a power of a prime). Now, by Theorem 7.26, two cyclic groups of the same order are isomorphic. Let $\theta_i\colon D_i \to E_i$ be an isomorphism of D_i onto E_i. Then, it may be verified that the mapping $\theta\colon G \to G'$ defined by

8.34 $$(d_1 + d_2 + \cdots + d_n)\theta = d_1\theta_1 + d_2\theta_2 + \cdots + d_n\theta_n$$

where $d_i \in D_i$, is an isomorphism of G onto G'. (See Exercise 4 below.)

As a simple application of this theorem, let us determine all non-isomorphic abelian groups of order 24. Since the product of the invariants must be 24, we find the following possible systems of invariants: 3, 2^3; 3, 2^2, 2; 3, 2, 2, 2. Thus there are three nonisomorphic abelian groups of order 24. If, as above, we let C_n denote a cyclic group of order n, these three nonisomorphic abelian groups of order 24 are respectively isomorphic to

$$C_3 \oplus C_{2^3}, \quad C_3 \oplus C_{2^2} \oplus C_2, \quad C_3 \oplus C_2 \oplus C_2 \oplus C_2.$$

EXERCISES

1. If an abelian group G has invariants 2^2, 5, 5; verify that there exist elements of G of order 20 and none of higher order. Determine the number of elements of order 20.

2. In the notation used in the proof of Theorem 8.21, prove that the set 8.22 is a basis of G_p.

3. In the notation of the same proof, prove that the set 8.23 is a basis of pG.

4. Verify that the mapping θ defined in 8.34 is an isomorphism of G onto G'.

5. Prove: If $\{a_1, a_2, \cdots, a_n\}$ is a basis of an abelian group G and if $\theta: G \to G'$ is an isomorphism of G onto G', then $\{a_1\theta, a_2\theta, \cdots, a_n\theta\}$ is a basis of G', and G and G' have the same invariants.

6. If $p_1, p_2, \cdots, p_k$ are distinct primes, show that any two abelian groups of order $p_1p_2 \cdots p_k$ are isomorphic (and therefore isomorphic to the cyclic group of this order).

7. Suppose that an abelian group G has order $n = p_1^{e_1}, p_2^{e_2}, \cdots p_k^{e_k}$, where the p's are distinct primes and each $e_i \geq 1$. If among the invariants of G the highest powers of these primes which occur are $p_1^{t_1}, p_2^{t_2}, \cdots, p_k^{t_k}$, prove that there exists an element of G of order $p_1^{t_1}p_2^{t_2} \cdots p_k^{t_k}$ and no element of higher order. [*Cf.* Exercise 14 at the end of Section 7.4. Observe also that Exercise 1 above involves a verification of a special case of this result.]

8. Verify that there are exactly four nonisomorphic abelian groups of order 100. For each of these groups, determine the maximal order of an element.

9. Show that if a cyclic group G has order p^m (p a prime) and if $t \in \mathbf{Z}$ such that $0 \leq t \leq m$, then G has a subgroup of order p^t.

10. Prove that if p and t are as in the preceding exercise, any abelian group G of order p^m has a subgroup of order p^t. [Hint: Consider the invariants of G, the result of the preceding exercise, and Exercise 2 of the preceding set.]

11. Use Theorem 8.2, Lemma 8.27 and the results of the two preceding exercises to prove the following general result: If an abelian group G has order n and $k \mid n$, then G has a subgroup of order k.

NOTES AND REFERENCES

The results obtained in this chapter may be found in most general books on group theory and in many books on abstract algebra. See, in particular, Lederman [22] and Hall [20].

If there exists a finite number of elements a_1, a_2, $\cdots$, a_m of an abelian group G such that all elements of G are expressible in the form

$$x_1 a_1 + x_2 a_2 + \cdots + x_m a_m,$$

the x's being integers, the group is said to be *finitely generated*. Of course, every finite abelian group is finitely generated, but so also are some infinite groups. As the simplest example, the additive group of the integers is generated by the single integer 1. Our Fundamental Theorem (8.29) can be suitably generalized to arbitrary finitely generated abelian groups by allowing the possibility that some of the basis elements have infinite order. The number of basis elements of infinite order is unique, as are the orders of the basis elements of finite order (these being required to have order a power of a prime). See, e.g., Fuchs [19], Lederman [22], Hall [20], Macdonald [23] or Rotman [25].

THE SYLOW THEOREMS

The most fundamental results about finite abelian groups were presented in the preceding chapter. We now return to the study of arbitrary finite (not necessarily abelian) groups and, in particular, shall concentrate on that part of the theory having to do with the existence of subgroups of certain orders. The main theorems in this connection are called the *Sylow Theorems*, after the Norwegian mathematician L. Sylow who first proved them in 1872. We shall begin by presenting several topics, of some interest in themselves, which will be useful in the proofs of these theorems.

Throughout this chapter, we shall let G denote a group of finite order and shall consider the operation on G to be multiplication.

9.1 CONJUGATE ELEMENTS AND TRANSFORMS

We begin with the following definition.

9.1 Definition. If $a, x \in G$ and $b = x^{-1}ax$, then b is said to be the *transform of a by x*. If b is a transform of a (by some element of the group), we also say that b is *conjugate* to a.

It follows readily that if a is the transform of b by x, then b is the transform of a by x^{-1}; hence b is conjugate to a if and only if a is conjugate to b. Clearly, each element a of G is its own transform by the identity of G, so that a is conjugate to a. Finally, suppose that b is the transform of a by x and c is the transform of b by y, then c is the transform of a by xy. Accordingly, we have shown that "being conjugate to" satisfies the properties required for an equivalence relation on G. In accordance with previous usage, let us denote the equivalence set which contains the element a (relative to this equivalence relation) by $[a]$. Thus $[a]$ consists of all transforms of a.

We may observe that a is itself equal to its transform by an element y if and only if $a = y^{-1}ay$ or $ya = ay$, that is, if and only if a commutes with y.

9.2 Definition. If $a \in G$, the set N of all elements y of G which transform a into itself is called the *normalizer* of a in G.

In view of the preceding remarks, the normalizer N of a in G may be characterized as follows:

$$N = \{y \mid y \in G, \ ya = ay\}.$$

It is quite simple to verify that N is a subgroup of G. (See Exercise 8 at end of Section 7.1.)

9.3 Definition. The set C of those elements of G which commute with all elements of G is called the *center* of G.

Note that C cannot be empty since it contains the identity of G. It is easily verified (Exercise 3 at end of Section 7.7) that C is a *normal subgroup* of G.

The following observations are immediate consequences of these various definitions. The equivalence set $[a]$ contains *only* the one element a if and only if $a \in C$. If $a \in G$, then $a \in C$ if and only if a is in the normalizer of *every* element of G. In other words, the center C is the intersection of the normalizers of all elements of G.

As an illustration of some of these concepts, let G be the symmetric group S_3, whose multiplication table is given by 7.10. Since the identity ϵ is in the center of this group, we see that $[\epsilon] = \{\epsilon\}$. By computing $t^{-1}\alpha_2 t$ for each element t of S_3, we find that ϵ and α_2 are the only elements which transform α_2 into itself. That is, the normalizer of α_2 is the subgroup $\{\epsilon, \alpha_2\}$ of S_3. Moreover, $[\alpha_2] = \{\alpha_2, \alpha_3, \alpha_4\}$. Similarly, we find that $[\alpha_5] = \{\alpha_5, \alpha_6\}$. The three equivalence sets $[\epsilon]$, $[\alpha_2]$, and $[\alpha_5]$ are thus a complete set of the different equivalence sets. As must be the case, the different equivalence sets form a partition of G since each element of G occurs in exactly one of them. The number of elements in these different equivalence sets are 1, 3, and 2, respectively. We observe that all of these integers are divisors of the order 6 of S_3, a fact which illustrates the last part of the next theorem to be established below. We may observe also that the center of S_3 consists *only* of the identity ϵ, and this is equivalent to the statement that the equivalence set $[\epsilon]$ is the only equivalence set which contains exactly one element.

Now, again, let G be a group of order n, and suppose that

9.4 $\{[a_1], [a_2], \cdots, [a_s]\}$

is a complete set of distinct equivalence sets in G. If t_i denotes the number of elements in $[a_i]$, the fact that each element of G occurs in exactly one of the sets 9.4 assures us that

9.5 $n = t_1 + t_2 + \cdots + t_s.$

Moreover, $t_i = 1$ if and only if a_i is in the center of G. We therefore know that at least one of the t_i is equal to one since the equivalence set which contains the identity of G certainly has only the identity in it.

We have already pointed out the truth of the first sentence of the following theorem, and we proceed to prove the rest of it.

9.6   Theorem.   *If N is the normalizer of the element a of G, then N is a subgroup of G. If*

$$\{Ny_1, Ny_2, \cdots, Ny_t\}$$

is the set of distinct right cosets of N in G, then there are exactly t elements in the equivalence set $[a]$. More precisely,

$$[a] = \{y_1^{-1}ay_1, y_2^{-1}ay_2, \cdots, y_t^{-1}ay_t\},$$

these indicated elements all being distinct. The number t of elements in $[a]$ is therefore the index of N in G (and hence is a divisor of the order n of G).

PROOF: We shall show that all elements of a right coset Ny transform a into the same element $y^{-1}ay$ of G, and that elements of different right cosets necessarily transform a into different elements. Let $xy \in Ny$, $x \in N$. If we transform a by xy, we obtain

$$(xy)^{-1}axy = y^{-1}x^{-1}axy = y^{-1}ay$$

since x, being in the normalizer of a, commutes with a. Thus all elements of the right coset Ny transform a into the element $y^{-1}ay$.

Let us next prove that elements of different right cosets transform a into different elements. Suppose, that Ny and Nz are different right cosets of N in G. Then, by what we have just proved, all elements of the coset Ny transform a into $y^{-1}ay$, and all elements of the coset Nz transform a into $z^{-1}az$. Suppose that $y^{-1}ay = z^{-1}az$, and let us seek a contradiction. We have

$$a = yz^{-1}azy^{-1} = (zy^{-1})^{-1}azy^{-1},$$

that is, zy^{-1} transforms a into itself, and hence $zy^{-1} \in N$. But this implies that $Ny = Nz$, and we have a contradiction since the cosets Ny and Nz were assumed to be distinct. All the statements of the theorem follow from these observations.

Before proceeding, let us pause to prove a result which will be of later use.

9.7   **Lemma.** *Suppose that the group G has order n and that p is a prime divisor of n. If p divides the index of every proper subgroup of G, then p divides the order of the center of G. In particular, the center of G cannot consist of the identity alone.*

PROOF: The result is trivial if G is abelian, so we assume now that G is nonabelian. In the notation used in Equation 9.5, we know that $t_i = 1$ if and only if a_i is in the center of G. Moreover, if a_i is not in the center of G, its normalizer has more than one element (in particular, the identity and a_i) and is not all of G. Hence if a_i is not in the center of G, then $p \mid t_i$ since, by the preceding theorem, t_i is the index of the normalizer of a_i, and this normalizer is a proper subgroup of G. If the center of G has order l, Equation 9.5 then shows that

$$n = l + px$$

for some integer x. Since $p \mid n$, it is clear that also $p \mid l$, and this completes the proof of the lemma.

As a special case, this lemma implies that *if the order of a group is a power of a prime p, the order of the center is divisible by p.*

9.2   CONJUGATE SUBGROUPS

In this section we do for *subgroups* some of the things that were done in the preceding section for *elements*. The definitions and results are analogous to those just presented.

If H is a subgroup of G and $x \in G$, let us define

$$x^{-1}Hx = \{x^{-1}hx \mid h \in H\},$$

that is, $x^{-1}Hx$ is the set of all transforms of elements of H by x. It is easy to verify (see Exercise 1 at the end of Section 7.7) that $x^{-1}Hx$ is a subgroup of G and that H is isomorphic to $x^{-1}Hx$ under the mapping $h \to x^{-1}hx$, $h \in H$.

9.8   Definition.   If H is a subgroup of G and $x \in G$, the subgroup $x^{-1}Hx$ of G is called the *transform* of H by x. If K is a transform of H by some element of G, we say that K is *conjugate* to H.

We leave it to the reader to verify that "is conjugate to" is an equivalence relation on the set of all subgroups of G. Moreover, H is a normal subgroup of G if and only if the *only* subgroup of G which is conjugate to H is H itself.

Corresponding to Definition 9.2 we make the following definition.

9.9   Definition.   If H is a subgroup of G, the subgroup N of G defined by

$$N = \{x \mid x \in G,\ xH = Hx\}$$

is called the *normalizer* of H in G.

Clearly, $x \in N$ if and only if $x^{-1}Hx = H$, that is, if and only if x transforms H into H.

We ask the reader to verify that N is indeed a subgroup of G. Moreover, $H \subseteq N$ and, as a matter of fact, H *is a normal subgroup of* N. For if $x \in N$, the right coset Hx of H in N is equal to the left coset xH of H in N.

If H is a normal subgroup of G, then by the very definition of normal subgroup, $N = G$.

We may now prove the following principal theorem of this section.

9.10   Theorem.   *Let N be the normalizer of the subgroup H of G. If*

9.11 $$\{Ny_1, Ny_2, \cdots, Ny_k\}$$

is the set of all distinct right cosets of N in G, then there are exactly k distinct subgroups of G which are conjugate to H in G, namely, the subgroups

9.12 $$y_1^{-1}Hy_1,\ y_2^{-1}Hy_2,\ \cdots,\ y_k^{-1}Hy_k.$$

The number k of such subgroups, being the index of N in G, is therefore a divisor of the order n of G.

The proof of this theorem follows closely the method of proof of Theorem 9.6. We shall prove that all the elements of a right coset of N in G transform H into the same conjugate subgroup, and that elements of different right cosets necessarily transform H into different conjugate subgroups.

First, consider an arbitrary element of a right coset, say, Ny. Such an element is of the form ay, where $a \in N$. Then

$$(ay)^{-1}Hay = y^{-1}(a^{-1}Ha)y = y^{-1}Hy,$$

since a is in the normalizer of H. Thus all elements of the right coset Ny transform H into the same subgroup $y^{-1}Hy$.

Second, suppose that Ny and Nz are different right cosets of N in G, and suppose that ay and bz, with $a, b \in N$, are elements of these respective cosets. Then, by what we have just proved, the transform of H by ay is $y^{-1}Hy$, and the transform of H by bz is $z^{-1}Hz$. Let us assume that $y^{-1}Hy = z^{-1}Hz$, and seek a contradiction. This assumption leads to the conclusion that $Hyz^{-1} = yz^{-1}H$. However, this implies that $yz^{-1} \in N$, from which it follows that $Ny = Nz$. However, we started with *different* right cosets Ny and Nz of N in G, and we have the desired contradiction. Thus elements of different right cosets of N in G transform H into different conjugate subgroups. The last statement of the theorem is already known (7.32).

9.3 DOUBLE COSETS

If A and B are nonempty subsets of a group G, we define

$$AB = \{ab \mid a \in A , b \in B\}.$$

If A is the set $\{a\}$ consisting of one element a, we shall write aB and Ba in place of $\{a\}B$ and $B\{a\}$, respectively. We know by Theorem 7.4 that a nonempty subset A of a finite group G is a subgroup of G if and only if A is closed with respect to the operation (here multiplication), that is, if and only if $A^2 = AA \subseteq A$. However, if A is a subgroup, it is clear that $A^2 = A$, so we have that *a nonempty set A of elements of a finite group G is a subgroup of G if and only if $A^2 = A$.*

We shall next prove the following lemma.

9.13 Lemma. *Let G be a group of order n, and let H and K be subgroups of G of respective orders h and k. Then*

(i) *If the subgroup $H \cap K$ has order d, HK contains exactly hk/d distinct elements.*

(ii) *HK is a subgroup of G if and only if $HK = KH$.*

PROOF OF (i):   Let $D = H \cap K$, D of order d. Then D is a subgroup of K (and of H also). Now suppose that

9.14 $\{Dk_1, Dk_2, \cdots, Dk_m\}$

is a complete set of distinct cosets of D in K, so that these cosets form a partition of K. It follows that $k = dm$. Moreover, every element of

HK is in one of the sets HDk_1, HDk_2, $\cdots$, HDk_m. Since $D \subseteq H$, we see that $HD = H$ and we have shown that every element of HK is contained in one of the following cosets of H in G:

9.15 $\{Hk_1, Hk_2, \cdots, Hk_m\}$.

Each of these cosets contains h elements, h the order of H. Let us show that the cosets 9.15 are disjoint, that is, that no two of them have an element in common. Suppose, on the contrary, that $Hk_i \cap Hk_j \neq \varnothing$ for some $i \neq j$. Thus there exist elements a and b of H such that $ak_i = bk_j$. From this, it follows that $b^{-1}a = k_j k_i^{-1}$, so that $k_j k_i^{-1} \in H \cap K = D$. But this implies that $Dk_i = Dk_j$ and in 9.14 these were assumed to be different cosets of D in K. We therefore have the desired contradiction, and the cosets 9.15 are disjoint. Thus there are hm distinct elements of G appearing in the cosets of 9.15 and these are just the elements of HK. We already know that $k = dm$, and it follows that HK has hk/d elements. This completes the proof of the first part of the lemma.

PROOF OF (*ii*): Suppose that $HK = KH$. Since H and K are groups, we know that $H^2 = H$ and $K^2 = K$. Thus $(HK)^2 = HKHK = H^2K^2 = HK$, and HK is a subgroup of the finite group G by the observation made just before the statement of the lemma. Conversely, suppose that HK is a subgroup of G and let us prove that $HK = KH$. If $a \in H$ and $b \in K$, then $a^{-1}b^{-1} \in HK$. Since HK is a group, $(a^{-1}b^{-1})^{-1} = ba \in HK$. This calculation shows that $KH \subseteq HK$. Similarly, $HK \subseteq KH$, and we conclude that $HK = KH$, completing the proof.

We may observe that if either H or K is a normal subgroup of G, then $HK = KH$ is a subgroup of G.

Before stating the theorem whose proof will make essential use of this lemma, we need another definition.

9.16 Definition. If H and K are subgroups of the group G and $a \in G$, the set

$$HaK = \{xay \mid x \in H, y \in K\}$$

is called a *double coset* of H and K in G.

Double cosets have the property, in common with right (or left) cosets with respect to a single subgroup, that the distinct double cosets form a partition of G. Let us prove this fact by showing first that if $a, b \in G$ and $HaK \cap HbK \neq \varnothing$, then $HaK = HbK$. Suppose that $h_1, h_2 \in H$ and $k_1, k_2 \in K$ such that $h_1 a k_1 = h_2 b k_2$. It follows that

$$Hh_1 a k_1 K = Hh_2 b k_2 K.$$

But $Hh_1 = H$, $k_1K = K$, etc., so we conclude that

$$HaK = HbK,$$

as we wished to show. Second, we observe that $a \in HaK$, so that every element of G is in some one (and therefore in exactly one) double coset of H and K. The distinct double cosets of H and K thus form a partition of G.

As a simple illustration of double cosets, let G be the octic group given by 7.12, and let $H = \{\epsilon, \beta\}$ and $K = \{\epsilon, \gamma\}$. It may then be verified that

$$
\begin{aligned}
H\epsilon K &= \{\epsilon, \alpha^2, \beta, \gamma\}, & H\beta K &= \{\epsilon, \alpha^2, \beta, \gamma\}, \\
H\alpha K &= \{\alpha, \delta\}, & H\gamma K &= \{\epsilon, \alpha^2, \beta, \gamma\}, \\
H\alpha^2 K &= \{\epsilon, \alpha^2, \beta, \gamma\}, & H\delta K &= \{\alpha, \delta\}, \\
H\alpha^3 K &= \{\alpha^3, \sigma\}, & H\sigma K &= \{\alpha^3, \sigma\}.
\end{aligned}
$$

As we have proved must be the case in general, we observe that two of these double cosets are identical if they have an element in common, and that every element of G occurs in at least one of these double cosets. However, in contrast to right (or left) cosets, not all double cosets have the same number of elements. The following theorem of Frobenius, part of which we have already proved, gives some information about the number of elements in a specified double coset.

9.17 Theorem. *If G is a group of order n, and H and K are subgroups of G of respective orders h and k, then*

(i) *There exist elements $a_1, a_2, \cdots, a_r$ of G (r some positive integer) such that*

9.18 $\{Ha_1K, Ha_2K, \cdots, Ha_rK,\}$ *is a partition of G.*

(ii) *If $a \in G$, the double coset HaK contains hk / d distinct elements, where d is the order of the subgroup $(a^{-1}Ha) \cap K$ of G.*

We have already proved the first part of the theorem in that we only need to choose $a_1, a_2, \cdots, a_r$ in such a way that the set 9.18 is a complete set of distinct cosets. To prove the second part of the theorem, suppose that HaK consists of the t elements $\{c_1, c_2, \cdots, c_t\}$. Let $H' = a^{-1}Ha$, the transform of H by a. Then the order of H' is also h, and $H'K$ has the t distinct elements

$$\{a^{-1}c_1, a^{-1}c_2, \cdots, a^{-1}c_t\}.$$

By Lemma 9.13 (i), applied to H' and K, we see that $t = hk/d$, where d is the order of $H' \cap K = (a^{-1}Ha) \cap K$, and this completes the proof.

Since the double cosets 9.18 form a partition of G, by use of part
(*ii*) of the theorem we have the following result.

9.19 Corollary. *In the notation of the preceding theorem, the order n of G
satisfies the following equation*

$$n = \frac{hk}{d_1} + \frac{hk}{d_2} + \cdots + \frac{hk}{d_r},$$

where d_i is the order of $(a_i^{-1}Ha_i) \cap K$.

EXERCISES

1. Prove that two conjugate elements of a group have the same order.

2. Let a and b be the following elements of the symmetric group S_5:

$$a = \begin{pmatrix} 1 & 2 & 3 & 4 & 5 \\ 3 & 1 & 5 & 4 & 2 \end{pmatrix}, \qquad b = \begin{pmatrix} 1 & 2 & 3 & 4 & 5 \\ 4 & 3 & 1 & 5 & 2 \end{pmatrix}.$$

Determine the element $b^{-1}ab$ of S_5.

3. Let a and b be any elements of the symmetric group S_n. Thus

$$a = \begin{pmatrix} 1 & 2 & 3 & \cdots & n \\ i_1 & i_2 & i_3 & \cdots & i_n \end{pmatrix}, \qquad b = \begin{pmatrix} 1 & 2 & 3 & \cdots & n \\ j_1 & j_2 & j_3 & \cdots & j_n \end{pmatrix}.$$

where $i_1, i_2, i_3, \cdots, i_n$ and $j_1, j_2, \cdots, j_n$ are arrangements of
$1, 2, 3, \cdots, n$. Show that

$$b^{-1}ab = \begin{pmatrix} j_1 & j_2 & \cdots & j_n \\ j_{i_1} & j_{i_2} & \cdots & j_{i_n} \end{pmatrix},$$

and observe that the answer obtained in the preceding exercise is
consistent with this general result.

4. If G is the octic group (7.12), find the normalizer N of the element
α and verify (Theorem 9.6) that the number of elements in the
equivalence set $[\alpha]$ is equal to the index of N in G.

5. If a and b are conjugate elements of a finite group G, prove that the
number of elements of G which transform a into itself is the same
as the number of elements of G which transform a into b.

6. Let G be the octic group given by 7.12. Find a complete set of
equivalence sets of elements of G, as in 9.4, and verify Equation
9.5 by direct calculation.

7. If H is the subgroup $\{\epsilon, \beta\}$ of the octic group G given by 7.12, find (i) all subgroups which are congugate to H and (ii) the normalizer of H in G. For this particular case, verify Theorem 9.10 by direct calculation.

8. If G is the octic group, verify Theorem 9.17 (ii) for each of the double cosets of H and K exhibited as an example before the statement of that theorem.

9. Fill in the details of the following outline of a proof that if p is a prime, a group G of order p^2 is necessarily abelian. [The center C of G has order p or p^2. If C has order p, the quotient group G/C has order p and is therefore cyclic. If the coset aC is a generator of this group, every element of G is of the form $a^m c$, where $m \in \mathbf{Z}$ and $c \in C$.]

10. If H is a subgroup of a group G, prove that the intersection of all subgroups conjugate to H is a normal subgroup of G.

9.4 PROOFS OF THE SYLOW THEOREMS

Exercise 11 at the end of the preceding chapter requires a proof of the fact that if G is an *abelian* group of order n and $k \mid n$, then there exists a subgroup of G of order k. It can be shown by examples that the corresponding result for a nonabelian group need not be true. In this section we shall prove some results which assert that if G is an arbitrary group of order n, for *certain* divisors k of n there do exist subgroups of order k. Precise statements will occur later.

The following lemma will be useful in later proofs. This result was obtained in Lemma 8.27(ii), but we shall now give an alternate proof which does not make use of the machinery developed in Chapter 8.

9.20 Lemma. *If G is an abelian group of order n and p is a prime divisor of n, then G contains an element of order p.*

PROOF: Since a group of order a prime p is necessarily cyclic, it certainly contains elements of order p. In particular, the result is true for $n = 2$ or $n = 3$ (or any prime p).

Our proof is by induction on the order n of G. Let us therefore assume that the result is true for groups of order less than n, and prove that it is true for G of order n. We therefore may consider n to be composite and let $p \mid n$. Since n is composite, it is easy to show that G has proper subgroups. (See Exercise 4 at end of Section 7.5). Let H be a proper subgroup of maximum order, say m. That is, if E denotes the subgroup consisting of the identity alone, we have $E \subset H \subset G$, and there is no proper subgroup of G of order greater than m. We now make two cases as follows:

CASE 1. $p \mid m$. Since H has order $m < n$, our induction hypothesis assures us that H has an element of order p. This element is then an element of G of order p.

CASE 2. $(m , p) = 1$. Since $H \subset G$, there exists an element a of G such that $a \not\subset H$. Suppose that a has order s, and let A be the cyclic subgroup (a) generated by a. Thus A has s elements. We now form the product HA and apply Lemma 9.13. Since G is assumed to be an abelian group, Lemma 9.13 (ii) assures us that HA is a subgroup of G. Since $a \in HA$, $a \not\subset H$, we see that $H \subset HA$. But H was a proper subgroup of maximum order; hence we conclude that $HA = G$. If d is the order of $H \cap A$, Lemma 9.13 (i) states that there are ms / d elements in HA, and hence $n = ms / d$ or $ms = dn$. Now since $p \mid n$ and $(p , m) = 1$, it follows that $p \mid s$. If we write $s = pt$, then a^t has order p, and again we have found an element of G of order p. This completes the proof of the lemma.

We next prove the following result.

9.21 Theorem. *Let G be a group of order $n = p^s n_1$, where p is a prime, $s \geq 1$ and $(n_1 , p) = 1$. If t is any integer such that $0 \leq t \leq s$, then G has a subgroup of order p^t.*

PROOF: Again, we use induction on the order n of G. If n is a prime, G is cyclic and the theorem merely states that G has the trivial subgroups. Let us therefore assume as an induction hypothesis that the desired result is true for all groups of order less than n. We make two cases as follows:

CASE 1. Suppose that G has a proper subgroup H whose index is not divisible by p. If H has order h and index k, then (by Theorem 7.32) $hk = p^s n_1$, and since $(p^s , k) = 1$, we have that $p^s \mid h$. Since $h < n$, our induction hypothesis states that H has a subgroup of order p^t for each t such that $0 \leq t \leq s$. These subgroups of H are subgroups of G, and this case is disposed of.

CASE 2. Suppose that the index of every proper subgroup of G is divisible by p. By Lemma 9.7 the order of the center C of G is divisible by p. Since C is an abelian group, we know by Lemma 9.20 that C contains an element a of order p. The subgroup $H = (a)$ of C is therefore a subgroup of G of order p. Moreover, since $H \subseteq C$, H is a normal subgroup of G and we may consider the quotient group

G/H. Now G/H has order $n / p = p^{s-1}n_1 < n$. Applying the induction hypothesis, we know that for each integer r such that $0 \leq r \leq s - 1$, G/H has a subgroup of order p^r. By 7.62, G has a subgroup of order p^{r+1}. This shows that G has a subgroup of order t for any t such that $1 \leq t \leq s$. It is trivial that any group has a subgroup of order $p^0 = 1$, namely, the trivial subgroup consisting of only the identity. This completes the proof of the theorem.

One of Sylow's Theorems is the following special case of this result.

9.22 Corollary (Sylow). *Let G be a group of order n, and p a prime divisor of n. If p^s is the highest power of p which divides n, then G contains a subgroup of order p^s.*

In view of this result, let us make the following definition.

9.23 Definition. Suppose that G is a group of order n and p is a prime which divides n. If the highest power of p which divides n is p^s, a subgroup of G of order p^s is said to be a *Sylow subgroup of G (corresponding to p)*.

The result just established may then be simply expressed by saying that a group of order n has at least one Sylow subgroup corresponding to each prime divisor of n.

Before proceeding to a further study of Sylow subgroups, let us observe that the case in which $t = 1$ in the preceding theorem yields the following generalization of Lemma 9.20, due to Cauchy.

9.24 Corollary. *If the prime p divides the order of an arbitrary finite group G, then G contains an element of order p.*

To see this result, one uses the fact that, by Theorem 9.21, G contains a subgroup H of order p. But H, having order the prime p, is cyclic and, in fact, is generated by any element other than the identity. Thus H, and therefore G, has elements of order p.

Now if H is a Sylow subgroup of a group G, the transform $a^{-1}Ha$ of H by any element a of G is a subgroup with the same order as H. Accordingly, if H is a Sylow subgroup corresponding to the prime p, any subgroup conjugate to H is also a Sylow subgroup corresponding to the same prime. The following theorem asserts that the converse of this statement is also true.

9.25 Theorem (Sylow). *Any two Sylow subgroups of G which correspond to the same prime p are conjugate subgroups.*

PROOF: Suppose that G has order $n = p^s n_1$, $s \geq 1$, p a prime and $(n_1, p) = 1$. Moreover, let H and K be Sylow subgroups of G corresponding to the prime p. Thus both H and K have order p^s. Let $a_1, a_2, \cdots, a_r$ be elements of G such that the double cosets of H and K

9.26 $\{Ha_1K, Ha_2K, \cdots, Ha_rK\}$

form a partition of G. Let d_i be the order of the subgroup $(a_i^{-1}Ha_i) \cap K$ of K. Since K has order p^s, d_i is of the form p^{k_i}, with $0 \leq k_i \leq s$. By Corollary 9.19, we then have

9.27 $n = p^{2s-k_1} + p^{2s-k_2} + \cdots + p^{2s-k_r}.$

Since p^s is the highest power of p which divides n, we cannot have $k_i < s$ for every i. Hence, for some i, we must have $k_i = s$ and thus the group $a_i^{-1}Ha_i \cap K$ has order p^s. But this group is a subgroup of K and K has order p^s. We conclude that $a_i^{-1}Ha_i \cap K = K$, and we see that $a_i^{-1}Ha_i = K$, and therefore that H and K are conjugate subgroups of G. This completes the proof of the theorem.

9.28   Corollary.   *A Sylow subgroup of G, corresponding to the prime p, is a normal subgroup of G if and only if it is the only Sylow subgroup of G corresponding to the prime p.*

This follows at once from the fact that a subgroup is normal if and only if it coincides with all of its conjugate subgroups.

Our final result gives some information about the number of Sylow subgroups. In the proof of this result, we shall find it convenient to denote the order of the group G by g, and reserve n for the order of a group N which will appear in the proof.

9.29   Theorem (Sylow).   *Let G be a group of order g, and p a prime factor of g. If m is the number of distinct Sylow subgroups of G which correspond to the prime p, then $m \mid g$ and $m \equiv 1 \pmod{p}$.*

Let H be one Sylow subgroup corresponding to p. By Theorem 9.25 the number m of distinct Sylow subgroups corresponding to p is equal to the number of distinct conjugates of the subgroup H. If N is the normalizer of H in G, then by Theorem 9.10, m is the index of N in G and therefore $m \mid g$. There remains to prove that $m \equiv 1 \pmod{p}$.

Suppose that p^s is the highest power of p which divides the order g of G, so that H has order p^s. Let n denote the order of the normalizer N of H in G. Then $g = nm$.

Following Definition 9.9 of normalizer, it was observed that H is a normal subgroup of its normalizer N. Since N is a subgroup of G and H is a Sylow subgroup of G, it follows that H must be a Sylow subgroup of N corresponding to the prime p. Thus we have $n = p^s n_1$, where $(n_1, p) = 1$.

We now apply Theorem 9.17 to the subgroups H and N of G of orders p^s and n, respectively. Thus there exist elements $a_1, a_2, \cdots, a_r$ of G such that

9.30 $$\{Ha_1N, Ha_2N, \cdots, Ha_rN\}$$

is a complete set of distinct double cosets of H and N, so that these cosets form a partition of G. Let us set $D_i = (a_i^{-1}Ha_i) \cap N$, and let the order of D_i be $d_i(i = 1, 2, \cdots, r)$. Then counting elements in 9.30 (or by applying Corollary 9.19 directly), we obtain

9.31 $$g = \frac{np^s}{d_1} + \frac{np^s}{d_2} + \cdots + \frac{np^s}{d_r}.$$

Now the identity e of G occurs in exactly one of the cosets 9.30 and, without loss of generality, let us assume that it occurs in the first one Ha_1N. Then $Ha_1N = HeN$ since e is in both of these double cosets. Let us henceforth assume, as we may, that $a_1 = e$. Then $D_1 = (e^{-1}He) \cap N = H \cap N = H$, since $H \subseteq N$. Hence $d_1 = p^s$. In 9.31, let us replace g by nm and divide throughout by n, thus obtaining

9.32 $$m = 1 + \frac{p^s}{d_2} + \cdots + \frac{p^s}{d_r}.$$

Now D_i is a subgroup of $a_i^{-1}Ha_i$ and hence d_i is a divisor of the order of $a_i^{-1}Ha_i$, which is p^s. Accordingly, $d_i = p^{t_i}$, where $0 \le t_i \le s$. Thus Equation 9.32 can be written in the form

9.33 $$m = 1 + p^{s-t_2} + \cdots + p^{s-t_r}.$$

We proceed to show that $t_i < s$ for $i = 2, 3, \cdots, r$, hence all terms on the right except the first are divisible by p. Suppose, for example, that $t_2 = s$, that is, that $d_2 = p^s$. Then $a_2^{-1}Ha_2 \cap N$ has the same order as $a_2^{-1}Ha_2$, and therefore $a_2^{-1}Ha_2 \subseteq N$. Thus H and $a_2^{-1}Ha_2$ are Sylow subgroups of N corresponding to the same prime p. From the definition of normalizer it follows that H is a normal subgroup of its normalizer N. By Corollary 9.28, we see that $H = a_2^{-1}Ha_2$, that is, that $a_2 \in N$. Hence $Ha_2N = HN = HeN = Ha_1N$, since $a_1 = e$. But the cosets in 9.30 are distinct, and we have the desired contradiction. We conclude, therefore, that we cannot have $d_2 = p^s$, and therefore $d_2 = p^{t_2}$ with $t_2 < s$, and therefore, $\dfrac{p^s}{d_2} = p^{s-t_2}$ with $s - t_2 \geq 1$. In like manner, all terms after the first on the right in Equation 9.32 are divisible by p. It follows that $m \equiv 1 \pmod{p}$, thus completing the proof of the theorem.

EXERCISES

1. Prove that a group of order 30 must have a normal subgroup of order 5 or a normal subgroup of order 3. [Hint: If not, use Theorem 9.29 to show that the sum of the number of elements of order 5 and the number of elements of order 3 is greater than 30.]

2. Prove that a group of order pq, where p and q are primes with $p > q$, has exactly one subgroup (necessarily normal) of order p.

3. If p and q are distinct primes with $p \not\equiv 1 \pmod{q}$ and $q \not\equiv 1 \pmod{p}$, prove that a group of order pq is necessarily abelian. [Hints: There exists a normal subgroup H of order p and a normal subgroup K of order q. Then $H \cap K = \{e\}$, e the identity of G, and $G = HK$. (See Exercise 4 at end of Section 7.7.)

4. Suppose that $p^m (m \geq 1)$ is the highest power of the prime p which divides the order of a group G. If K is a subgroup of G of order p^t, where $0 \leq t \leq m$, prove that K is contained in at least one Sylow subgroup of G. [Hints: If H is a Sylow subgroup corresponding to p, count the numbers of elements in the distinct double cosets 9.18. Show that for at least one i, $(a_i^{-1} H a_i) \cap K = K$.]

NOTES AND REFERENCES

For additional results involving Sylow subgroups, see Hall [20], Macdonald [23], or Rotman [25]. A table, listing all nonisomorphic groups of order $n \leq 15$ is given in Rotman, p. 96. On page 52 of Hall there is a table listing the *number* of nonisomorphic groups of order $n \leq 20$. The largest number, namely 14, occurs for $n = 16$. There is no general known formula for the number of nonisomorphic groups of order n.

POLYNOMIALS

In elementary algebra an important role is played by polynomials in a symbol "x" with coefficients that are real or complex numbers. In the next section we shall introduce polynomials with coefficients in a commutative ring S with unity, and show that under suitable definitions of addition and multiplication the set of all such polynomials is a ring. Actually, we could just as well start by letting S be an entirely arbitrary ring, but in most of the chapter it is essential that it be commutative and so we simplify matters by making this assumption from the beginning. The restriction that S have a unity is not very important but it does serve to simplify the notation somewhat.

The purpose of this chapter is to introduce polynomials with coefficients in a commutative ring S with unity, and to establish a number of properties of such polynomials. We shall frequently find it necessary or desirable to make additional restrictions on the ring S. In particular, we shall sometimes require that it be a field or a specified one of the fields that have already been studied in detail in previous chapters.

It will be found that a ring of polynomials with coefficients in a *field* has a considerable number of properties in common with the ring $\mathbf{Z}$ of integers. Accordingly, several of the sections of this chapter will closely parallel corresponding material of Chapter 4.

10.1 POLYNOMIAL RINGS

Let S be a commutative ring with unity. Heretofore we have used letters to denote sets or elements of sets, but we now use the letter x in a different way. It is not an element of S, but is just a symbol which we shall use in an entirely formal way. It is customary to call such a symbol an *indeterminate*. It is our purpose in this section to construct a ring which contains S and also has x as an element. This goal will motivate the definitions which we proceed to give.

Let x be an indeterminate and let us consider expressions of the form

10.1 $a_0x^0 + a_1x^1 + a_2x^2 + \cdots + a_nx^n$,

where n is some nonnegative integer and $a_i \in S$ $(i = 0, 1, \cdots, n)$. Such an expression is called "a *polynomial* in x with coefficients in S" or simply, "a polynomial in x over S." If i is an integer such that $0 \leq i \leq n$, we say that a_i is the *coefficient* of x^i in the polynomial 10.1; also we say that a_ix^i is a *term* of the polynomial 10.1 with coefficient a_i.

At this stage we are to think of 10.1 as a purely formal expression. That is, the $+$ signs are not to be considered as representing addition in a ring, and neither is x^i to be considered as a product $x \cdot x \cdots x$ with i factors. Later on, after we have proved the existence of a ring which contains S as well as x, we shall see that in this larger ring we can make these familiar interpretations and thus justify the notation we are using. At the present time, we could logically use some such symbol as $(a_0, a_1, a_2, \cdots, a_n)$ to designate the polynomial 10.1, but the definitions of addition and multiplication of polynomials to be given below will seem more natural with the familiar notation used in 10.1.

For the moment, let S be the ring $\mathbf{Z}$ of integers. Then the following are examples of polynomials in x over $\mathbf{Z}$:

(i) $2x^0 + (-3)x^1 + 4x^2$,   (ii) $3x^0$,   (iii) $0x^0 + 0x^1 + 4x^2$,
(iv) $0x^0 + 2x^1 + (-1)x^2 + 0x^3$.

In order to avoid writing so many terms with zero coefficients, we could agree in the third of these examples to write merely $4x^2$ with the understanding that x^0 and x^1 are assumed to have zero coefficients. Also, it would certainly agree with usual practice if we omitted the terms with zero coefficients in the fourth example and wrote $2x^1 + (-1)x^2$ to designate this polynomial. These simplifications will be possible under general agreements which we now make.

Let us designate the polynomial 10.1 over S by the symbol $f(x)$, and let $g(x)$ be the following polynomial over S:

10.2 $b_0x^0 + b_1x^1 + \cdots + b_mx^m$,

where $m \geq 0$ and $b_i \in S$ $(i = 0, 1, \cdots, m)$. By the *equality* of $f(x)$ and $g(x)$, written in the usual way as $f(x) = g(x)$, we shall mean that the expressions 10.1 and 10.2 are identical except for terms with zero coefficients. We therefore consider a polynomial as being unchanged by the insertion, or omission, of any number of terms with zero coefficients. In particular, with reference to the above examples, we may write

$$0x^0 + 0x^1 + 4x^2 = 4x^2,$$

and

$$0x^0 + 2x^1 + (-1)x^2 + 0x^3 = 2x^1 + (-1)x^2.$$

Also, if we wish, we could write

$$3x^0 = 3x^0 + 0x^1 + 0x^2 + 0x^3,$$

and so on.

With this understanding about zero coefficients, if $f(x)$ is a polynomial over S and i is an *arbitrary* nonnegative integer, we may speak of the coefficient of x^i in $f(x)$. For example, in the polynomial $1x^0 + 2x^1 + 3x^2$ over $\mathbf{Z}$, the coefficient of x^{10} is zero. This language often helps to simplify statements about polynomials. As an illustration, we may state again our definition of equality of two polynomials as follows. If $f(x)$ and $g(x)$ are polynomials over S, by $f(x) = g(x)$ we mean that for *every* nonnegative integer i, the coefficients of x^i in $f(x)$ and in $g(x)$ are equal elements of S.

Using the familiar sigma notation for sums, the polynomial 10.1 can be formally written as follows:

$$\sum_{i=0}^{n} a_i x^i.$$

Moreover, in view of our agreement about zero coefficients, we can write an arbitrary polynomial in x over S in the form

$$\sum_{i=0} a_i x^i,$$

with the tacit understanding that all coefficients are zero from some point on, so that this sum may be considered to be a finite sum with an unspecified number of terms.

Now let $S[x]$ denote the set of all polynomials in the indeterminate x over S. We proceed to define operations of addition and multiplication on the set $S[x]$. Of course, these definitions are suggested by the way that one adds and multiplies polynomials in elementary algebra. Let

10.3
$$f(x) = \sum_{i=0} a_i x^i$$

and

10.4
$$g(x) = \sum_{i=0} b_i x^i$$

be elements of $S[x]$. We define addition as follows:

10.5
$$f(x) + g(x) = \sum_{i=0} (a_i + b_i)x^i,$$

that is, for every nonnegative integer i, the coefficient of x^i in $f(x) + g(x)$ is the sum of the coefficients of x^i in $f(x)$ and in $g(x)$. Multiplication in $S[x]$ is defined as follows:

10.6
$$f(x)g(x) = \sum_{i=0} \left(\sum_{k=0}^{i} a_k b_{i-k} \right) x^i.$$

Another way of stating this definition of the product of $f(x)$ and $g(x)$ is to say that for each nonnegative integer i, the coefficient of x^i in the product is the sum (in the ring S) of all products of the form $a_r b_s$, where r and s are nonnegative integers such that $r + s = i$. The first few terms in the product given in 10.6 are as follows:

$$(a_0 b_0)x^0 + (a_0 b_1 + a_1 b_0)x^1 + (a_0 b_2 + a_1 b_1 + a_2 b_0)x^2 + \cdots.$$

We are now ready to state the following theorem.

10.7   Theorem.   *Let $S[x]$ be the set of all polynomials in the indeterminate x over the commutative ring S with unity. If operations of addition and multiplication are defined on $S[x]$ by 10.5 and 10.6, respectively, then*

  (i) $S[x]$ *is a commutative ring with unity,*
  (ii) $S[x]$ *contains a subring isomorphic to S,*
  (iii) $S[x]$ *is an integral domain if and only if S is an integral domain.*

The commutative and associative laws for addition in $S[x]$ follow from 10.5 since these laws hold in the ring S. Moreover, the polynomial

$0x^0$ (which is equal to the polynomial with *all* coefficients zero) is the zero of $S[x]$ since, by 10.5, for each polynomial $f(x)$ we have

$$f(x) + 0x^0 = f(x).$$

Moreover, our definition of addition also shows that

$$\sum_{i=0} a_i x^i + \sum_{i=0} (-a_i)x^i = \sum_{i=0} [a_i + (-a_i)]x^i = 0x^0,$$

and each element of $S[x]$ has an additive inverse in $S[x]$.

To establish that multiplication is commutative, we observe that if $f(x)$ and $g(x)$ are given by 10.3 and 10.4, respectively, then the coefficient of x^i in $g(x)f(x)$ is

$$b_0 a_i + b_1 a_{i-1} + \cdots + b_i a_0,$$

and since S is assumed to be commutative, this is equal to the coefficient

$$a_0 b_i + a_1 b_{i-1} + \cdots + a_i b_0$$

of x^i in $f(x)g(x)$. Inasmuch as this statement is true for every nonnegative integer i, it follows that $f(x)g(x) = g(x)f(x)$, and hence that multiplication in $S[x]$ is commutative.

If $f(x)$ and $g(x)$ are given by 10.3 and 10.4, respectively, and

10.8 $$h(x) = c_0 x^0 + c_1 x^1 + \cdots + c_p x^p$$

is also an element of $S[x]$, the coefficient of x^i in the product $(f(x)g(x))h(x)$ is found to be the sum of all products of the form $(a_r b_s)c_t$, where r, s, and t are nonnegative integers such that $r + s + t = i$. Similarly, the coefficient of x^i in the product $f(x)(g(x)h(x))$ is the sum of all products of the form $a_r(b_s c_t)$, with the same restriction on r, s, and t. However, since $(a_r b_s)c_t = a_r(b_s c_t)$ by the associative law of multiplication in S, it follows that

$$(f(x)g(x))h(x) = f(x)(g(x)h(x)),$$

that is, that multiplication is associative in $S[x]$.

We leave as exercises the proof of the distributive laws, and that if 1 is the unity of S, then $1x^0$ is the unity of $S[x]$. It follows then that $S[x]$ is a commutative ring with unity.

To establish part (ii) of the theorem, let S' denote the set of elements of $S[x]$ of the form ax^0, $a \in S$. It is easy to verify that S' is a subring of $S[x]$. Now the mapping $\theta \colon S' \to S$ defined by $(ax^0)\theta = a$, $a \in S$, is a one-one mapping of S' onto S. Moreover,

$$(ax^0 + bx^0)\theta = [(a + b)x^0]\theta = a + b = (ax^0)\theta + (bx^0)\theta,$$

and

$$[(ax^0)(bx^0)]\theta = [(ab)x^0]\theta = ab = [(ax^0)\theta][(bx^0)\theta],$$

and it follows that θ is an isomorphism of S' onto S. Part (ii) of the theorem is therefore established.

Before proceeding to the proof of part (iii) of the theorem, let us introduce some simplifications of our notation as follows. We shall henceforth identify S' with S, and therefore write simply a in place of ax^0; that is, we shall omit x^0 in writing polynomials. In particular, the zero polynomial will then be designated by the familiar symbol 0. We shall also write x in place of x^1, x^i in place of $1x^i$, and $-ax^i$ in place of $(-a)x^i$. We may now observe that x is itself an element of the ring $S[x]$. If $a \in S$, then also $a \in S[x]$, and ax^i can be interpreted as the product (in the ring $S[x]$) of a times x to the power i. Also, since each individual term of a polynomial 10.1 is itself equal to a polynomial, the $+$ signs occurring in 10.1 can be correctly interpreted as addition in the ring $S[x]$. In other words, we have finally justified the use of the notation appearing in 10.1. Of course, addition is commutative in $S[x]$ and we can write the polynomial 10.1 with the terms in any order. For example, we could just as well write the polynomial 10.1 in the form

$$a_n x^n + a_{n-1}x^{n-1} + \cdots + a_1x + a_0.$$

In this case, it is customary to say that it is written in *decreasing* powers of x. As given in 10.1, it is written in *increasing* powers of x.

The following familiar concepts are of such great importance that we give a formal definition.

10.9   Definition.   Let $f(x)$ be a nonzero element of the ring $S[x]$. If n is the largest nonnegative integer such that x^n has a nonzero coefficient in $f(x)$, we say that $f(x)$ has *degree* n. If $f(x)$ has degree n, the nonzero coefficient of x^n is sometimes called the *leading coefficient* of $f(x)$. The zero polynomial has no degree and therefore also no leading coefficient. The coefficient of x^0 in a polynomial—that is, as now written, the term that does not involve x—is sometimes referred to as the *constant term* of the polynomial.

It will be observed that the nonzero elements of S, considered as elements of $S[x]$, are just the polynomials of degree zero. The degree of a polynomial $f(x)$ may be conveniently designated by $\deg f(x)$.

If S is the ring $\mathbf{Z}$ of integers, the polynomials $2 + 3x - x^2$, $4x$, 3, and $x^4 - 2x$ have respective degrees 2, 1, 0, and 4; and respective leading coefficients -1, 4, 3, and 1. The constant terms are, respectively, 2, 0, 3, and 0.

The third part of Theorem 10.7 will follow immediately from the following lemma.

10.10   **Lemma.**   *Let S be an integral domain and let $f(x)$ and $g(x)$ be nonzero elements of S[x]. Then*

10.11 $deg\ (f(x)g(x)) = deg\ f(x) + deg\ g(x).$

Since $f(x)$ and $g(x)$ are not zero, they have degrees, and let us suppose that $\deg f(x) = n$ and $\deg g(x) = m$. Then $f(x)$ can be written in the form 10.3 with $a_n \neq 0$, and $g(x)$ in the form 10.4 with $b_m \neq 0$. It now follows by the definition of multiplication (10.6) that $f(x)g(x)$ cannot have degree greater than $n + m$. Moreover, since S is an integral domain and we know that $a_n \neq 0$ and $b_m \neq 0$, it follows that the coefficient $a_n b_m$ of x^{n+m} is not zero, and 10.11 follows at once.

Lemma 10.10 assures us that if $f(x)$ and $g(x)$ are nonzero elements of $S[x]$, with S an integral domain, then the element $f(x)g(x)$ of $S[x]$ has a degree and therefore is not zero. Hence, $S[x]$ is also an integral domain. Since $S \subset S[x]$, it is trivial that if $S[x]$ is an integral domain, then S must be an integral domain. We have thus completed the proof of Theorem 10.7.

The familiar property 10.11 is not necessarily true if S is not an integral domain since, in the above proof, $a_n b_m$ might be zero without either factor being zero. For example, let $S = \mathbf{Z}_6$. If $f(x) = [1] + [2]x$, and $g(x) = [2] + [4]x + [3]x^2$, then $\deg f(x) = 1$ and $\deg g(x) = 2$. However, $f(x)g(x) = [2] + [2]x + [5]x^2$, and $\deg f(x)g(x) = 2$. In this case,

$$deg\ (f(x)g(x)) < deg\ f(x) + deg\ g(x).$$

In this section we have introduced polynomials in *one* indeterminate x. However, this procedure can easily be generalized as follows. If S is a commutative ring with unity, then the polynomial ring $S[x]$ is a commutative ring with unity. If now y is another indeterminate, we may as above construct a ring $(S[x])[y]$ consisting of polynomials in y with coefficients in the ring $S[x]$. It is easy to verify that the elements of this new ring can also be expressed as polynomials in x with coefficients in the ring $S[y]$; in other words, that the rings $(S[x])[y]$ and $(S[y])[x]$ are identical. Accordingly, we may denote this ring by $S[x, y]$ and call its elements polynomials in the indeterminates x and y. A double application of Theorem 10.7(iii) then assures us that $S[x, y]$ is an integral domain if and only if S is an integral domain. These statements may be extended in an obvious way to polynomials in any finite number of indeterminates. However, for the most part we shall study polynomials in just one indeterminate.

10.2 THE SUBSTITUTION PROCESS

In defining the polynomial ring $S[x]$, where S is a commutative ring with unity, we have emphasized that x is not to be considered as an element of S. However, if $f(x) = a_0 + a_1 x + \cdots + a_n x^n$ is an element of $S[x]$ and $s \in S$, let us define

10.12 $$f(s) = a_0 + a_1 s + \cdots + a_n s^n.$$

It follows that $f(s)$ is a uniquely determined element of S associated with the polynomial $f(x)$ and the element s of S. Now the importance of this "substitution process" stems from the fact that our definitions of addition and multiplication in $S[x]$ have the same form as though x were an element of S. Let us state this fact more precisely in terms of the mapping $\theta: S[x] \to S$ defined by

10.13 $$f(x)\theta = f(s), \qquad\qquad f(x) \in S[x].$$

We may emphasize that in this mapping we are thinking of s as being a fixed element of S. Different elements s of S would, of course, lead to different mappings of $S[x]$ into S. When we said above that addition and multiplication of polynomials were defined "as though x were an element of S," what we really meant was that the operations of addition and multiplication are preserved under the mapping θ, that is, that θ is a homomorphism. Actually, the mapping θ is a homomorphism of $S[x]$ *onto* S (no matter what element s of S is used) since if $a_0 \in S$ and $f(x) = a_0$, clearly $f(x)\theta = a_0$.

We are frequently interested in considering elements r of S such that $f(r) = 0$, and so we make the following definition.

10.14 Definition. If $f(x) \in S[x]$ and $r \in S$ such that $f(r) = 0$, we say that r is a *root* of the polynomial $f(x)$.*

---

* In elementary algebra, r is usually said to be a root of the *equation* $f(x) = 0$, in which case x is thought of as an unknown number. However, this is not consistent with the definitions of the preceding section, and we shall continue to write $f(x) = 0$ to mean that $f(x)$ is the zero polynomial.

In later sections we shall obtain various results about roots of polynomials. However, in order to obtain results of a familiar nature, we shall find it necessary to make some additional restrictions on the ring S. In particular, we shall frequently assume that S is a *field*. As an example to show what may happen if we do not restrict the ring of coefficients, let T be the ring of all subsets of a given set (Example 10 of Section 2.3), and $T[x]$ the ring of polynomials in the indeterminate x with coefficients in T. Since $a^2 = a$ for every element a of T, it is clear that the polynomial $x^2 - x$ of $T[x]$ has as a root *every* element of T. We thus have an example of a polynomial of degree 2 that has more than two roots (if the given set has more than one element). In the next section we shall see that this cannot happen in case the ring of coefficients is restricted to be a field.

EXERCISES

1. Prove the distributive laws in $S[x]$.

2. If S is a commutative ring with unity, verify that the set of all polynomials of $S[x]$ with zero constant terms is a subring of $S[x]$.

3. Verify that the set of all polynomials of $S[x]$ with the property that all odd powers of x have zero coefficients is a subring of $S[x]$. Is the same true if the word "odd" is replaced by the word "even"?

4. If $\mathbf{Z}$ is the ring of integers and x an indeterminate, let $(\mathbf{Z}[x])^+$ be the subset of $\mathbf{Z}[x]$ consisting of those nonzero polynomials which have as leading coefficient a *positive* integer. Show that the set $(\mathbf{Z}[x])^+$ has all the properties required in 3.4, and hence that $\mathbf{Z}[x]$ is an ordered integral domain.

5. Generalize the preceding exercise by showing that if D is an ordered integral domain, then the polynomial ring $D[x]$ is also an ordered integral domain.

6. Let $h(x)$ be the element $5x^2 - 3x + 4$ of $\mathbf{Z}_6[x]$. (Here we are writing 5, -3, and 4 in place of the more cumbersome [5], $[-3]$, and [4].) By simply trying all the elements of $\mathbf{Z}_6$, find all roots of $h(x)$ in $\mathbf{Z}_6$.

7. If $g(x)$ is the element $x^7 - x$ of $\mathbf{Z}_7[x]$, verify that all elements of $\mathbf{Z}_7$ are roots of $g(x)$.

8. If m is a positive integer, how many polynomials are there of degree m over the ring $\mathbf{Z}_n$ of integers modulo n?

9. Let S and T be commutative rings, each with a unity, and suppose that $\theta: S \to T$ is a given homomorphism of S onto T. If a mapping $\phi: S[x] \to T[x]$ is defined by

$$(a_0 + a_1 x + \cdots + a_n x^n)\phi = a_0\theta + (a_1\theta)x + \cdots + (a_n\theta)x^n,$$

    prove that ϕ is a homomorphism of $S[x]$ onto $T[x]$.

10. If $f(x) = g(x)h(x)$, where these are elements of $\mathbf{Z}[x]$, and every coefficient of $f(x)$ is divisible by the prime p, prove that every coefficient of $g(x)$ is divisible by p or every coefficient of $h(x)$ is divisible by p. [Hint: Use the preceding exercise with $S = \mathbf{Z}$, $T = \mathbf{Z}_p$, and $\theta: \mathbf{Z} \to \mathbf{Z}_p$ as defined near the end of Section 4.7. Then consider what $[f(x)]\phi = 0$ implies about the polynomial $f(x)$.]

11. If

$$f(x) = \sum_{i=0} a_i x^i$$

    is a polynomial over a commutative ring S, let us define the *derivative* $f'(x)$ of $f(x)$ as follows:

$$f'(x) = \sum_{i=1} ia_i x^{i-1}.$$

    Prove that

$$[f(x) + g(x)]' = f'(x) + g'(x),$$

    and that

$$[f(x)g(x)]' = f(x)g'(x) + f'(x)g(x).$$

10.3   DIVISORS AND THE DIVISION ALGORITHM

In this and the next two sections we shall study polynomials with coefficients in an arbitrary *field* F. We then know, by Theorem 10.7, that $F[x]$ is necessarily an integral domain. The following definition is essentially a restatement of Definition 4.1 as applied to the integral domain $F[x]$ instead of the integral domain $\mathbf{Z}$.

10.15   Definition.   Let $F[x]$ be the ring of polynomials in the indeterminate x over an arbitrary field F. If $f(x)$, $g(x) \in F[x]$, $g(x)$ is said to be a *divisor* (or *factor*) of $f(x)$ if there exists $h(x) \in F[x]$ such that $f(x) = g(x)h(x)$. If $g(x)$ is a divisor of $f(x)$, we say also that $f(x)$ is *divisible* by $g(x)$ or that $f(x)$ is a *multiple* of $g(x)$.

It follows immediately from this definition that if c is a nonzero element of F (that is, a polynomial of $F[x]$ of degree zero), then c is a divisor of every element $f(x)$ of $F[x]$. For, since c has a multiplicative inverse c^{-1} in F, we can write $f(x) = c(c^{-1}f(x))$, and this shows that c is a divisor of $f(x)$.

It is also important to observe that if $f(x) = g(x)h(x)$, then also $f(x) = (cg(x))(c^{-1}h(x))$, where c is any nonzero element of F. That is, if $g(x)$ is a divisor of $f(x)$, then $cg(x)$ is also a divisor of $f(x)$ for every nonzero element c of F.

The following result plays just as important a role in the study of divisibility in $F[x]$ as the corresponding result (4.4) does in establishing divisibility properties of the integers.

10.16 Division Algorithm. *If* $f(x)$, $g(x) \in F[x]$ *with* $g(x) \neq 0$, *there exist unique elements* $q(x)$ *and* $r(x)$ *of* $F[x]$ *such that*

10.17 $$f(x) = q(x)g(x) + r(x), \qquad r(x) = 0 \text{ or } deg\ r(x) < deg\ g(x).$$

We may recall that the zero polynomial has no degree and this fact explains the form of the condition which $r(x)$ is required to satisfy.

If $f(x)$ and $g(x)$ are given polynomials, the polynomials $q(x)$ and $r(x)$ can easily be computed by the usual process of long division. The existence of such polynomials therefore seems almost obvious. However, we shall give a detailed proof of their existence, and for the moment leave aside the question of their uniqueness. Let us first dispose of two easy cases as follows.

(A) If $f(x) = 0$ or deg $f(x) <$ deg $g(x)$, then 10.17 is trivially satisfied with $q(x) = 0$ and $r(x) = f(x)$.

(B) If deg $g(x) = 0$, so that $g(x) = c$ with c a nonzero element of F, then $f(x) = [c^{-1}f(x)]c$ and 10.17 holds with $q(x) = c^{-1}f(x)$ and $r(x) = 0$.

We are now ready to complete the proof by induction on the degree of $f(x)$. In this case, we shall use the form of the Induction Principle given in Exercise 9 of Section 3.3. If n is a positive integer, let S_n be the statement, "For every polynomial $f(x)$ of degree n and every nonzero polynomial $g(x)$, there exist polynomials $q(x)$ and $r(x)$ satisfying Equation 10.17." Let us now consider the statement S_1. By (A) and (B), we need only consider the case in which deg $g(x) = 1$; that is, $g(x) = cx + d$, $c \neq 0$. Since $f(x) = ax + b$, $a \neq 0$, we can easily see that

10.18 $$f(x) = ac^{-1}(cx + d) + b - ac^{-1}d,$$

and 10.17 is satisfied with $q(x) = ac^{-1}$ and $r(x) = b - ac^{-1}d$. Hence, S_1 is true. Now suppose that k is a positive integer with the property that S_i is true for every positive integer $i \leq k$, and let us prove that S_{k+1} is true. Let $f(x) = ax^{k+1} + \cdots$, where $a \neq 0$, be a polynomial of degree $k + 1$ and let $g(x)$ be an entirely arbitrary polynomial. Cases (A) and (B) show that we may assume that $0 < \deg g(x) \leq k + 1$ since otherwise the existence of $q(x)$ and $r(x)$ satisfying 10.17 follows immediately. Suppose that $\deg g(x) = m$, hence that $g(x) = bx^m + \cdots$, with $b \neq 0$ and $0 < m \leq k + 1$. Now it is easily verified that

10.19 $$f(x) = b^{-1}ax^{k+1-m}g(x) + [f(x) - b^{-1}ax^{k+1-m}g(x)].$$

Perhaps we should point out that this equation is merely the result of taking one step in the usual long-division process of dividing $f(x)$ by $g(x)$. If we set $t(x) = f(x) - b^{-1}ax^{k+1-m}g(x)$, it is easy to see that the coefficient of x^{k+1} in $t(x)$ is zero; hence that $t(x) = 0$ or $\deg t(x) < k + 1$. By (A), or by the assumption that S_i is true for every positive integer $i \leq k$, we know that there exist polynomials $s(x)$ and $r(x)$, with $r(x) = 0$ or $\deg r(x) < \deg g(x)$, such that $t(x) = s(x)g(x) + r(x)$. Substituting in 10.19, we see that

$$f(x) = [b^{-1}ax^{k+1-m} + s(x)]g(x) + r(x),$$

and 10.17 is satisfied. Hence S_{k+1} is true, and it follows that S_n is true for every positive integer n. This completes the proof of the *existence* part of the Division Algorithm. The proof of the fact that $q(x)$ and $r(x)$ are *unique* will be left as an exercise. It is customary to call $q(x)$ and $r(x)$ satisfying 10.17 the *quotient* and the *remainder*, respectively, in the division of $f(x)$ by $g(x)$. Clearly, $f(x)$ is divisible by $g(x)$ if and only if the remainder in the division of $f(x)$ by $g(x)$ is zero.

A special case of the Division Algorithm of importance is that in which the divisor $g(x)$ is of the special form $x - c$, $c \in F$. In this case the remainder must be zero or have degree zero, that is, it is an element of F. We can thus write

$$f(x) = q(x)(x - c) + r, \qquad\qquad r \in F.$$

From this equation it is clear that $f(c) = r$, and hence that

$$f(x) = q(x)(x - c) + f(c).$$

The next two theorems then follow immediately.

10.20   Remainder Theorem.   *If $f(x) \in F[x]$ and $c \in F$, the remainder in the division of $f(x)$ by $x - c$ is $f(c)$.*

10.21   Factor Theorem.   *If $f(x) \in F[x]$ and $c \in F$, $f(x)$ is divisible by $x - c$ if and only if $f(c) = 0$, that is, if and only if c is a root of the polynomial $f(x)$.*

We shall now make use of the Factor Theorem to prove the following result.

10.22   Theorem.   *Let F be a field and $f(x)$ an element of $F[x]$ of positive degree n and with leading coefficient a. If $c_1, c_2, \cdots, c_n$ are distinct elements of F, all of which are roots of $f(x)$, then*

10.23
$$f(x) = a(x - c_1)(x - c_2) \cdots (x - c_n).$$

The proof of this theorem is by induction on the degree n of $f(x)$. If n is a positive integer, let S_n be the statement, "The statement of the theorem is true for every polynomial of degree n." We then wish to prove that S_n is true for every positive integer n. The truth of the statement S_1 follows quite easily. If $f(x)$ is of degree 1 and has leading coefficient a, then $f(x) = ax + b$, $a \neq 0$. If c_1 is a root of $f(x)$, we have $f(c_1) = 0$ or $ac_1 + b = 0$. Then $b = -ac_1$ and hence $f(x) = a(x - c_1)$, which is the desired form 10.23 in case $n = 1$.

Now let k be a positive integer such that S_k is true, and consider S_{k+1}. Accordingly, we let $f(x)$ be a polynomial of degree $k + 1$ with leading coefficient a, and let $c_1, c_2, \cdots, c_{k+1}$ be distinct roots of $f(x)$. Since c_1 is a root of $f(x)$, we have $f(c_1) = 0$ and by the Factor Theorem it follows that

10.24
$$f(x) = q(x)(x - c_1).$$

Now it is clear that deg $q(x) = k$, and the leading coefficient of $q(x)$ is a since a is the coefficient of x^{k+1} in $f(x)$. If c_i $(i \neq 1)$ is any other of the given roots of $f(x)$, it follows, using 10.24 and the fact that $f(c_i) = 0$, that

$$q(c_i)(c_i - c_1) = 0.$$

Since the c's are distinct, $c_i - c_1 \neq 0$ and therefore $q(c_i) = 0$. We have therefore shown that the polynomial $q(x)$ in 10.24 is of degree k, has leading coefficient a, and has $c_2, c_3, \cdots, c_{k+1}$ as distinct roots. Since S_k is assumed to be true, it follows that

$$q(x) = a(x - c_2)(x - c_3) \cdots (x - c_{k+1}).$$

Substituting this expression for $q(x)$ in 10.24, we get

$$f(x) = a(x - c_1)(x - c_2) \cdots (x - c_{k+1}).$$

Hence, S_{k+1} is true, and the Induction Principle assures us that S_n is true for every positive integer n. This completes the proof of the theorem.

We next establish the following corollary.

10.25 Corollary. *A polynomial $f(x)$ of degree n over a field F cannot have more than n distinct roots in F.*

Since polynomials of degree zero have no roots, in verifying this corollary we may assume that $n \geq 1$. If $c_1, c_2, \cdots, c_n$ are distinct roots of $f(x)$, then $f(x)$ can be written in the form 10.23. Now let c be an arbitrary root of $f(x)$. Since $f(c) = 0$, it follows at once from 10.23 that

$$a(c - c_1)(c - c_2) \cdots (c - c_n) = 0.$$

Since $a \neq 0$, some one of the other factors must be zero, that is, $c = c_i$ for some i. Hence, $c_1, c_2, \cdots, c_n$ are the *only* roots of $f(x)$, and $f(x)$ cannot have more than n distinct roots.

The next corollary is now a simple consequence of this one.

10.26 Corollary. *Let $g(x)$ and $h(x)$ be polynomials over a field F with the property that $g(s) = h(s)$ for every element s of F. If the number of elements in F exceeds the degrees of both $g(x)$ and $h(x)$, then necessarily $g(x) = h(x)$.*

Let us set $f(x) = g(x) - h(x)$, and we then have that $f(s) = 0$ for every element s of F. If $f(x) \neq 0$, its degree can certainly not exceed the degrees of both $g(x)$ and $h(x)$, and hence $f(x)$ would have more distinct roots than its degree. Since, by the preceding corollary, this is impossible, we must have $f(x) = 0$. Hence, $g(x) = h(x)$, as required.

The following example shows that this last result is not true without the restriction on the number of elements of the field F. Let F be the field $\mathbf{Z}_3$, a field of three elements. If $g(x) = x^3$ and $h(x) = x$, it is easy to show by direct substitution that $g(s) = h(s)$ for every element s of F, but $g(x)$ and $h(x)$ are not equal elements of the polynomial ring $F[x]$. See also Exercise 7 of the preceding set.

10.4   GREATEST COMMON DIVISOR

It has been pointed out earlier that if c is a nonzero element of the field F, then the element $f(x)$ of $F[x]$ is divisible by the element $g(x)$ of $F[x]$ if and only if $f(x)$ is divisible by $cg(x)$. By choosing c as the multiplicative inverse of the leading coefficient of $g(x)$, the polynomial $cg(x)$ will have the unity 1 of F as its leading coefficient. Hence, we will know *all* the divisors of $f(x)$ when we have determined all those divisors that have 1 as leading coefficient. The following definition makes it easy to refer to such polynomials.

10.27 Definition. A nonzero element of $F[x]$ is said to be a *monic* polynomial if its leading coefficient is the unity 1 of F.

The greatest common divisor of two elements of $F[x]$ may now be defined as follows.

10.28 Definition. The monic polynomial $d(x)$ of $F[x]$ is said to be the *greatest common divisor* (g.c.d.) of the nonzero polynomials $f(x)$ and $g(x)$ of $F[x]$ if the following conditions are satisfied:

(i) $d(x)$ is a divisor of both $f(x)$ and $g(x)$,

(ii) Every divisor of both $f(x)$ and $g(x)$ is a divisor of $d(x)$.

As in the case of integers, it is quite easy to verify that two polynomials cannot have more than one g.c.d. We proceed to outline a proof of the existence of the g.c.d. and to develop a method for actually computing the g.c.d. of two given polynomials. Inasmuch as the procedure follows quite closely the material of Section 4.3, we shall omit most of the details.

First, we make the following definition.

10.29 Definition. If $f(x), g(x) \in F[x]$, we say that a polynomial of the form

$$f(x)s(x) + g(x)t(x), \qquad s(x), t(x) \in F[x],$$

is a *linear combination* of $f(x)$ and $g(x)$.

The following theorem can now be established by a simple modification of the proof of Theorem 4.12.

10.30 Theorem. *If $f(x)$ and $g(x)$ are nonzero elements of $F[x]$, the monic polynomial of least degree which is expressible as a linear combination of $f(x)$ and $g(x)$ is the g.c.d. of $f(x)$ and $g(x)$. Hence, if $d(x)$ is the g.c.d. of $f(x)$ and $g(x)$, there exist elements $s_1(x)$ and $t_1(x)$ of $F[x]$ such that*

$$d(x) = f(x)s_1(x) + g(x)t_1(x),$$

and $d(x)$ is the monic polynomial of least degree which is expressible in this form.

In order to *compute* the g.c.d. of two nonzero polynomials $f(x)$ and $g(x)$ of $F[x]$, we use the Euclidean Algorithm as in the case of integers. By repeated use of the Division Algorithm we obtain the following sequence of equations, it being understood that $r_k(x)$ is the last nonzero remainder (and $r_k(x) = g(x)$ if $r(x) = 0$):

10.31

$$
\begin{aligned}
f(x) &= q(x)g(x) + r(x) & \deg r(x) &< \deg g(x), \\
g(x) &= q_1(x)r(x) + r_1(x) & \deg r_1(x) &< \deg r(x), \\
r(x) &= q_2(x)r_1(x) + r_2(x) & \deg r_2(x) &< \deg r_1(x), \\
& \quad \cdots & & \cdots \\
r_{k-2}(x) &= q_k(x)r_{k-1}(x) + r_k(x) & \deg r_k(x) &< \deg r_{k-1}(x), \\
r_{k-1}(x) &= q_{k+1}(x)r_k(x). & &
\end{aligned}
$$

Now from these equations it follows that $r_k(x)$ is a divisor of both $f(x)$ and $g(x)$; also that any divisor of both $f(x)$ and $g(x)$ is a divisor of $r_k(x)$. If c is the leading coefficient of $r_k(x)$, then $c^{-1}r_k(x)$ also has these same properties and, moreover, it is a *monic* polynomial. We have therefore outlined a proof of the following result.

10.32 Theorem. *Let $r_k(x)$ be the last nonzero remainder in the Euclidean Algorithm as applied to the nonzero polynomials $f(x)$ and $g(x)$ of $F[x]$. If c is the leading coefficient of $r_k(x)$, then $c^{-1}r_k(x)$ is the g.c.d. of $f(x)$ and $g(x)$.*

In a numerical case, the actual calculations may often be simplified by the following observation. If $d(x)$ is the g.c.d. of $f(x)$ and $g(x)$, then also $d(x)$ is the g.c.d. of $af(x)$ and $bg(x)$, where a and b are nonzero elements of F. Hence, instead of the first of Equations 10.31, we might use the similar equation obtained by dividing $af(x)$ by $bg(x)$. In like manner, instead of the second equation we might work with $dg(x)$ and $er(x)$, where d and e are nonzero elements of F; and so on for the other equations. This modification will not affect the validity of the arguments used to show that $c^{-1}r_k(x)$ is the g.c.d. of $f(x)$ and $g(x)$, and may greatly simplify the work involved. Let us give an illustration by finding the g.c.d. of the polynomials

$$f(x) = x^3 + \tfrac{1}{2}x^2 + \tfrac{1}{3}x + \tfrac{1}{6}$$

and

$$g(x) = x^2 - \tfrac{1}{2}x - \tfrac{1}{2}$$

over the field $\mathbf{Q}$ of rational numbers. In order to avoid fractions, we divide $6f(x)$ by $2g(x)$, obtaining

$$6f(x) = (3x + 3)[2g(x)] + 8x + 4,$$

so that $r(x) = 8x + 4$. If we now divide $2g(x)$ by $r(x)/4$, we see that

$$2g(x) = (x - 1)[r(x)/4].$$

Since $r_1(x) = 0$, the g.c.d. of $f(x)$ and $g(x)$ is obtained from the last non-zero remainder, namely, $8x + 4$ by multiplying it by the multiplicative inverse of its leading coefficient. Hence the g.c.d. of $f(x)$ and $g(x)$ is $x + 1/2$.

It is sometimes convenient to use the following terminology, which is suggested by the corresponding definition for the integers.

10.33 Definition. Two nonzero elements $f(x)$ and $g(x)$ of $F[x]$ are said to be *relatively prime* if and only if their g.c.d. is 1.

EXERCISES

1. Complete the proof of the Division Algorithm by showing that the quotient and the remainder are unique.

2. If $f(x) \in F[x]$, show that $f(x)$ has as a factor a polynomial of $F[x]$ of degree one if and only if $f(x)$ has a root in F.

3. If F is the field $\mathbf{Z}_7$, use the result of Exercise 7 of the preceding set to show, without calculation, that in $F[x]$ we have

$$x^7 - x = x(x - 1)(x - 2)(x - 3)(x - 4)(x - 5)(x - 6).$$

4. State and prove a corresponding result for the field $\mathbf{Z}_p$, where p is an arbitrary prime. [Hint: Consider the multiplicative group of $\mathbf{Z}_p$.]

5. Prove Theorem 10.30.

6. Find the g.c.d. of each of the following pairs of polynomials over the field $\mathbf{Q}$ of rational numbers, and express it as a linear combination of the two polynomials:

   (i) $2x^3 - 4x^2 + x - 2$ and $x^3 - x^2 - x - 2$,
   (ii) $x^4 + x^3 + x^2 + x + 1$ and $x^3 - 1$,
   (iii) $x^5 + x^4 + 2x^3 - x^2 - x - 2$ and $x^4 + 2x^3 + 5x^2 + 4x + 4$,
   (iv) $x^3 - 2x^2 + x + 4$ and $x^2 + x + 1$.

7. Find the g.c.d. of each of the following pairs of polynomials over the indicated field, and express it as a linear combination of the two polynomials:

    (i) $x^3 + 2x^2 + 3x + 2$ and $x^2 + 4$; field $\mathbf{Z}_5$,
    (ii) $x^3 + (2i + 1)x^2 + ix + i + 1$ and $x^2 + (i - 1)x - 2i - 2$; field $\mathbf{C}$ of complex numbers,
    (iii) $x^2 + (1 - \sqrt{2})x - \sqrt{2}$ and $x^2 - 2$; field $\mathbf{R}$ of real numbers,
    (iv) $x^4 + x + 1$ and $x^2 + x + 1$; field $\mathbf{Z}_2$.

8. Let $f(x)$ and $g(x)$ be nonzero elements of $F[x]$, where F is a field. If the field F' is an extension of the field F, then $F[x] \subseteq F'[x]$ and we may also consider $f(x)$ and $g(x)$ to be elements of $F'[x]$. Show that the quotient and the remainder in the division of $f(x)$ by $g(x)$ are the same whether these polynomials are considered as elements of $F[x]$ or of $F'[x]$. In particular, conclude that if there exists an element $h(x)$ of $F'[x]$ such that $f(x) = g(x)h(x)$, then $h(x) \in F[x]$.

9. Verify that the Division Algorithm (10.16) remains true if the field F is replaced by an arbitrary commutative ring S with unity, provided only that $g(x)$ is required to have as leading coefficient an element of S with a multiplicative inverse in S.

10. By using the result of the preceding exercise, verify that the Factor Theorem and the Remainder Theorem are true if the field F is replaced by a commutative ring S with unity.

11. Give an example to show that Theorem 10.22 is not necessarily true if the field F is replaced by an arbitrary commutative ring S with unity. Where does the proof break down? Verify that the proof of this theorem will remain valid if F is replaced by an integral domain.

10.5   UNIQUE FACTORIZATION IN $F[x]$

We begin this section with the following definition.

10.34   Definition. A polynomial $p(x)$ of positive degree over a field F is said to be a *prime* (or *irreducible*) polynomial over F if it cannot be expressed as the product of two polynomials of positive degree over F.

If c is a nonzero element of the field F and $f(x) \in F[x]$, then we always have $f(x) = c^{-1}(cf(x))$, so that every polynomial of the form $cf(x)$ is a divisor of $f(x)$. It is easy to verify that a polynomial $f(x)$ of positive degree over F is a prime polynomial over F if and only if the *only* elements of $F[x]$ of positive degree that are divisors of $f(x)$ are of the form $cf(x)$, $c \neq 0$.

Since the degree of the product of two polynomials over F is the sum of the degrees of the factors, it follows at once from Definition 10.34 that *every element of $F[x]$ of the first degree is necessarily prime over F.*

We may emphasize that the possible divisors of $p(x)$ that are being considered in Definition 10.34 are those which are elements of $F[x]$; that is, they must have coefficients in F. For example, consider the polynomial $x^2 - 2$ over the field $\mathbf{Q}$ of rational numbers. Now $x^2 - 2$ cannot be factored into the product of two polynomials of the first degree in $\mathbf{Q}[x]$, and hence $x^2 - 2$ is a prime polynomial over $\mathbf{Q}$. However, if we should consider the same polynomial as a polynomial over the field $\mathbf{R}$ of real numbers, we find that it is *not* prime over $\mathbf{R}$ since we have the factorization $x^2 - 2 = (x - \sqrt{2})(x + \sqrt{2})$ with these factors of the first degree having coefficients in $\mathbf{R}$. As this example shows, the concept of a polynomial being a prime polynomial is relative to a specified field which contains the coefficients of the given polynomial.

In later sections we shall discuss prime polynomials over each of the familiar fields of elementary algebra. As for the finite fields of the form $\mathbf{Z}_p$, where p is a prime integer, we may here state without proof the following fact. For each prime p and each positive integer n, there exists at least one polynomial of degree n over the field $\mathbf{Z}_p$, which is prime over $\mathbf{Z}_p$.

The prime polynomials play essentially the same role in the factorization of an element of $F[x]$ as do the prime integers in the factorization of an integer. We therefore state without proof the following lemma and theorem, which are analogous to 4.18 and 4.20, respectively.

10.35 Lemma. *If $f(x)$ and $g(x)$ are nonzero polynomials over the field F such that $f(x)g(x)$ is divisible by the prime polynomial $p(x)$ over F, then $f(x)$ is divisible by $p(x)$ or $g(x)$ is divisible by $p(x)$.*

10.36 Theorem. *If $f(x)$ is a polynomial of positive degree over the field F and a is its leading coefficient, then there exist distinct monic prime polynomials $p_1(x), \cdots, p_k(x)$ $(k \geq 1)$ over F such that*

10.37
$$f(x) = a[p_1(x)]^{n_1}[p_2(x)]^{n_2} \cdots [p_k(x)]^{n_k},$$

where the n's are positive integers. Moreover, such a factorization is unique except for the orders of the factors.

We may emphasize that the prime polynomials in 10.37 are restricted to be monic polynomials, and hence the leading coefficient of the right side is just a, which is given as the leading coefficient of $f(x)$. A proof of the above theorem can be given by a simple modification of the proof of the Fundamental Theorem of Arithmetic. Although Theorem 10.36 certainly has some theoretical significance, it is not so very useful from a computational point of view. For example, from the factorizations of two polynomials in the form 10.37 it is easy to write down their g.c.d. just as in the case of two integers. However, it is often very difficult to *find* the prime factors of a given polynomial and hence to write it in the form 10.37. Accordingly, it will usually be very much easier to apply the method of Section 10.4 to find the g.c.d. of two polynomials than to make use of Theorem 10.36.

As an important special case, one or more of the monic prime polynomials occurring in a factorization 10.37 of $f(x)$ may be of the first degree. In particular, the Factor Theorem (10.11) assures us that $x - c$, $c \in F$, is a factor of $f(x)$ if and only if $f(c) = 0$; that is, if and only if c is a root of the polynomial $f(x)$. The following definition introduces a terminology which is sometimes convenient.

10.38   Definition.   The element c of F is said to be a root of *multiplicity* $m \geq 1$ of the polynomial $f(x)$ over F if $f(x)$ is divisible by $(x - c)^m$ but not by $(x - c)^{m+1}$. A root of multiplicity two is called a *double root*.

It follows that c is a root of $f(x)$ of multiplicity m if and only if in the factorization 10.37 of $f(x)$ one of the prime factors occurring is $x - c$ and, furthermore, it occurs with the exponent m.

EXERCISES

1.   (a) Prove that a polynomial $f(x)$ of degree two or three over a field F is a prime polynomial over F if and only if the polynomial $f(x)$ has no root in F.

   (b) Show, by means of an example, that a corresponding statement does not hold for polynomials of degree four.

2.   Determine whether or not each of the following polynomials is prime over each of the given fields. If it is not prime, factor it into a product of prime factors over each given field. As usual, **Q** is the field of rational numbers, **R** the field of real numbers, and **C** the field of complex numbers.

   (a) $x^2 + x + 1$ over **Q, R,** and **C**;

   (b) $x^2 + 2x - 1$ over **Q, R,** and **C**;

(c) $x^2 + 3x - 4$ over **Q, R,** and **C;**

(d) $x^3 + 2$ over **Q, R,** and **C;**

(e) $x^2 + x + 1$ over $\mathbf{Z}_2$, $\mathbf{Z}_3$, and $\mathbf{Z}_5$;

(f) $x^3 + x + 1$ over $\mathbf{Z}_2$, $\mathbf{Z}_5$, and $\mathbf{Z}_{11}$;

(g) $x^4 - 1$ over $\mathbf{Z}_{17}$;

(h) $x^3 + x^2 + 1$ over $\mathbf{Z}_{11}$;

(i) $x^2 + 15$ over **R** and **C.**

3. Find all prime polynomials of degree not more than five over the field $\mathbf{Z}_2$.

4. In each case the polynomial over the given field has as a root the specified element of the field. Find the multiplicity of this root and complete the factorization of the polynomial into prime factors over the given field.

(a) $x^4 + x^3 - 3x^2 - 5x - 2$ over **Q,** root -1;

(b) $x^4 + 1$ over $\mathbf{Z}_2$, root 1;

(c) $x^4 + 2x^2 + 1$ over **C,** root i;

(d) $x^4 + 6x^3 + 3x^2 + 6x + 2$ over $\mathbf{Z}_7$, root 4.

5. Prove that there are $(p^2 - p)/2$ monic quadratic polynomials which are prime over the field $\mathbf{Z}_p$.

6. Suppose that $f(x)$ is a polynomial over the field F and let $f'(x)$ be the derivative of $f(x)$, as defined in Exercise 11 of Section 10.2. Prove each of the following:

(i) If an element c of F is a root of $f(x)$ of multiplicity greater than one, then c is also a root of the polynomial $f'(x)$.

(ii) If an element c of F is a root of $f(x)$ of multiplicity one, then c is not a root of $f'(x)$.

(iii) If $f(x)$ can be expressed as a product of elements of $F[x]$ of the first degree, then $f(x)$ and $f'(x)$ are relatively prime if and only if $f(x)$ has no root of multiplicity greater than one.

10.6 RATIONAL ROOTS OF A POLYNOMIAL OVER THE RATIONAL FIELD

If $f(x)$ is a polynomial of degree $n > 0$ over a field F, then clearly $f(x)$ and $cf(x)$ have the same roots for any nonzero element c of F. If, in particular, $f(x)$ has coefficients in the field **Q** of rational numbers and we choose c as the l.c.m. of the denominators of the coefficients of $f(x)$, $cf(x)$

will have coefficients that are integers. In studying the roots of a polynomial with rational coefficients there is therefore no loss of generality in restricting attention to polynomials that have integral coefficients. We shall now prove the following theorem.

10.39   Theorem.   *Let*

$$f(x) = a_n x^n + a_{n-1} x^{n-1} + \cdots + a_0, \qquad (a_n \neq 0),$$

be a polynomial of positive degree n with coefficients that are integers. If r/s is a rational number, in lowest terms, which is a root of the polynomial f(x), then r is a divisor of a_0 and s is a divisor of a_n.

We may recall that by saying that r/s is in lowest terms we mean that r and s are relatively prime integers and $s > 0$. However, the requirement that s be positive plays no role in the proof of this theorem.

Since r/s is assumed to be a root of $f(x)$, we have that

$$a_n \left(\frac{r}{s}\right)^n + a_{n-1} \left(\frac{r}{s}\right)^{n-1} + \cdots + a_0 = 0.$$

If we multiply throughout by the nonzero integer s^n, we obtain

10.40 $a_n r^n + a_{n-1} r^{n-1} s + \cdots + a_1 r s^{n-1} + a_0 s^n = 0.$

By transposing the last term to the right side, this equation can be written in the form

$$(a_n r^{n-1} + a_{n-1} r^{n-2} s + \cdots + a_1 s^{n-1}) r = -a_0 s^n.$$

Since all letters here represent integers, we see that the integer $a_0 s^n$ is divisible by the integer r. But we are given that r and s are relatively prime, and it therefore follows that a_0 is divisible by r.

By a similar argument, if in 10.40 we transpose $a_n r^n$ to the other side, we can see that a_n is divisible by s.

As an example of the use of this theorem, let us find all rational roots of the polynomial

$$g(x) = 4x^5 + x^3 + x^2 - 3x + 1.$$

If r/s is a rational number, in lowest terms, which is a root of this polynomial, then r must be a divisor of 1 and s a positive divisor of 4. It follows that $r = \pm 1$, $s = 1, 2$, or 4; and we see that the only possible rational roots are the following: $1, 1/2, 1/4, -1, -1/2, -1/4$. It is easy to verify by direct calculation that $g(1) \neq 0$, $g(1/2) = 0$, $g(1/4) \neq 0$, $g(-1) = 0$, $g(-1/2) \neq 0$, and $g(-1/4) \neq 0$. Hence, 1/2 and -1 are the *only* rational roots. If we divide $g(x)$ by $x - 1/2$ and then divide the quotient by $x + 1$, we find that

$$g(x) = (x - \tfrac{1}{2})(x + 1)(4x^3 - 2x^2 + 4x - 2).$$

Any root of this third degree factor is naturally a root of $g(x)$, so its only possible rational roots are therefore $1/2$ and -1. It is easy to verify that $1/2$ is a root and if we again divide by $x - 1/2$, we can express $g(x)$ in the form

$$g(x) = (x - \tfrac{1}{2})^2(x + 1)(4x^2 + 4)$$

or

10.41 $$g(x) = 4(x - \tfrac{1}{2})^2(x + 1)(x^2 + 1).$$

We see therefore that $1/2$ is a double root of $g(x)$. Since the quadratic polynomial $x^2 + 1$ has no rational root, it is a prime polynomial over $\mathbf{Q}$ and hence in 10.41 we have $g(x)$ expressed as a product of prime polynomials over $\mathbf{Q}$. For that matter, the polynomial $x^2 + 1$ is prime over the field $\mathbf{R}$ of real numbers and so 10.41 also gives the factorization of $g(x)$ into prime polynomials over $\mathbf{R}$.

EXERCISES

1. Complete the proof of Theorem 10.39 by showing that s is a divisor of a_n.

2. Prove the following corollary of Theorem 10.39. A rational root of a *monic* polynomial with coefficients that are integers is necessarily an integer which is a divisor of the constant term of the polynomial.

3. Find the factorization of the polynomial $g(x)$ of the example given above into prime factors over the field $\mathbf{C}$ of complex numbers.

4. Find all rational roots of each of the following polynomials over the rational field $\mathbf{Q}$:

   (a) $3x^3 + 5x^2 + 5x + 2$,
   (b) $2x^4 - 11x^3 + 17x^2 - 11x + 15$,
   (c) $x^5 - x^4 - x^3 - x^2 - x - 2$,

(d) $x^3 + x^2 - 2x - 3$,

(e) $6x^3 - 7x^2 - 35x + 6$,

(f) $x^5 + 5x^4 + 13x^3 + 19x^2 + 18x + 8$,

(g) $x^3 - (1/5)x^2 - 4x + 4/5$,

(h) $x^7 + x^6 + x^5 + x^4 + x^3 + x^2 + x + 1$.

5. Find all rational roots of each of the following polynomials over the rational field **Q**, and factor each polynomial into a product of prime polynomials over **Q**:

   (a) $9x^4 + 6x^3 + 19x^2 + 12x + 2$,

   (b) $x^5 - x^4 - 3x^3 + 6x^2 - 4x + 1$,

   (c) $4x^4 + 20x^3 + 33x^2 + 20x + 4$,

   (d) $2x^4 + 3x^3 + 4x + 6$.

6. Show that each of the following polynomials over **Q** has no rational root:

   (a) $x^{1000} - x^{500} + x^{100} + x + 1$,

   (b) $x^{12} - x^9 + x^6 - x^3 + 1$,

   (c) $x^m + 2x^{m-1} - 2$,   (m a positive integer ≥ 2).

10.7 PRIME POLYNOMIALS OVER THE RATIONAL FIELD (OPTIONAL)

It was pointed out in Section 10.5 that every polynomial of the first degree over a field F is necessarily a prime polynomial over F. Also, the first exercise at the end of that section asserts that a polynomial of degree two or three over F is a prime polynomial over F if and only if it has no root in F. If the field F is now taken to be the field **Q** of rational numbers, it is easy to apply Theorem 10.39 to find whether or not a polynomial of degree at most three is prime over **Q**. For a polynomial of higher degree it may be exceedingly difficult to determine whether or not it is prime. For example, a polynomial of degree four over **Q** may not have a rational root, and therefore may have no factor of the first degree over **Q**, but may be a product of two prime polynomials of degree two. In this section we shall give some rather special results, which will enable us to show that for *every* positive integer n, there exist polynomials of degree n that are prime over **Q**.

We shall begin by proving two lemmas, the first of which is the following. As usual, $\mathbf{Z}[x]$ is the ring of polynomials in the indeterminate x with coefficients in the ring $\mathbf{Z}$ of integers.

10.42 Lemma. *Let $f(x)$, $g(x)$, and $h(x)$ be elements of the ring $\mathbf{Z}[x]$ such that $f(x) = g(x)h(x)$. If p is a prime integer which is a divisor of every coefficient of $f(x)$, then p is a divisor of every coefficient of $g(x)$ or a divisor of every coefficient of $h(x)$.*

The proof of this lemma was stated as Exercise 10 at the end of Section 10.2, and one method of proof was suggested in a hint given there. We here indicate a more elementary proof which, however, does involve a little more calculation. Let us set

$$f(x) = a_0 + a_1 x + \cdots + a_n x^n,$$
$$g(x) = b_0 + b_1 x + \cdots + b_m x^m,$$

and

$$h(x) = c_0 + c_1 x + \cdots + c_k x^k.$$

We are given that each coefficient a_i $(i = 0, 1, \cdots, n)$ is divisible by the prime p. Suppose now that $g(x)$ has at least one coefficient which is not divisible by p, and also that $h(x)$ has at least one coefficient which is not divisible by p, and let us seek a contradiction. To be more precise, let b_s be the *first* coefficient of $g(x)$, when $g(x)$ is written in increasing powers of x, that is not divisible by p; and let c_t be the *first* coefficient of $h(x)$ that is not divisible by p. Since $f(x) = g(x)h(x)$, by considering the coefficients of x^{s+t} on both sides of this equation, we find that

$$a_{s+t} = \cdots + b_{s-1}c_{t+1} + b_s c_t + b_{s+1}c_{t-1} + \cdots.$$

Now, by our choice of s and t, p is seen to be a divisor of every term on the right except the term $b_s c_t$. Since also p is a divisor of a_{s+t}, it follows that p is a divisor of $b_s c_t$. In view of the fact that p is a prime, this implies that p must be a divisor of b_s or a divisor of c_t. We have therefore obtained the desired contradiction. It follows that either $g(x)$ or $h(x)$ must have all coefficients divisible by p, and the proof is complete.

The following lemma, whose proof will be based on the preceding lemma, shows that a polynomial with *integral* coefficients is prime over the field $\mathbf{Q}$ if and only if it cannot be factored into a product of two polynomials of positive degree with *integral* coefficients. It will then be possible to prove that certain polynomials are prime over $\mathbf{Q}$ by making use of special properties of the integers.

10.43 Lemma. *Let $f(x)$ be an element of $\mathbf{Z}[x]$ such that $f(x) = g(x)h(x)$, where $g(x)$, $h(x) \in \mathbf{Q}[x]$. Then there exist polynomials $g'(x)$, $h'(x)$ of $\mathbf{Z}[x]$ having the same degrees as $g(x)$ and $h(x)$, respectively, such that $f(x) = g'(x)h'(x)$.*

Let k be the l.c.m. of the denominators of the coefficients of $g(x)$, so that $kg(x)$ has integral coefficients. Similarly, let l be an integer such that $lh(x)$ has integral coefficients. Since $f(x) = g(x)h(x)$, it follows that

10.44 $klf(x) = g_1(x)h_1(x),$

where $g_1(x)$ and $h_1(x)$ have integral coefficients. We may then apply the preceding lemma as follows. If p is a prime divisor of kl, it must be a divisor of all coefficients of $g_1(x)$ or of $h_1(x)$; hence p can be divided from both sides of the equation 10.44, and we still have polynomials with integral coefficients. By a repetition of this process, we can divide out every prime factor of kl and finally get $f(x) = g'(x)h'(x)$, where $g'(x)$ and $h'(x)$ have integral coefficients. It is almost trivial that $g'(x)$ has the same degree as $g(x)$, and also that $h'(x)$ has the same degree as $h(x)$. The proof is therefore complete.

We are now ready to prove the following theorem of Eisenstein.

10.45   Theorem.   *Let $f(x) = a_0 + a_1x + \cdots + a_nx^n$ be a polynomial of positive degree n over the ring $\mathbf{Z}$ of integers, and p a prime integer such that $a_i \equiv 0 \pmod{p}$ for $i = 0, 1, \cdots, n - 1$; $a_n \not\equiv 0 \pmod{p}$, and $a_0 \not\equiv 0 \pmod{p^2}$. Then $f(x)$ is a prime polynomial over $\mathbf{Q}$.*

The preceding lemma shows that we need only prove that $f(x)$ cannot be factored into a product of two factors of positive degree over $\mathbf{Z}$. Let us assume that

10.46 $a_0 + a_1x + \cdots + a_nx^n$
$$= (b_0 + b_1x + \cdots + b_mx^m)(c_0 + c_1x + \cdots + c_kx^k),$$

where all these coefficients are integers, and clearly $m + k = n$. Since $a_0 = b_0c_0$, the fact that $a_0 \equiv 0 \pmod{p}$ but $a_0 \not\equiv 0 \pmod{p^2}$ shows that exactly one of the integers b_0 and c_0 is divisible by p. Suppose, for convenience of notation, that $c_0 \equiv 0 \pmod{p}$ and that $b_0 \not\equiv 0 \pmod{p}$. Now $a_n = b_mc_k$ and $a_n \not\equiv 0 \pmod{p}$; so $c_k \not\equiv 0 \pmod{p}$. Let s be chosen as the smallest positive integer such that $c_s \not\equiv 0 \pmod{p}$. From what we have just shown we know that there exists such an integer s and that $0 < s \leq k$. Now by a consideration of the coefficients of x^s on both sides of 10.46, we see that

$$a_s = b_0c_s + b_1c_{s-1} + \cdots,$$

and, in view of our choice of s, every term on the right with the single exception of b_0c_s is divisible by p. Moreover, $b_0 \not\equiv 0 \pmod{p}$ and $c_s \not\equiv 0 \pmod{p}$, so $a_s \not\equiv 0 \pmod{p}$. However, by our assumptions, the only coefficient of $f(x)$ that is not divisible by p is the leading coefficient a_n. Hence $s = n$, and therefore we must have $k = n$. This shows that in any factorization of $f(x)$ into a product of polynomials with integral coefficients, one of the factors must have degree n. It follows that $f(x)$ is necessarily a prime polynomial over $\mathbf{Q}$.

10.47 Corollary. *If n is an arbitrary positive integer, there exist polynomials of degree n over $\mathbf{Q}$ that are prime over $\mathbf{Q}$.*

This result is easily established by examples. As an illustration, the polynomial $x^n - 2$ over $\mathbf{Q}$ satisfies all the conditions of the preceding theorem with $p = 2$. Hence, $x^n - 2$ is a prime polynomial over $\mathbf{Q}$ for each positive integer n. In like manner, each of the following polynomials of degree n over $\mathbf{Q}$ is prime over $\mathbf{Q}$: $x^n + 2$, $x^n + 3$, $3x^n + 2x^{n-1} + 2x^{n-2} + \cdots + 2x + 2$, $x^n + 9x + 3$ $(n > 1)$. The reader will have no difficulty in constructing other examples.

Perhaps we should emphasize that we have not presented a general method for determining whether or not a given polynomial over $\mathbf{Q}$ is prime over $\mathbf{Q}$. This is a difficult problem, and we shall not discuss it further in this book.

10.8 POLYNOMIALS OVER THE REAL OR COMPLEX NUMBERS

In this section we shall discuss some properties of polynomials over the field $\mathbf{R}$ of real numbers or the field $\mathbf{C}$ of complex numbers. We begin with a few remarks, essentially established in elementary algebra, about quadratic polynomials; that is, polynomials of degree two.

Let

$$g(x) = ax^2 + bx + c, \qquad\qquad a \neq 0,$$

be a quadratic polynomial with coefficients in the field $\mathbf{C}$. Then it is well-known that the polynomial $g(x)$ has roots r_1 and r_2, where

10.48 $$r_1 = \frac{-b + \sqrt{b^2 - 4ac}}{2a}, \quad r_2 = \frac{-b - \sqrt{b^2 - 4ac}}{2a}.$$

We may point out that, by a special case of Theorem 6.20, every non-zero complex number has two square roots. Hence, r_1 and r_2, given by 10.48, are complex numbers and it is easy to verify by direct calculation that

10.49 $$g(x) = a(x - r_1)(x - r_2).$$

Since these first-degree factors have coefficients in **C**, it is apparent that no quadratic polynomial over **C** is a prime polynomial over **C**.

It is customary to call $b^2 - 4ac$ the *discriminant* of the quadratic polynomial $ax^2 + bx + c$. For convenience, let us designate this discriminant by D.

From 10.48 it follows that $r_1 = r_2$ if and only if $D = 0$. However, the factorization 10.49 holds in any case, so $D = 0$ is a necessary and sufficient condition that the polynomial $g(x)$ have a double root.

Now let us assume that the quadratic polynomial $g(x)$ has *real* coefficients. Then the roots r_1 and r_2 will also be real if and only if $D \geq 0$, for only in this case will D have real square roots. The factorization 10.49 of $g(x)$ into factors of the first degree is therefore a factorization over **R** if and only if $D \geq 0$. If $D < 0$, $g(x)$ has no real root and $g(x)$ is therefore prime over **R**.

Let us summarize some of these observations in the following theorem.

10.50 Theorem. *No quaratic polynomial over the field **C** of complex numbers is prime over **C**. A quadratic polynomial over the field **R** of real numbers is prime over **R** if and only if its discriminant is negative.*

We have referred above to Theorem 6.20, where it was proved by use of the trigonometric form of a complex number that every nonzero complex number has n nth roots. It may be worth pointing out that the *square* roots of a complex number may also be computed by an algebraic process. As an illustration, let us seek the roots of the polynomial $x^2 + x - (1 + 3i)$ over **C**. By 10.48, these roots can immediately be written down in the form

10.51
$$\frac{-1 \pm \sqrt{5 + 12i}}{2}.$$

Now in order to express these roots in the usual form of complex numbers, we need to compute the square roots of $5 + 12i$. To do so, suppose that s and t are unknown real numbers such that $s + ti$ is a square root of $5 + 12i$. Thus we have

$$(s + ti)^2 = 5 + 12i,$$

or

$$s^2 - t^2 + 2sti = 5 + 12i.$$

In turn, this implies both of the following equations involving the real numbers s and t:

$$s^2 - t^2 = 5, \quad 2st = 12.$$

If we solve these two simultaneous equations by elementary methods and remember that s and t are real (so that $s^2 \geq 0$ and $t^2 \geq 0$), we find the solutions to be $s = 3, t = 2$ and $s = -3, t = -2$. Hence, the square roots of $5 + 12i$ are $\pm(3 + 2i)$. Substituting in 10.51, we find that the roots of the polynomial $x^2 + x - (1 + 3i)$ are $1 + i$ and $-(2 + i)$.

We have shown above that no quadratic polynomial is prime over **C**. Another special case of some interest is the following. Let us consider a polynomial of the form $ax^n + b$, where a and b are nonzero complex numbers and n is an arbitrary positive integer greater than 1. Since, by Theorem 6.20, the complex number $-b/a$ has n distinct nth roots and these are obviously roots of the polynomial $ax^n + b$, Theorem 10.22 asserts that this polynomial can be factored over **C** into a product of factors of the first degree. In particular, such a polynomial can never be prime over **C**.

The general theorem which we shall next state is partially suggested by the special cases already discussed. The theorem was first proved by the famous German mathematician Carl Friedrich Gauss (1777–1855), and is of such importance that it has often been called "The Fundamental Theorem of Algebra." Unfortunately, there is no really elementary proof of this theorem and we shall therefore have to omit the proof.*

10.52 Theorem. *If $f(x)$ is an element of **C**[x] of positive degree, there exists an element of **C** which is a root of the polynomial $f(x)$.*

If r is a complex number which is a root of the polynomial $f(x)$ of degree n over **C**, then in **C**[x] we can use the Factor Theorem and write

$$f(x) = (x - r)f_1(x),$$

where $f_1(x)$ is of degree $n - 1$. It is then apparent from this observation and Theorem 10.36 that the preceding theorem can be expressed in either of the following alternate forms.

10.53 Theorem. *The only prime polynomials of **C**[x] are the polynomials of the first degree.*

10.54 Theorem. *If $f(x)$ is an element of **C**[x] of positive degree, then $f(x)$ is itself of the first degree or it can be factored in **C**[x] into a product of polynomials of the first degree.*

---

* For a proof of this theorem see, e. g., Birkhoff and MacLane [2] or MacLane and Birkhoff [12].

We next consider the question of which polynomials over the real field $\mathbf{R}$ are prime over $\mathbf{R}$. Of course, the polynomials of the first degree are always prime, and we have shown in Theorem 10.50 that the quadratic polynomials over $\mathbf{R}$ that are prime over $\mathbf{R}$ are those with negative discriminant. A little later we shall prove that these are the only prime polynomials over $\mathbf{R}$. First, however, we need a preliminary result, which is of some interest in itself.

Let

$$f(x) = a_n x^n + \cdots + a_1 x + a_0$$

be a polynomial of positive degree with real coefficients. Since $\mathbf{R} \subset \mathbf{C}$, then also $f(x) \in \mathbf{C}[x]$ and Theorem 10.52 states that there exists an element r of $\mathbf{C}$ such that $f(r) = 0$. We now want to make use of the concept of the conjugate of a complex number, introduced in Section 6.4. We recall that if $u = a + bi$ is a complex number, then the conjugate u^* of u is defined by: $u^* = a - bi$. It was shown that the mapping $u \to u^*$ is a one-one mapping of $\mathbf{C}$ onto $\mathbf{C}$, which preserves the operations of addition and multiplication. Now since $f(x)$ is assumed to have real coefficients and a real number is equal to its conjugate, it is not difficult to verify that

$$[f(r)]^* = a_n(r^*)^n + \cdots + a_1 r^* + a_0 = f(r^*).$$

But, since $f(r) = 0$, it follows that $[f(r)]^* = 0$ and therefore $f(r^*) = 0$. That is, r^* is also a root of the polynomial $f(x)$. This result we state as the following theorem.

10.55 Theorem. *If r is a complex number which is a root of the polynomial $f(x)$ with real coefficients, then the conjugate r^* of r is also a root of $f(x)$.*

If it happens that r is a real number, then $r^* = r$, and this theorem has no content. However, if r is not real, then r^* and r are distinct roots of $f(x)$. It follows that in $\mathbf{C}[x]$ we have

$$f(x) = (x - r)(x - r^*)f_1(x),$$

with the degree of $f_1(x)$ two less than the degree of $f(x)$. If $r = a + bi$, then $r^* = a - bi$, and a simple calculation shows that

$$(x - r)(x - r^*) = x^2 - 2ax + a^2 + b^2.$$

We can therefore write

10.56 $$f(x) = (x^2 - 2ax + a^2 + b^2)f_1(x),$$

and the quadratic factor on the right clearly has *real* coefficients. Since also $f(x)$ has real coefficients, it is easy to verify that $f_1(x)$ must have real coefficients (cf. Exercise 8, Section 10.4). It follows that 10.56 gives a factorization of $f(x)$ in $\mathbf{R}[x]$. If $\deg f(x) > 2$, $f(x)$ can therefore not be a prime polynomial over $\mathbf{R}$. This result, combined with Theorem 10.50, completes the proof of the following theorem.

10.57 Theorem. *The only polynomials of $\mathbf{R}[x]$ that are prime over $\mathbf{R}$ are the polynomials of the first degree and the quadratic polynomials with negative discriminant.*

Now a polynomial of *odd* degree clearly cannot be factored into a product of quadratic polynomials. Therefore, if a polynomial $f(x)$ of $\mathbf{R}[x]$ of odd degree is expressed as a product of prime polynomials over $\mathbf{R}$, at least one of these prime polynomials (in fact, an odd number of them) must be of the first degree. This implies that $f(x)$ has at least one real root, and the following is therefore an almost immediate consequence of the preceding theorem.

10.58 Corollary. *A polynomial with real coefficients and of odd degree necessarily has a real root.*

Except for quadratic polynomials, and polynomials of the special form $ax^n + b$, we have not given any indication as to how one might actually *find* the real or complex roots of a given polynomial. This is a difficult problem but some information can be found in texts on the "theory of equations." In particular, there do exist algebraic formulas for the roots of polynomials of degrees 3 or 4 with real or complex coefficients. Although these formulas are of great theoretical interest, they are not convenient to use in a numerical case. It is, however, not too difficult to develop methods of approximating the roots to any desired accuracy, and this is what is usually done in practical applications.

EXERCISES

1. Find the roots of each of the following polynomials and express each root in the standard form $a + bi$ of a complex number:

(a) $x^2 - (3i - 2)x - 5 - i$,　(b) $x^2 + ix + 1$,
(c) $x^2 - (2 + i)x - 1 + 7i$,　(d) $x^2 + x + 4$,
(e) $x^2 - x + 2 + \sqrt{2}i$,　(f) $x^2 + 2x + i$.

2. Factor each of the following polynomials of **R**[x] into a product of prime polynomials over **R**:

(a) $x^3 - 2x - 4$,   (b) $x^3 - x^2 - 3x + 6$,
(c) $x^4 + 1$,   (d) $x^4 + 2x^2 - 8$,
(e) $x^4 + x^3 + 2x^2 + x + 1$,   (f) $x^5 + 1$.

10.9 PARTIAL FRACTIONS (OPTIONAL)

In calculus, partial fractions are used to carry out the integration of rational functions. In this section we shall briefly outline a proof of the existence of the required partial fraction decompositions.

It was pointed out in Section 5.4 that, starting with an integral domain D, it is possible to construct a field of quotients of D whose elements are the formal quotients a/b, where a, $b \in D$ and $b \neq 0$. Now if F is a given field, we know that the polynomial ring $F[x]$ is an integral domain, and we are now interested in the field of quotients of this integral domain. An element of this field of quotients is therefore expressible as $f(x)/g(x)$, where $f(x)$, $g(x) \in F[x]$, $g(x) \neq 0$. Such an element is called a *rational form* over F, and the field whose elements are these rational forms is often called the field of rational forms (in the indeterminate x) over F. This field is usually denoted by $F(x)$. It should be observed that, by the same conventions we made in constructing the rational numbers from the integers, a polynomial is a special case of a rational form, and therefore $F[x] \subset F(x)$. However, we are not now primarily interested in properties of the field $F(x)$, but only in individual elements of this field.

If $g(x)$ is a polynomial over F of positive degree, we know by Theorem 10.36 that $g(x)$ can be expressed uniquely as a product of its leading coefficient times a product of powers of distinct monic polynomials that are prime over F. This fact is implicitly used in the proof of the following theorem.

10.59 Theorem. *A rational form $f(x)/g(x)$ over F is expressible as a polynomial over F plus a sum of rational forms over F of the special type $r(x)/[p(x)]^k$, where $p(x)$ is a prime polynomial over F, $[p(x)]^k$ is a divisor of $g(x)$, and deg $r(x) <$ deg $p(x)$.*

The expressing of $f(x)/g(x)$ as described in this theorem is said to be "expressing $f(x)/g(x)$ as a sum of partial fractions."

As an illustration of the theorem, it may be verified that over the field of real numbers

10.60 $$\frac{x^2 + x - 1}{x^3(x^2 + 1)} = \frac{2}{x} + \frac{1}{x^2} - \frac{1}{x^3} - \frac{2x + 1}{x^2 + 1}.$$

In this case, the polynomial mentioned in the theorem is the zero polynomial. Moreover, there are just two prime factors of the denominator, namely, x and $x^2 + 1$, and therefore only these two choices for $p(x)$.

We prove the theorem in two steps as follows. First, suppose that $g(x) = h(x)k(x)$, where $h(x)$ and $k(x)$ are relatively prime polynomials over F. Then we know that there exist polynomials $s(x)$, $t(x)$ over F such that

$$1 = h(x)s(x) + k(x)t(x),$$

from which it follows that

$$\frac{1}{g(x)} = \frac{s(x)}{k(x)} + \frac{t(x)}{h(x)}.$$

Then, since

$$\frac{f(x)}{g(x)} = \frac{f(x)s(x)}{k(x)} + \frac{f(x)t(x)}{h(x)},$$

we see that $f(x)/g(x)$ is expressible as a sum of rational forms with respective denominators $k(x)$ and $h(x)$. If, say, $h(x)$ is now expressible as a product of two relatively prime polynomials, the same procedure can be applied to the rational form $f(x)t(x)/h(x)$. By a repetition of this process we can finally write $f(x)/g(x)$ as a sum of rational forms having denominators which cannot be expressed as a product of two relatively prime polynomials. Each denominator is then a power of a single prime polynomial and therefore each of these rational forms is of the type $u(x)/[p(x)]^n$, where $p(x)$ is a prime polynomial over F, and $[p(x)]^n$ is a divisor of $g(x)$.

We next consider any one such form of the type $u(x)/[p(x)]^n$. If $\deg u(x) < \deg p(x)$, $u(x)/[p(x)]^n$ is already one of the rational forms described in the statement of the theorem. If $\deg u(x) \geq \deg p(x)$, we use the Division Algorithm and write

10.61
$$u(x) = q_0(x)p(x) + r_0(x),$$

where, as usual, $r_0(x) = 0$ or $\deg r_0(x) < \deg p(x)$. If $\deg q_0(x) \geq \deg p(x)$, we divide $q_0(x)$ by $p(x)$ and obtain

$$q_0(x) = q_1(x)p(x) + r_1(x),$$

and by substitution in 10.61 we obtain

$$u(x) = q_1(x)[p(x)]^2 + r_1(x)p(x) + r_0(x).$$

If deg $q_1(x) \geq$ deg $p(x)$, we divide $q_1(x)$ by $p(x)$, and continue this process. We omit the details, but essentially as in the proof of Theorem 4.7 it can be shown that for some positive integer m,

10.62 $$u(x) = r_m(x)[p(x)]^m + r_{m-1}(x)[p(x)]^{m-1} + \cdots$$
$$+ r_1(x)p(x) + r_0(x),$$

where $r_m(x) \neq 0$ and $r_i(x) = 0$ or deg $r_i(x) <$ deg $p(x)$ for $i = 0$, $1, \cdots, m$. It follows at once from 10.62 that the rational form $u(x)/[p(x)]^n$ is expressible as a polynomial (possibly zero) plus a sum of forms $r(x)/[p(x)]^k$, with $k \leq n$ and therefore $[p(x)]^k$ a divisor of $g(x)$. Since we have already shown that $f(x)/g(x)$ can be expressed as a sum of terms of the form $u(x)/[p(x)]^n$, the proof is therefore complete.

In a numerical case, the steps of the above proof can be actually carried out in order to express a rational form as a sum of partial fractions. Let us give an illustration by carrying out the calculations involved in establishing the example 10.60 given above. Since x^3 and $x^2 + 1$ are relatively prime, by the usual method involving the Euclidean Algorithm, we find that

$$1 = x^3 \cdot x + (x^2 + 1)(1 - x^2),$$

and therefore

$$\frac{1}{x^3(x^2 + 1)} = \frac{x}{x^2 + 1} + \frac{1 - x^2}{x^3}.$$

If we multiply by the given numerator, $x^2 + x - 1$, we obtain

10.63 $$\frac{x^2 + x - 1}{x^3(x^2 + 1)} = \frac{x^3 + x^2 - x}{x^2 + 1} + \frac{-x^4 - x^3 + 2x^2 + x - 1}{x^3}.$$

We now consider the first term on the right. By the Division Algorithm we see that

$$x^3 + x^2 - x = (x + 1)(x^2 + 1) - 2x - 1,$$

and therefore

$$\frac{x^3 + x^2 - x}{x^2 + 1} = x + 1 - \frac{2x + 1}{x^2 + 1}.$$

Using this equation, we can write Equation 10.63 in the form

$$\frac{x^2 + x - 1}{x^3(x^2 + 1)} = x + 1 - \frac{2x + 1}{x^2 + 1} - x - 1 + \frac{2}{x} + \frac{1}{x^2} - \frac{1}{x^3},$$

and we conclude that

$$\frac{x^2 + x - 1}{x^3(x^2 + 1)} = \frac{2}{x} + \frac{1}{x^2} - \frac{1}{x^3} - \frac{2x + 1}{x^2 + 1}.$$

It will be observed that in simplifying each of the terms on the right of 10.63 a nonzero polynomial occurred, but no polynomial occurred in the final result. It can be shown that whenever $\deg f(x) < \deg g(x)$, as is true in this example, in expressing $f(x)/g(x)$ as a sum of partial fractions no polynomial occurs. Also, it is proved in more advanced texts that the expression of a rational form as a sum of partial fractions is *unique*. However, we shall not prove these facts here.

Over the real field, which is the case of most importance, the only prime polynomials are of the first or second degree. Hence, in this case, the prime polynomials $p(x)$ in the statement of Theorem 10.59 are of the first or second degree. This fact is important in the proof that every rational function can be integrated in terms of elementary functions.

EXERCISES

Use the method of proof of Theorem 10.59 to express each of the following rational forms over the field of real numbers as a sum of partial fractions.

1. $\dfrac{x^2 - x + 1}{x(x^2 + x + 1)}.$

2. $\dfrac{x^2 + x - 2}{x(x^2 - 1)}.$

3. $\dfrac{x + 1}{x(x^2 + 1)^2}.$

4. $\dfrac{1}{(x - 1)^2(x^2 + 2)}.$

5. $\dfrac{2x^2 + x - 1}{x(x - 1)^3}.$

6. $\dfrac{x^4 + 2x^3 + 4}{(x^2 + 1)^2}.$

IDEALS AND QUOTIENT RINGS

In an early chapter we defined homomorphisms of rings and established a few simple properties of homomorphisms. Later on we introduced homomorphisms of groups and carried the theory far enough to show the importance of normal subgroups and quotient groups. We now return to the study of rings and bring that theory up to approximately the same level as was reached with groups. In particular, we shall introduce the concept of ideal in a ring as an analogue of normal subgroup of a group, and then define quotient rings and indicate their fundamental connection with homomorphisms. It will be seen that the ring $\mathbf{Z}_n$ of integers modulo n is an important special case of a quotient ring. We shall also study in some detail another important special case involving a polynomial ring $F[x]$ over a field. This will give us a method of constructing many new rings and fields in addition to those previously mentioned.

11.1 IDEALS

Let us begin with the following definition.

11.1 Definition. Let A be a subring of the ring R. Then

  (i) A is said to be a *right ideal* in R if A is closed with respect to multiplication on the right by elements of R (if $a \in A$ and $r \in R$, then $ar \in A$).

  (ii) A is said to be a *left ideal* in R if A is closed with respect to multiplication on the left by elements of R (if $a \in A$ and $r \in R$, then $ra \in A$).

(iii) A is said to be an *ideal* in R if it is both a right ideal in R and a left ideal in R (that is, it is closed with respect to multiplication on either side by elements of R).

We shall primarily be interested in ideals in a ring although the study of right (or left) ideals plays an important role in more advanced ring theory.

In any ring R, the subring consisting only of the zero element is clearly an ideal, and the entire ring R is also an ideal. These two ideals are often called trivial ideals. Another simple observation is that if R has a unity e and a right ideal A in R contains an element a with a multiplicative inverse, then $A = R$. For if $a \in A$ and $aa^{-1} = e$, then $e \in A$ and $ex = x \in A$ for every x in R. Clearly, a similar result holds for left ideals and ideals.

As a first example of an ideal (other than the trivial ones mentioned above), we may observe that the subring E of even integers in the ring $\mathbf{Z}$ is an ideal in $\mathbf{Z}$. This is true since the product of an even integer by an arbitrary integer is an even integer.

The subring $\mathbf{Z}$ of integers in the ring $\mathbf{Q}$ of rational numbers is not an ideal in $\mathbf{Q}$ since, for example, $3 \in \mathbf{Z}$ and $\frac{1}{2} \in \mathbf{Q}$, but $3 \cdot \frac{1}{2} \notin \mathbf{Z}$.

In order to give an example of a right ideal (or left ideal) which is not an ideal, we must clearly have a noncommutative ring. It is easy to verify that the subring $\{a, b\}$ of the ring K of Example 6 of Section 2.3 is a left ideal, but not a right ideal, in K. A more significant example is the following. Let W be the ring of all matrices of order two over the integers (Example 9 of Section 2.3). Then the set of all elements of W of the form

$$\begin{bmatrix} x & y \\ 0 & 0 \end{bmatrix}, \qquad\qquad x, y \in \mathbf{Z},$$

is a right ideal but not a left ideal; the set of all elements of W of the form

$$\begin{bmatrix} x & 0 \\ y & 0 \end{bmatrix}, \qquad\qquad x, y \in \mathbf{Z},$$

is a left ideal but not a right ideal; and the set of all elements of W of the form

$$\begin{bmatrix} x & y \\ z & t \end{bmatrix},$$

where x, y, z, and t are *even* integers, is an ideal in W. We leave to the reader the verification of these statements.

Throughout the rest of this section we shall consider *commutative* rings only, and hence there will be no distinction between ideals and right (or left) ideals. Moreover, for our purposes the most important case is that in which the ring has a unity. Accordingly, let S be a commutative ring with unity e. If $a \in S$, let

$$A = \{as \mid s \in S\},$$

and let us verify that A is an ideal in S. If s, $t \in S$, then $as + at = a(s + t)$ and $(as)t = a(st)$, so that A is clearly closed with respect to addition and with respect to multiplication by arbitrary elements of S. Moreover, $-(as) = a(-s) \in A$, and hence additive inverses of elements of A are elements of A. Thus, A is indeed an ideal in S. This conclusion holds whether or not S has a unity, but the presence of a unity now assures us that $a \in A$ since $a = ae$. It is customary to denote this ideal A by (a). As an example of this notation, the ideal of all even integers in the ring **Z** would be denoted by (2). Similarly, the ideal consisting of all multiples of 3 would be denoted by (3), and so on.

Some convenient terminology is introduced in the following definition.

11.2   Definition.   Let S be a commutative ring with unity. If $a \in S$, an ideal of the form

$$(a) = \{as \mid s \in S\}$$

is called a *principal ideal*. It is also called the *principal ideal generated by a*.

The next theorem shows that in certain important rings there are no ideals except principal ideals.

11.3   Theorem.   *Every ideal is a principal ideal*

(*i*)   *in the ring **Z** of integers,*

(*ii*)   *in a polynomial ring F[x] over a field.*

We shall prove the first case and outline the proof for the other case. Suppose that K is an ideal in the ring **Z**. If K is the zero ideal, then K is the principal ideal (0) generated by the zero of **Z**. If $K \neq (0)$, then K must contain positive integers. (Why?) Suppose that m is the least positive integer in K, and let k denote an arbitrary element of K. By the division algorithm, we may write $k = qm + r$, where $0 \leq r < m$. Now $qm \in K$ since $m \in K$, and $r = k - qm$ is an element of K. Since $r < m$ and m is the least positive integer in K, we conclude that $r = 0$

and $k = qm$. It follows that $K = (m)$, completing this part of the proof.*

Suppose now that K is an ideal in the polynomial ring $F[x]$, where F is a field with unity 1, and again we may assume that $K \neq (0)$. If K contains a nonzero element r of F, then $1 = rr^{-1} \in K$ and $K = F[x] = (r)$. If $K \neq (0)$ and $K \neq F[x]$, let $f(x)$ be a polynomial of least degree in the ideal K. Then $f(x)$ has positive degree and the method of proof of the previous case will show that $K = (f(x))$. We leave the details as an exercise.

Let us observe that the rings $\mathbf{Z}$ and $F[x]$ are quite special rings, and the result just proved for these rings does not hold in general. We shall now emphasize this fact by giving an example of an ideal which is not a principal ideal. For our ring we take $\mathbf{Z}[x]$, the ring of polynomials over $\mathbf{Z}$. It may be verified that the set T of all elements of $\mathbf{Z}[x]$ with *even* constant terms is an ideal in $\mathbf{Z}[x]$. However, we shall show that T is not a principal ideal. Suppose, on the contrary, that $T = (f(x))$. Since $2 \in T$, we must have $2 = f(x)g(x)$ for some element $g(x)$ of $\mathbf{Z}[x]$. It follows that both $f(x)$ and $g(x)$ are of degree zero, that is, they are integers. Now $f(x) \neq \pm 1$ since this would imply that $(f(x)) = \mathbf{Z}[x]$, which is false. Accordingly, we must have $f(x) = \pm 2$, $g(x) = \pm 1$. However, there are many elements of T (for example, $x + 2$) which are not multiples of ± 2. We have obtained a contradiction, and T is therefore not a principal ideal in $\mathbf{Z}[x]$.

EXERCISES

1. If A and B are ideals (right ideals, left ideals) in a ring R, prove that $A \cap B$ is an ideal (right ideal, left ideal) in R. Generalize to any number of ideals.

2. If A and B are ideals (right ideals, left ideals) in a ring R, let us define

$$A + B = \{a + b \mid a \in A, b \in B\}.$$

Prove that $A + B$ is an ideal (right ideal, left ideal) in R and that $A \subseteq A + B$ and $B \subseteq A + B$.

3. Let s and t be nonzero integers with d as their g.c.d. and m as their l.c.m. Prove that in the ring $\mathbf{Z}$, $(s) \cap (t) = (m)$ and $(s) + (t) = (d)$.

---

* This argument should seem familiar since it is essentially the proof (Theorem 7.27) that every subgroup of a cyclic group is cyclic. In fact, we have really proved that the ideals in $\mathbf{Z}$ coincide with the cyclic subgroups of the additive group of $\mathbf{Z}$.

4. Find integers s and t such that $(s) \cup (t)$ is not an ideal in **Z**.

5. Complete the proof of Theorem 11.3 for the ring $F[x]$.

6. Verify that a *field* F has only the two trivial ideals (0) and F.

7. Verify that the set of all matrices of the form

$$\begin{bmatrix} x - 2y & y \\ 2x - 4y & 2y \end{bmatrix}, \qquad x, y \in \mathbf{Z},$$

is a right ideal in the ring of all matrices of order two over **Z**.

8. An element a of a ring R is said to be *nilpotent* if $a^n = 0$ for some positive integer n (which may depend on a). Prove that the set of all nilpotent elements in a commutative ring R is an ideal in R.

9. Let a and b be elements of a commutative ring with unity. If a has a multiplicative inverse and b is nilpotent, prove that $a + b$ has a multiplicative inverse. [Hint: If $b^2 = 0$, then $(a + b)^{-1} = a^{-1} - a^{-2}b$. What if $b^3 = 0$. In general, what if $b^n = 0$?]

10. Let U be an infinite set (for example, the set $\mathbf{Z}^+$), and let R be the ring of all subsets of U. Prove that the set S of all elements of R consisting of *finite* subsets of U is an ideal in R. Prove that S is not a principal ideal in R.

11.2   QUOTIENT RINGS

Let us first make a few additional observations about homomorphisms of rings. Since a ring is an abelian group with respect to the operation of addition, and zero is the identity of this group, the following definition is at least partly suggested by the corresponding definition for groups.

11.4   Definition. If $\theta: R \to S$ is a homomorphism of the ring R into the ring S, the set of all elements a of R such that $a\theta = 0$ is called the *kernel* of the homomorphism θ, and denoted by ker θ.

Corresponding to Theorem 7.18 for groups, we have the following theorem for rings.

11.5   Theorem. *If $\theta: R \to S$ is a homomorphism of the ring R into the ring S, then ker θ is an ideal in R. Moreover, θ is an isomorphism if and only if ker $\theta = \{0\}$.*

PROOF: If $a \in$ ker θ and $r \in R$, then

$$(ar)\theta = (a\theta)(r\theta) = 0(r\theta) = 0,$$

and hence $ar \in \ker \theta$. Similarly, $ra \in \ker \theta$. Moreover, if $a, b \in \ker \theta$, then

$$(a + b)\theta = a\theta + b\theta = 0 + 0 = 0,$$

and $a + b \in \ker \theta$. Finally, if $a \in \ker \theta$, Theorem 2.32(ii) assures us that $(-a)\theta = -(a\theta) = 0$, and $-a \in \ker \theta$. We have thus shown that $\ker \theta$ is an ideal in R.

If θ is a one-one mapping and $a \in \ker \theta$ then $a\theta = 0\theta$ and we must have $a = 0$; hence $\ker \theta = \{0\}$. To go the other way, suppose that $\ker \theta = \{0\}$ and that $a, b \in R$ such that $a\theta = b\theta$. Then $(a - b)\theta = 0$ and this implies that $a - b = 0$. It follows that the mapping is a one-one mapping and therefore an isomorphism. This completes the proof of the theorem.

Now let K be an ideal in an arbitrary ring R. The additive group of K is clearly a subgroup of the additive group of R. We wish to consider cosets with respect to this subgroup. A typical such coset is of the form

$$a + K = \{a + k \mid k \in K\},$$

where a is an element of R. From our previous study of cosets, we know that $c + K = d + K$ if and only if $c \in d + K$, that is, if and only if $c - d \in K$. Moreover, we also know that addition of cosets is well-defined as follows:

11.6 $$(a + K) + (b + K) = (a + b) + K, \qquad a, b \in R.$$

So far we have only used the fact that the additive group of K is a subgroup of the additive group of R. Now, however, since K is an ideal we can show that multiplication of cosets is well-defined by

11.7 $$(a + K)(b + K) = ab + K, \qquad a, b \in R.$$

Suppose that $a + K = a_1 + K$ and that $b + K = b_1 + K$. Thus there exist elements $k, k' \in K$ such that $a = a_1 + k$ and $b = b_1 + k'$. It follows that

$$\begin{aligned}
ab &= (a_1 + k)(b_1 + k') \\
&= a_1 b_1 + a_1 k' + k b_1 + k k' \\
&= a_1 b_1 + k'',
\end{aligned}$$

where $k'' = a_1 k' + k b_1 + k k'$ is an element of K. Hence $ab + K = a_1 b_1 + K$, and multiplication of cosets is well-defined by 11.7.

We now have the following result (cf. Theorem 7.50 for groups).

11.8   Theorem.   *Let K be an ideal in the ring R. With respect to addition and multiplication of cosets defined by 11.6 and 11.7, the set of all cosets of K in R is a ring, usually called the* quotient ring *of R by K, and denoted by R/K. Moreover, the mapping $\theta \colon R \to R/K$ defined by $a\theta = a + K$, $a \in R$, is a homomorphism of R onto the ring R/K, with kernel K.*

The proof that we get a ring is straightforward and we leave it as an exercise. However, it may be well to observe here that the zero of the ring R/K is the coset $0 + K = K$. Moreover, if R has a unity e, then R/K has the unity $e + K$.

The last statement of the theorem is an almost immediate consequence of the definitions 11.6 and 11.7 of addition and multiplication in the ring R/K.

We now give an important example of a quotient ring with which we are already familiar. Let n be a positive integer and let us consider the principal ideal (n) in the ring $\mathbf{Z}$. A coset $a + (n)$ of the ideal (n) in $\mathbf{Z}$ consists of all integers x expressible in the form $a + nt$ for some $t \in \mathbf{Z}$. Thus, $x \in a + (n)$ if and only if $x \equiv a \pmod{n}$. In the notation of equivalence sets modulo n, introduced in Section 4.7, we see therefore that $a + (n) = [a]$. Moreover, our definitions of addition and multiplication of cosets coincide with the previous definitions of addition and multiplication of equivalence sets modulo n. Thus the ring $\mathbf{Z}_n$ of integers modulo n is, in the language and notation of the present section, precisely the quotient ring $\mathbf{Z}/(n)$. Some additional examples of quotient rings will be presented in the following section.

11.3   QUOTIENT RINGS $F[x]/(s(x))$

We now consider the ring $F[x]$ of all polynomials in an indeterminate x over a *field F*, and let $s(x)$ be a fixed element of $F[x]$ of *positive* degree. Moreover, for convenience in writing, we shall sometimes let $S = (s(x))$, that is, S is the ideal in $F[x]$ consisting of all polynomials of the form $s(x)g(x)$, $g(x) \in F[x]$. Our purpose is to study the quotient ring $F[x]/(s(x))$. An element of this ring is a coset of the form

$$f(x) + S, \qquad\qquad f(x) \in F[x],$$

where $S = (s(x))$. We shall first prove the following theorem.

11.9   Theorem.   *The ring $F[x]/(s(x))$ is a field if and only if $s(x)$ is a prime polynomial over F. In any case, the ring $F[x]/(s(x))$ contains a subring isomorphic to the field F.*

PROOF: Suppose, first, that $s(x)$ is not prime over F. Then there exist elements $s_1(x)$ and $s_2(x)$ of $F[x]$ of positive degrees such that $s(x) = s_1(x)s_2(x)$. Since deg $s_1(x) <$ deg $s(x)$, $s_1(x)$ cannot be divisible by $s(x)$ and therefore $s_1(x) \not\subset S$. Similarly, $s_2(x) \not\subset S$. It follows that neither $s_1(x) + S$ nor $s_2(x) + S$ is the zero S of $F[x]/S$. However,

$$(s_1(x) + S)(s_2(x) + S) = s_1(x)s_2(x) + S = s(x) + S = S,$$

since $s(x) \in S$. Hence a product of two nonzero elements is the zero element of $F[x]/S$. This shows that $F[x]/S$ is not even an integral domain, and therefore certainly not a field.

Next, suppose that $s(x)$ is prime over F and let $f(x) + S$ be a nonzero element of $F[x]/S$, that is, $f(x) \not\subset S$. Thus $f(x)$ is not divisible by $s(x)$ and since $s(x)$ is prime over $F[x]$, this implies that $f(x)$ and $s(x)$ are relatively prime. By Theorem 10.30, there must then exist elements $h(x)$ and $k(x)$ of $F[x]$ such that

$$f(x)h(x) + s(x)k(x) = 1,$$

where 1 is the unity of F. Since $s(x)k(x) \in S$, this implies that

$$(f(x) + S)(h(x) + S) = 1 + S.$$

However, $1 + S$ is the unity of $F[x]/S$, and this shows that the arbitrary nonzero element $f(x) + S$ of $F[x]/S$ has a multiplicative inverse $h(x) + S$. Hence $F[x]/S$ is indeed a field. The part of the theorem proved so far closely parallel corresponding results for the ring of integers modulo n.

We now proceed to the proof of the last sentence of the theorem. Let F' be the set of all elements of $F[x]/S$ of the form $a + S$, where $a \in F$. Since $S = (s(x))$ and $s(x)$ has positive degree, S contains no nonzero element of F and we see that

$$a + S = b + S, \qquad\qquad a, b \in F$$

if and only if $a - b \in S$, that is, if and only if $a = b$. This shows that the mapping $a \rightarrow a + S$ of F into F' is one-one, and it is clearly an onto mapping. The proof of the theorem is completed by verifying that F' is a field and that this mapping is an isomorphism of F onto F'. We leave the details as an exercise.

In the future we shall often find it convenient to identify F' with F, that is, we merely change the notation by writing a in place of $a + S$, where $a \in F$, whenever it is clear from the context that we are working in the ring $F[x]/S$.

We proceed to point out a convenient, and somewhat more explicit, way to specify the elements of the ring $F[x]/S$. As soon as we have done this, we shall give a number of examples that may help to clarify the material of this and of the preceding section.

We have assumed that the fixed polynomial $s(x)$ of $F[x]$ has positive degree, say k. If c is a nonzero element of F, then a polynomial is a multiple of $s(x)$ if and only if it is a multiple of $cs(x)$, that is, $(s(x)) = (cs(x))$. Accordingly, there is no loss of generality in assuming that $s(x)$ is a monic polynomial since this would only involve choosing c to be the multiplicative inverse of the leading coefficient of $s(x)$. We shall henceforth assume that $s(x)$ is monic and, for later convenience, we choose the notation

11.10 $$s(x) = x^k - s_{k-1}x^{k-1} - \cdots - s_1 x - s_0,$$

the coefficients being elements of F. Now let $f(x) + S$ be an element of $F[x]/S$. By the Division Algorithm, we have $f(x) = q(x)s(x) + r(x)$, where $r(x) = 0$ or deg $r(x) < k$. Since $q(x)s(x) \in S$, it follows that

$$f(x) + S = r(x) + S.$$

Thus every element of $F[x]/S$ can be expressed in the form

11.11 $$a_0 + a_1 x + \cdots + a_{k-1}x^{k-1} + S, \qquad \text{each } a_i \in F.$$

We shall next show that every element is *uniquely* expressible in this form. Let $g(x) = a_0 + a_1 x + \cdots + a_{k-1}x^{k-1}$ and $h(x) = b_0 + b_1 x + \cdots + b_{k-1}x^{k-1}$, and suppose that $g(x) + S = h(x) + S$. This implies that $g(x) - h(x) \in S$ and since S contains no polynomial of degree less than k, we conclude that $g(x) - h(x) = 0$, or $g(x) = h(x)$. Thus each element of $F[x]/S$ can be expressed in exactly one way in the form 11.11.

We proceed to simplify our notation by introducing a simple symbol for the particular element $x + S$ of $F[x]/S$. Let us agree to set

$$j = x + S.$$

Then $j^2 = (x + S)(x + S) = x^2 + S$ and, more generally, for each positive integer m we have

$$j^m = x^m + S.$$

Now, for example, let us consider an element of the form $(a + bx + cx^2) + S$, where a, b, $c \in F$. Clearly,

$$(a + bx + cx^2) + S = (a + S) + (b + S)(x + S) + (c + S)(x^2 + S)$$
$$= (a + S) + (b + S)j + (c + S)j^2.$$

We agreed above to write a for $a + S$, $a \in F$, so using this notation we have

$$(a + bx + cx^2) + S = a + bj + cj^2.$$

By generalizing this argument, we see that an element $f(x) + S$ of $F[x]/S$ may be written in the simple form $f(j)$. In particular, from 11.11 it follows that the elements of $F[x]/S$ are uniquely expressible in the form

11.12 $$a_0 + a_1j + \cdots + a_{k-1}j^{k-1}, \qquad \text{each } a_i \in F.$$

Since $s(x) \in S$, $s(x) + S$ is the zero of $F[x]/S$, and we have $s(j) = s(x) + S = 0$. Thus, in particular, the element j is a root of the polynomial $s(x)$ (although j is in the ring $F[x]/S$, not in F). Accordingly, we can operate with the elements 11.12 of $F[x]/S$ by merely considering j to be a symbol such that $s(j) = 0$. The sum of two elements of the form 11.12 is immediately an element of the same form. The product of two elements can be expressed in the form 11.12 by multiplying out in the usual way and then replacing each power of j higher than the $(k - 1)$st by the element of the form 11.12 to which it is equal. Since $s(j) = 0$, we have from 11.10 that

11.13 $$j^k = s_0 + s_1j + \cdots + s_{k-1}j^{k-1},$$

and the right side is of the form 11.12. To compute j^{k+1}, we multiply the preceding equation by j and obtain

$$j^{k+1} = s_0j + s_1j^2 + \cdots + s_{k-2}j^{k-1} + s_{k-1}j^k.$$

Now the right side is not of the form 11.12, but we can get it into this form by substituting for j^k from 11.13 and collecting coefficients of the different powers of j. In this way we obtain

11.14 $\quad j^{k+1} = s_{k-1}s_0 + (s_0 + s_{k-1}s_1)j + \cdots + (s_{k-2} + s_{k-1}^2)j^{k-1}.$

We could proceed in this way to compute higher powers of j. However, the general formulas are not very useful since it is much easier to apply the method directly in any specific case. The following examples will illustrate how this is done.

EXAMPLE 1.   Let F be the field $\mathbf{R}$ of real numbers, and let $s(x)$ be the polynomial $x^2 + 1$. Since $x^2 + 1$ is prime over $\mathbf{R}$, we know by Theorem 11.9 that $\mathbf{R}[x]/(x^2 + 1)$ is a field. We proceed to describe this field in some detail.

As a special case of the general discussion above, we may observe that since $x^2 + 1$ is of the second degree, every element of the field $\mathbf{R}[x]/(x^2 + 1)$ is uniquely expressible in the form

11.15 $a + bj$, $a, b \in \mathbf{R}$,

where $j^2 + 1 = 0$. Let us now characterize the field $\mathbf{R}[x]/(x^2 + 1)$ by specifying the operations of addition and multiplication of the elements 11.15. Addition is trivial since

11.16 $(a + bj) + (c + dj) = (a + c) + (b + d)j$,

which is immediately of the form 11.15. As for multiplication, we have

$$(a + bj)(c + dj) = ac + (ad + bc)j + bdj^2,$$

or, replacing j^2 by -1,

11.17 $(a + bj)(c + dj) = (ac - bd) + (ad + bc)j$.

We have thus shown how to express the product of two elements of the form 11.15 in the same form. The field $\mathbf{R}[x]/(x^2 + 1)$ can now be simply characterized as the field with elements 11.15 and with addition and multiplication given by 11.16 and 11.17, respectively.

Except for an almost trivial difference in notation, the field we have just constructed coincides with the field $\mathbf{C}$ under the mapping

$$a + bj \to a + bi, \qquad\qquad a, b \in \mathbf{R}.$$

Hence, we have now given another method of constructing the field of complex numbers from the field of real numbers.

EXAMPLE 2.   Let F be the field $\mathbf{Z}_2$ of integers modulo 2, whose two elements we shall now write as 0 and 1; and let $s(x) = x^2 + x + 1$. Since neither of the elements of $\mathbf{Z}_2$ is a root of this quadratic polynomial, it follows that this polynomial is prime over $\mathbf{Z}_2$. Hence the ring $\mathbf{Z}_2[x]/(x^2 + x + 1)$ is a field which, for simplicity, we shall designate by F^*. Since also in this example $s(x)$ is a quadratic polynomial, it follows as in the preceding example that the elements of F^* are uniquely expressible in the form

11.18 $a + bj$, $a, b \in \mathbf{Z}_2$.

As usual, addition of two of these elements is carried out in an almost trivial way as follows:

11.19 $(a + bj) + (c + dj) = (a + c) + (b + d)j.$

As for multiplication, we have as in the previous example

$$(a + bj)(c + dj) = ac + (ad + bc)j + bdj^2.$$

However, since $s(j) = 0$, in this example we have $j^2 + j + 1 = 0$, or $j^2 = -j - 1$. Since our coefficients are from the field $\mathbf{Z}_2$, we can just as well write $j^2 = j + 1$. Replacing j^2 by $j + 1$ in the above expression for $(a + bj)(c + dj)$, we obtain

11.20 $(a + bj)(c + dj) = (ac + bd) + (ad + bc + bd)j,$

as the general formula for the product of two elements of F^*. Since there are only two elements of $\mathbf{Z}_2$, and therefore only two choices for a and b in 11.18, we see that F^* has only the four elements 0, 1, j, $1 + j$. Using 11.19 and 11.20 or, better still, simply carrying out the calculations in each case, we can construct the following addition and multiplication tables for F^*.

$(+)$	0	1	j	$1+j$	$(\cdot)$	0	1	j	$1+j$
0	0	1	j	$1+j$	0	0	0	0	0
1	1	0	$1+j$	j	1	0	1	j	$1+j$
j	j	$1+j$	0	1	j	0	j	$1+j$	1
$1+j$	$1+j$	j	1	0	$1+j$	0	$1+j$	1	j

The reader may verify that this field F^* of four elements is isomorphic to the ring of Example 7 of Section 2.3.

EXAMPLE 3.   Let F be the field $\mathbf{Z}_2$, as in the preceding example, but let $s(x) = x^2$. In this case, $s(x)$ is certainly not prime over $\mathbf{Z}_2$. For convenience, let us denote the ring $\mathbf{Z}_2[x]/(x^2)$ by T. We know then, by Theorem 11.9, that T is not a field. The elements of T are again of the form

$$a + bj, \qquad\qquad a, b \in \mathbf{Z}_2,$$

only this time $j^2 = 0$. Using this fact, we can obtain the following addition and multiplication tables for T.

$(+)$	0	1	j	$1+j$		$(\cdot)$	0	1	j	$1+j$
0	0	1	j	$1+j$		0	0	0	0	0
1	1	0	$1+j$	j		1	0	1	j	$1+j$
j	j	$1+j$	0	1		j	0	j	0	j
$1+j$	$1+j$	j	1	0		$1+j$	0	$1+j$	j	1

The addition table coincides with the addition table of Example 2, but the multiplication table is different, as it would have to be since T is not a field.

EXAMPLE 4. Let $s(x)$ be the polynomial $x^3 + x^2 + 1$ over the field $\mathbf{Q}$ of rational numbers, and consider the ring $\mathbf{Q}[x]/(x^3 + x^2 + 1)$, which we shall denote by U. It is easy to verify that $x^3 + x^2 + 1$ has no rational root and, since it is of degree 3, it must therefore be prime over $\mathbf{Q}$. Hence, U is a field. Since the degree of $s(x)$ is 3 in this case, it follows, as a special case of 11.12, that the elements of U are uniquely expressible in the form

11.21 $$a + bj + cj^2, \qquad\qquad a, b, c \in \mathbf{Q}.$$

Let us consider the product of two of these elements as an illustration of the procedure by which we obtained 11.13 and 11.14. Since $s(j) = 0$, we have that $j^3 + j^2 + 1 = 0$, or

11.22 $$j^3 = -1 - j^2.$$

If we multiply this equation by j and substitute $-1 - j^2$ for j^3, we get

$$j^4 = -j - j^3 = -j - (-1 - j^2);$$

that is,

11.23 $$j^4 = 1 - j + j^2.$$

The product of two elements 11.21 can now be computed by using the distributive laws and then substituting for j^3 and j^4 from 11.22 and 11.23. If we do so, we finally obtain

11.24 $(a + bj + cj^2)(d + ej + fj^2) = ad - bf - ce + cf$
$$+ (ae + bd - cf)j + (af + be + cd - bf - ce + cf)j^2.$$

The field U can therefore be characterized as the field with elements 11.21, with multiplication given by 11.24, and addition carried out in the obvious way. It should perhaps be remarked that the formula 11.24 is obviously too complicated to be of much practical use. For example, it would be extremely difficult to find the multiplicative inverse of a given element of U by using this formula for the product of two elements. Instead, one would use the method of proof of Theorem 11.9 in order to carry out such a calculation.

There is one further theorem which is implicit in what we have done, and which is of sufficient importance to warrant an explicit statement as follows.

11.25   Theorem.   *If F is a field and $f(x)$ is an arbitrary element of $F[x]$ of positive degree, there exists an extension F' of the field F such that $f(x)$ has a root in F'.*

If $f(x)$ has a root in F, then the result is trivial with $F' = F$. Otherwise, there exists a factor $s(x)$ of $f(x)$, which is of degree at least two and is prime over F. Then let us set $F' = F[x]/(s(x))$. We know that the field F' is an extension of the field F, and we may therefore also consider $f(x)$ to be a polynomial over F'. Moreover, using the notation in which the element $x + (s(x))$ of F' is denoted by j, we have that $s(j) = 0$. That is, the element j of F' is a root of the polynomial $s(x)$ and therefore also of $f(x)$. This completes the proof.

The following result is an easy consequence of the theorem just established.

11.26   Corollary.   *If F is a field and $f(x)$ is an element of $F[x]$ of positive degree, there exists an extension F^* of the field F with the property that $f(x)$ factors in $F^*[x]$ into factors of the first degree.*

Using the notation of the proof of the theorem, the Factor Theorem assures us that in $F'[x]$ the polynomial $f(x)$ has $x - j$ as a factor. If $f(x)$ does not factor entirely into factors of the first degree over F'; that is, if $f(x)$ contains a prime factor over F' which is of degree at least two, the process can be repeated by constructing a field F'' which contains F' and in which $f(x)$ has another root. It is clear that by a continuation of this process, there exists a field F^* containing F such that $f(x)$ factors in $F^*[x]$ into factors of the first degree, and the corollary is proved.

EXERCISES

1. Find a homomorphism of the ring Z_{12} onto the ring Z_4. What is the kernel of this homomorphism?

2. Let R be the ring of all matrices of the form

$$\begin{bmatrix} a & 0 \\ b & a \end{bmatrix}, \qquad\qquad a, b \in Z.$$

   Find a homomorphism of R onto Z and verify by direct calculation that the kernel K of this homomorphism is an ideal in R.

3. For the given field F and the given polynomial $s(x)$ over F, construct a multiplication table for the ring $F[x]/(s(x))$. Which of these rings are fields?

   (a) $F = Z_2$, $s(x) = x^2 + 1$;
   (b) $F = Z_3$, $s(x) = x^2 + 1$;
   (c) $F = Z_3$, $s(x) = x^2 + x + 1$;
   (d) $F = Z_2$, $s(x) = x^3 + x + 1$;
   (e) $F = Z_2$, $s(x) = x^3 + x^2 + 1$.

4. Determine all positive integers n with $1 < n \leq 7$ such that $Z_n[x]/(x^2 + x + 1)$ is a field.

5. Discuss the field $Q[x]/(x^2 - 2)$ and verify that it is isomorphic to the field of all real numbers of the form $a + b\sqrt{2}$, where $a, b \in Q$.

6. Discuss the field $Q[x]/(x^3 - 2)$, and describe a field of real numbers to which it is isomorphic.

7. It was stated earlier that for each positive integer n and each positive prime p, there exists a polynomial of degree n with coefficients in the field Z_p which is prime over this field. Use this fact to show that there exists a field with p^n elements. (See Exercise 16 below.)

8. In each case describe a field in which the given polynomial over the specified field has a root. In particular, give a general formula for the product of two elements of the field you describe.

   (a) $x^3 + x + 1$ over Q,
   (b) $x^3 + x^2 + x + 2$ over Q,

(c) $x^2 - x + 1$ over **R**,

(d) $x^3 + x + 1$ over $\mathbf{Z}_2$.

9. (a) Compute the multiplicative inverse of $1 + j + j^2$ in the field U of Example 4 above, and check by use of Formula 11.24.

   (b) Verify that in $U[x]$,

$$x^3 + x^2 + 1 = (x - j)(x^2 + (1 + j)x + j + j^2).$$

10. If R is a commutative ring and N is the ideal in R consisting of all nilpotent elements of R (Exercise 8 of preceding set), show that the quotient ring R/N contains no nilpotent element except the zero.

11. An ideal P in a commutative ring R is said to be a *prime ideal* if whenever a, $b \in R$ such that $ab \in P$, then $a \in P$ or $b \in P$. Determine all prime ideals in the ring **Z** and in the ring $F[x]$, where F is a field.

12. Prove: If R is a commutative ring with unity, an ideal $P \neq R$ in R is a prime ideal if and only if R/P is an integral domain.

13. In the notation of Exercise 2 above, show that the ring R/K is isomorphic to the ring **Z**.

14. Let $\theta: R \to S$ be a homomorphism of the ring R onto the ring S. Prove each of the following (*Cf.* with Theorem 7.60):

   (i) If A is a right ideal (left ideal, ideal) in R, then $A\theta$ is a right ideal (left ideal, ideal) in S.

   (ii) If A and B are right ideals (left ideals, ideals) in R, both of which contain ker θ, then $A\theta = B\theta$ if and only if $A = B$.

   (iii) If R is commutative, an ideal P in R such that ker $\theta \subseteq P$ is a prime ideal (Exercise 11 above) if and only if $P\theta$ is a prime ideal in S.

15. Let p be a positive prime and n a positive integer, and consider the polynomial $f(x) = x^{p^n} - x$ as a polynomial over the field $\mathbf{Z}_p$. By Corollary 11.26, there exists an extension F of $\mathbf{Z}_p$ such that $f(x)$ factors in $F[x]$ into factors of the first degree. Prove that $f(x)$ has p^n distinct roots in F. [Hint: See Exercise 6 of Section 10.5.]

16. In the notation of the preceding exercise, prove that the p^n distinct roots of $f(x)$ in F are the elements of a subfield of F, and hence conclude that there exists a field with p^n elements. [Hint: See Exercise 8 of Section 5.3.]

11.4   THE FUNDAMENTAL THEOREM ON RING HOMOMORPHISMS

We conclude this chapter by presenting the following theorem which corresponds to Theorem 7.52 for groups.

11.27   Theorem.   *Let $\phi: R \to S$ be a homomorphism of the ring R onto the ring S, with kernel K. Then K is an ideal in R, and S is isomorphic to the quotient ring R/K. More precisely, the mapping $\alpha: R/K \to S$ defined by*

11.28 $$(a + K)\alpha = a\phi, \qquad\qquad a \in R,$$

is an isomorphism of R/K onto S.

   We have already shown that K is an ideal in R. Moreover, by a suitable change in notation (addition replacing multiplication), the corresponding proof for groups will show that 11.28 actually defines a mapping of R/K onto S. We leave it as an exercise to show that α indeed is a homomorphism. If $a + K$ is in ker α, then $(a + K)\alpha = a\phi = 0$ and $a \in$ ker ϕ. But ker $\phi = K$, so $a \in K$ and $a + K = K$. Hence ker α consists only of the zero K of R/K and α is an isomorphism, as we wished to show.

   This theorem may be interpreted as stating that if isomorphic rings are not considered as different, the *only* homomorphic images of a ring R are the quotient rings R/K, where K is an ideal in R.

EXERCISES

1.   Prove in detail, giving reasons for each step, that 11.28 actually defines a mapping of R/K onto S, and that it is a homomorphism.

2.   Show that for each positive integer n, there is exactly one ring (not counting isomorphic rings as different) with n elements which is a homomorphic image of the ring **Z** of integers.

3.   Prove: If $\theta: F \to S$ is a homomorphism of a *field F* onto a ring S with more than one element, then θ is an isomorphism and S is a field.

4.   Let A and B be ideals in a ring R and define $A + B$ as in Exercise 2 of Section 11.1. Verify that B is an ideal in the ring $A + B$ and that $A \cap B$ is an ideal in the ring A. Then prove that the quotient

ring $A/(A \cap B)$ is isomorphic to the quotient ring $(A + B)/B$. [Hint: The mapping $a \to a + B$, $a \in A$ is a homomorphism of A onto $(A + B)/B$. What is its kernel?]

NOTES AND REFERENCES

A few additional topics in the theory of rings will be presented in the last chapter of this book. The subject is covered fairly extensively in references [26] through [31] of the bibliography. Additional references will be found in bibliographies which appear in [27] through [31].

VECTOR SPACES

In this chapter we shall introduce and study a new class of algebraic systems called *vector spaces*. The concept of a vector, used here to indicate an element of a vector space, is a generalization and abstraction of the concept of vector as the term is used in physics. We begin with a short discussion of vectors in the latter sense, as a partial motivation of the material to follow. We then proceed to give the abstract definition of a vector space and to establish some of the most important properties of such systems.

12.1 VECTORS IN A PLANE

Physical entities such as displacements, forces, and velocities have both magnitude and direction, and are usually called *vectors*. Geometrically, a vector may be represented by a directed line segment, the length of the segment indicating the magnitude of the vector and the direction of the segment specifying the direction of the vector. We shall here consider vectors in a given coordinate plane and, moreover, shall represent the vectors by directed segments emanating from the origin of coordinates. A vector X, as shown in Figure 15, is then completely determined by the coordinates (r , s) of its terminal point. Accordingly, we may just as well call (r , s) the vector; that is, we may identify the vector X with the ordered pair of real numbers that specifies its terminal point, and write $X = (r , s)$.

If X and Y are vectors in the same plane, the so-called parallelogram law states that the *sum* (or resultant) $X + Y$ of these vectors is the vector determined by the diagonal of the parallelogram, two of whose adjacent sides are the line segments representing the vectors X

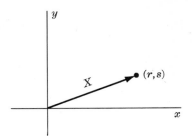

Figure 15

and Y, respectively (Figure 16). If $X = (r, s)$ and $Y = (u, v)$, it is not difficult to show that

12.1 $$X + Y = (r + u, s + v).$$

From our point of view, we propose to take 12.1 as the *definition* of the sum of two vectors. Let us now denote by V_2 the set of all vectors (x, y), where x and y are real numbers. Then, using 12.1 as the definition of addition, we have an operation of addition defined on V_2, and it is easy to verify that V_2 is an abelian group with respect to this operation. The identity $(0, 0)$ of this group we may call the *zero vector*.

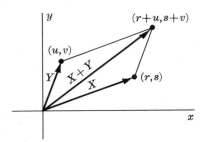

Figure 16

When using vectors in physical problems it is customary to consider, for example, that $2X$ is a vector having twice the magnitude of X and the same direction as X. The vector $(-2)X$ is considered to be the vector having twice the magnitude of X and the opposite direction to X. In general, if a is a real number, aX has magnitude $|a|$ times the magnitude of X and has the same or opposite direction to X according as $a > 0$ or $a < 0$. If $X = (r, s)$, simple geometric considerations show that if a is any real number,

12.2 $$aX = a(r, s) = (ar, as).$$

Now real numbers are often called *scalars* to distinguish them from vectors, so 12.2 gives us a multiplication of vectors by scalars. Again, although this scalar multiplication was suggested by a procedure used in physics, we propose to take 12.2 as the *definition* of scalar multiplication.

The set V_2 with addition defined by 12.1 and scalar multiplication defined by 12.2 is an example of a vector space according to the definition to be given presently. Actually, since the scalars are real numbers, it is customary to call V_2 a vector space *over the field* **R** of real numbers and to recognize this fact by the more explicit notation $V_2(\mathbf{R})$, instead of V_2 as used so far.

It is apparent that the above procedure could be generalized in various ways. For example, a consideration of vectors in space instead of in a plane would lead to vectors designated by ordered triples of real numbers, and the set of all such vectors with analogous definitions of addition and scalar multiplication would be a vector space which we might denote by $V_3(\mathbf{R})$. From a purely algebraic point of view, there is no reason why we might not go on and consider vectors to be ordered n-tuples of real numbers, and likewise the field **R** might be replaced by any other field. Actually, we shall not be so much concerned with the nature of the vectors themselves as with certain formal properties involving addition and scalar multiplication of vectors. Of course, the particular properties which are of primary interest are those which will be exhibited in the definition of a vector space we now proceed to give.

12.2 DEFINITION AND SIMPLE PROPERTIES OF A VECTOR SPACE

The following definition will assign a precise meaning to some of the terms which have been used in the preceding section.

12.3 Definition. Let F be a field, and V a nonempty set on which there is defined an operation of addition. The elements of F and of V may be called *scalars* and *vectors*, respectively. We assume that there is also defined on V a scalar multiplication by elements of F; that is, if $a \in F$ and $X \in V$, then aX is a uniquely determined element of V. The set V is then called a *vector space over the field F* if the following conditions are satisfied:

(i) V is an abelian group with respect to addition,

(ii) $a(X + Y) = aX + aY$, $a \in F; X, Y \in V,$

(iii) $(a + b)X = aX + bX$, $a, b \in F; X \in V,$

(iv) $a(bX) = (ab)X$, $\qquad\qquad\qquad\qquad$ $a, b \in F;\, X \in V$,

(v) $1X = X$, $\qquad\qquad\qquad\qquad\qquad$ 1 the unity of F, $X \in V$.

When it is desirable to exhibit explicitly the particular field F over which V is a vector space, we shall find it convenient to designate the vector space by $V(F)$. However, we shall omit the "F" when the context makes it clear what field is being considered.

Let us now clarify the preceding definition by several examples.

EXAMPLE 1. Let F be an arbitrary field, n a positive integer, and let $V_n(F)$ be the set of all ordered n-tuples of elements of F. That is, the elements of $V_n(F)$ are of the form $(a_1, a_2, \cdots, a_n)$, where $a_i \in F$ $(i = 1, 2, \cdots, n)$. In $V_n(F)$ we define addition as follows:

12.4
$$(a_1, a_2, \cdots, a_n) + (b_1, b_2, \cdots, b_n) = (a_1 + b_1, a_2 + b_2, \cdots, a_n + b_n).$$

Moreover, if $c \in F$, we define scalar multiplication in the following way:

12.5 $\qquad\qquad c(a_1, a_2, \cdots, a_n) = (ca_1, ca_2, \cdots, ca_n).$

It is then easy to verify that all properties of a vector space are satisfied, and hence that $V_n(F)$ is a vector space over the field F. Vector spaces of this type are of great importance and will be referred to often in the future. We shall consistently use the notation $V_n(F)$ to designate this vector space.

It is obvious that 12.4 and 12.5 are generalizations of 12.1 and 12.2, so that the use of $V_2(\mathbf{R})$ to designate the vector space discussed in the preceding section is consistent with the more general notation introduced in this example.

EXAMPLE 2. We now modify the preceding example by using *infinite* sequences of elements of F. Let $W(F)$ be the set of all infinite sequences of elements of F; that is, all expressions of the form

$$(a_1, a_2, a_3, \cdots), \qquad\qquad\qquad a_i \in F (i = 1, 2, 3, \cdots).$$

In $W(F)$ we define addition and scalar multiplication as follows:

$$(a_1, a_2, a_3, \cdots) + (b_1, b_2, b_3, \cdots) = (a_1 + b_1, a_2 + b_2, a_3 + b_3, \cdots),$$

and

$$c(a_1, a_2, a_3, \cdots) = (ca_1, ca_2, ca_3, \cdots).$$

Then $W(F)$ is a vector space over F.

If, instead of using *all* infinite sequences of elements of F, we use just those infinite sequences in which at most a finite number of elements of F are different from zero, we again obtain a vector space. (*Cf.* Exercise 8 at the end of this section.)

EXAMPLE 3. Let H be a given field and F a subfield of H. We can consider H to be a vector space over the field F if we use as addition the addition already defined in the field H, and define scalar multiplication in the following obvious way. If $a \in F$ and $c \in H$, let ac be the product of these elements as already defined in the field H. The vector space that we obtain in this way might be designated by $H(F)$. In this special case, Property (i) of Definition 12.3 is satisfied since we are using the additive group of the field H. Properties (ii) and (iii) follow from the distributive laws in H, and Property (iv) is just the associative law in H.

EXAMPLE 4. Let $P(F)$ be the set of polynomials in an indeterminate x over a field F. We use the usual addition of polynomials, and scalar multiplication is defined in the following way. If $a \in F$ and $f(x) \in P(F)$, then $af(x)$ is the polynomial obtained from $f(x)$ by multiplying all its coefficients by a. Of course, this coincides with the product of two polynomials, as defined previously, where one of the polynomials is just a. It is easily verified that $P(F)$ is then a vector space over the field F.

This example and the preceding one have a common generalization as follows. Let R be a ring which contains a field F as a subring, with R and F having the same unity. Then R is a vector space over F, using addition as already defined in R and scalar multiplication as ring multiplication of elements of R by elements of F. The vector space of Example 3 is obtained by specializing the ring R to be a field, and the vector space of Example 4 by taking R to be the ring $F[x]$ of polynomials in x over F.

EXAMPLE 5. Let T be the set of all polynomials in an indeterminate x over a field F that have degree at most three, together with the zero polynomial. Then T is a vector space over F if we define addition and scalar multiplication as in the preceding example. We may point out, however, that T is not a ring since it is not closed under multiplication of polynomials.

Now that we have given the definition of a vector space and exhibited some examples, let us prove a few simple properties of vector spaces in general. If X is an element of a vector space V, we shall use the familiar notations of abelian groups with respect to the operation of addition. In particular, we shall denote the additive inverse of X by $-X$. The identity of the abelian group V we shall call the *zero vector* and, for the moment, we shall designate it by O to distinguish it from the zero 0 of the field F. The most fundamental properties of vector spaces are stated in the following theorem.

12.6   **Theorem.**   *Let V be a vector space over the field F, and let O be the zero vector of V. The following are then true:*

   (i)   *If $a \in F$, then $aO = O$,*
   (ii)   *If $X \in V$, then $0X = O$,*
   (iii)   *If $a \in F$ and $X \in V$, then $a(-X) = (-a)X = -(aX)$,*
   (iv)   *If $aX = O$, then $a = 0$ or $X = O$.*

We shall prove (i) and (iii), and leave the proofs of the others as exercises.

To prove (i), let $a \in F$ and $X \in V$. Then

$$aX = a(X + O) = aX + aO,$$

by Definition 12.3(ii). This shows that aO is the zero vector; that is, that $aO = O$.

One part of (iii) is a consequence of the following calculation:

$$O = aO = a(X - X) = aX + a(-X).$$

It follows that $a(-X)$ is the additive inverse of aX, and hence that $a(-X) = -(aX)$. In this calculation we have tacitly used 12.3(ii) and 12.6(i). To get the other part of (iii) we use the following calculation in which we assume the truth of 12.6(ii) although the proof has not been written out, and also make use of 12.3(iii):

$$O = 0X = (a - a)X = aX + (-a)X.$$

Hence, $(-a)X = -(aX)$, as we wished to show.

Up to this point we have used different symbols to designate the zero vector and the zero element of the field F. However, in the future we shall not find it necessary to distinguish between these zeros since the context will always make it clear which one is intended. Accordingly, we shall henceforth use the familiar symbol 0 to designate either the zero vector or the zero scalar.

If V is a vector space over a field F, a nonempty subset U of V is naturally called a *subspace* of V if U is itself a vector space over F with respect to the addition and scalar multiplication already defined in V.

The following theorem is helpful in identifying subspaces of a given vector space.

12.7   Theorem.   *A nonempty subset U of a vector space V over a field F is a subspace of V if and only if U is closed under addition and scalar multiplication.*

If U is a subspace of V, it is trivial that U must be closed under addition and scalar multiplication. To show the converse, suppose that U is a nonempty subset of the vector space V, which is closed under addition and scalar multiplication, and let us show that U is indeed a vector space. If $X \in U$ and 1 is the unity of F, we have $(-1)X \in U$. But, by 12.6(iii) and 12.3(v), we see that

$$(-1)X = -(1X) = -X,$$

so that the additive inverse $-X$ of X is in U. Since U is closed under addition, Theorem 7.4 now shows that U is a subgroup of V; that is, that part (i) of Definition 12.3 is satisfied. Properties (ii)–(v) hold in U since they hold in the larger set V. Hence, U is a vector space over F and therefore is a subspace of V.

As an illustration of the use of this theorem, let us show that the set W of all elements of the vector space $V_3(F)$ of the form $(x + 2y , y , -x + 3y)$, where x and y are elements of F, is a subspace of $V_3(F)$. If $(a + 2b , b , -a + 3b)$ and $(c + 2d , d , -c + 3d)$ are elements of W, we see that their sum can be written in the form

$$(a + c + 2(b + d), b + d, -(a + c) + 3(b + d)),$$

and this is seen to be the element of W in which $x = a + c$ and $y = b + d$. This shows that W is closed under addition. Also, if $(a + 2b , b , -a + 3b)$ is an element of W and $r \in F$, it follows that

$$r(a + 2b , b , -a + 3b) = (ra + 2rb , rb , -ra + 3rb),$$

and we have the desired form with $x = ra$ and $y = rb$. Hence, W is also closed under scalar multiplication and, by the preceding theorem, W is therefore a subspace of $V_3(F)$.

EXERCISES

1. In each case, using natural definitions of addition and scalar multiplication, which of the following are vector spaces over the indicated field?

   (a) The set of all real numbers of the form $a + b\sqrt{2} + c\sqrt[3]{3}$, where a, b and c are elements of the field $\mathbf{Q}$ of rational numbers; field $\mathbf{Q}$.

   (b) The set of all polynomials of degree greater than five over a field F; field F.

   (c) The set of all real functions f such that $f(x + 1) = f(x)$; field $\mathbf{R}$ of real numbers.

   (d) The set $\{0 , x + 2 , 2x + 4 , 3x + 1 , 4x + 3\}$ of polynomials in the indeterminate x over the field $\mathbf{Z}_5$; field $\mathbf{Z}_5$.

   (e) The set of all polynomials with zero constant terms over a field F; field F.

2. Prove Theorem 12.6(ii) and (iv).

3. Let V be a vector space over a field F. Prove each of the following "cancellation laws":

   (i) If a, $b \in F$ and X is a nonzero element of V such that $aX = bX$, then $a = b$.

   (ii) If X, $Y \in V$ and a is a nonzero element of F such that $aX = aY$, then $X = Y$.

4. If F is a field and a_1, a_2, and a_3 are fixed elements of F, show that the set of all ordered triples (x_1 , x_2 , x_3) of elements of F such that $a_1x_1 + a_2x_2 + a_3x_3 = 0$ is a subspace of $V_3(F)$.

5. Find all subspaces of $V_2(\mathbf{Z}_2)$; of $V_3(\mathbf{Z}_2)$.

6. (a) How many elements are there in the vector space $V_n(\mathbf{Z}_p)$?

   (b) Show that the number of elements in any subspace of $V_n(\mathbf{Z}_p)$ is of the form p^k for some nonnegative integer k.

7. Which of the following are subspaces of $V_3(\mathbf{R})$?

   (a) The set of all elements of the form $(x , 2y , 3z)$, where x, y, $z \in \mathbf{R}$.

   (b) The set of all elements of the form (x , y , z), where x, y, and z are rational numbers.

(c) The set of all elements of the form $(x, 2x, x + 1)$, where $x \in \mathbf{R}$.

(d) The set of all elements of the form $(x, 0, z)$, where $x, z \in \mathbf{R}$.

(e) The set of all elements of the form $(x, y, 2)$, where $x, y \in \mathbf{R}$.

(f) The set of all elements of the form $(x + 2y, x - 3z, 2x + y + z)$, where $x, y, z \in \mathbf{R}$.

8. Verify that the set of all elements of the vector space $W(F)$ of Example 2 in which at most a finite number of elements of F are different from zero is a subspace of $W(F)$.

12.3 LINEAR DEPENDENCE

Throughout this section V will denote a vector space over a field F. Unless otherwise explicitly stated, when we refer to a set $\{X_1, X_2, \cdots, X_m\}$ of vectors, it will be understood that m is a positive integer and the set is therefore a nonempty finite set. The concept which we now define plays a central role in the study of vector spaces.

12.8 Definition. A set $\{X_1, X_2, \cdots, X_m\}$ of vectors of a vector space V is said to be a *linearly dependent* set if there exist elements $a_1\, a_2, \cdots, a_m$ of F, *not all of which are zero*, such that

12.9 $$a_1X_1 + a_2X_2 + \cdots + a_mX_m = 0.$$

If the set $\{X_1, X_2, \cdots, X_m\}$ is not linearly dependent, it is said to be *linearly independent*.

As a matter of language, we shall also sometimes say that the vectors $X_1, X_2, \cdots, X_m$ are linearly dependent or independent according as the set $\{X_1, X_2, \cdots, X_m\}$ is linearly dependent or independent.

Let us emphasize the meaning of the definition by the following remarks. Certainly, a relation of the form 12.9 will always hold if the a's are all equal to zero. If such a relation holds *only* in this case, the set $\{X_1, X_2, \cdots, X_m\}$ is linearly independent. However, if a relation 12.9 holds with at least one of the a's unequal to zero, the set $\{X_1, X_2, \cdots, X_m\}$ is linearly dependent.

EXAMPLE 1.   Let us consider the set $\{X_1, X_2, X_3\}$, where these are the following vectors of $V_3(\mathbf{R})$: $X_1 = (1, 3, 2)$, $X_2 = (1, -7, -8)$, $X_3 = (2, 1, -1)$. It is easily verified that $3X_1 + X_2 - 2X_3 = 0$, and hence that this set is linearly dependent.

EXAMPLE 2. Find whether the vectors $X_1 = (2, 1, 1, 1)$, $X_2 = (1, 3, 1, -2)$, and $X_3 = (1, 2, -1, 3)$ of $V_4(\mathbf{R})$ are linearly dependent or independent.

In order to solve this problem we need to determine whether there exist real numbers y_1, y_2, y_3, not all of which are zero, such that

12.10 $$y_1 X_1 + y_2 X_2 + y_3 X_3 = 0.$$

Using the definitions of addition and scalar multiplication in $V_4(\mathbf{R})$, Equation 12.10 is equivalent to the following system of simultaneous equations in the unknowns y_1, y_2, and y_3:

$$2y_1 + y_2 + y_3 = 0,$$
$$y_1 + 3y_2 + 2y_3 = 0,$$
$$y_1 + y_2 - y_3 = 0,$$
$$y_1 - 2y_2 + 3y_3 = 0.$$

Systems of equations of this form will be studied in detail in the next chapter, but a systematic use of the methods of elementary algebra is sufficient for our present purpose. First, we proceed as follows to eliminate y_1 from every equation but one. Let us multiply the second equation by 2 and subtract it from the first; then also subtract the second equation from the third and from the fourth. There then results the following system of equations:

$$-5y_2 - 3y_3 = 0,$$
$$y_1 + 3y_2 + 2y_3 = 0,$$
$$-2y_2 - 3y_3 = 0,$$
$$-5y_2 + y_3 = 0.$$

We could, by a similar method, proceed to eliminate y_2 from all the equations of this new system except, say, the first. However, it is not necessary to do so, for if we subtract the first equation from the last, we find that $4y_3 = 0$, and hence we must have $y_3 = 0$. Now, setting $y_3 = 0$ in the first equation, we see that $y_2 = 0$. Finally, if we set $y_2 = y_3 = 0$ in the second equation, it follows that $y_1 = 0$. We have shown that if y_1, y_2, y_3 are real numbers such that 12.10 holds, then $y_1 = y_2 = y_3 = 0$, and the vectors X_1, X_2, X_3 are therefore linearly independent.

We now state in the following theorem a number of simple, but fundamental, properties of linear dependence or independence.

12.11 Theorem. *In the following, the indicated vectors are elements of a vector space V over a field F.*

(i)   *The set* $\{X_1, X_2, \cdots, X_m\}$ *is a linearly dependent set if one of the vectors of the set is the zero vector.*

(ii)   *The set* $\{X\}$, *consisting of the one vector* X, *is linearly independent if and only if* $X \neq 0$.

(iii)   *If the set* $\{X_1, X_2, \cdots, X_m\}$ *is linearly independent, then any nonempty subset of this set is linearly independent.*

(iv)   *If the set* $\{X_1, X_2, \cdots, X_m\}$ *is linearly dependent, then the set* $\{X_1, X_2, \cdots, X_m, X\}$ *is linearly dependent for each* $X \in V$.

(v)   *If* $\{X_1, X_2, \cdots, X_m\}$ *is a linearly independent set and if* b_i, $c_i \in F$ $(i = 1, 2, \cdots, m)$ *such that*
$$b_1 X_1 + b_2 X_2 + \cdots + b_m X_m = c_1 X_1 + c_2 X_2 + \cdots + c_m X_m,$$
then $b_i = c_i (i = 1, 2, \cdots, m)$.

(vi)   *If* $X_i \in V$ $(i = 1, 2, \cdots, m)$ *and* $r_i \in F$ $(i = 2, 3, \cdots, m)$, *are such that the set* $\{X_2 + r_2 X_1, X_3 + r_3 X_1, \cdots, X_m + r_m X_1\}$ *is a linearly dependent set, then the set* $\{X_1, X_2, \cdots, X_m\}$ *is a linearly dependent set.*

The reader should try to prove the various parts of this theorem before looking at the proofs below. There should be no difficulty in carrying out the proofs provided the definitions of a vector space and of linear dependence and independence are clearly in mind.

PROOF OF (i).   Suppose, for convenience of notation, that $X_1 = 0$. Then, since $1X_1 = 0$ by 12.3(v), and $0X_i = 0$ by 12.6(ii), it follows that

$$1X_1 + 0X_2 + \cdots + 0X_m = 0.$$

This relation is of the form 12.9 with $a_1 \neq 0$; hence the set $\{X_1, X_2, \cdots, X_m\}$ is linearly dependent.

PROOF OF (ii).   Suppose that $X \neq 0$. If $aX = 0$, it follows from 12.6(iv) that $a = 0$. Hence, the set $\{X\}$ is linearly independent. Of course, in this case a relation of the form 12.9 has just one term on its left side. If $X = 0$, the special case of (i) in which $m = 1$ shows at once that the set $\{X\}$ is linearly dependent.

PROOF OF (iii).   For convenience of notation, let us consider a subset of the form $\{X_1, \cdots, X_i\}$, where $1 \leq i < m$, and suppose that $a_1 X_1 + \cdots + a_i X_i = 0$. Then, obviously,

$$a_1 X_1 + \cdots + a_i X_i + 0X_{i+1} + \cdots + 0X_m = 0.$$

Since the set $\{X_1, \cdots, X_m\}$ is linearly independent, it follows that we must have $a_1 = a_2 = \cdots = a_i = 0$. We have therefore shown that

$a_1 X_1 + \cdots + a_i X_i = 0$ only if all a's are equal to zero, and hence that the set $\{X_1, \cdots, X_i\}$ is linearly independent.

PROOF OF (iv). Suppose that $a_1 X_1 + \cdots + a_m X_m = 0$ with $a_j \neq 0$, where j is some integer such that $1 \leq j \leq m$. Then

$$a_1 X_1 + \cdots + a_m X_m + 0X = 0,$$

and since $a_j \neq 0$, we conclude that the set $\{X_1, \cdots, X_m, X\}$ is a linearly dependent set.

PROOF OF (v). From what is given it follows that

$$b_1 X_1 + b_2 X_2 + \cdots + b_m X_m - (c_1 X_1 + c_2 X_2 + \cdots + c_m X_m) = 0.$$

Then, using 12.6(iii), 12.3(iii), and the fact that V is an abelian group with respect to addition, it is not difficult to show that

$$(b_1 - c_1)X_1 + (b_2 - c_2)X_2 + \cdots + (b_m - c_m)X_m = 0.$$

Since the set $\{X_1, \cdots, X_m\}$ is linearly independent, this equation implies that $b_i - c_i = 0$ and therefore that $b_i = c_i (i = 1, 2, \cdots, m)$.

PROOF OF (vi). By what is given we know that there must exist elements $a_i (i = 2, 3, \cdots, m)$ of F, not all of which are zero, such that

$$a_2(X_2 + r_2 X_1) + a_3(X_3 + r_3 X_1) + \cdots + a_m(X_m + r_m X_1) = 0.$$

However, it follows from this equation that

$$(a_2 r_2 + \cdots + a_m r_m)X_1 + a_2 X_2 + \cdots + a_m X_m = 0$$

and, since the a's are not all zero, we see that the set $\{X_1, X_2, \cdots, X_m\}$ is a linearly dependent set. This completes the proof of the theorem.

EXERCISES

1. Determine whether each of the following sets of vectors of $V_3(\mathbf{R})$ is linearly dependent or independent:

    (a) $\{(-1, 2, 1), (3, 1, -2)\}$,

    (b) $\{(1, 3, 2), (2, 1, 0), (0, 5, 4)\}$,

    (c) $\{(2, -1, 1), (1, 2, 3), (0, 1, 2)\}$,
    (d) $\{(1, 0, 0), (0, 1, 0), (0, 0, 1)\}$,
    (e) $\{(1, -2, 1), (0, 1, 2), (1, 1, 1)\}$,
    (f) $\{(1, 0, -1), (2, 1, 3), (-1, 0, 0), (1, 0, 1)\}$.

2.   Determine whether each of the following sets of vectors of $V_4(\mathbf{R})$ is linearly dependent or independent:

    (a) $\{(1, -1, 2, 1), (2, 1, 1, 2)\}$,
    (b) $\{(1, 2, 1, 2), (0, 1, 1, 0), (1, 4, 3, 2)\}$,
    (c) $\{(0, 1, 0, 1), (1, 2, 3, -1), (1, 0, 1, 0), (0, 3, 2, 0)\}$,
    (d) $\{(1, 2, -1, 1), (0, 1, -1, 2), (2, 1, 0, 3), (1, 1, 0, 0)\}$.

3.   Determine whether each of the following sets of vectors of $V_3(\mathbf{Z}_5)$ is linearly dependent or independent:

    (a) $\{(1, 3, 2), (2, 1, 3)\}$,
    (b) $\{(1, 1, 2), (2, 1, 0), (0, 4, 1)\}$.
    (c) $\{(2, 1, 0), (1, 1, 2), (3, 0, 2)\}$.

4.   Prove, giving the reason for each step, that a set consisting of *two* vectors of a vector space is a linearly dependent set if and only if one of these vectors is equal to a scalar times the other.

5.   If X_1 and X_2 are vectors of a vector space over the field F, and $a, b \in F$, show that the set $\{X_1, X_2, aX_1 + bX_2\}$ is a linearly dependent set.

6.   Let X_1, X_2, and X_3 be vectors of a vector space over the field F, and let a and b be arbitrary elements of F. Show that the set $\{X_1, X_2, X_3\}$ is a linearly dependent set if and only if the set $\{X_1 + aX_2 + bX_3, X_2, X_3\}$ is linearly dependent.

7.   Let X_1 and X_2 be linearly independent vectors of a vector space over a field F. If a, b, c, and d are elements of F, prove that the vectors $aX_1 + bX_2$ and $cX_1 + dX_2$ are linearly independent if and only if $ad - bc \neq 0$.

12.4 LINEAR COMBINATIONS AND SUBSPACES

We shall continue to let V be a vector space over a field F.

12.12 **Definition.** A vector of the form $a_1X_1 + a_2X_2 + \cdots + a_mX_m$, where $X_i \in V$ and $a_i \in F$ $(i = 1, 2, \cdots, m)$, is called a *linear combination* (over F) of the vectors $X_1, X_2, \cdots, X_m$.

In the linear combination $a_1X_1 + a_2X_2 + \cdots + a_mX_m$, it is sometimes convenient to call a_i the *coefficient* of X_i $(i = 1, 2, \cdots, m)$.

We shall now verify the important fact that *the set U of all linear combinations of given vectors $X_1, X_2, \cdots, X_m$ of V is a subspace of V.* By Theorem 12.7, we only need to show that U is closed under addition and scalar multiplication. Suppose that Y and Z are elements of U. Then,

$$Y = c_1X_1 + c_2X_2 + \cdots + c_mX_m$$

and

$$Z = d_1X_1 + d_2X_2 + \cdots + d_mX_m,$$

where the c's and d's are elements of F. It follows that

$$Y + Z = (c_1 + d_1)X_1 + (c_2 + d_2)X_2 + \cdots + (c_m + d_m)X_m.$$

Hence, $Y + Z$ is a linear combination of $X_1, X_2, \cdots, X_m$; and therefore an element of U. This shows that U is closed under addition. Now if $r \in F$ and Y is as above, we see that

$$rY = r(c_1X_1 + c_2X_2 + \cdots + c_mX_m) = (rc_1)X_1 \\ + (rc_2)X_2 + \cdots + (rc_m)X_m.$$

It follows that $rY \in U$; that is, that U is also closed under scalar multiplication. We have therefore proved that U is a subspace of V.

We now make the following definition.

12.13 Definition. If $X_1, X_2, \cdots, X_m$ are elements of a vector space V, the subspace of V which consists of all linear combinations of these vectors will be designated by $[X_1, X_2, \cdots, X_m]$, and called the subspace *generated by* (or *spanned by*) the vectors $X_1, X_2, \cdots, X_m$.

Perhaps we should emphasize the distinction between the sets $\{X_1, X_2, \cdots, X_m\}$ and $[X_1, X_2, \cdots, X_m]$. The former is the set consisting of just the m vectors $X_1, X_2, \cdots X_m$; whereas the latter consists of all vectors which are expressible as linear combinations of the vectors $X_1, X_2, \cdots, X_m$. Since

$$X_1 = 1X_1 + 0X_2 + \cdots + 0X_m,$$

it is clear that X_1 is a linear combination of the vectors $X_1, X_2, \cdots, X_m$; and hence that $X_1 \in [X_1, X_2, \cdots, X_m]$. In like manner we see that $X_i \in [X_1, X_2, \cdots, X_m]$ for $i = 1, 2, \cdots, m$; and it follows that

$$\{X_1, X_2, \cdots, X_m\} \subseteq [X_1, X_2, \cdots, X_m].$$

Actually, $[X_1, X_2, \cdots, X_m]$ is the smallest subspace of V which contains all the vectors $X_1, X_2, \cdots X_m$; and this is the reason that we call it the subspace of V *generated by* these vectors.

As a consequence of the fact that $[X_1, X_2, \cdots, X_m]$ is a subspace of V, or by a simple direct calculation, it follows that a linear combination of vectors, each of which is a linear combination of $X_1 X_2, \cdots, X_m$, is itself a linear combination of $X_1, X_2, \cdots, X_m$. Otherwise expressed, if $Y_1, Y_2, \cdots, Y_k$ are elements of the subspace $[X_1, X_2, \cdots, X_m]$, then

$$[Y_1, Y_2, \cdots, Y_k] \subseteq [X_1, X_2, \cdots, X_m].$$

Moreover, we have that

$$[Y_1, Y_2, \cdots, Y_k] = [X_1, X_2, \cdots, X_m]$$

if and only if each of the Y's is a linear combination of the X's, and each of the X's is a linear combination of the Y's. This observation is frequently useful in proving the equality of two subspaces of V.

As an illustration of a subspace generated by given vectors, let us consider the vector space $V_3(\mathbf{R})$ and let $X = (1, 0, -1)$ and $Y = (2, 1, 3)$. Then the subspace $[X, Y]$ of $V_3(\mathbf{R})$ is the set of all vectors of the form $aX + bY$, where $a, b \in \mathbf{R}$. However,

$$aX + bY = a(1, 0, -1) + b(2, 1, 3) = (a + 2b, b, -a + 3b),$$

and hence $[X, Y]$ may be characterized as the set of all vectors of the form $(a + 2b, b, -a + 3b)$, with $a, b \in \mathbf{R}$.

Now let n be an arbitrary positive integer, and consider the vector space $V_n(F)$, where F is an arbitrary field. Let $E_1, E_2, \cdots, E_n$ be the following vectors of $V_n(F)$:

$$E_1 = (1, 0, 0, \cdots, 0),$$
$$E_2 = (0, 1, 0, \cdots, 0),$$
$$E_3 = (0, 0, 1, \cdots, 0),$$
$$\cdot \quad \cdot \quad \cdot \quad \cdot \quad \cdot \quad \cdot$$
$$E_n = (0, 0, 0, \cdots, 1).$$

These are often called the *unit vectors* of $V_n(F)$, and we shall in the future use the notation we have introduced here for these vectors. We observe now that these unit vectors are linearly independent since

$$a_1E_1 + a_2E_2 + \cdots + a_nE_n = (a_1, a_2, \cdots, a_n),$$

and this is the zero vector if and only if all a's are equal to zero. It is also almost obvious that the entire space $V_n(F)$ is generated by these unit vectors, that is, that

$$V_n(F) = [E_1, E_2, \cdots, E_n].$$

For if $(c_1, c_2, \cdots, c_n)$ is an arbitrary element of $V_n(F)$, we have

$$(c_1, c_2, \cdots, c_n) = c_1E_1 + c_2E_2 + \cdots + c_nE_n,$$

and hence every element of $V_n(F)$ is a linear combination of the unit vectors.

Before stating the next theorem let us observe that in the notation introduced in this section, Theorem 12.11(v) may be stated in the following convenient form.

12.14 Corollary. *If $X_1, X_2, \cdots, X_m$ are linearly independent vectors of V, each vector of the subspace $[X_1, X_2, \cdots, X_m]$ of V is uniquely expressible as a linear combination of $X_1, X_2, \cdots, X_m$.*

Several important properties are collected in the following theorem.

12.15 Theorem. *Let m be a positive integer and let $X_1, X_2, \cdots, X_m$ be vectors of the vector space V over the field F. The following are then true:*

(i) *If $Y = a_1X_1 + a_2X_2 + \cdots + a_mX_m$, where the a's are scalars and $a_k \neq 0$ for an integer k such that $1 \leq k \leq m$, then the subspace $[X_1, X_2, \cdots, X_m]$ is unchanged if X_k is replaced by Y; that is,*

$$[X_1, \cdots, X_k, \cdots, X_m] = [X_1, \cdots, Y, \cdots, X_m].$$

(ii) *If $X \in V$, then $[X_1, X_2, \cdots, X_m, X] = [X_1, X_2, \cdots, X_m]$ if and only if $X \in [X_1, X_2, \cdots, X_m]$.*

(iii) *If $\{X_1, X_2, \cdots, X_m\}$ is a linearly independent set and if $X \notin [X_1, X_2, \cdots, X_m]$, then $\{X_1, X_2, \cdots, X_m, X\}$ is a linearly independent set.*

We shall prove parts (i) and (iii) of this theorem, and leave the proof of part (ii) as an exercise.

First, let us consider part (i). Since Y is a linear combination of the X's, it follows at once that

$$[X_1, \cdots, Y, \cdots, X_m] \subseteq [X_1, \cdots, X_k, \cdots, X_m].$$

To obtain inclusion the other way, it is necessary to show that $X_k \in [X_1, \cdots, Y, \cdots, X_m]$. However, since it is given that $a_k \neq 0$, we may solve the given relation for X_k as follows:

$$X_k =$$
$$-a_k^{-1}(-Y + a_1X_1 + \cdots + a_{k-1}X_{k-1} + a_{k+1}X_{k+1} + \cdots + a_mX_m).$$

Hence $X_k \in [X_1, \cdots, Y, \cdots, X_m]$, and this completes the proof.

To establish part (iii), suppose that $c_1, c_2, \cdots, c_m, c$ are scalars such that

$$c_1X_1 + c_2X_2 + \cdots + c_mX_m + cX = 0,$$

and let us show that all of these scalars must be zero. If $c \neq 0$, we may write

$$X = -c^{-1}(c_1X_1 + c_2X_2 + \cdots + c_mX_m),$$

and it follows that $X \in [X_1, X_2, \cdots, X_m]$, thus violating our hypothesis. Hence we must have $c = 0$ and it then follows that $c_1X_1 + c_2X_2 + \cdots + c_mX_m = 0$. But since $X_1, X_2, \cdots, X_m$ are linearly independent, we conclude that $c_i = 0$ $(i = 1, 2, \cdots, m)$. These calculations therefore prove that the vectors $X_1, X_2, \cdots, X_m, X$ are linearly independent, as we wished to show.

Two special cases of the first part of this theorem are of sufficient interest to warrant specific mention. We therefore state them as the following corollary.

12.16   Corollary. *If $X_1, X_2, \cdots, X_m$ are vectors of a vector space V over a field F, then each of the following is true:*

  (i) *The subspace $[X_1, X_2, \cdots, X_m]$ is unchanged if a vector X_k $(1 \leq k \leq m)$ is replaced by aX_k, where a is a nonzero scalar; that is,*

$$[X_1, \cdots, X_k, \cdots, X_m] = [X_1, \cdots, aX_k, \cdots, X_m].$$

  (ii) *The subspace $[X_1, X_2, \cdots, X_m]$ is unchanged if a vector X_k $(1 \leq k \leq m)$ is replaced by $X_k + bX_l$, where $1 \leq l \leq m$, $l \neq k$, and b is any scalar. That is, we have*

$$[X_1, \cdots, X_k, \cdots, X_l, \cdots, X_m]$$
$$= [X_1, \cdots, X_k + bX_l, \cdots, X_l, \cdots, X_m].$$

We conclude this section with the following theorem, which will prove to be extremely useful in the further study of vector spaces.

12.17   Theorem. *If $X_1, X_2, \cdots, X_m$ are vectors in the vector space V, any $m + 1$ vectors in the subspace $[X_1, X_2, \cdots, X_m]$ of V are linearly dependent.*

The proof is by induction on m. For the case in which $m = 1$ we need only show that any two vectors of $[X_1]$ are linearly dependent. Let $Y_1 = aX_1$ and $Y_2 = bX_1$ be two vectors of the subspace $[X_1]$. If $a = 0$, then $Y_1 = 0$ and the equation $1Y_1 + 0Y_2 = 0$ shows that Y_1 and Y_2 are linearly dependent. If $a \neq 0$, the equation $-bY_1 + aY_2 = 0$ shows that Y_1 and Y_2 are linearly dependent. This disposes of the case in which $m = 1$.

To complete the proof by induction, let k be a positive integer such that the statement of the theorem is true for $m = k$, and let us prove it for $m = k + 1$. We shall do so by showing that if $Y_1, Y_2, \cdots,$ Y_{k+2} are arbitrary vectors in the subspace $[X_1, X_2, \cdots, X_{k+1}]$, then these vectors are linearly dependent. Since each Y_i is a linear combination of $X_1, X_2, \cdots, X_{k+1}$, we can write

12.18
$$
\begin{aligned}
Y_1 &= a_1X_1 + a_2X_2 + \cdots + a_{k+1}X_{k+1}, \\
Y_2 &= b_1X_1 + b_2X_2 + \cdots + b_{k+1}X_{k+1}, \\
Y_3 &= c_1X_1 + c_2X_2 + \cdots + c_{k+1}X_{k+1}, \\
&\ \cdot \quad \cdot \quad \cdot \quad \cdot \quad \cdot \quad \cdot \quad \cdot \\
Y_{k+2} &= s_1X_1 + s_2X_2 + \cdots + s_{k+1}X_{k+1},
\end{aligned}
$$

it being understood that the various coefficients are elements of F. If it happens that in these equations the coefficients of X_1 are all zero, then the Y's are, in fact, linear combinations of the k vectors X_2, $X_3, \cdots, X_{k+1}$. This means that they are elements of the subspace $[X_2, X_3, \cdots, X_{k+1}]$ and, by our assumption that the statement of the theorem is true for $m = k$, we see that any $k + 1$ vectors of the set $\{Y_1, Y_2, \cdots, Y_{k+2}\}$ are linearly dependent. Theorem 12.11(iv) then shows that the set $\{Y_1, Y_2, \cdots, Y_{k+2}\}$ is linearly dependent and we have the desired result.

There remains to dispose of the case in which not all the coefficients of X_1 in Equations 12.18 are zero. Let us assume, for convenience of notation, that $a_1 \neq 0$. Then from the first of Equations 12.18 we have that

$$a_1^{-1}Y_1 = X_1 + a_1^{-1}a_2X_2 + \cdots + a_1^{-1}a_{k+1}X_{k+1},$$

and from this and the second of Equations 12.18 it follows that the vector $Y_2 - b_1a_1^{-1}Y_1$ is a linear combination of $X_2, \cdots, X_{k+1}$; and is therefore an element of $[X_2, \cdots, X_{k+1}]$. Similarly, using the third of Equations 12.18, we see that $Y_3 - c_1a_1^{-1}Y_1$ is an element of $[X_2, \cdots, X_{k+1}]$. Continuing in this manner, we find that the $k + 1$ vectors

$$Y_2 - b_1a_1^{-1}Y_1, \ Y_3 - c_1a_1^{-1}Y_1, \cdots, Y_{k+2} - s_1a_1^{-1}Y_1$$

are elements of $[X_2, \cdots, X_{k+1}]$. But by our assumption that the statement of the theorem is true for $m = k$, these $k + 1$ vectors must be linearly dependent. Theorem 12.11(vi) then shows that the vectors $Y_1, Y_2, \cdots, Y_{k+2}$ are linearly dependent, and the proof of the theorem is complete.

The following simple corollary of this theorem follows immediately from the observation made above that if $E_1, E_2, \cdots, E_n$ are the unit vectors of $V_n(F)$, then $V_n(F) = [E_1, E_2, \cdots, E_n]$.

12.19   Corollary.   *Any $n + 1$ vectors of $V_n(F)$ are linearly dependent.*

EXERCISES

1. Prove that if $\{X_1, X_2, \cdots, X_m\}$ (where $m > 1$) is a linearly dependent set of vectors, then some one of these vectors is a linear combination of the others.

2. Prove Theorem 12.15(ii).

3. Show that if the set $\{X_1, X_2, \cdots, X_m\}$ is linearly independent but the set $\{X_1, X_2, \cdots, X_m, X\}$ is linearly dependent, then X is a linear combination of the vectors $X_1, X_2, \cdots, X_m$.

4. If $m > 1$, $X \in [X_1, X_2, \cdots, X_m]$, and $X \notin [X_1, X_2, \cdots, X_{m-1}]$, prove that $X_m \in [X_1, X_2, \cdots, X_{m-1}, X]$.

5. If $X \in [X_1, X_2, \cdots, X_m]$, show that the set $\{X, X_1, X_2, \cdots, X_m\}$ is a linearly dependent set.

6. Show that if $[X_1, X_2, \cdots, X_m] = [Y_1, Y_2, \cdots, Y_n]$ with $m \neq n$, then at least one of the sets $\{X_1, X_2, \cdots, X_m\}$ and $\{Y_1, Y_2, \cdots, Y_n\}$ is a linearly dependent set.

7. Show that if the nonzero vectors $X_1, X_2, \cdots, X_m$ $(m \geq 2)$ are linearly dependent, there exists an integer k with $2 \leq k \leq m$ such that X_k is a linear combination of $X_1, X_2, \cdots, X_{k-1}$.

12.5   BASIS AND DIMENSION

We now make the following definition.

12.20 **Definition.** The set $\{X_1, X_2, \cdots, X_n\}$ of elements of a vector space V is said to be a *basis* of V if the following two conditions are satisfied:

   (i) The set $\{X_1, X_2, \cdots, X_n\}$ is a linearly independent set.
   (ii) V is generated by $X_1, X_2, \cdots, X_n$; that is,

$$V = [X_1, X_2, \cdots, X_n].$$

In view of Corollary 12.14, we see that if the set $\{X_1, X_2, \cdots, X_n\}$ is a basis of V, every vector of V is *uniquely* expressible as a linear combination of the vectors $X_1, X_2, \cdots, X_n$.

As an example of the concept of basis of a vector space, we have already observed that the set $\{E_1, E_2, \cdots, E_n\}$ of unit vectors of $V_n(F)$ has both the defining properties and is therefore a basis of $V_n(F)$. In particular, let us now consider the vector space $V_3(\mathbf{R})$. Then, as a special case of the observation just made, the set $\{(1, 0, 0), (0, 1, 0), (0, 0, 1)\}$ is a basis of $V_3(\mathbf{R})$. However, $V_3(\mathbf{R})$ may have other bases as well. For example, let us consider the set $A = \{(1, 2, 1), (2, 1, 0), (1, -1, 2)\}$ of elements of $V_3(\mathbf{R})$. By the method used in Section 10.3 it can be shown that this is a linearly independent set, and we shall not give the details here. Moreover, that each of the unit vectors is a linear combination of the vectors of this set A follows from the following easily verified equations:

$$(1, 0, 0) = -\tfrac{2}{9}(1, 2, 1) + \tfrac{5}{9}(2, 1, 0) + \tfrac{1}{9}(1, -1, 2).$$
$$(0, 1, 0) = \tfrac{4}{9}(1, 2, 1) - \tfrac{1}{9}(2, 1, 0) - \tfrac{2}{9}(1, -1, 2).$$
$$(0, 0, 1) = \tfrac{1}{3}(1, 2, 1) - \tfrac{1}{3}(2, 1, 0) + \tfrac{1}{3}(1, -1, 2).$$

Since $V_3(\mathbf{R})$ is generated by the unit vectors, we see therefore that every element of $V_3(\mathbf{R})$ is a linear combination of the vectors of the set A. Hence, the vectors of this set form a basis of $V_3(\mathbf{R})$.

We have just indicated that a vector space may have more than one basis. However, it is easy to verify that not every vector space has a basis according to our definition.* As an example of a vector space without a basis, let us consider the vector space $P(F)$ of polynomials in an indeterminate x over a field F (Example 4 of Section 12.2). If n is an arbitrary positive integer and $f_1, f_2, \cdots, f_n$ are any n elements of $P(F)$, then no linear combination of these vectors can have a degree exceeding the maximum of the degrees of $f_1, f_2, \cdots, f_n$. Hence, there exist elements of $P(F)$ that are not in the subspace $[f_1 f_2, \cdots, f_n]$, and condition (ii) of Definition 12.20 cannot be satisfied. This shows that the vector space $P(F)$ cannot have a basis. Another example of a vector

---

* In more advanced treatises, what we have called a basis is usually called a *finite* basis, and every vector space has either a finite or an infinite basis. See Theorem 17.33 in the last chapter of this book.

space without a basis is the vector space $W(F)$ of Example 2 of Section 12.2. However, we shall be primarily concerned with vector spaces that do have bases, and for them the following theorem is fundamental.

12.21   Theorem.   *If the vector space V has a basis consisting of n vectors, then every basis of V has exactly n vectors.*

Suppose that $\{X_1, X_2, \cdots, X_n\}$ and $\{Y_1, Y_2, \cdots, Y_m\}$ are bases of V, and let us show that necessarily $m = n$. We observe that $V = [X_1, X_2, \cdots, X_n] = [Y_1, Y_2, \cdots, Y_m]$ and apply Theorem 12.17 as follows. If $m > n$, any $n + 1$ of the vectors $Y_1, Y_2, \cdots, Y_m$ are linearly dependent, and hence the entire set $\{Y_1, Y_2, \cdots, Y_m\}$ is linearly dependent. However, this contradicts the fact that $\{Y_1, Y_2 \cdots, Y_m\}$ is a basis of V. We conclude therefore that we cannot have $m > n$. By interchanging the roles of the X's and the Y's in this argument, we find also that we cannot have $n > m$. Hence, $m = n$, and the proof is complete.

Since all bases of a vector space have the same number of elements, it is convenient to have a name for the number of such elements.

12.22   Definition.   A vector space V is said to have *dimension n ($n \geq 1$)* if V has a basis consisting of n elements. The vector space consisting of only the zero vector is said to have *dimension zero*. A vector space is said to have *finite* dimension if it has dimension m for some nonnegative integer m.

We shall write dim $V = n$, to indicate that the vector space V has dimension n.

It is now clear that dim $V_n(F) = n$, since $V_n(F)$ has the basis $\{E_1, E_2, \cdots, E_n\}$. In particular, the vector space $V_2(\mathbf{R})$ discussed in Section 12.1, and which we described geometrically as the set of all vectors in a plane, has dimension 2. This fact should at least help to make our definition of dimension seem a reasonable one.

We shall now prove the following theorem.

12.23   Theorem.   *If dim $V = n$ with $n > 0$, the following are true:*

   (*i*)   *Any $n + 1$ vectors of V are linearly dependent.*

   (*ii*)   *Any set of n linearly independent vectors of V is a basis of V.*

   (*iii*) *V cannot be generated by fewer than n vectors.*

   (*iv*)   *If $V = [Z_1, Z_2, \cdots, Z_n]$, then $\{Z_1, Z_2, \cdots, Z_n\}$ is necessarily a linearly independent set and therefore a basis of V.*

If $\{X_1, X_2, \cdots, X_n\}$ is a basis of V, then $V = [X_1, X_2, \cdots, X_n]$ and the first statement of the theorem follows at once from Theorem 12.17.

To prove the second statement let, $\{Y_1, Y_2, \cdots, Y_n\}$ be a set of n linearly independent vectors of V. If this set were not a basis, there would exist an element Y of V such that $Y \not\subset [Y_1, Y_2, \cdots, Y_n]$. By Theorem 12.15(iii), this would imply that the set $\{Y_1, Y_2, \cdots, Y_n, Y\}$ is a linearly independent set. However, this is impossible by the first part of the present theorem, and we conclude that $\{Y_1, Y_2, \cdots, Y_n\}$ must be a basis of V.

If V were generated by m vectors with $m < n$, Theorem 12.17 would show that V could not contain n linearly independent vectors. However, dim $V = n$ implies that there do exist n linearly independent vectors in V, and we have established part (iii) of the theorem.

To prove part (iv), suppose that $V = [Z_1, Z_2, \cdots, Z_n]$, and let us assume that the set $\{Z_1, Z_2, \cdots, Z_n\}$ is linearly dependent and seek a contradiction. The case in which $n = 1$ is trivial, so we may assume that $n > 1$. Then the linear dependence of the set $\{Z_1, Z_2, \cdots, Z_n\}$ implies that some one of these vector is a linear combination of the others. (See Exercise 1 of the preceding set.) For convenience of notation, let us suppose that Z_1 is a linear combination of $Z_2, \cdots, Z_n$. By Theorem 12.15(ii), we then see that

$$V = [Z_1, Z_2, \cdots, Z_n] = [Z_2, \cdots, Z_n].$$

However, this violates part (iii) of the present theorem since we now have V generated by fewer than n vectors. This contradiction shows that the set $\{Z_1, Z_2, \cdots, Z_n\}$ is linearly independent, and the proof of the theorem is therefore complete.

The next theorem shows that any set of linearly independent vectors of a vector space of finite dimension is a part of a basis of the space.

12.24 **Theorem.** *Let V be a vector space of dimension $n > 1$. If $\{X_1, X_2, \cdots, X_r\}$, where $1 \leq r < n$, is a set of linearly independent vectors of V, there exist vectors $X_{r+1}, \cdots, X_n$ of V such that $\{X_1, X_2, \cdots, X_n\}$ is a basis of V.*

This result is easily established as follows. Since $r < n$, the set $\{X_1, X_2, \cdots, X_r\}$ is not a basis of V and hence there exists a vector X_{r+1} of V such that $X_{r+1} \not\subset [X_1, X_2, \cdots, X_r]$. By Theorem 12.15(iii), the set $\{X_1, X_2, \cdots, X_r, X_{r+1}\}$ is a linearly independent set. If $r + 1 < n$, we can repeat the argument. Continuing in this way, we must eventually obtain a set of n linearly independent vectors and, by the preceding theorem, this set is a basis of V.

We next consider a few questions about the dimensions of subspaces of a given vector space.

12.25   Theorem.

(i)   *If dim V = n and U is a subspace of V, then U has finite dimension and dim U ≤ n. Moreover, U = V if and only if dim U = n.*

(ii) *If the nonzero subspace U is generated by the vectors of the set $\{X_1, X_2, \cdots, X_k\}$, there exists a subset of $\{X_1, X_2, \cdots, X_k\}$ which is a basis of U.*

The first part of this theorem is trivial if $n = 0$; hence we assume that $n > 0$. If U consists only of the zero vector, dim $U = 0$ and clearly dim $U \le n$, so there is nothing to prove. Suppose, then, that X_1 is a nonzero vector in U. If $U \ne [X_1]$, let X_2 be an element of U which is not in $[X_1]$. Then X_1 and X_2 are linearly independent. If $U \ne [X_1, X_2]$, let X_3 be an element of U which is not in $[X_1, X_2]$, and again we know that X_1, X_2, and X_3 are linearly independent. Continuing in this way, we must eventually come to the point at which $U = [X_1, X_2, \cdots, X_r]$, where $r \le n$ since there can exist at most n linearly independent vectors in V. This shows that dim $U = r \le n$, and the first statement of part (i) is established. The second statement of this part is an immediate consequence of Theorem 12.23(ii).

Part (ii) can be proved by a simple modification of the above proof. Instead of choosing an arbitrary vector of U not in a specified subspace one can always choose an element of the generating set $\{X_1, X_2, \cdots, X_k\}$. We leave the details as an exercise. (*Cf.* also Exercise 6 below.)

If U_1 and U_2 are subspaces of the same vector space V, let us define

12.26 $$U_1 + U_2 = \{X + Y \mid X \in U_1, Y \in U_2\}.$$

As will soon be stated in the next theorem, it can be shown that $U_1 + U_2$ is a *subspace* of V. We may remark that since the subspace U_2 contains the zero vector, it follows that if $X \in U_1$, then $X = X + 0$ is also an element of $U_1 + U_2$. That is, $U_1 \subseteq U_1 + U_2$; and, similarly, $U_2 \subseteq U_1 + U_2$. However, in general, $U_1 + U_2$ will contain many vectors other than those in U_1 or U_2. It is quite easy to show that the intersection $U_1 \cap U_2$ of the two subspaces U_1 and U_2 is also a subspace of V. An interesting relationship between the subspaces U_1, U_2, $U_1 + U_2$, and $U_1 \cap U_2$ is given in the second part of the following theorem.

12.27   Theorem.   *Let U_1 and U_2 be subspaces of a vector space V. Then*

(i)   *$U_1 \cap U_2$ and $U_1 + U_2$ are subspaces of V,*

(ii) *If V has finite dimension,*
      dim $(U_1 + U_2)$ = dim U_1 + dim U_2 − dim $(U_1 \cap U_2)$.

We shall leave as exercises the proof of part (i) of this theorem and the proof of part (ii) for the special case in which dim $(U_1 \cap U_2) =$

0. We then proceed to the proof of part (ii) under the assumption that $\dim (U_1 \cap U_2) > 0$ We may remark that since $U_1 \cap U_2$ is a subspace of U_1, it follows that

$$\dim (U_1 \cap U_2) \le \dim U_1,$$

and, similarly,

$$\dim (U_1 \cap U_2) \le \dim U_2.$$

First, we dispose of an easy special case as follows. Suppose that

$$\dim (U_1 \cap U_2) = \dim U_1,$$

which implies that $U_1 \cap U_2 = U_1$. It follows that $U_1 \subseteq U_2$, and 12.26 then shows that $U_1 + U_2 = U_2$. Hence, in this case, 12.27 (ii) takes the form

$$\dim U_2 = \dim U_1 + \dim U_2 - \dim U_1,$$

which is obviously true. Similar remarks hold if it happens that

$$\dim (U_1 \cap U_2) = \dim U_2.$$

Let us now set $\dim (U_1 \cap U_2) = r$, $\dim U_1 = r + s$, and $\dim U_2 = r + t$. In view of the preceding remarks, we henceforth assume that $r > 0$, $s > 0$, and $t > 0$. The proof will be completed by showing that

$$\dim (U_1 + U_2) = r + s + t.$$

Let $\{X_1, \cdots, X_r\}$ be a basis of $U_1 \cap U_2$. Then, by Theorem 12.24, there exist vectors $Y_1, \cdots, Y_s$ such that $\{X_1, \cdots, X_r, Y_1, \cdots, Y_s\}$ is a basis of U_1; and vectors $Z_1, \cdots, Z_t$ such that $\{X_1, \cdots, X_r, Z_1, \cdots, Z_t\}$ is a basis of U_2. It now follows from 12.26 that every vector of the subspace $U_1 + U_2$ is a linear combination of vectors of the set

12.28 $$\{X_1, \cdots, X_r, Y_1, \cdots, Y_s, Z_1, \cdots, Z_t\}.$$

We shall show that this is a linearly independent set and hence a basis of $U_1 + U_2$.

Suppose that

12.29 $$a_1 X_1 + \cdots + a_r X_r + b_1 Y_1 + \cdots$$
$$+ b_s Y_s + c_1 Z_1 + \cdots + c_t Z_t = 0,$$

where all the coefficients are elements of F. Let $Z = c_1Z_1 + \cdots + c_tZ_t$. It is then clear that $Z \in U_2$, and we see from 12.29 that

$$Z = -(a_1X_1 + \cdots + a_rX_r + b_1Y_1 + \cdots + b_sY_s),$$

and hence also $Z \in U_1$. This shows that $Z \in (U_1 \cap U_2)$, and hence Z is a linear combination of the basis elements $X_1, \cdots, X_r$ of $U_1 \cap U_2$. Thus there exist scalars $e_1, \cdots, e_r$ such that

$$Z = c_1Z_1 + \cdots + c_tZ_t = e_1X_1 + \cdots + e_rX_r,$$

and from this it follows that

$$e_1X_1 + \cdots + e_rX_r - c_1Z_1 - \cdots - c_tZ_t = 0.$$

But since $\{X_1, \cdots, X_r, Z_1, \cdots, Z_t\}$ is a basis of U_2, this is a linearly independent set and hence all e's and all c's must equal zero. Now, setting all c's equal to zero in 12.29, the linear independence of the set $\{X_1, \cdots, X_r, Y_1, \cdots, Y_s\}$ shows that we must have all a's and all b's equal to zero. Hence, a relation of the form 12.29 holds only if all coefficients are zero. This shows that the set 12.28 is a linearly independent set and therefore a basis of $U_1 + U_2$. Finally, we see that dim $(U_1 + U_2) = r + s + t$ since this is the number of vectors in the basis 12.28. The proof is therefore complete.

EXERCISES

1. Prove Theorem 12.25(ii).

2. Prove Theorem 12.27(i).

3. Prove Theorem 12.27 (ii) for the case in which dim $(U_1 \cap U_2) = 0$.

4. Find a basis for $V_3(\mathbf{R})$ which contains the vectors $(1, -1, 0)$ and $(2, 1, 3)$.

5. If $\mathbf{C}(\mathbf{R})$ is the vector space of the field of complex numbers over the field $\mathbf{R}$ of real numbers (*cf.* Example 3 of Section 12.2),

   (i) Find the dimension of $\mathbf{C}(\mathbf{R})$.

   (ii) Show that $\{a + bi, c + di\}$ is a basis of $\mathbf{C}(\mathbf{R})$ if and only if $ad - bc \neq 0$.

6. Let $A = \{X_1, X_2, \cdots, X_m\}$ be a set of nonzero vectors of a vector space V. A subset $\{Y_1, Y_2, \cdots, Y_k\}$ of A is said to be a *maximal linearly independent subset* of A if (i) the set $\{Y_1, Y_2, \cdots, Y_k\}$ is linearly independent, and (ii) the set $\{Y_1, Y_2, \cdots, Y_k, Y\}$ is a linearly dependent set for each Y in A other than Y_1, $Y_2, \cdots, Y_k$. Show that if $\{Y_1, Y_2, \cdots, Y_k)$ is a maximal linearly independent subset of A, then $[X_1, X_2, \cdots, X_m] = [Y_1, Y_2, \cdots, Y_k]$ and, in particular,

$$\dim [X_1, X_2, \cdots, X_m] = k.$$

7. Find the dimension of the subspace
   $[(1, 2, 1, 0), (-1, 1, -4, 3), (2, 3, 3, -1), (0, 1, -1, 1)]$
   of $V_4(\mathbf{R})$.

8. Let U_1 and U_2 be subspaces of $V_4(\mathbf{R})$ as follows: $U_1 = [(1, 2, -1, 0), (2, 0, 1, 1)]$ and $U_2 = [(0, 0, 0, 1), (1, 0, 1, 0), (0, 4, -3, -1)]$. Find $\dim U_1$, $\dim U_2$, $\dim (U_1 \cap U_2)$, $\dim (U_1 + U_2)$, and verify the truth of Theorem 12.27 (ii) in this particular case.

9. Give an example to show that the following statement is false: If $\{X_1, X_2, \cdots, X_n\}$ is a basis of V, and U is a subspace of V, then some subset of $\{X_1, X_2, \cdots, X_n\}$ is a basis of U.

10. Let T be the set of all subspaces of a nonzero vector space V, and let an operation of addition be defined on the set T by 12.26. Verify that T is not a group with respect to this operation of addition.

11. We have observed that a field may be considered to be a vector space over any subfield. Suppose that F_1, F_2, and F_3 are fields such that $F_1 \subset F_2 \subset F_3$. If $\{X_1, X_2, \cdots, X_m\}$ is a basis of F_2 over F_1, and $\{Y_1, Y_2, \cdots, Y_n\}$ is a basis of F_3 over F_2, prove that the mn elements $X_i Y_j (i = 1, 2, \cdots, m; j = 1, 2, \cdots, n)$ are a basis of F_3 over F_1.

12. If U_1 is a subspace of a vector space V of finite dimension, prove that there exists a subspace U_2 of V such that $V = U_1 + U_2$ and $U_1 \cap U_2 = \{0\}$. Exhibit an example to show that there may be more than one such subspace U_2.

13. If U_1, U_2, and U_3 are subspaces of a vector space V, and $U_1 \subseteq U_3$, prove that $U_1 + (U_2 \cap U_3) = (U_1 + U_2) \cap U_3$.

12.6 HOMOMORPHISMS OF VECTOR SPACES

The familiar concept of homomorphism of rings or of groups can easily be modified so as to apply to vector spaces over the same field.

12.30 Definition. Let V and W be vector spaces over the same field F. A mapping $\theta \colon V \to W$ is called a *homomorphism* (or a *linear transformation*) of V into W if the following are true:

(i) $(X + Y)\theta = X\theta + Y\theta$, $\qquad\qquad\qquad\qquad$ $X, Y \in V$,

(ii) $(cX)\theta = c(X\theta)$, $\qquad\qquad\qquad\qquad\qquad$ $c \in F, X \in V$.

The first of these conditions merely states that addition is preserved under the mapping θ; that is, if we ignore scalar multiplication, θ is a homomorphism of the abelian group V into the abelian group W. The second condition asserts that also scalar multiplication is preserved under the mapping θ.

Just as in the case of rings or of groups, if there exists a homomorphism of V *onto* W, we may say that V is *homomorphic to* W or that W is a *homomorphic image* of V. Naturally, a homomorphism which is a one-one mapping is called an *isomorphism,* and if there exists an isomorphism of V onto W we say that V is *isomorphic to* W or that W is an *isomorphic image* of V, and may indicate this fact by writing $V \cong W$.

The following are some examples of homomorphisms of vector spaces. We leave it to the reader to verify that they are indeed homomorphisms.

EXAMPLE 1. Let $\theta \colon V_3(F) \to V_2(F)$ be defined by

$$(a_1, a_2, a_3)\theta = (a_1, a_3).$$

Then θ is a homomorphism of $V_3(F)$ onto $V_2(F)$.

EXAMPLE 2. Let $\phi \colon V_2(F) \to V_3(F)$ be defined by

$$(a_1, a_2)\phi = (a_1 + a_2, a_1, a_2).$$

This mapping ϕ is a homomorphism, but it is not an onto mapping.

EXAMPLE 3. Let $\gamma \colon V_2(\mathbf{R}) \to V_2(\mathbf{R})$ be defined by

$$(a_1, a_2)\gamma = (2a_1 - 3a_2, a_1 + 2a_2).$$

Then γ is a homomorphism of $V_2(\mathbf{R})$ into $V_2(\mathbf{R})$. (See Exercise 1 below.)

The following theorem lists a few of the basic facts about homomorphisms of vector spaces

12.31 Theorem. *Let $\theta \colon V \to W$ be a homomorphism of the vector space V over the field F into the vector space W over F. Then each of the following is true:*

(*i*)   *If 0 is the zero of V, then 0θ is the zero of W.*

(*ii*)   *If $X \in V$, then $(-X)\theta = -(X\theta)$.*

(*iii*)   *Let k be an arbitrary positive integer. If $X_i \in V$ and $c_i \in F$ $(i = 1, 2, \cdots, k)$, then*
$$(c_1 X_1 + c_2 X_2 + \cdots + c_k X_k)\theta = c_1(X_1\theta) + c_2(X_2\theta) + \cdots + c_k(X_k\theta).$$

(*iv*)   *If U is a subspace of V and $U\theta = \{X\theta \mid X \in U\}$, then $U\theta$ is a subspace of W.*

Since parts (i) and (ii) do not involve scalar multiplication, they are properties of group homomorphisms which have already been established. They also follow easily from 12.30(ii) by letting c be 0 and -1, respectively. The proofs of (iii) and (iv) are straightforward, and we leave them as an exercise.

We may emphasize that both of the properties (i) and (ii) of 12.30, used to define a homomorphism, are special cases of 12.31(*iii*), so that we *could* have used property 12.31(*iii*) as the definition of a homomorphism.

If $\theta: V \to W$ is a homomorphism (always assuming that V and W are vector spaces over the *same* field), let us define the *kernel* of θ, which we shall write as ker θ, as follows:

$$\ker \theta = \{X \mid X \in V,\ X\theta = 0\}.$$

We may now state the following result.

12.32   Theorem.   *If $\theta: V \to W$ is a homomorphism of V into W, then ker θ is a subspace of V. Moreover, θ is an isomorphism if and only if ker $\theta = \{0\}$.*

We shall leave the first statement as an exercise, and give only the proof of the second.

Since, by Theorem 12.31(*i*), we know that $0\theta = 0$, it follows that if θ is a one-one mapping, no other element can have 0 as an image; hence ker $\theta = \{0\}$. Conversely, if ker $\theta = \{0\}$ and $X\theta = Y\theta$, it follows from Theorem 12.31 that $(X - Y)\theta = 0$. Thus, $(X - Y) \in$ ker θ, and therefore $X - Y = 0$, or $X = Y$. This shows that θ is a one-one mapping, as we wished to prove.

In the case of vector spaces of finite dimension, we have the following result.

12.33   Theorem.   *If V and W are vector spaces of finite dimension over a field F, then $V \cong W$ if and only if dim $V =$ dim W.*

We shall give an outline of a proof of this theorem and suggest that the reader supply the details. Suppose, first, that $\theta: V \to W$ is an isomorphism of V onto W. Let us assume that dim $V = n$ and dim $W = m$. The desired result is trivial in case $n = 0$, so we assume that $n > 0$. If $\{X_1, X_2, \cdots, X_n\}$ is a basis of V, it can be verified that $\{X_1\theta, X_2\theta, \cdots, X_n\theta\}$ is a basis of W. Hence dim $W = n$, and therefore $n = m$.

Conversely, suppose that dim $V = $ dim $W = n > 0$. Let $\{X_1, X_2, \cdots, X_n\}$ be a basis of V and $\{Y_1, Y_2, \cdots, Y_n\}$ a basis of W. Each element X of V can be uniquely expressed as a linear combination of the basis elements of V. We leave it to the reader to verify that the mapping θ defined by

$$(a_1X_1 + a_2X_2 + \cdots + a_nX_n)\theta = a_1Y_1 + a_2Y_2 + \cdots + a_nY_n,$$

where the a's are arbitrary elements of F, is the desired isomorphism of V onto W.

Since for each $n > 0$, $V_n(F)$ has dimension n, we have the following immediate consequence of the preceding theorem.

12.34   Corollary.   *If the vector space V has dimension $n > 0$ over the field F, then $V \cong V_n(F)$.*

The content of this theorem suggests that when studying vector spaces of finite dimension we could limit ourselves to vector spaces of the form $V_n(F)$. However, it is often simpler not to make this restriction. Moreover, the most important properties of vector spaces are, and should be, independent of notation. This is the reason that we have waited until this point to prove Corollary 12.34.

The next result gives some important information about the *existence* of homomorphisms of V into W, in case V has finite dimension.

12.35   Theorem.   *Let V and W be vector spaces over the field F, and suppose that dim $V = n > 0$. If $\{X_1, X_2, \cdots, X_n\}$ is a basis of V, and Y_1, $Y_2, \cdots, Y_n$ are arbitrary elements of W, there exists exactly one homomorphism α of V into W such that $X_i\alpha = Y_i$ $(i = 1, 2, \cdots, n)$.*

PROOF: If $X \in V$, there exist unique elements $a_1, a_2, \cdots, a_n$ of F such that

12.36 $X = a_1X_1 + a_2X_2 + \cdots + a_nX_n\,.$

We now define a mapping α of V into W as follows:

12.37 $\quad (a_1X_1 + a_2X_2 + \cdots + a_nX_n)\alpha = a_1Y_1 + a_2Y_2 + \cdots + a_nY_n .$

Although the proof is straightforward let us verify that α is indeed a homomorphism. If X, given by 12.36, and

12.38 $\qquad\qquad X' = b_1X_1 + b_2X_2 + \cdots + b_nX_n$

are any elements of V, then

$$\begin{aligned}(X + X')\alpha &= [(a_1 + b_1)X_1 + (a_2 + b_2)X_2 + \cdots + (a_n + b_n)X_n]\alpha \\ &= (a_1 + b_1)Y_1 + (a_2 + b_2)Y_2 + \cdots + (a_n + b_n)Y_n \\ &= (a_1Y_1 + a_2Y_2 + \cdots + a_nY_n) + (b_1Y_1 + b_2Y_2 \\ &\quad + \cdots + b_nY_n) \\ &= X\alpha + X'\alpha,\end{aligned}$$

and thus addition is preserved under the mapping α.

Also, if X is given by 12.36 and $c \in F$, then

$$\begin{aligned}(cX)\alpha &= (ca_1X_1 + ca_2X_2 + \cdots + ca_nX_n)\alpha \\ &= ca_1Y_1 + ca_2Y_2 + \cdots + ca_nY_n \\ &= c(a_1Y_1 + a_2Y_2 + \cdots + a_nY_n) \\ &= c(X\alpha).\end{aligned}$$

This shows that scalar multiplication is preserved, and we have that α is a homomorphism. Moreover, if in 12.37 we choose all a's to be zero except $a_i = 1$, we see that $X_i\alpha = Y_i$ for $i = 1, 2, \cdots, n$.

These calculations verify that the mapping α, defined by 12.37, is one homomorphism of V into W satisfying the requirement of the theorem. To show that there is only one such homomorphism, let $\theta: V \to W$ be any homomorphism of V into W with the property that $X_i\theta = Y_i$ for $i = 1, 2, \cdots, n$. Then if $X \in V$, given by 12.36, we have from Theorem 12.31(*iii*) that

$$\begin{aligned}X\theta &= (a_1X_1 + a_2X_2 + \cdots + a_nX_n)\theta \\ &= a_1(X_1\theta) + a_2(X_2\theta) + \cdots + a_n(X_n\theta) \\ &= a_1Y_1 + a_2Y_2 + \cdots + a_nY_n.\end{aligned}$$

It follows that $X\alpha = X\theta$ for every X in V, and $\alpha = \theta$, as we wished to show.

It may be emphasized that we have just shown that if two homomorphisms of V into W have the same effect upon the elements of a basis of V, then the homomorphisms are equal. This fact is often expressed by saying that *a homomorphism of V into W is completely determined by its effect upon a basis of V.* In particular, if we wish to show that two homomorphisms β and γ of V into W are equal, we may do so by showing that each element of a basis of V has the same image under β as under γ.

If V and W are vector spaces over the same field F, it is customary to denote the set of all homomorphisms of V into W by $\text{Hom}_F(V, W)$. In the following section we shall give definitions of addition and scalar multiplication in such a way that $\text{Hom}_F(V, W)$ becomes itself a vector space over F.

EXERCISES

1. If $\theta: V_3(F) \to V_2(F)$ is the homomorphism defined in Example 1, determine ker θ and verify that it is a subspace of $V_3(F)$.

2. Prove that the homomorphism γ of Example 3 is an isomorphism of $V_2(\mathbf{R})$ onto $V_2(\mathbf{R})$.

3. Prove Theorem 12.31(iii) and (iv).

4. Prove the first statement of Theorem 12.32.

5. Complete the proof of Theorem 12.33.

6. Let V be the vector space of all polynomials with real coefficients (*Cf.* Example 4 of Section 12.2), and denote the derivative of $f(x)$ by $f'(x)$. Verify that the mapping $\theta: V \to V$ defined by $f(x)\theta = f'(x)$ is a homomorphism of V into V. What is the kernel of this homomorphism?

12.7 HOM$_F$(V, W) AS A VECTOR SPACE

Throughout this section, V and W will be vector spaces over the same field F. For simplicity, we shall often denote the set of all homomorphisms of V into W by H instead of using the more explicit, but more cumbersome, $\text{Hom}_F(V, W)$. Our present goal is to define addition in H and scalar multiplication of elements of H by elements of F in such a way that H becomes a vector space over F. We may observe that if V has positive dimension and $W \neq \{0\}$, Theorem 12.35 assures us that H has elements other than the trivial homomorphism which maps every element of V into the zero of W.

If $\alpha, \beta \in H$, we propose to define a mapping $\alpha + \beta$ as follows:

12.39 $$X(\alpha + \beta) = X\alpha + X\beta, \qquad\qquad X \in V.$$

It is clear that, as so defined, $\alpha + \beta$ is a mapping of V into W. The proof that it is a homomorphism follows from the defining properties (12.3) of a vector space and properties of homomorphisms. The details of the proof are as follows, in which $X_1, X_2 \in V$ and $a \in F$:

$$
\begin{aligned}
(X_1 + X_2)(\alpha + \beta) &= (X_1 + X_2)\alpha + (X_1 + X_2)\beta && (by\ 12.39) \\
&= X_1\alpha + X_2\alpha + X_1\beta + X_2\beta && (by\ 12.30(i)) \\
&= X_1\alpha + X_1\beta + X_2\alpha + X_2\beta && (by\ 12.3(i)) \\
&= X_1(\alpha + \beta) + X_2(\alpha + \beta) && (by\ 12.39),
\end{aligned}
$$

and

$$
\begin{aligned}
(aX_1)(\alpha + \beta) &= (aX_1)\alpha + (aX_1)\beta && (by\ 12.39) \\
&= a(X_1\alpha) + a(X_1\beta) && (by\ 12.30(ii)) \\
&= a(X_1\alpha + X_1\beta) && (by\ 12.3(ii)) \\
&= a[X_1(\alpha + \beta)] && (by\ 12.39).
\end{aligned}
$$

These calculations show that both addition and scalar multiplication are preserved under the mapping $\alpha + \beta$ of V into W; hence $\alpha + \beta \in H$, and 12.39 defines an addition on the set H.

Next, if $\alpha \in H$ and $c \in F$, we define a mapping $c\alpha$ of V into W as follows:

12.40 $$X(c\alpha) = (cX)\alpha \qquad\qquad X \in V.$$

Again, we show that $c\alpha \in H$ by verifying that the mapping $c\alpha$ is a homomorphism of V into W. Let $X_1, X_2 \in V$ and $a \in F$. Then

$$
\begin{aligned}
(X_1 + X_2)(c\alpha) &= [c(X_1 + X_2)]\alpha && (by\ 12.40) \\
&= (cX_1 + cX_2)\alpha && (by\ 12.3(ii)) \\
&= (cX_1)\alpha + (cX_2)\alpha && (by\ 12.30(i)) \\
&= X_1(c\alpha) + X_2(c\alpha) && (by\ 12.40),
\end{aligned}
$$

and

$$
\begin{aligned}
(aX_1)(c\alpha) &= [c(aX_1)]\alpha && (by\ 12.40) \\
&= [(ca)X_1]\alpha && (by\ 12.3(iv)) \\
&= [(ac)X_1]\alpha && (comm.\ of\ F) \\
&= [a(cX_1)]\alpha && (by\ 12.3(iv)) \\
&= a[(cX_1)\alpha] && (by\ 12.30(ii)) \\
&= a[X_1(c\alpha)] && (by\ 12.40).
\end{aligned}
$$

Thus, both addition and scalar multiplication are preserved under the mapping $c\alpha$, and therefore $c\alpha \in H$.

We can now state the following significant result.

12.41   Theorem.   *Let V and W be vector spaces over the same field F, and let H be the set of all homomorphisms of V into W. If addition and scalar multiplication by elements of F are defined respectively by 12.39 and 12.40, H becomes a vector space over F.*

In order to establish this result, it is necessary to verify all the defining properties 12.3 of a vector space. We shall sketch a proof that H is an abelian group with respect to addition, and leave the proofs of 12.3(ii)–(v) as an exercise.

If $\alpha, \beta, \gamma \in H$ and $X \in V$, we have

$$
\begin{aligned}
X[(\alpha + \beta) + \gamma] &= X(\alpha + \beta) + X\gamma & \text{(by 12.39)} \\
&= (X\alpha + X\beta) + X\gamma & \text{(by 12.39)} \\
&= X\alpha + (X\beta + X\gamma) & \text{(by 12.3(i))} \\
&= X\alpha + X(\beta + \gamma) & \text{(by 12.39)} \\
&= X[\alpha + (\beta + \gamma)] & \text{(by 12.39)}.
\end{aligned}
$$

Since $X[(\alpha + \beta) + \gamma] = X[\alpha + (\beta + \gamma)]$ for every X in V, we have $(\alpha + \beta) + \gamma = \alpha + (\beta + \gamma)$, and addition in H is associative.

Moreover, since for α, β in H and X in V,

$$
\begin{aligned}
X(\alpha + \beta) &= X\alpha + X\beta \\
&= X\beta + X\alpha \\
&= X(\beta + \alpha),
\end{aligned}
$$

we conclude that $\alpha + \beta = \beta + \alpha$, and addition is commutative.

If we define $\zeta \colon V \to W$ by $X\zeta = 0$ for every X in V, then ζ is the identity for the abelian group H since clearly $X(\alpha + \zeta) = X\alpha + X\zeta = X\alpha$, and therefore $\alpha + \zeta = \alpha$ for $\alpha \in H$.

Finally, if $\alpha \in H$, then the inverse $-\alpha$ of α is the mapping (clearly a homomorphism) defined by

$$
X(-\alpha) = -(X\alpha).
$$

For then

$$
\begin{aligned}
X(\alpha + (-\alpha)) &= X\alpha + X(-\alpha) \\
&= X\alpha - (X\alpha) = 0 = X\zeta
\end{aligned}
$$

for every X in V, and it follows that $\alpha + (-\alpha) = \zeta$.

We have verified the defining properties of an abelian group, and hence we have shown that H is an abelian group with respect to addition. As stated above, we shall omit the proofs of the other properties of a vector space.

In case both V and W have finite dimension over the field F, the dimension of the vector space $\mathrm{Hom}_F(V , W)$ is given by the following theorem.

12.42 Theorem. *If the vector spaces V and W have respective dimensions n > 0 and m > 0 over the field F, then the vector space $\mathrm{Hom}_F(V, W)$ has dimension nm over F.*

PROOF: The proof consists in exhibiting a basis of the space $H = \mathrm{Hom}_F(V , W)$ with nm elements. Let $\{X_1, X_2, \cdots, X_n\}$ be a basis of V and $\{Y_1, Y_2, \cdots, Y_m\}$ a basis of W. For each $i = 1, 2, \cdots, n$ and $j = 1, 2, \cdots, m$, there exists (by Theorem 12.35) a unique homomorphism α_{ij} of V into W such that

12.43
$$\begin{aligned} X_i\alpha_{ij} &= Y_j \\ X_k\alpha_{ij} &= 0 \text{ for } k \neq i. \end{aligned}$$

Since $1 \leq i \leq n$ and $1 \leq j \leq m$, there are n choices for i and m choices for j; hence we have nm elements α_{ij} of H. We propose to prove that these elements form a basis of the vector space H. First of all, let us show that these α_{ij} are linearly independent. Suppose that

$$\beta = \sum_{j=1}^{m} \sum_{i=1}^{n} c_{ij}\alpha_{ij} = 0,$$

the c_{ij} being elements of F. Let k be an arbitrary, but fixed, element of the set $1, 2, \cdots, n$. Since we are assuming that $\beta = 0$, we have

$$0 = X_k\beta = \sum_{j=1}^{m} \sum_{i=1}^{n} c_{ij}(X_k\alpha_{ij}).$$

But, using the definition 12.43 of the α_{ij}, we see that we have

$$0 = \sum_{j=1}^{m} c_{kj}Y_j.$$

However, the Y's form a basis of W and hence are linearly independent. Accordingly, we conclude that $c_{kj} = 0$ for $j = 1, 2, \cdots, m$. Since k was an arbitrary element of the set $1, 2, \cdots, n$, we have shown that $c_{ij} = 0$ for all choices of i and j; hence the α_{ij} are linearly independent elements of the vector space H.

We must now show that any element of H is a linear combination of the elements α_{ij}. Let γ be an arbitrary element of H. For each $k \in \{1, 2, \cdots, n\}$, $X_k\gamma \in W$ and therefore $X_k\gamma$ can be expressed as a linear combination of the basis elements of W. Thus there exist elements a_{kj} of F such that

12.44 $$X_k\gamma = a_{k1}Y_1 + a_{k2}Y_2 + \cdots + a_{km}Y_m \qquad (k = 1, 2, \cdots, n).$$

We shall show that

$$\gamma = \sum_{j=1}^{m} \sum_{i=1}^{n} a_{ij}\alpha_{ij}$$

by showing that the elements of H occurring on the two sides of this equation have the same effect upon the elements of the basis $\{X_1, X_2, \cdots, X_n\}$ of V. If X_k is any one of these basis elements, we find (using 12.43) that

$$X_k\left(\sum_{j=1}^{m} \sum_{i=1}^{n} a_{ij}\alpha_{ij}\right) = \sum_{j=1}^{m} \sum_{i=1}^{n} a_{ij}(X_k\alpha_{ij})$$

$$= \sum_{j=1}^{m} a_{kj}Y_j$$

$$= X_k\gamma \qquad\qquad (by\ 12.44).$$

It follows that

$$\gamma = \sum_{j=1}^{m} \sum_{i=1}^{n} a_{ij}\alpha_{ij},$$

and we conclude that the α_{ij} do indeed form a basis of the vector space H over F. Since there are nm of the elements α_{ij}, we have shown that the vector space H over F has a basis with nm elements, and therefore has dimension nm. This completes the proof of the theorem.

In this section we have shown that under appropriate definitions of addition and scalar multiplication. $\mathrm{Hom}_F(V, W)$ is a vector space over F. In the next section we shall study in detail the important special case in which $\dim V = n > 0$ and $\dim W = 1$. The special case in which $V = W$ will be the principal subject of Chapter 16.

EXERCISES

1. Complete the proof of Theorem 12.41 by verifying that the defining properties 12.3(ii)–(v) of a vector space hold in H.

2. In the notation of Theorem 12.42, let $V = W = V_2(Q)$ and use the basis of unit vectors in both V and W. Determine the element $2\alpha_{11} + 3\alpha_{21}$ by exhibiting its effect upon the basis of unit vectors.

3. If V is a vector space over a field F and $\alpha, \beta \in \mathrm{Hom}_F(V, V)$, verify that the mapping $\alpha\beta$ is defined and that it is in fact an element of $\mathrm{Hom}_F(V, V)$.

4. If V and W are vector spaces over a field F with dim $V = n > 0$, and dim $W = m > 0$, what is the dimension of the vector space $\mathrm{Hom}_F(\mathrm{Hom}_F(V, W), V)$?

12.8 DUAL VECTOR SPACES

Throughout this section, V will denote a vector space of finite dimension over the field F, and W will have dimension 1, that is, W is F considered as a vector space over itself. We shall thus be concerned with the vector space $\mathrm{Hom}_F(V, F)$ of homomorphisms of V into F.

An element of $\mathrm{Hom}_F(V, F)$ is thus a mapping * $\alpha\colon V \to F$ such that if $X, Y \in V$ and $a \in F$, then

$$(X + Y)\alpha = X\alpha + Y\alpha$$

and

$$(aX)\alpha = a(X\alpha).$$

As a special case of Theorem 12.42, we see that if dim $V = n > 0$, then the dimension of $\mathrm{Hom}_F(V, F)$ is also n.

In order to emphasize that we are considering $\mathrm{Hom}_F(V, F)$ as a vector space, let us now denote it by V', and let us denote elements of V' by X', Y', and so on. Thus if $X' \in V'$, X' is a homomorphism of V into F, so that for each $X \in V$, $XX' \in F$. If $\{X_1, X_2, \cdots, X_n\}$ is a

---

* A mapping of V into F which has these properties is sometimes called a *linear functional* on V. In this language, $\mathrm{Hom}_F(V, F)$ consists of all linear functionals on V.

basis of V and we take as a basis of F the unity 1 of F, following the proof of Theorem 12.42 with $m = 1$ (and using the new notation) we see that V' has a basis $\{X_1', X_2', \cdots, X_n'\}$ where for each $k = 1, 2, \cdots, n$, the homomorphism X_k' of V into F is defined by

12.45 $X_k X_k' = 1, \quad X_i X_k' = 0$ for $i \neq k$.

Let us now make the following definition.

12.46 **Definition.** The vector space $V' = \mathrm{Hom}_F(V, F)$ is called the *dual* of the vector space V. If $\{X_1, X_2, \cdots, X_n\}$ is a basis of V and the X_k' are defined by 12.45, the basis $\{X_1', X_2', \cdots X_n'\}$ of V' is called the *dual basis* to $\{X_1, X_2, \cdots, X_n\}$.

Now that we have the vector space V' over F, for the moment we need not try to keep in mind what its elements are, but just consider that we have a vector space V' over F. There is then no reason why we should not consider *its* dual, which we may denote by V''. Thus elements of V'' are homomorphisms of V' into F, that is, $V'' = \mathrm{Hom}_F(V', F)$. If dim $V = n$, we know that dim $V' = n$ and dim $V'' = n$, so that these vector spaces are all isomorphic (by Theorem 12.33). This fact in itself is of no great importance, but it is significant that there exists a *natural* isomorphism of V onto V''. As we proceed to obtain this result, it will become apparent that the roles of V and V' are essentially interchangeable in that the dual of V', although not V itself, is isomorphic to V in a special way.

We observed above, when the present notation was introduced, that if $X \in V$ and $X' \in V'$, then $XX' \in F$. If X' is fixed, the mapping X' of V into F may be indicated by writing

$$X \to XX', \qquad\qquad X \in V.$$

Now if X is fixed, let us consider the mapping

$$X' \to XX', \qquad\qquad X' \in V'$$

of V' into F. For convenience, let us denote this last mapping by T_X, that is, T_X is defined by

12.47 $X'T_X = XX', \qquad\qquad X' \in V'.$

Not only is T_X a mapping of V' into F, we shall show that it is actually a homomorphism of V' into F, and is therefore an element of V''. Then we shall prove an important result which asserts that the mapping $X \to T_X$ is actually an isomorphism of V onto V''.

We proceed to verify that addition and scalar multiplication are preserved under the mapping T_X. If Y', $Z' \in V'$, we have

$$
\begin{aligned}
(Y' + Z')T_X &= X(Y' + Z') && \text{(by 12.47)}\\
&= XY' + XZ' && \text{(by 12.39)}\\
&= Y'T_X + Z'T_X && \text{(by 12.47)}.
\end{aligned}
$$

Also, if $Y' \in V'$ and $a \in F$,

$$
\begin{aligned}
(aY')T_X &= X(aY')\\
&= (aX)Y' && \text{(by 12.40)}\\
&= a(XY') && \text{(Y' is a}\\
& && \text{homomorphism)}\\
&= a(Y'T_X) && \text{(by 12.47)}.
\end{aligned}
$$

Thus, T_X is a homomorphism of V' into F and hence an element of V'', the dual of V'. As a matter of fact, *every* element of V'' is of the form T_X for some $X \in V$. This is one consequence of the following principal theorem about dual vector spaces of finite dimension.

12.48 Theorem. *Let V be a vector space of finite dimension and let $\theta\colon V \to V''$ be the mapping defined by $X\theta = T_X$, $X \in V$; where T_X is given by 12.47. Then θ is an isomorphism of V onto V''.*

PROOF: Let us first verify that θ is a homomorphism of V into V''. If X, $Y \in V$ and $X' \in V'$, we have (by use of 12.47 and the fact that X' is a homomorphism of V into F) that

$$
\begin{aligned}
X'T_{X+Y} &= (X + Y)X'\\
&= XX' + YX'\\
&= X'T_X + X'T_Y\\
&= X'(T_X + T_Y),
\end{aligned}
$$

by definition of addition in V''. Also, if $X' \in V'$ and $c \in F$, we have

$$
\begin{aligned}
X'T_{cX} &= (cX)X'\\
&= c(XX')\\
&= c(X'T_X)\\
&= X'(cT_X),
\end{aligned}
$$

by definition of the element cT_X of V''. These calculations show that $T_{X+Y} = T_X + T_Y$ and that $T_{cX} = cT_X$, that is, that $\theta\colon V \to V''$ has the properties that

$$(X + Y)\theta = X\theta + Y\theta$$

and

$$(cX)\theta = c(X\theta),$$

and θ is indeed a homomorphism of V into V''. There are various ways of showing that the mapping θ is one-one and onto. One method is as follows.

Let $\{X_1, X_2, \cdots, X_n\}$ be a basis of V and $\{X'_1, X'_2, \cdots, X'_n\}$ the dual basis (12.45) of V'. For each $k = 1, 2, \cdots, n$, the following hold (by 12.47):

$$X'_k T_{X_k} = X_k X'_k = 1,$$
$$X'_i T_{X_k} = X_k X'_i = 0 \quad \text{for } i \neq k.$$

By the same argument that led to the conclusion that $\{X'_1, \cdots, X'_n\}$ was a basis of V' (dual to the basis $\{X_1, \cdots, X_n\}$ of V), it follows that $\{T_{X_1}, T_{X_2}, \cdots, T_{X_n}\}$ is a basis of V'' dual to the basis $\{X'_1, X'_2, \cdots, X'_n\}$ of V'. Now if $X \in V$ and we write $X = a_1 X_1 + a_2 X_2 + \cdots + a_n X_n$, it is true that

$$X\theta = (a_1 X_1 + a_2 X_2 + \cdots + a_n X_n)\theta$$
$$= a_1 T_{X_1} + a_2 T_{X_2} + \cdots + a_n T_{X_n}.$$

We leave the verification of this fact as an exercise. Now since $\{X_1, X_2, \cdots, X_n\}$ is a basis of V and $\{T_{X_1}, T_{X_2}, \cdots, T_{X_n}\}$ is a basis of V'', it follows easily, as indicated near the end of the sketch of the proof of Theorem 12.33, that θ is an isomorphism of V onto V'', as we wished to show.

12.9   QUOTIENT VECTOR SPACES AND DIRECT SUMS

In this section we shall present very briefly a few additional concepts about vector spaces which will be useful for later reference. Since they are analogous to concepts which have previously been introduced for rings or groups, we shall sometimes state the basic results without proofs or with only an outline of a proof.

First, let us present the concept of a quotient space, which corresponds to the idea of a quotient ring or a quotient group. Let V be a vector space over a field F, and let U be a subspace of V. With respect to addition (ignoring scalar multiplication for the moment), we know that U is a subgroup of V. Accordingly, we may consider the set of all cosets of U in V, such a coset being of the form

$$X + U = \{X + Y \mid Y \in U\},$$

X being a fixed element of V. We know from our study of groups that addition of cosets is well-defined by

12.49 $$(X_1 + U) + (X_2 + U) = (X_1 + X_2) + U.$$

We now propose to define scalar multiplication of cosets by elements of F. If $X + U$ is a coset and $a \in F$, we define

12.50 $$a(X + U) = aX + U,$$

that is, $a(X + U)$ is the coset which contains aX. Let us show that scalar multiplication is well-defined by 12.50. To this end, suppose that $X_1 + U = X_2 + U$, and let us show that $aX_1 + U = aX_2 + U$. Now $X_1 + U = X_2 + U$ implies that $X_1 - X_2 \in U$. Then since U is a subspace of V, we see that $a(X_1 - X_2) \in U$ and it follows that $aX_1 + U = aX_2 + U$, and this completes the proof.

We may now state the following theorem (*cf.* Theorem 7.50).

12.51 Theorem. *Let U be a subspace of the vector space V over F. With respect to the definition 12.49 of addition and 12.50 of scalar multiplication, the set of all cosets of U in V is a vector space over F, usually called the* quotient space *of V by U and denoted by V/U. Moreover, the mapping $\theta: V \rightarrow V/U$ defined by $X\theta = X + U$, $X \in V$, is a homomorphism of V onto V/U with kernel U.*

We know from our study of groups that V/U is an abelian group with respect to addition and that the zero element is the coset U. To verify that it is in fact a vector space over F, the remaining properties (12.3) of the definition of a vector space must be verified. This will be listed as an exercise below.

If V has finite dimension, the following theorem states how dim V and dim U/V are related.

12.52 Theorem. *Suppose that the vector space V has finite dimension $n > 0$ over the field F, and let U be a subspace of V of dimension m. Then the vector space V/U has dimension $n - m$.*

PROOF: We know that $m \le n$. If $m = 0$, then $U = \{0\}$ and $V/U \cong V$, so this case is trivial. Let us therefore assume that $m > 0$.

Let $\{X_1, X_2, \cdots, X_m\}$ be a basis of U. By Theorem 12.24, this set can be extended to a basis

12.53 $\{X_1, \cdots, X_m, X_{m+1}, \cdots, X_n\}$

of V. We shall show that

12.54 $\{X_{m+1} + U, \cdots, X_n + U\}$

is a basis of the vector space V/U.

First, let $X + U$ be any element of V/U, and let us write X as a linear combination of the basis elements 12.53 of V,

$$X = a_1 X_1 + \cdots + a_n X_n.$$

Then since $a_1 X_1 + \cdots + a_m X_m$ is an element of U, we see that by 12.49 and 12.50

$$\begin{aligned} X + U &= (a_{m+1} X_{m+1} + \cdots + a_n X_n) + U \\ &= a_{m+1}(X_{m+1} + U) + \cdots + a_n(X_n + U). \end{aligned}$$

Thus every element of V/U is a linear combination of the elements 12.54.

Next, let us show that the elements 12.54 are linearly independent. Suppose that the b's are elements of F such that

$$b_{m+1}(X_{m+1} + U) + \cdots + b_n(X_n + U) = U,$$

U being the zero of the space V/U. This equation implies that $b_{m+1} X_{m+1} + \cdots + b_n X_n$ is an element of U. However, this fact implies that $b_{m+1} = \cdots = b_n = 0$ since the set 12.53 is linearly independent and each element of U is expressible as a linear combination of the basis elements $X_1, X_2, \cdots, X_m$ of U. Accordingly, we have shown that the elements 12.54 of V/U are linearly independent. We have thus completed the proof that the elements 12.54 are a basis of V/U. Since there are $n - m$ of these basis elements, the dimension of V/U is indeed $n - m$.

We now state the following theorem which is analogous to Theorem 11.27 for rings and Theorem 7.52 for groups. We shall list its proof as an exercise below.

12.55 Theorem. *Let V and W be vector spaces over the same field, and let $\theta: V \to W$ be a homomorphism of V onto W. Then $W \cong V/(\ker \theta)$.*

Next let us introduce the concept of direct sum of subspaces. If $U_1, U_2, \cdots, U_r$ are subspaces of the vector space V over the field F, by 12.26 we see that $U_1 + U_2 + \cdots + U_r$ is the subspace of V consisting of all elements of V expressible in the form

$$X_1 + X_2 + \cdots + X_r, \quad X_i \in U_i \ (i = 1, 2, \cdots, r).$$

In keeping with the concept of the direct sum of subgroups of a given abelian group, let us make the following definition.

12.56 Definition. If $U_i \ (i = 1, 2, \cdots, r)$ are subspaces of the vector space V, the sum $U_1 + U_2 + \cdots + U_r$ is said to be a *direct sum* if and only if each element X of this sum is *uniquely* expressible in the form

$$X = X_1 + X_2 + \cdots + X_r, \qquad\qquad X_i \in U_i.$$

As was pointed out when direct sums of abelian groups were introduced, an equivalent way of stating that a sum $U_1 + U_2 + \cdots + U_r$ is direct is to assert that *if* $X_i \in U_i \ (i = 1, 2, \cdots, r)$ *are such that* $X_1 + X_2 + \cdots + X_r = 0$, *then every* $X_i = 0$.

We may indicate that a sum $U_1 + U_2 + \cdots + U_r$ is direct by writing it in the form $U_1 \oplus U_2 + \cdots \oplus U_r$.

Let us conclude this section by proving the following simple consequence of previously established facts.

12.57 Theorem. *If* U_1 *and* U_2 *are subspaces of the vector space* V *such that* $V = U_1 \oplus U_2$, *then* $U_1 \cong V/U_2$ *and* $U_2 \cong V/U_1$.

PROOF: Each element X of V is uniquely expressible in the form $X_1 + X_2$, where $X_1 \in U_1$ and $X_2 \in U_2$. The mapping $\theta: V \to U_1$ defined by $X\theta = X_1$ is a homomorphism of V onto U_1. Moreover, $\ker \theta = U_2$. From Theorem 12.55, it follows that $U_1 \cong V/U_2$. Similarly, $U_2 \cong V/U_1$.

12.10 INNER PRODUCTS IN $V_n(F)$

For the moment, we consider only vector spaces of the form $V_n(F)$. The concept now to be introduced will be particularly useful in the following chapter.

12.58 Definition. If $X = (a_1, a_2, \cdots, a_n)$ and $Y = (b_1, b_2, \cdots, b_n)$ are elements of $V_n(F)$, the *inner product* $X \cdot Y$ of X and Y is defined as follows:

$$X \cdot Y = a_1 b_1 + a_2 b_2 + \cdots + a_n b_n.$$

It is clear that the inner product of two vectors is a scalar; that is, it is an element of F. The following theorem gives the most important properties of inner products. Since the proofs are quite simple, we leave them as exercises.

12.59 Theorem.

   (*i*) *If* $X, Y \in V_n(F)$, *then* $X \cdot Y = Y \cdot X$.

   (*ii*) *If* $X, Y, Z \in V_n(F)$, *then* $(X + Y) \cdot Z = X \cdot Z + Y \cdot Z$.

   (*iii*) *If* $X, Y \in V_n(F)$ *and* $a \in F$, *then*

$$(aX) \cdot Y = X \cdot (aY) = a(X \cdot Y).$$

   (*iv*) *If* $Y, X_1, X_2, \cdots, X_m$ *are elements of* $V_n(F)$, *and* $a_1, a_2, \cdots, a_m$ *are elements of* F, *then*

$$(a_1X_1 + a_2X_2 + \cdots + a_mX_m) \cdot Y$$
$$= a_1(X_1 \cdot Y) + a_2(X_2 \cdot Y) + \cdots + a_m(X_m \cdot Y).$$

EXERCISES

1. Let $\theta: V \to V''$ be the mapping defined in the statement of Theorem 12.48. If $X_1, X_2, \cdots, X_n$ are elements of V, verify in detail that

$$(a_1X_1 + a_2X_2 + \cdots + a_nX_n)\theta = a_1T_{X_1} + a_2T_{X_2} + \cdots + a_nT_{X_n}.$$

2. If θ is as in the preceding exercise, prove that θ is a one-one mapping by verifying that $\ker \theta = \{0\}$.

3. In the notation of Theorem 12.51 verify that all the defining properties of a vector space are satisfied in V/U.

4. Let U_1 and U_2 be subspaces of the vector space V such that $V = U_1 \oplus U_2$. If $\{X_1, X_2, \cdots, X_h\}$ is a basis of U_1 and $\{Y_1, Y_2, \cdots, Y_k\}$ is a basis of U_2, prove that $\{X_1, X_2, \cdots, X_h, Y_1, Y_2, \cdots, Y_k\}$ is a basis of V. Prove that not every basis of V is the union of bases of U_1 and of U_2.

5. State and prove a generalization of the preceding exercise to the case in which V is the direct sum of any finite number of subspaces.

6. Prove Theorem 12.55.

7. Prove Theorem 12.59.

8. If X and Y are nonzero vectors of $V_2(\mathbf{R})$, show that $X \cdot Y = 0$ if and only if the directed line segments which represent these vectors, in the sense described in Section 12.1, are perpendicular.

9. If $Y \in V_n(F)$, use Theorem 12.59 to show that the set of all vectors X of $V_n(F)$ such that $X \cdot Y = 0$ is a subspace of $V_n(F)$.

10. If S is a nonempty *subset* of $V_n(\mathbf{R})$, let us define $S^{\perp} = \{X \mid X \in V_n(\mathbf{R}), Y \cdot X = 0 \text{ for every } Y \text{ in } S\}$.

    (i) Prove that $S^{\perp}$ is a *subspace* of $V_n(\mathbf{R})$.

    (ii) Prove that $S \cap S^{\perp} = \{0\}$ or $S \cap S^{\perp} = \varnothing$.

    (iii) Show, by an example, that part (ii) would be false if we were using $V_n(\mathbf{C})$ in place of $V_n(\mathbf{R})$.

NOTES AND REFERENCES

General references to the material of this chapter (and of Chapter 16) are [**32**]—[**35**] and vol. 2 of [**8**] in the bibliography. In particular, Halmos [**34**] and Malcev [**35**] give good expositions of a number of topics not treated in this book.

The commutativity of multiplication in a field F plays essentially no role in obtaining many properties of a vector space over F. With proper care, everything which we have done can be done as well for vector spaces over a "noncommutative field" or, as it is usually called, a "division ring." That is, all field properties are assumed, including the existence of a multiplicative inverse for each nonzero element, except that multiplication is not required to be commutative. Vector spaces over a division ring are studied in detail in vol. 2 of Jacobson [**8**]. Chapter 9 of this same reference is an exposition of results about infinite dimensional vector spaces, including such concepts as infinite bases of such spaces. See also Section 17.5 in the last chapter of this book.

FIELD EXTENSIONS

If F and K are fields with $F \subseteq K$, then F is a *subfield* of K and K is an *extension* of F. If $F \subset K$, that is, if F is a subfield of K and $F \neq K$, we may call F a *proper* subfield of K and K a *proper* extension of F.

If F is a subfield of K, we proved in Section 5.6 that F and K have the same unity, which we shall now usually denote by 1. This fact implies that F and K have the same characteristic, which we know is either zero or a prime.

We proved in Theorem 5.28 that a field of characteristic zero has a subfield isomorphic to the field $\mathbf{Q}$ of rational numbers, and in Theorem 5.10 that a field of characteristic the prime p has a subfield isomorphic to $\mathbf{Z}_p$. Another way of stating these facts is to say that every field of characteristic zero is (essentially) an extension of the field $\mathbf{Q}$, and every field of characteristic p is (essentially) an extension of $\mathbf{Z}_p$. The word "essentially" as used here is to be interpreted as "if we do not distinguish between isomorphic fields."

In this chapter we shall present briefly a few of the basic concepts and results about extensions of a given field, and (at the end of the chapter) give references to some further aspects of this very extensive branch of abstract algebra.

In previous chapters we have already obtained some results which are important for our present purposes, and, we shall refer to them and in some cases, give a short review of them at appropriate points in the exposition.

13.1 THE PROCESS OF ADJUNCTION

Throughout this section we shall assume that fields F and K are given, with $F \subseteq K$. That is, K is an extension of F. What we have to say will be quite trivial if $F = K$, so we shall usually tacitly assume that F is a proper subfield of K. In the following section we shall start with just the field F, and consider the problem of *constructing* extension fields of F.

Suppose that S is a set of elements of the extension K of F. Then there certainly exists one field (K itself) which contains F and also contains the set S. It may be verified that the intersection of all subfields of K which contain F and S is a field with these same properties. It is clearly the smallest (in the sense of set inclusion) field with these properties. Let us make the following convenient definition.

13.1 Definition. Let K be an extension of the field F, and S a set of elements of K. The intersection of all subfields of K which contain F and S is a subfield of K which we may denote by $F(S)$ and call the field *generated by* S *over* F. We also say that $F(S)$ is the field obtained from F by *adjunction* of the elements of S. If the set S has exactly *one* element, $F(S)$ is called a *simple extension* of F.

In view of this definition, $F(S)$ may be completely characterized by the following properties:

(i) $F(S)$ is a field with $F \subset F(S) \subset K$.

13.2 (ii) $S \subseteq F(S)$.

(iii) If J is any subfield of K such that $F \subseteq J$ and $S \subseteq J$, then $F(S) \subseteq J$.

It is clear that if $S \subseteq F$, then $F = F(S)$. We shall mainly be interested in the case in which S is a finite set, say $S = \{u_1, u_2, \cdots, u_n\}$. If S is such a finite set, we shall usually write $F(u_1, u_2, \cdots, u_n)$ in place of $F(S)$.

The *definition* of $F(S)$ gives no clue as to how one might determine the elements of this field if F and S are given. We proceed to consider this question and let us first consider the case of a simple extension, that is, the case in which S has *one* element, say $S = \{u\}$, where $u \in K$. Otherwise expressed, we seek the form of the elements of the field $F(u)$ obtained from the field F by adjunction of the one element u. Let us assume that $u \notin F$ since otherwise we clearly get $F(u) = F$.

Since $F(u)$ is a field that contains F and u, we see that $F(u)$ must contain all elements of K which can be obtained from u and elements of F by a finite number of the so-called rational operations (addition, subtraction, multiplication, and division by nonzero elements). In order to state this fact in a more precise way, let us introduce the following notation and terminology. If $F[x]$ is the ring of all polynomials in an indeterminate x over F and $f(x) \in F[x]$, let us call the element $f(u)$ of $F(u)$ a *polynomial in u over F*. The set of all polynomials in u over F may be denoted by $F[u]$. The new feature here is that we have previously used the notation $F[u]$ only in the case in which u is an *indeterminate,* but we now do not make this restriction. It is readily verified that $F[u]$ is a subring of the field $F(u)$. This implies that $F[u]$ is an integral domain. As indicated near the end of Section 5.4, the *field of quotients* of any integral domain may be obtained much as the field of rational numbers is obtained from the integers. The elements of the field of quotients of $F[u]$ may be written in the form $f(u)/g(u)$, with $g(u) \neq 0$. Let us call an element of this field a *rational expression* in u over F. Since the field of quotients of the integral domain $F[u]$ is a field which contains F and the element u, and every field which contains F and u must contain this field of quotients, it follows that this field of quotients is, in fact, the field $F(u)$. Thus $F(u)$ *consists of all the rational expressions in u over F.*

Perhaps we should emphasize the distinction between $F[u]$ and $F(u)$. The former is the smallest *ring* which contains F and u, whereas the latter is the smallest *field* which contains F and u.

It will be observed that the assumed extension field K of F does not play any explicit role in the determination of the field $F(u)$. The existence of K is used only to assure us that the rational expressions in u over F actually belong to some field.

EXAMPLE 1.   Since $\mathbf{Q} \subseteq \mathbf{R}$, we have that $\sqrt[3]{2} \in \mathbf{R}$. Let us consider the simple extension field $\mathbf{Q}(\sqrt[3]{2})$ of $\mathbf{Q}$. First of all, we consider $\mathbf{Q}[\sqrt[3]{2}]$ and the field we seek will have elements which are expressible as quotients of elements of $\mathbf{Q}[\sqrt[3]{2}]$. Since any polynomial in $\sqrt[3]{2}$ over $\mathbf{Q}$ can be written in the form

$$a + b\sqrt[3]{2} + c\sqrt[3]{4}, \qquad\qquad a\,,b\,,c \in \mathbf{Q},$$

we see that these are the elements of $\mathbf{Q}[\sqrt[3]{2}]$. The elements of the field $\mathbf{Q}(\sqrt[3]{2})$ are then of the form

13.3
$$\frac{a + b\sqrt[3]{2} + c\sqrt[3]{4}}{d + e\sqrt[3]{2} + f\sqrt[3]{4}},$$

where all coefficients are rational numbers and the denominator is different from zero. We shall find later on that $\mathbf{Q}[\sqrt[3]{2}]$ is itself a field, so that in this case, $\mathbf{Q}(\sqrt[3]{2}) = \mathbf{Q}[\sqrt[3]{2}]$.

Let us now briefly consider the field $F(u_1\,,u_2\,,\cdots,u_n)$ obtained by adjunction of the finite set $\{u_1\,,u_2\,,\cdots,u_n\}$ of elements of K to F. As a matter of fact, $F(u_1\,,u_2) = (F(u_1))(u_2)$, that is, $F(u_1\,,u_2)$ may be considered to be a simple extension of $F(u_1)$, and we could continue in this way for arbitrary n. But in order to state in a simple way what the elements of F are, let us first introduce some convenient new notation.

If x_1, x_2, $\cdots$, x_n are distinct *indeterminates*, let us use the method just suggested above and define $F[x_1, x_2]$ as the ring of all polynomials in the indeterminate x_2 with coefficients in the ring $F[x_1]$, that is, the coefficients are polynomials in the indeterminate x_1 over F. More generally, if $F[x_1, x_2, \cdots, x_k]$ has been defined, we define $F[x_1, x_2, \cdots, x_k, x_{k+1}]$ to be $(F[x_1, x_2, \cdots, x_k])[x_{k+1}]$. By suitable conventions and notation, it follows that the elements of $F[x_1, x_2, \cdots, x_n]$ may be expressed as a finite sum of terms of the form

$$a x_1^{i_1} x_2^{i_2} \cdots x_n^{i_n},$$

where $a \in F$ and the i's are nonnegative integers. An element of $F[x_1, x_2, \cdots, x_n]$ is naturally called a *polynomial* in the indeterminates x_1, x_2, $\cdots$, x_n over F.

Let us now return to our problem. If u_1, u_2, $\cdots$, u_n are elements of K and $f(x_1, x_2, \cdots, x_n)$ is an element of the ring $F[x_1, x_2, \cdots, x_n]$, then we denote by $f(u_1, u_2, \cdots, u_n)$ the element of K obtained by replacing x_i by $u_i (i = 1, 2, \cdots, n)$ in the polynomial $f(x_1, x_2, \cdots, x_n)$, and call $f(u_1, u_2, \cdots, u_n)$ a polynomial in $u_1, u_2, \cdots, u_n$ over F. It may be verified that the set of all polynomials in $u_1, u_2, \cdots, u_n$ over F is a ring, that we shall denote by $F[u_1, u_2, \cdots, u_n]$. As in the case in which $n = 1$, previously considered, $F[u_1, u_2, \cdots, u_n]$ is an integral domain since it is a subring of the field K. Moreover, the field of quotients of this integral domain, whose elements are quotients of polynomials in $u_1, u_2, \cdots, u_n$ over K, is the smallest field which contains F and the elements u_1, u_2, $\cdots$, u_n; that is, it is precisely the field $F(u_1, u_2, \cdots, u_n)$. It may sometimes be convenient to call an element of this field a *rational expression* in the elements $u_1, u_2, \cdots, u_n$ of K over F.

EXAMPLE 2. Determine the form of the elements of the field obtained from the rational field **Q** by adjunction of $\sqrt{2}$ and $\sqrt{3}$, that is, the field $\mathbf{Q}(\sqrt{2}, \sqrt{3})$.

In accordance with the procedure outlined above, we first consider polynomials in $\sqrt{2}$ and $\sqrt{3}$ over **Q,** and then take quotients of such polynomials. Since the square of each of these adjoined elements is in **Q,** every polynomial in these two elements is expressible in the form

$$a + b\sqrt{2} + c\sqrt{3} + d\sqrt{6} \qquad a, b, c, d \in \mathbf{Q}.$$

Hence the elements of $\mathbf{Q}(\sqrt{2}, \sqrt{3})$ are expressible in the form

13.4
$$\frac{a + b\sqrt{2} + c\sqrt{3} + d\sqrt{6}}{e + f\sqrt{2} + g\sqrt{3} + h\sqrt{6}},$$

where the coefficients are rational numbers and the denominator is different from zero. In Section 13.5, we shall find a different form for the elements of this field.

13.2   THE EXISTENCE OF CERTAIN EXTENSIONS

In the previous section we have assumed that an extension K of the field F was given. We now change our point of view and start with a field F and proceed to *construct* some extensions of F. As a matter of fact, in previous chapters we have already obtained (or at least outlined) results which establish the existence of two types of simple extensions of a given field. Let us begin by briefly reviewing these results.

TYPE 1.   Let F be a given field, and $F[x]$ the ring of all polynomials in an indeterminate x over F. Then $F[x]$ is an integral domain, and its field of quotients has elements expressible as rational forms in x over F, that is, they are of the form

$$\frac{f(x)}{g(x)},$$

where $f(x)$ and $g(x)$ are polynomials over F and $g(x) \neq 0$. The field consisting of all these rational forms contains x (by choosing $f(x) = x$, $g(x) = 1$). Also, by suitable agreements (similar to those made when the rational numbers were constructed from the integers), we may consider that this field contains F. Using a notation suggested in the previous section, we denote this new field by $F(x)$, and say that it has been obtained from F by *adjunction of the indeterminate x*.

TYPE 2.   A quite different type of extension was presented in some detail in Section 11.3. Let us review it briefly inasmuch as this construction of an extension field is of fundamental importance for our present purposes.

Let F be a given field and let $s(x)$ be an element of the polynomial ring $F[x]$ which is prime over F. In the ring $F[x]$, let $S = (s(x))$; that is, S is the principal ideal consisting of all multiples of $s(x)$. We proved that the quotient ring $F[x]/S$ is a field whose elements are cosets of S in $F[x]$, that is, they are of the form $f(x) + S$, where $f(x) \in F[x]$. For the moment, let us denote the field $F[x]/S$ by F' The elements of F' of the form $a + S$, $a \in F$, are a subfield of F' which is isomorphic to F; and we identify it with F. In other words, we write simply a for an element of F' of the form $a + S$, $a \in F$. With this identification, F' is an extension of F. We showed that if we write j for the element $x + S$

of the field F' and deg $s(x) = k$, then every element of the field F is uniquely expressible in the form

13.5 $$a_0 + a_1 j + \cdots + a_{k-1} j^{k-1}, \qquad \text{each } a_i \in F.$$

Moreover, since $F \subseteq F'$, if we wish to do so, we may consider $s(x)$ to be a polynomial over F'. As a polynomial over F', $s(j) = 0$, that is, the element j of F' is a root of the polynomial $s(x)$. Since (by Theorem 10.36) every polynomial of positive degree over F has a divisor which is prime over F, the following result, originally stated as Theorem 11.25, is an immediate consequence of these remarks.

13.6 Theorem. *If F is a field and $f(x)$ an element of $F[x]$ of positive degree, there exists an extension F' of the field F in which $f(x)$ has a root.*

Let us now make the following definition.

13.7 Definition. If $f(x) \in F[x]$ and K is an extension of F in which $f(x)$ can be expressed as a product of factors of the first degree, then we say that $f(x)$ *splits in K.*

For example, the polynomial $x^2 - 2$ of $\mathbf{Q}[x]$ does not split in $\mathbf{Q}$ but it does split in $\mathbf{R}$ since in $\mathbf{R}$ we have $x^2 - 2 = (x - \sqrt{2})(x + \sqrt{2})$.

We next use the preceding theorem to give a formal proof of the following result (*Cf.* Corollary 11.26, where an outline of a proof is given).

13.8 Theorem. *If F is a field and $f(x)$ is an element of the polynomial ring $F[x]$ of positive degree, there exists an extension of F in which $f(x)$ splits.*

PROOF: The result is clearly true if the degree of $f(x)$ is 1, since in this case $f(x)$ splits in F itself. We complete the proof by induction on the degree of $f(x)$. Suppose that the statement is true for all fields F and all polynomials of degree k, and let $f(x)$ be of degree $k + 1$ over a field F. Then $f(x)$ has a prime factor $s(x)$ over F (which might be $f(x)$ itself), and we may write $f(x) = f_1(x)s(x)$ over F. By the preceding theorem, there exists an extension F' of F in which $s(x)$ has a root, which we may denote by j. Thus $s(x)$, and therefore $f(x)$, has $x - j$ as a factor over F'. Accordingly, we have over F',

$$f(x) = (x - j)g(x),$$

where $g(x)$ has degree k. By our induction hypothesis, there exists an extension K of F' in which $g(x)$, and therefore $f(x)$, splits. This completes the proof of the theorem by induction.

If a polynomial splits in a certain field, it also splits in any proper extension of that field. We are sometimes interested in a *smallest* field in which a given polynomial splits. The following definition will make it easy to refer to such fields.

13.9 Definition. Let $f(x)$ be an element of the polynomial ring $F[x]$. An extension L of F is called a *splitting field of $f(x)$ over F* if L is an extension of F in which $f(x)$ splits, but $f(x)$ does not split in any proper subfield of L.

Using a notation which was introduced in the previous section, we may now establish the following result.

13.10 Theorem. *Let $f(x)$ be an element of degree $n > 1$ of the polynomial ring $F[x]$, and let K be a field in which $f(x)$ splits. Hence, over K, we may write $f(x)$ in the following form:*

13.11 $$f(x) = a(x - u_1)(x - u_2) \cdots (x - u_n),$$

where $a \in F$ and the u's are elements of K. Then $F(u_1, u_2, \cdots, u_n)$ is a splitting field of $f(x)$ over F.

For convenience, let us denote the field $F(u_1, u_2, \cdots, u_n)$ by F^*. Then all coefficients on the right in 13.11 are elements of F^*; hence $f(x)$ splits in F^*. Now $f(x)$ can be *uniquely* expressed as a product of prime polynomials (here of the first degree) over K; hence any splitting field of $f(x)$ which is contained in K must contain the coefficients of all polynomials occurring on the right in 13.11. That is, any subfield of K in which $f(x)$ splits must contain $u_1, u_2, \cdots, u_n$; and therefore must contain the extension $F(u_1, u_2, \cdots, u_n)$ of F. It is then clear that $F(u_1, u_2, \cdots, u_n)$ is indeed a splitting field of $f(x)$, and the proof is complete.

Another way of stating what we have just proved is to assert that a splitting field of a polynomial $f(x)$ over F is obtained by adjoining to F all the roots of $f(x)$ (which are assumed to be in some field in which $f(x)$ splits).

It should be noted that in this theorem we started with a field K in which $f(x)$ splits and have then shown that there is in fact a *unique subfield* of K which is a splitting field of $f(x)$. In a later section we shall consider whether we get different splitting fields if we start with different fields K in which $f(x)$ splits. It will turn out that in a certain sense (to be described precisely later) there is a unique splitting field for a given polynomial.

EXERCISES

By Theorem 10.54, every polynomial over the field **C** of complex numbers splits in **C**. In the following exercises the indicated fields are all subfields of **C**. As usual, **Q** will denote the field of rational numbers and **R** the field of real numbers.

1. Verify that $\mathbf{Q}(\sqrt{2}) = \mathbf{Q}[\sqrt{2}]$.

2. Prove that $\mathbf{Q}(\sqrt{2}, \sqrt{3}) = \mathbf{Q}(\sqrt{2} + \sqrt{3})$. [Hint: Use the fact that $\mathbf{Q}(\sqrt{2} + \sqrt{3})$ contains the multiplicative inverse of $\sqrt{2} + \sqrt{3}$; hence show that $\sqrt{2} \in \mathbf{Q}(\sqrt{2} + \sqrt{3})$ and that $\sqrt{3} \in \mathbf{Q}(\sqrt{2} + \sqrt{3})$.]

3. Generalize the preceding exercise by proving that if a and b are positive rational numbers, then $\mathbf{Q}(\sqrt{a}, \sqrt{b}) = \mathbf{Q}(\sqrt{a} + \sqrt{b})$.

4. Determine a splitting field of the polynomial $x^2 + 1$ over **R** and over **Q**.

5. Show that for each positive integer n, a splitting field of the polynomial $x^n - 1$ over **R** can be obtained by adjunction of *one* element to **R**. [Hint: See Corollary 6.25.]

13.3 CLASSIFICATIONS OF EXTENSIONS

Throughout this section, K will be a fixed extension of the field F. We begin with the following definition.

13.12 Definition. If $F \subseteq K$, an element u of K is said to be *algebraic over F* if there exists some nonzero element $f(x)$ of the polynomial ring $F[x]$ such that $f(u) = 0$. An element of K which is not algebraic over F is said to be *transcendental* over F.

The real number $\sqrt{2}$ is algebraic over **Q** since it is a root of the polynomial $x^2 - 2$ with coefficients in **Q**. It is known (although the proof is not elementary) that the real number π is transcendental over **Q**.

From the definition, it is clear that if $F \subseteq F' \subseteq K$ and u is an element of K which is algebraic over F, it is also algebraic over F'.

13.13   Definition.   An extension K of a field F is said to be an *algebraic extension* of F if every element of K is algebraic over F. If K contains at least one element which is transcendental over K, K is called a *transcendental* extension of F.

Let us pause here to obtain a few results about an *element* which is algebraic over a given field F, and a little later return to a consideration of extensions of F.

Suppose that K is an extension of the field F and that u is an element of K which is algebraic over F. One way of stating that u is algebraic over F is to assert that the homomorphic mapping $\theta: F[x] \to K$, defined by $f(x)\theta = f(u)$ for $f(x) \in F[x]$, is such that ker $\theta \neq \{0\}$. Clearly, $f(x) \in$ ker θ if and only if $f(u) = 0$. Now ker θ is an ideal in $F[x]$ and, by Theorem 11.3, it is a principal ideal. Moreover, as generator of this ideal we may take any polynomial $m(x)$ of least degree in the ideal. Since ker θ then consists of the multiples of $m(x)$, the following theorem is an immediate consequence of the observations just made.

13.14   Theorem.   *Let K be an extension of the field F, and let u be an element of K which is algebraic over F. If $m(x)$ is a polynomial of $F[x]$ of least degree such that $m(u) = 0$ and $f(x) \in F[x]$, then $f(u) = 0$ if and only if $m(x)$ is a divisor of $f(x)$.*

If $m(x)$ is a polynomial over F of least degree such that $m(u) = 0$, the same is also true for any polynomial $am(x)$, where a is a nonzero element of F. Accordingly, there will always exist a *monic* polynomial of least degree which has u as a root. By the theorem just established, if we have two polynomials of least degree which have u as a root, each would be a divisor of the other. Accordingly, the *monic* polynomial of least degree which has u as a root is *unique*.

13.15   Definition.   If u is algebraic over the field F, the unique monic polynomial of least degree over F of which u is a root may be called *the minimal polynomial* of u over F.

It is now easy to establish the following additional result.

13.16   Theorem. *If u is algebraic over F, the minimal polynomial $m(x)$ of u over F is a prime polynomial over F.*

The proof goes as follows. If $m(x)$ were not prime over F, we would have $m(x) = m_1(x)m_2(x)$, where both $m_1(x)$ and $m_2(x)$ are elements of $F[x]$ with deg $m_1(x) <$ deg $m(x)$ and deg $m_2(x) <$ deg $m(x)$. Now $m(u) = 0$ implies that $m_1(u)m_2(u) = 0$, and therefore $m_1(u) = 0$ or

$m_2(u) = 0$. However, these are both impossible since $m(x)$ is an element of $F[x]$ of *least* degree which has u as a root. This proves that $m(x)$ must be prime over F, and the proof of the theorem is complete.

In view of Theorems 13.14 and 13.16, we see that if u is algebraic over F, and $\theta: F[x] \to F[u]$ is the homomorphism defined by $f(x)\theta = f(u)$, then ker $\theta = (m(x))$, where we may take $m(x)$ to be the (prime) minimal polynomial of u over F. This fact will be useful in the following section.

Let us now introduce another way of classifying extensions of a given field. If K is an extension of a field F, we may consider K to be a vector space over F (Example 3 of Section 12.2).

13.17 **Definition.** Let the field K be an extension of the field F. If the dimension of K considered as a vector space over F is finite, we say that K is a *finite extension* of F; otherwise, it is an *infinite extension* of F. If the dimension of K over F is the integer $n \geq 0$, we may say that n is the *degree* of K over F.

If K is a finite extension of F, it is customary to denote the degree of K over F by $[K : F]$.

We next prove the following theorem.

13.18 **Theorem.** *If K is a finite extension of F, it is an algebraic extension of F.*

The proof is as follows. If $[K : F] = n$, by Theorem 12.23(i) any set of $n + 1$ elements of K is linearly dependent over F. Thus, if $u \in K$, the $n + 1$ elements $1, u, u^2, \cdots, u^n$ of K are linearly dependent over F. But this implies that there exist elements $a_0, a_1, \cdots, a_n$ of F, not all of which are zero, such that $a_0 + a_1u + a_2u^2 + \cdots + a_nu^n = 0$. Thus each element u of K is algebraic over F, and K is an algebraic extension of F.

The following theorem plays a fundamental role in the study of finite extensions. (See Exercise 11 of Section 12.5.)

13.19 **Theorem.** *If the field K is a finite extension of the field F and the field L is a finite extension of K, then L is a finite extension of K and*

13.20 $$[L : F] = [K : F][L : K].$$

PROOF: Let $n = [K : F]$ and $m = [L : K]$. Thus K has a basis $\{u_1, u_2, \cdots, u_n\}$ over F, and L has a basis $\{v_1, v_2, \cdots, v_m\}$ over K. We shall establish the theorem by showing that the set of nm elements

13.21 $u_i v_j$ $(i = 1, 2 \cdots, n; j = 1, 2, \cdots, m)$

is a basis of L over F.

First, let us verify that the elements 13.21 are linearly independent. Suppose that a_{ij} are elements of F such that

$$\sum a_{ij} u_i v_j = 0,$$

it being understood that in this sum i takes values from 1 to n, and j independently takes values from 1 to m. A somewhat more explicit way of writing the preceding equation is as follows:

$$\sum_{j=1}^{n} (a_{1j} u_1 + a_{2j} u_2 + \cdots + a_{nj} u_n) v_j = 0.$$

But the coefficient of each v_j is an element of K and since the v's are linearly independent over K, it follows that

$$a_{1j} u_1 + a_{2j} u_2 + \cdots + a_{nj} u_n = 0$$

for each $j = 1, 2, \cdots, m$. However, the u's are linearly independent over F and we conclude that $a_{ij} = 0$ for all i and j. Thus the elements 13.21 are linearly independent over F.

There remains to show that every element of L is expressible as a linear combination over F of the elements 13.21. Since the v's form a basis of L over K, every element of L is expressible in the form

13.22 $c_1 v_1 + c_2 v_2 + \cdots + c_m v_m ,$

the c's being elements of K. But since the u's form a basis of K over F, each c is expressible as a linear combination of $u_1, u_2, \cdots, u_n$ over F. Substituting in 13.22, these linear expressions for the c's, we find that the expression 13.22 is a linear combination of the elements 13.21 over F. We have thus completed the proof that the nm elements 13.21 of L are indeed a basis for L over F, and the theorem is established.

EXERCISES

1.   If $F \subseteq F' \subseteq K$ and u is an element of K which is algebraic over F, prove that the minimal polynomial of u over F' is a divisor (in $F'[x]$) of the minimal polynomial of u over F.

2.   Find the minimal polynomial of $\sqrt{2} + \sqrt{3}$ over **Q**, and also over **Q**$(\sqrt{2})$. Verify the result of the preceding exercise for the case in which $F = $ **Q**, $F' = $ **Q**$(\sqrt{2})$, $K = $ **Q**$(\sqrt{2}, \sqrt{3})$, and $u = \sqrt{2} + \sqrt{3}$.

3.   If $F \subseteq F_1 \subseteq F_2$, where both F_1 and F_2 are finite extensions of F, verify that $F_1 = F_2$ if and only if $[F_1 : F] = [F_2 : F]$.

4.   Suppose that $F \subseteq K$ and that $u \in K$. Prove that u^2 is algebraic over F if and only if u is algebraic over F.

5.   If $[F' : F]$ is a prime number, prove that the only fields F_1 such that $F \subseteq F_1 \subseteq F'$ are $F_1 = F$ or $F_1 = F'$, that is, there are no fields "between" F and F'.

13.4   SIMPLE EXTENSIONS

We now return to the study of simple extensions which were introduced in Section 13.2.

13.23   **Theorem.**   *Let u be an element of an extension K of the field F, and let x be an indeterminate. Then each of the following is true:*

   (*i*)   *If u is transcendental over F, the mapping $\alpha : F(x) \to F(u)$ defined by*

13.24
$$\frac{f(x)}{g(x)} \alpha = \frac{f(u)}{g(u)}$$

   is an isomorphism of the field $F(x)$ of all rational forms in x over F onto the simple extension $F(u)$.

   (*ii*)   *If u is algebraic over F, and $m(x)$ is the minimal polynomial of u over F, the mapping $\alpha : F[x]/(m(x)) \to F[u]$ defined by*

13.25
$$[f(x) + (m(x))]\alpha = f(u)$$

   is an isomorphism of the field $F[x]/(m(x)$ onto the ring $F[u]$, and therefore $F(u) = F[u]$. In this case, $F(u)$ is a finite extension whose degree over F is equal to the degree of $m(x)$ over F.

   PROOF: Let x be an indeterminate, and consider the mapping $\theta : F[x] \to F[u]$, defined by $f(x)\theta = f(u)$, $f(x) \in F[x]$. It is readily verified that θ is a homomorphism of the polynomial ring $F[x]$ onto the ring $F[u]$ of all polynomials in u, with coefficients from F. If K is the kernel of the homomorphism θ, we know from the Fundamental Theorem on Ring Homomorphisms (Theorem 11.27) that $\alpha : F[x]/K \to F[u]$ defined by $(f(x) + K)\alpha = f(u)$ is an isomorphism of the ring $F[x]/K$ onto the ring $F[u]$.

Now suppose that u is transcendental over F. This implies that $K = \{0\}$, and the mapping α is actually an isomorphism of $F[x]$ onto $F[u]$, and, in fact, $f(x)\alpha = f(u)$. By Exercise 9 of Section 5.6, it follows that the corresponding fields of quotients $F(x)$ and $F(u)$ are isomorphic under the mapping defined by 13.24.

If, on the other hand, u is algebraic over F, $K = \ker \theta$ is the set of all polynomials $g(x)$ of $F[x]$ such that $g(u) = 0$. In this case, $K \neq \{0\}$ and Theorems 13.14 and 13.16 show that K is the principal ideal $(m(x))$ in $F[x]$, where $m(x)$ is the minimal polynomial of u over F, and that $m(x)$ is prime over F. Hence, as indicated in Section 13.2 (reviewing material of Section 11.3), $F[x]/(m(x))$ is an extension of F of degree over F equal to the degree of $m(x)$ over F. Theorem 11.27 then asserts that the mapping α defined by 13.25 is an isomorphism of the field $F[x]/(m(x))$ onto the ring $F[u]$. Accordingly, the *ring* $F[u]$ of polynomials in u over F must be a *field*, and thus $F(u) = F[u]$.

In this second case, $F(u)$ is a finite extension of F, and Theorem 13.18 shows that it is an algebraic extension of F. Accordingly, we see that a simple extension $F(u)$ of F is a transcendental or an algebraic extension according as the element u is transcendental or algebraic over F.

There is a fairly important corollary of the theorem just established, but first it will be convenient to make another definition.

13.26 Definition. Two extensions K and L of a field F are said to be *equivalent* extensions of F if there exists an isomorphism θ of K onto L with the property that $a\theta = a$ for every element a of F.

The fact that $a\theta = a$ for every element a of F is often expressed by saying that all elements of F are *left fixed* (or are *invariant*) under θ. We now establish the following corollary of Theorem 13.23.

13.27 Corollary.

(i) *If u and v are transcendental over F, then the simple transcendental extensions $F(u)$ and $F(v)$ of F are equivalent.*

(ii) *If u and v are algebraic over F and are roots (in some extension field) of the same prime polynomial over F, then the simple algebraic extensions $F(u)$ and $F(v)$ of F are equivalent under an isomorphism which maps $f(u)$ into $f(v)$ for each $f(x) \in F[x]$.*

To verify the first part of this corollary, let α be the isomorphism 13.24, and let β be the corresponding isomorphism of $F(x)$ onto $F(v)$. It follows that $\alpha^{-1}\beta$ is an isomorphism of $F(u)$ onto $F(v)$. Actually,

$$\frac{f(u)}{g(u)}\,(\alpha^{-1}\beta) = \frac{f(v)}{g(v)},$$

and elements of F are left fixed under this isomorphism. Hence $F(u)$ and $F(v)$ are equivalent extensions of F.

Part (ii) follows by a similar argument. Suppose that u and v are roots of the same minimal polynomial $m(x)$ over F. Then, by Theorem 13.14, $m(x)$ is prime over F, and the mapping α given by 13.25 is an isomorphism of $F[x]/(m(x))$ onto $F(u)$. If β is the corresponding isomorphism of $F[x]/m(x))$ onto $F(v)$, then again $\alpha^{-1}\beta$ is an isomorphism of $F(u)$ onto $F(v)$ and for $f(x) \in F[x]$, $f(u)(\alpha^{-1}\beta) = f(v)$. Elements of F are left fixed under this isomorphism, so again we see that $F(u)$ and $F(v)$ are equivalent extensions of F.

13.5   FINITE ALGEBRAIC EXTENSIONS

Suppose, now, that $u_1, u_2, \cdots, u_n$ are a finite number of elements of some extension field of F which are algebraic over F, and let us consider the extension field $F(u_1, u_2, \cdots, u_n)$ obtained by adjoining all these elements to F. We shall prove the following theorem.

13.28   Theorem. *If $u_1, u_2, \cdots, u_n$ are algebraic over F (in some extension field of F), then $F(u_1, u_2, \cdots, u_n)$ is a finite algebraic extension of F.*

For simplicity, let us set $F_1 = F(u_1)$, $F_2 = F(u_1, u_2)$ and, in general, $F_i = F(u_1, u_2, \cdots, u_i)$. Next, we observe that F_2 is obtained from F_1 by adjoining the element u_2. Since u_2 is algebraic over F, it is certainly algebraic over F_1. Similarly, each of the fields in the following sequence is a simple algebraic extension of the preceding:

$$F \subseteq F_1 \subseteq F_2 \subseteq \cdots \subseteq F_n.$$

By part (ii) of the preceding theorem, $[F_i : F_{i-1}]$ is equal to the degree of the minimal polynomial of u_i over F_{i-1}; in particular, the degree is finite. Accordingly, by repeated use of Theorem 13.19, we see that

$$[F_n : F] = [F_1 : F] \cdot [F_2 : F_1] \cdots [F_n : F_{n-1}].$$

Accordingly, F_n has finite degree over F, and Theorem 13.18 implies that F_n is algebraic over F.

The following result is an interesting special case of the theorem just proved.

13.29 Corollary. *If u and v are algebraic over F (in some extension field of F), then so also is each of the following: $u + v$, $u - v$, uv, and u/v if $v \neq 0$.*

This is an immediate consequence of the fact (from the preceding theorem) that if u and v are algebraic over F, then $F(u, v)$ is an algebraic extension of F. Hence each element of $F(u, v)$; in particular, each of the elements specified in the statement of the corollary, is algebraic over F.

As an example, let us consider the real numbers $\sqrt{2}$ and $\sqrt{3}$ which are algebraic over the rational field $\mathbf{Q}$, and let us verify directly that $\sqrt{2} + \sqrt{3}$ is algebraic over $\mathbf{Q}$.

If we let $w = \sqrt{2} + \sqrt{3}$, then $(w - \sqrt{2})^2 = 3$, and this implies that $w^2 - 2\sqrt{2}w - 1 = 0$. Thus $-2\sqrt{2}w = 1 - w^2$, and by squaring both sides we obtain

$$w^4 - 10w^2 + 1 = 0.$$

This shows that w is a root of the polynomial $f(x) = x^4 - 10x^2 + 1$, with rational coefficients. By Theorem 10.39, we see that $f(x)$ has no rational root. Moreover, it may be verified that $f(x)$ cannot be factored into the product of two quadratic polynomials over $\mathbf{Q}$. Accordingly, $f(x)$ is prime over $\mathbf{Q}$ and is therefore the minimal polynomial of $\sqrt{2} + \sqrt{3}$ over $\mathbf{Q}$. Thus the field $\mathbf{Q}(\sqrt{2} + \sqrt{3})$ has degree 4 over $\mathbf{Q}$.

Now consider the fields

$$\mathbf{Q} \subseteq \mathbf{Q}(\sqrt{2}) \subseteq \mathbf{Q}(\sqrt{2}, \sqrt{3}).$$

Since $\sqrt{2}$ is of degree 2 over $\mathbf{Q}$, and $\sqrt{3}$ is of degree 2 over $\mathbf{Q}$ and therefore of degree no more than 2 over $\mathbf{Q}(\sqrt{2})$, we see that

$$[\mathbf{Q}(\sqrt{2}, \sqrt{3}) : \mathbf{Q}] = [\mathbf{Q}(\sqrt{2}) : \mathbf{Q}] \cdot [\mathbf{Q}(\sqrt{2}, \sqrt{3}) : \mathbf{Q}(\sqrt{2})] \leq 4.$$

But we have just proved that the field $\mathbf{Q}(\sqrt{2} + \sqrt{3})$ has degree 4 over $\mathbf{Q}$, and $\mathbf{Q} \subseteq \mathbf{Q}(\sqrt{2} + \sqrt{3}) \subseteq \mathbf{Q}(\sqrt{2}, \sqrt{3})$. Accordingly, we conclude that $\mathbf{Q}(\sqrt{2} + \sqrt{3}) = \mathbf{Q}(\sqrt{2}, \sqrt{3})$, that is, the field obtained from $\mathbf{Q}$ by adjoining $\sqrt{2}$ and $\sqrt{3}$ may also be obtained by the adjunction of the single algebraic element $\sqrt{2} + \sqrt{3}$. (See Exercise 2 of Section 13.2.)

Although we shall not go further into questions of this kind, we may remark that the final conclusion in the preceding example illustrates an interesting general result. The statement of this result in its greatest generality involves some concepts which we have not introduced, but it does include the fact that any finite algebraic extension of a field with characteristic zero can be obtained by adjoining *one* element, that is, it is a simple extension.*

13.6 EQUIVALENCE OF SPLITTING FIELDS OF A POLYNOMIAL

The main purpose of this section is to prove that two splitting fields of the same polynomial over a field F are necessarily equivalent extensions of F. However, it will be convenient to start by proving a somewhat more general result.

Let us begin with the following definition.

13.30 **Definition.** Let $\alpha : R \to S$ be an isomorphism of the ring R onto the ring S. Suppose that R_1 and S_1 are rings such that $R \subseteq R_1$ and $S \subseteq S_1$. If there exists an isomorphism $\beta : R_1 \to S_1$ of R_1 onto S_1 with the property that $a\beta = a\alpha$ for each element a of R, we call the isomorphism β an *extension* of the isomorphism α, and also say that the given isomorphism of R onto S *can be extended to* an isomorphism of R_1 onto S_1.

Let us point out one case, important for our present purposes, in which a rather natural extension of an isomorphism does exist. Let $\alpha : F \to F'$ be a given isomorphism of the field F onto the field F', and let us consider the polynomial rings $F[x]$ and $F'[x]$ in an indeterminate x over F and F', respectively. By straightforward calculations (see Exercise 9 of Section 10.2), the mapping $\gamma : F[x] \to F'[x]$ defined by

13.31 $\quad (a_0 + a_1 x + \cdots + a_n x^n)\gamma = (a_0\alpha) + (a_1\alpha)x + \cdots + (a_n\alpha)x^n$

is an isomorphism of the ring $F[x]$ onto the ring $F'[x]$. Note that $F \subseteq F[x]$ and that $F' \subseteq F'[x]$. Moreover, if $a \in F$, by 13.31, we see that $a\gamma = a\alpha$, and hence γ is an extension of α. It will sometimes be convenient to denote the mapping γ, defined by 13.31, by α_x to emphasize that it is an extension of α to appropriate rings of polynomials in an indeterminate x.

We may observe that if in $F[x]$, we have an equation of the form $f(x) = g(x)h(x)$, by applying the isomorphism α_x it follows that $f(x)\alpha_x = [g(x)\alpha_x][h(x)\alpha_x]$. In particular, a polynomial $p(x)$ over F will be prime over F if and only if $p(x)\alpha_x$ is prime over F'.

The following lemma will play a central role in the proof of our principal result on splitting fields.

---

* See, e.g., Zariski and Samuel [38], p. 84.

13.32 Lemma. *Let $\alpha : F \to F'$ be an isomorphism of the field F onto the field F', and let α_x be the extension of α to an isomorphism of $F[x]$ onto $F'[x]$, as defined in 13.31. If $p(x)$ is a prime polynomial over F with a root u in some extension field of F, and v is a root of the corresponding prime polynomial $p(x)\alpha_x$ in some extension field of F', there exists an isomorphism β of $F(u)$ onto $F'(v)$ which is an extension of the given isomorphism α and has the property that $u\beta = v$.*

PROOF: For the present, let us simplify the notation somewhat by writing $f'(x)$ in place of $f(x)\alpha_x$, for each element $f(x)$ of $F[x]$. In particular, if $a \in F$, then $a\alpha = a\alpha_x = a'$. It will turn out that the isomorphism will be given by $f(u)\beta = f'(v)$. Let us prove that this is indeed the case.

Without loss of generality, we may assume that $p(x)$ is a monic polynomial, in which case the minimal polynomial of u over F is $p(x)$ itself. In like manner, $p(x)\alpha_x = p'(x)$ will be the minimal polynomial of v over F'. By Theorem 13.23 *(ii)*, the mapping $\gamma : F[x] / (p(x)) \to F(u)$ defined by $[f(x) + (p(x))]\gamma = f(u)$ is an isomorphism. Similarly, the mapping $\delta : F'[x]/(p'(x)) \to F'(v)$ defined by $[f'(x) + (p'(x))]\delta = f'(v)$ is an isomorphism. Finally, it may be verified that the mapping $\psi : F[x]/(p(x) \to F'[x]/(p'(x))$ defined by $[f(x) + (p(x))]\psi = f'(x) + (p'(x))$ is an isomorphism. Moreover, all of these isomorphisms are onto mappings. It follows that $\beta = \gamma^{-1}\psi\delta$ is an isomorphism of $F[u]$ onto $F'[v]$, and that for each polynomial $f(x)$ of $F[x]$, we have that $f(u)\beta = f'(v)$. Hence, in particular, if $a \in F$, then $a\beta = a' = a\alpha$, so that β is an extension of α. Finally, we see that $u\beta = v$, and the proof is complete.

We are now ready to prove the principal theorem of this section.

13.33 Theorem. *Let $\alpha : F \to F'$ be an isomorphism of the field F onto the field F', and let $f(x)$ be an arbitrary element of the polynomial ring $F[x]$. Moreover, let $f'(x) = f(x)\alpha_x$ be the element of $F'[x]$ corresponding to $f(x)$ under the extension α_x of α. If K is a splitting field of $f(x)$ over F and K' is a splitting field of $f'(x)$ over F', there exists an isomorphism of K onto K' which is an extension of the given isomorphism α of F onto F'.*

PROOF: In what follows, we shall speak of the degree of $f(x)$, but it should be kept in mind that $f'(x)$ always has the same degree as $f(x)$.

We shall prove the theorem by induction on the degree of $f(x)$. The result is trivially true for $f(x)$ of degree one, since in this case F is itself the only splitting field of $f(x)$ over F; and, similarly, F' is the only splitting field of $f'(x)$ over F'.

As an induction hypothesis, let us assume that for arbitrary isomorphic fields F and F' and an arbitrary isomorphism $\alpha : F \to F'$, the statement of the theorem is true for all polynomials $f(x)$ (and $f'(x)$) of degree k over F (over F'). Now suppose that fields F and F' are given, and that an isomorphism $\alpha : F \to F'$ of F onto F' is given. Moreover, let $f(x)$ be a polynomial of degree $k + 1$ over F, and therefore $f'(x)$ is also of degree $k + 1$ over F'. By Theorem 10.36, there exists a monic divisor $p(x)$ of $f(x)$ which is prime over F. Since $f(x)$ splits in K, $p(x)$ also splits in K. Let u be a root of $p(x)$ in K. Then in the field $F(u)$, $p(x)$ has $x - u$ as a divisor. Accordingly, we have

13.34
$$f(x) = (x - u)f_1(x),$$

where $f_1(x)$ has degree k and its coefficients are in the simple extension $F(u)$ of F. By a similar argument, $p'(x)$ is prime over F' and if v is a root of $p'(x)$ in the splitting field K' of $f'(x)$ over F', we know by the lemma that there exists an isomorphism $\beta : F(u) \to F'(v)$ which is an extension of α and is such that $u\beta = v$. Then β_x (the extension of β to an isomorphism of the ring of polynomials in an indeterminate x over $F(u)$ onto the ring of polynomials in x over $F'(v)$) is an extension of α_x and when applied to 13.34 yields

$$f'(x) = f(x)\beta_x = (x - v)[f_1(x)\beta_x].$$

If we set $f_2(x) = [f_1(x)]\beta_x$, we therefore have

13.35
$$f'(x) = (x - v)f_2(x),$$

where all coefficients are in the field $F'(v)$.

Now let us return to a consideration of 13.34. It was given that K is a splitting field of $f(x)$ over F. But, by 13.34, the roots of $f(x)$ in K are just u and the roots of $f_1(x)$, that is, K *is also a splitting field of $f_1(x)$ over* $F(u)$. In like manner K' *is a splitting field of $f_2(x)$ over $F'(v)$*. Now $f_1(x)$ and $f_2(x)$ are of degree k, and we apply the induction hypothesis to the fields $F(u)$ and $F(v)$ with isomorphism $\beta : F(u) \to F(v)$, using the fact that $f_2(x) = f_1(x)\beta_x$. Thus there exists an isomorphism γ of the splitting field K of $f_1(x)$ over $F(u)$ onto the splitting field K' of $f_2(x)$ over $F'(v)$, with γ an extension of β. Since β is an extension of α, clearly γ is also an extension of α. The statement of the theorem therefore holds for $f(x)$ of degree $k + 1$, completing the proof.

The most important application of this theorem is to the case in which $F = F'$ and α is the identity mapping on F. We obtain in this way the following result.

13.36   Corollary.   *Any two splitting fields of a polynomial $f(x)$ over a field F are equivalent extensions of F.*

EXERCISES

1. Suppose that $F \subset K$ and $u \in K$. If $f(u)$ is a polynomial in u over K (not an element of F), prove that u is algebraic over F if and only if $f(u)$ is algebraic over F. (This generalizes Exercise 4 at the end of Section 13.3.)

2. If $F \subseteq F' \subseteq K$, with F' an algebraic extension of F and K a transcendental extension of F', prove that K is a transcendental extension of F.

3. If $F(x)$ is a simple transcendental extension of F and u is the element $(x^3 + 1)/(x^2 + 1)$ of $F(x)$, prove that u is transcendental over F and that $F(x)$ is a simple algebraic extension of $F(u)$ of degree three.

4. By Theorem 13.23 (*ii*), the elements of the field $\mathbf{Q}(\sqrt[3]{2})$ can be written in the form $a + b\sqrt[3]{2} + c\sqrt[3]{4}$, where a, b, and c are elements of $\mathbf{Q}$. Express the element $(1 + \sqrt[3]{2} + \sqrt[3]{4})^{-1}$ of $\mathbf{Q}(\sqrt[3]{2})$ in this form.

5. If $F \subseteq K$, prove that the set F^* of all elements of K which are algebraic over F is a field with $F \subseteq F^* \subseteq K$. (The field F^* is called the *algebraic closure* of F in K.)

6. Prove that a field K is a finite extension of the field F if and only if there exist a finite set of elements $u_1, u_2, \cdots, u_m$ of K which are algebraic over F and are such that $K = F(u_1, u_2, \cdots, u_m)$.

7. Prove: If K is a finite extension of a field F and $m(x)$ is the minimum polynomial of an element u of K over F, the degree of $m(x)$ divides $[K : F]$.

8. Prove: If K is a finite extension of F of degree 2^n over F (for some positive integer n), a prime polynomial of odd prime degree over F is also prime over K.

NOTES AND REFERENCES

The further study of field extensions leads to an interesting and significant theory, known as Galois Theory, relating groups with certain extensions of a field. Let us make a few statements, without proof, which will give a hint as to the direction the theory takes.

With proper care, it is not essential that the fields involved have characteristic zero, but we shall now make this assumption for simplicity and accuracy of statement.

Let K be a splitting field of a polynomial $f(x)$ of positive degree over a field F of characteristic zero. The set of all automorphisms of K (isomorphisms of K onto itself) which leave elements of F fixed is a finite group G under the usual multiplication of mappings. The group G is called the *Galois group* of K over F (or of the polynomial $f(x)$ over F), and its order is equal to the degree of K over F. One of the principal theorems of the theory then asserts that *there is a one-to-one correspondence between subgroups H of G and fields J such that $F \subseteq J \subseteq K$.* If H is given, J is the field consisting of all elements of K which are left fixed under all automorphisms in H. If the field J is given, the corresponding subgroup H of G is the set of all automorphisms of K which leave all elements of J fixed.

It is also true that H will be a normal subgroup of G if and only if the corresponding field J is the splitting field of some polynomial over F. If H is a normal subgroup of G, the Galois group of the corresponding field J over F is isomorphic to the quotient group G/H.

For details and applications of this theory, see Artin [**36**], Postnikov [**37**], Zariski and Samuel [**38**], Ames [**1**], Dean [**3**], van der Waerden [**16**], Jacobson [**8**, Vol. 3]. Other references will be found in these sources.

SYSTEMS OF LINEAR EQUATIONS

There are several different ways of approaching the study of systems of linear equations. In this chapter we shall apply the theory of vector spaces as developed in Chapter 12. After determinants have been introduced in the next chapter we shall then indicate how the theory of determinants may be used as an alternate approach to the subject.

Section 14.2 is devoted to a systematic procedure which can be used to determine whether or not a given system of linear equations has a solution and, if it does have a solution, for finding all solutions. However, we shall be primarily interested in obtaining theoretical results such as various conditions under which a system of linear equations will have a solution. Matrices will be introduced in Section 14.3 and a few simple properties will be established. Finally, these properties will be used to obtain additional results about systems of linear equations.

14.1 NOTATION AND SIMPLE RESULTS

If F is a given field and $x_1, x_2, \cdots, x_n$ are indeterminates, it is customary to call a polynomial of the form $a_1 x_1 + a_2 x_2 + \cdots + a_n x_n$, where the coefficients are elements of F, a *linear form* (over F). Using the sigma notation for sums, such a linear form may be written as

$$\sum_{k=1}^{n} a_k x_k.$$

The linear form in which all coefficients are zero may be called the *zero linear form* and designated simply by 0.

Now let m and n be positive integers and let us consider a system of linear equations which we may write in the following explicit form:

14.1
$$
\begin{aligned}
a_{11}x_1 + a_{12}x_2 + \cdots + a_{1n}x_n &= b_1, \\
a_{21}x_1 + a_{22}x_2 + \cdots + a_{2n}x_n &= b_2, \\
\cdots \cdots \cdots \cdots \cdots \cdots \cdots \cdots \\
a_{m1}x_1 + a_{m2}x_2 + \cdots + a_{mn}x_n &= b_m.
\end{aligned}
$$

It is understood that all the coefficients a_{ij}, as well as the *constant terms* b_i, are elements of a given field F. If we wish to emphasize the particular field involved, we shall speak of a system of linear equations *over F*.

As a matter of notation, it should be observed that a_{ij} is the coefficient of x_j in the ith equation. That is, the first subscript of a_{ij} specifies the equation and the second one the indeterminate of which it is the coefficient.

Now the left sides of Equation 14.1 are linear forms over F, and the right sides are elements of F. Since a linear form over F is not an element of F, it is clear that the "$=$" is being used in a different sense than heretofore. However, it is common practice to write Equations 14.1 with the understanding that what we really mean is that we are seeking elements $t_1, t_2, \cdots, t_n$ of F such that if we replace x_i by t_i $(i = 1, 2, \cdots, n)$, each equation will yield a true equality of elements of F. Then, if $t_1, t_2, \cdots, t_n$ are such elements, it is customary to say that $x_1 = t_1, x_2 = t_2, \cdots, x_n = t_n$ is a *solution* of the Equations 14.1; also that in this solution x_i has the *value* t_i $(i = 1, 2, \cdots, n)$. Of course, it is quite possible for a given system of linear equations not to have any solution. In fact, we shall eventually obtain various tests for the existence of a solution.

The symbols $x_1, x_2, \cdots, x_n$ are often called *unknowns*, and we may therefore call 14.1 *a system of m linear equations in n unknowns*.

There are various alternative ways of writing the Equations 14.1, each of which is convenient for certain purposes. First, we observe that we may write them in the following form:

14.2
$$
\sum_{j=1}^{n} a_{ij}x_j = b_i, \qquad (i = 1, 2, \cdots, m).
$$

In this form, each value of i gives one equation, and in each equation j takes values from 1 to n. We next introduce a quite different notation which will be most useful.

Let us define elements of the vector space $V_n(F)$ as follows:

14.3
$$
\begin{aligned}
A_1 &= (a_{11}, a_{12}, \cdots, a_{1n}), \\
A_2 &= (a_{21}, a_{22}, \cdots, a_{2n}), \\
\cdots \cdots \cdots \cdots \cdots \cdots \cdots \\
A_m &= (a_{m1}, a_{m2}, \cdots, a_{mn}).
\end{aligned}
$$

It will be noted that A_i is composed of the coefficients in the ith equation of the system 14.1. Let us also formally write $X = (x_1, x_2, \cdots, x_n)$. Then in terms of the inner product of vectors as defined in the last section of Chapter 12, we may write the system 14.1 in the following form:

14.4 $A_1 \cdot X = b_1, \quad A_2 \cdot X = b_2, \quad \cdots, \quad A_m \cdot X = b_m.$

A *solution* of this system of equations is then an element $T = (t_1, t_2, \cdots, t_n)$ of $V_n(F)$ such that

$$A_1 \cdot T = b_1, \quad A_2 \cdot T = b_2, \quad \cdots, \quad A_m \cdot T = b_m.$$

It is now fairly easy to give one condition which must hold provided this system of linear equations has a solution. First, let us make the following definition.

14.5 Definition. The system 14.4 of linear equations is said to be *compatible* if for every choice of elements s_i of F such that $\sum_{i=1}^{m} s_i A_i = 0$, then necessarily $\sum_{i=1}^{m} s_i b_i = 0$ also.

We shall now show that if the system 14.4 of linear equations has a solution, the system is compatible. For if T is a solution and

$$\sum_{i=1}^{m} s_i A_i = 0,$$

it follows from Theorem 12.59 that

$$\sum_{i=1}^{m} s_i b_i = \sum_{i=1}^{m} s_i (A_i \cdot T) = \sum_{i=1}^{m} (s_i A_i) \cdot T = \left(\sum_{i=1}^{m} s_i A_i \right) \cdot T = 0 \cdot T = 0,$$

and the system is therefore compatible.

It should be clear that when we say that a system is compatible, we are only saying in a precise way that if the system has a solution and if there exist elements of F such that when we multiply both sides of the equations by these elements of F and add corresponding members we obtain the zero linear form on the left, then we must also obtain the zero element of F on the right. Later on we shall prove the converse of what was proved above, that is, we shall prove that if a system of linear equations is compatible, the system necessarily has a solution. This is a fairly deep result and in order to prove it we shall have to wait until the proper machinery is available.

There is still another useful way of writing Equations 14.1 (or 14.2 or 14.4). First, we shall introduce elements of $V_m(F)$ consisting of coefficients in our system of equations that lie in a fixed vertical line. Let us set

14.6 $\quad A^1 = \begin{bmatrix} a_{11} \\ a_{21} \\ \vdots \\ a_{m1} \end{bmatrix}, \quad A^2 = \begin{bmatrix} a_{12} \\ a_{22} \\ \vdots \\ a_{m2} \end{bmatrix}, \quad \cdots, \quad A^n = \begin{bmatrix} a_{1n} \\ a_{2n} \\ \vdots \\ a_{mn} \end{bmatrix}, \quad B^1 = \begin{bmatrix} b_1 \\ b_2 \\ \vdots \\ b_m \end{bmatrix}.$

The elements 14.3 of $V_n(F)$ are written as *row vectors*, and we may call these elements 14.6 of $V_m(F)$ *column vectors* to indicate that we have used a vertical arrangement instead of a horizontal one. Heretofore we have always used row vectors only because they are simpler to write. When we have occasion to use column vectors we shall use superscripts (not to be confused with exponents) to indicate this fact. Now in terms of the column vectors defined in 14.6 the entire system 14.1 of linear equations can be written in the following vector form:

14.7 $$x_1 A^1 + x_2 A^2 + \cdots + x_n A^n = B^1.$$

In the notation used here we may now observe that *the Equation 14.7 (or the system 14.1) has a solution if and only if the vector B^1 is a linear combination of the vectors A^1, A^2, $\cdots$, A^n*. In view of Theorem 12.15(ii) and Theorem 12.25(i), we can restate this result in the following useful form.

14.8 **Theorem.** *The Equation 14.7 (or the system 14.1) has a solution if and only if*

$$dim\ [A^1, A^2, \cdots, A^n, B^1] = dim\ [A^1, A^2, \cdots, A^n].$$

The usual method of finding solutions of a given system of linear equations involves a procedure for simplifying the form of the system. The following concept is a useful one in this connection.

14.9 **Definition.** Two systems of linear equations are said to be *equivalent* if they have exactly the same solutions.

There are simple operations on a system of linear equations that always yield equivalent systems. In order to simplify the wording, we shall speak of multiplying an equation by an element of F to mean the multiplying of both members of the equation by this element. Also, we shall speak of adding two equations to mean the adding of corresponding members of the two equations.

14.10   Definition.   We shall say that we perform an *elementary operation* on a system of linear equations if we do any one of the following:

>   *Type 1.* Interchange two equations.
>
>   *Type 2.* Multiply an equation by a nonzero element of F.
>
>   *Type 3.* Add to one equation d times a different equation, where $d \in F$.

As suggested by what was said above, the importance of these elementary operations stems from the following theorem.

14.11   Theorem.   *If a system of linear equations is obtained from a given system by applying in turn a finite number of elementary operations, the two systems are equivalent.*

It is obvious that we need only show that *one* elementary operation always yields an equivalent system. The desired result is quite trivial for an elementary operation of Type 1 or 2, and so we consider an elementary operation of Type 3. Let us write our given system of equations in the form 14.4 and, for convenience of notation, suppose that the operation consists of multiplying the second equation by $d \in F$ and adding it to the first equation. Using the fact that

$$A_1 \cdot X + d(A_2 \cdot X) = (A_1 + dA_2) \cdot X,$$

the resulting system can be written in the following form:

14.12 $(A_1 + dA_2) \cdot X = b_1 + db_2, \quad A_2 \cdot X = b_2, \quad \cdots, \quad A_m \cdot X = b_m.$

Now if T is a solution of 14.4 so that, in fact, $A_i \cdot T = b_i$ for $i = 1, 2, \cdots, m$, it is clear that T is also a solution of 14.12. Conversely, let T be a solution of 14.12, so that, in particular, $(A_1 + dA_2) \cdot T = b_1 + db_2$ and $A_2 \cdot T = b_2$. Since

$$(A_1 + dA_2) \cdot T = A_1 \cdot T + d(A_2 \cdot T) = b_1 + db_2,$$

it follows that $A_1 \cdot T = b_1$. Moreover, the two systems 14.4 and 14.12 are identical except for the first equation, and hence T is a solution of every equation of the system 14.4. We have thus shown that every solution of either of these systems is a solution of the other and they are therefore equivalent.

If one of the equations of a system is the *zero equation;* that is, if all the coefficients and the constant term are zero, the deletion of this equation from the system will clearly yield an equivalent system. We shall not call this an elementary operation, but we shall use this operation without hesitation whenever it is helpful to do so.

Theorem 14.11, together with the operation of deletion of one or more zero equations, may be applied in a systematic way to find all solutions (if any) of a given system. What we do is to apply a sequence of operations until a system is obtained in a simple enough form that the solutions are apparent. These solutions must then be the solutions of the original system. Although it is a very simple procedure, we shall find that it leads to interesting theoretical results as well as to a practical method for actually finding the solutions of a given system. This procedure will be discussed in detail in the following section.

14.2   ECHELON SYSTEMS

We shall begin by discussing two examples which will clarify the ideas involved. First, let us consider the following system of four equations in five unknowns over the field $\mathbf{Q}$ of rational numbers:

14.13
$$\begin{aligned}
x_1 + x_2 + x_3 + 2x_4 + 3x_5 &= 13, \\
-2x_1 - 2x_2 + x_3 + 3x_4 - 4x_5 &= 5, \\
3x_1 + 3x_2 \qquad\quad + x_4 + 5x_5 &= 10, \\
x_1 + x_2 + 2x_3 - x_4 + 9x_5 &= 18.
\end{aligned}$$

In order to eliminate x_1 from all equations but the first, we perform, in turn, the following three elementary operations of Type 3 on this system. First, we multiply the first equation by 2 and add it to the second equation, then multiply the first equation by -3 and add it to the third, and finally multiply the first equation by -1 and add it to the last equation. We thus obtain the following system which, by Theorem 14.11, must be equivalent to the system 14.13:

$$\begin{aligned}
x_1 + x_2 + x_3 + 2x_4 + 3x_5 &= 13, \\
3x_3 + 7x_4 + 2x_5 &= 31, \\
-3x_3 - 5x_4 - 4x_5 &= -29, \\
x_3 - 3x_4 + 6x_5 &= 5.
\end{aligned}$$

We now proceed to eliminate x_3 from all these equations but one. Since in the last equation the coefficient of x_3 is unity, we shall work with this equation and, in order to systematize the procedure, we use an elementary operation of Type 1 to interchange the second and fourth equation in order to get this equation in the second position. We then eliminate x_3 from all the equations except this new second one by multiplying it in turn by the proper elements of $\mathbf{Q}$ and adding to the other equations. In this way we obtain the system

$$
\begin{aligned}
x_1 + x_2 \quad + \quad 5x_4 - \quad 3x_5 &= 8, \\
x_3 - \quad 3x_4 + \quad 6x_5 &= 5, \\
- 14x_4 + 14x_5 &= -14, \\
16x_4 - 16x_5 &= 16.
\end{aligned}
$$

It is now clear that the third equation (as well as the fourth) can be simplified by an elementary operation of Type 2. Accordingly, we divide the third equation by -14 (multiply it by $-1/14$), and then proceed as above to eliminate x_4 from all equations except the third. We thus obtain the following system of equations:

$$
\begin{aligned}
x_1 + x_2 \quad + 2x_5 &= 3, \\
x_3 \quad + 3x_5 &= 8, \\
x_4 - \quad x_5 &= 1, \\
0 &= 0.
\end{aligned}
$$

Finally, we omit the last equation and rewrite the system in the following form:

14.14
$$
\begin{aligned}
x_1 &= 3 - x_2 - 2x_5, \\
x_3 &= 8 \quad\quad - 3x_5, \\
x_4 &= 1 \quad\quad + \quad x_5.
\end{aligned}
$$

This system is equivalent to the given system 14.13, and in the present form its solutions are apparent. If x_2 and x_3 are replaced by arbitrary elements of $\mathbf{Q}$, and the other unknowns are calculated from 14.14, we obtain a solution; and all solutions can be obtained in this way. To express this fact algebraically, let s and t be arbitrary elements of $\mathbf{Q}$. Then

$$
x_1 = 3 - s - 2t, \quad x_2 = s, \quad x_3 = 8 - 3t, \quad x_4 = 1 + t, \quad x_5 = t
$$

is a solution of the system 14.14, and any solution is of this form for suitable choices of s and t. We have therefore found all solutions of the given system 14.13 since it is equivalent to the system 14.14.

In the example just discussed, we found many solutions of the given system of equations. In other cases there might be exactly one solution or no solution. As a simple illustration of what happens when there is no solution, let us attempt to solve the following system of equations by the same method used above:

14.15
$$x_1 + x_2 - x_3 = 5,$$
$$x_1 + 2x_2 - 3x_3 = 8,$$
$$x_2 - 2x_3 = 1.$$

First, we multiply the first equation by -1 and add it to the second equation, obtaining the following system:

$$x_1 + x_2 - x_3 = 5,$$
$$x_2 - 2x_3 = 3,$$
$$x_2 - 2x_3 = 1.$$

Of course, it is obvious that this system has no solution, but let us proceed to eliminate x_2 from the first and third equations. After doing this, we have the system

$$x_1 \quad + x_3 = 2,$$
$$x_2 - 2x_3 = 3,$$
$$0 = -2.$$

Finally, in order to standardize the procedure, we divide the third equation by -2 and then multiply the new third equation by -2 and add it to the first; and also multiply the new third equation by -3 and add it to the second. We obtain in this way the following system of equations which is equivalent to the given system 14.15:

14.16
$$x_1 \quad + x_3 = 0,$$
$$x_2 - 2x_3 = 0,$$
$$0 = 1.$$

Now the symbol "0" on the left in the last of these equations stands for the zero linear form $0x_1 + 0x_2 + 0x_3$. It is clear that if the unknowns in this zero linear form are replaced by arbitrary elements of the field $\mathbf{Q}$, we obtain the zero element of $\mathbf{Q}$. Hence the last equation has no solution, and therefore the system 14.16 has no solution. We shall presently see that any system of linear equations which does not have a solution is reducible to a system in which one of the equations takes the form $0 = 1$.

We have considered these two examples in detail as illustrations of the procedure which can be applied to any system of linear equations. Suppose, now, that we wish to solve an arbitrary system 14.1 of m linear equations in n unknowns. We shall assume that not *all* the coefficients a_{ij} are zero since, otherwise, the problem is completely trivial. Moreover, if all the coefficients of x_1 were zero, we could just as well consider only $x_2, \cdots, x_n$ as the unknowns and ignore x_1. However, to use a general notation, let us suppose that x_{k_1} is the *first* one of the unknowns $x_1, x_2, \cdots, x_n$ which has a nonzero coefficient in any of the equations. Normally, of course, we will have $k_1 = 1$. By interchanging equations, if necessary, we can obtain an equivalent system in which the coefficient of x_{k_1} is not zero in the *first* of our equations. Then, by dividing the first equation by the coefficient of x_{k_1} in this equation, we can obtain unity as the coefficient of x_{k_1}. Next, by elementary operations of Type 3, as in the examples, we can obtain a system in which the coefficient of x_{k_1} is zero in every equation other than the first. The system is then of the following type:

$$x_{k_1} + b_{1\,k_1+1}x_{k_1+1} + \cdots + b_{1n}x_n = c_1,$$
$$b_{2\,k_1+1}x_{k_1+1} + \cdots + b_{2n}x_n = c_2,$$
$$\cdots \cdots \cdots \cdots \cdots \cdots \cdots$$
$$b_{m\,k_1+1}x_{k_1+1} + \cdots + b_{mn}x_n = c_m.$$

Now suppose that x_{k_2} is the first one of the unknowns $x_{k_1+1}, \cdots, x_n$ which has a nonzero coefficient in any of these equations *except the first*. By interchanging equations, if necessary, we can be sure that the coefficient of x_{k_2} is not zero in the second equation. We can then use elementary operations to make this coefficient unity and the coefficient of x_{k_2} zero in all equations except the second. By continuing this process, we find that for some positive integer r, with $r \le m$ and $r \le n$, there exist positive integers $k_1 < k_2 < \cdots < k_r$ such that our system of equations can be reduced by use of elementary operations to a system of the following form:

$$x_{k_1} + \cdots + 0x_{k_2} + \cdots + 0x_{k_r} + \cdots = d_1,$$
$$x_{k_2} + \cdots + 0x_{k_r} + \cdots = d_2,$$
$$\cdots \cdots \cdots \cdots \cdots \cdots \cdots$$

14.17
$$x_{k_r} + \cdots = d_r,$$
$$0 = d_{r+1},$$
$$\cdots \cdots \cdots$$
$$0 = d_m.$$

In this system if i is an integer such that $1 \le i \le r$, the coefficient of x_{k_i} is different from zero *only* in the ith equation. For example, the coefficients of $x_{k_2}, \cdots, x_{k_r}$ are all zero in the first equation, but if there are any other unknowns, their coefficients need not be zero. In the second equation the coefficient of x_j is zero for all $j < k_2$; also, the coefficients of $x_{k_3}, \cdots, x_{k_r}$ are zero. Corresponding remarks hold for the other equations. If it happens that $r = m$, then there will be no equations with 0 as left member.

Let us now assume that the given system 14.1, and therefore also the equivalent system 14.17, has a solution. It is then apparent that we must have $d_{r+1} = \cdots = d_m = 0$. Accordingly, we conclude that *if the system 14.1 has a solution, it can be reduced by elementary operations, together with the possible deletion of zero equations, to a system of the form*

14.18
$$\begin{aligned}
x_{k_1} + \cdots + 0x_{k_2} + \cdots + 0x_{k_r} + \cdots &= d_1, \\
x_{k_2} + \cdots + 0x_{k_r} + \cdots &= d_2, \\
\cdot \quad \cdot \quad \cdot \quad \cdot \quad \cdot \quad \cdot \quad \cdot \quad \cdot \quad &\cdot \\
x_{k_r} + \cdots &= d_r,
\end{aligned}$$

with the same understanding about zero coefficients as in 14.17. We now observe that it is easy to find all solutions of the system 14.18. If we assign arbitrary values from the field F to the unknowns (if any) other than $x_{k_1}, x_{k_2}, \cdots, x_{k_r}$, the value of x_{k_1} is uniquely determined from the first equation, the value of x_{k_2} is uniquely determined from the second equation, and so on. Not only does this procedure give a method of finding solutions but, since the values of $x_{k_1}, x_{k_2}, \cdots, x_{k_r}$ are uniquely determined by the values of the other unknowns, it follows that *every* solution of the system 14.18 can be obtained by the process just described.

Let us next assume that the given system 14.1, and therefore also the equivalent system 14.17, does not have a solution. If $d_{r+1} = \cdots = d_m = 0$, the argument given above would show that the system has a solution. Accordingly, at least one of the equations in 14.17 must be of the form $0 = d$ with $d \neq 0$. For theoretical purposes it is helpful to continue our simplification procedure a little further as follows. By interchanging equations, if necessary, we can consider this equation $0 = d$ to be the first one of those with 0 as left member. Then, by elementary operations, we can write this equation in the form $0 = 1$ and also reduce the constant terms in all other equations to 0. Finally, after deleting any zero equations, our system takes the following form:

14.19
$$\begin{aligned}
x_{k_1} + \cdots + 0x_{k_2} + \cdots + 0x_{k_r} + \cdots &= 0, \\
x_{k_2} + \cdots + 0x_{k_r} + \cdots &= 0, \\
\cdot \quad \cdot \quad \cdot \quad \cdot \quad \cdot \quad \cdot \quad \cdot \quad \cdot \quad &\cdot \\
x_{k_r} + \cdots &= 0, \\
0 &= 1.
\end{aligned}$$

A system of linear equations either of the form 14.18 or of the form 14.19 is said to be an *echelon* system.

The conclusions we have reached above may be summarized in the following theorem.

14.20   Theorem.   *Any system 14.1 of linear equations with coefficients over a field F can be reduced by means of elementary operations, and the possible deletion of zero equations, to an echelon system.*

The given system has a solution if and only if it is reducible to an echelon system of the form 14.18. In this case, the unknowns (if any) other than $x_{k_1}, x_{k_2}, \cdots, x_{k_r}$, can be assigned arbitrary values from F, and the corresponding values of $x_{k_1}, x_{k_2}, \cdots, x_{k_r}$, are then uniquely determined from the Equations 14.18. Moreover, all solutions can be obtained in this way.

The given system does not have a solution if and only if it is reducible to an echelon system of the form 14.19.

If $r = n$, the Equations 14.18 take the form $x_1 = d_1$, $x_2 = d_2, \cdots$, $x_n = d_n$; and the system clearly has exactly one solution. If $r < n$, there is at least one unknown which can be assigned arbitrary values; hence there will be more than one solution. The following result is therefore an immediate consequence of the preceding theorem.

14.21   Corollary.   *A system 14.1 of linear equations has a unique solution if and only if the number r of equations in the corresponding echelon system 14.18 is equal to the number n of unknowns.*

EXERCISES

In each of Exercises 1–6, reduce the given system of linear equations over the field **Q** to an echelon system, and find all solutions.

1.
$$x_1 - x_2 + 2x_3 = 5,$$
$$2x_1 + x_2 - x_3 = 2,$$
$$2x_1 - x_2 - x_3 = 4,$$
$$x_1 + 3x_2 + 2x_3 = 1.$$

2.
$$2x_1 - 2x_2 + 2x_3 - 3x_4 = 11,$$
$$x_1 - x_2 + x_3 - 2x_4 = 4,$$
$$-x_1 + x_2 \qquad + 6x_4 = -3,$$
$$9x_1 - 9x_2 + 7x_3 - 23x_4 = 43.$$

3.
$$2x_1 - x_2 + x_3 = 4,$$
$$3x_1 + x_2 - 5x_3 = 1,$$
$$x_1 - 5x_2 + 8x_3 = 5,$$
$$2x_1 - 2x_2 + x_3 = 3.$$

4. $\quad 2x_1 - 4x_2 + 3x_3 - 5x_4 = -3,$
$\qquad 4x_1 + 2x_2 + x_3 \qquad\quad = 4,$
$\qquad 6x_1 - 2x_2 + 4x_3 - 5x_4 = 1.$

5. $\quad 2x_1 - x_2 - x_3 + x_4 + 8x_5 = -4,$
$\qquad x_1 + x_2 + 4x_3 + x_4 + 4x_5 = 3,$
$\qquad -3x_1 + 2x_2 + 3x_3 + x_4 - 5x_5 = 3,$
$\qquad 2x_1 - 2x_2 - 3x_3 + 2x_4 + 12x_5 = -10.$

6. $\quad 3x_1 - x_2 + x_3 - x_4 = 1,$
$\qquad 2x_1 + 3x_2 - x_3 + 5x_4 = 7,$
$\qquad 2x_1 + 5x_2 - x_3 + 12x_4 = 8,$
$\qquad x_1 - 2x_2 + 2x_3 + x_4 = 5.$

In each of Exercises 7–9, the equations are over the field $\mathbf{Z}_3$. Reduce to an echelon system, find the number of solutions in each case, and actually exhibit all of them.

7. $\quad x_1 + 2x_2 + x_3 = 2,$
$\qquad 2x_1 + x_2 + 2x_3 = 1,$
$\qquad x_1 + x_2 + x_3 = 2.$

8. $\quad x_1 + 2x_2 + x_3 \qquad = 0,$
$\qquad x_2 + x_3 + x_4 = 0,$
$\qquad 2x_1 + 2x_2 + x_3 \qquad = 2,$
$\qquad 2x_2 \qquad + x_4 = 2.$

9. $\quad 2x_1 + x_2 + 2x_3 + x_4 = 1,$
$\qquad x_1 + 2x_2 + x_3 + 2x_4 = 2.$

In each of Exercises 10–12, apply Definition 14.5 to show that the given system of linear equations over the field $\mathbf{Q}$ is *not* compatible. Verify also that the system does not have a solution.

10. $\quad x_1 + x_2 + 3x_3 = 4,$
$\qquad 2x_1 + 2x_2 + 6x_3 = 12.$

11. $\quad 2x_1 - x_2 + x_3 = 1,$
$\qquad x_1 + x_2 - 3x_3 = 2,$
$\qquad 5x_1 - x_2 - x_3 = 1.$

12. $\quad x_1 - x_2 + x_3 - x_4 = 2,$
$\qquad x_1 + x_2 + x_3 + x_4 = 1,$
$\qquad 2x_1 \qquad + 2x_3 \qquad = 3,$
$\qquad x_1 + 3x_2 + x_3 + 3x_4 = 2.$

14.3   MATRICES

The concept of a matrix arises naturally in mathematics in several different ways. For example, in carrying out the calculations of the preceding section it is obvious that we could avoid writing down the unknowns, as well as the signs of addition and equality, and just work with the array of coefficients and constant terms. This possibility suggests the introduction of some suitable notation and terminology for discussing rectangular arrays of elements of a field. We proceed to give the necessary definition and to establish those properties which will be particularly useful in the study of systems of linear equations. Matrices will be studied in somewhat more detail in Chapter 16.

Let p and q be positive integers, and let c_{ij} ($i = 1, 2, \cdots, p$; $j = 1, 2, \cdots, q$) be elements of a field F. The rectangular array C defined by

14.22
$$C = \begin{bmatrix} c_{11} & c_{12} & \cdots & c_{1q} \\ c_{21} & c_{22} & \cdots & c_{2q} \\ \cdot & \cdot & \cdots & \cdot \\ c_{p1} & c_{p2} & \cdots & c_{pq} \end{bmatrix}$$

is called a *matrix* (over F) with p rows and q columns, or simply a $p \times q$ matrix. As suggested by this language, the elements of the matrix C that occur in a horizontal line constitute a *row* of the matrix, and those in a vertical line a *column* of the matrix. It will be observed that an element c_{ij} occurs at the intersection of the ith row and jth column.

The rows of the matrix C may be considered to be elements of the vector space $V_q(F)$. More precisely, we may define the *row vectors* of C to be the following vectors of $V_q(F)$:

$$C_1 = (c_{11}, c_{12}, \cdots, c_{1q}),$$
$$C_2 = (c_{21}, c_{22}, \cdots, c_{2q}),$$
$$\cdot \quad \cdot \quad \cdot \quad \cdot \quad \cdot \quad \cdot \quad \cdot \quad \cdot$$
$$C_p = (c_{p1}, c_{p2}, \cdots, c_{pq}).$$

Similarly, the *column vectors* of C are defined to be the following vectors of $V_p(F)$:

$$C^1 = \begin{bmatrix} c_{11} \\ c_{21} \\ \vdots \\ c_{p1} \end{bmatrix}, \quad C^2 = \begin{bmatrix} c_{12} \\ c_{22} \\ \vdots \\ c_{p2} \end{bmatrix}, \quad \cdots, \quad C^q = \begin{bmatrix} c_{1q} \\ c_{2q} \\ \vdots \\ c_{pq} \end{bmatrix}.$$

It will be observed that a row vector of the matrix C may be considered to be a matrix with one row and q columns, and likewise a column vector may be considered to be a matrix with p rows and one column.

The concepts introduced in the following definition play an important role in the sequel.

14.23   Definition.   The subspace of $V_q(F)$ generated by the row vectors of C, that is, in the notation of 12.13, the subspace $[C_1, C_2, \cdots, C_p]$ of $V_q(F)$, is called the *row space* of the matrix C. The dimension of this row space is called the *row rank* of the matrix C.

      Similarly, the subspace of $V_p(F)$ generated by the column vectors of C; that is, the subspace $[C^1, C^2, \cdots, C^q]$ of $V_p(F)$, is called the *column space* of C and its dimension is the *column rank* of C.

In order to compute the row rank, or the column rank, of a given matrix, we may use a method suggested by the way in which we simplified a system of linear equations in the preceding section. Let us first define elementary operations on a matrix as follows (*cf.* 14.10).

14.24   Definition.   Let C be a matrix over a field F. We shall say that we perform an *elementary row (column) operation* on C if we do any one of the following.

    Type 1.   Interchange two rows (columns).

    Type 2.   Multiply the elements of one row (column) by a nonzero element of F.

    Type 3.   Add to the elements of one row (column) d times the corresponding elements of a different row (column), where $d \in F$.

We thus have three different types of elementary row operations, and three types of elementary column operations. For simplicity of statement, we now restrict attention to elementary row operations. From our present point of view, the importance of the elementary row operations is that if a matrix D is obtained from a matrix C by means of an elementary row operation, C and D have the same row spaces and therefore also the same row rank. This fact is obvious for an elementary row operation of Type 1, and Corollary 12.16 assures us that it is also true for operations of Types 2 and 3. Since the row rank of a matrix is not changed by application of *one* elementary row operation, the same must also be true for a finite sequence of elementary row operations. Of course, similar remarks hold for column operations, and we summarize these remarks in the following theorem.

14.25   Theorem.   *If one matrix is obtained from another by a finite sequence of elementary row (column) operations, the two matrices have the same row space (column space), and therefore also the same row rank (column rank).*

In view of this theorem, we may compute the row rank of a given matrix by applying elementary row operations until a matrix is obtained in a form in which its row rank is apparent. This row rank must then also be the row rank of the given matrix. Let us illustrate this procedure by finding the row rank of the following matrix over the field **Q** of rational numbers:

14.26
$$\begin{bmatrix} 0 & -1 & 3 & -1 & 0 & 2 \\ -1 & 1 & -2 & -2 & 1 & -3 \\ 2 & -1 & 4 & 4 & -1 & 8 \\ 1 & -2 & 5 & 1 & -1 & 5 \end{bmatrix}.$$

It will be observed that the procedure is essentially that used in the preceding section to reduce a system of linear equations to an echelon system.

First, we get an element 1 in the upper left-hand position by interchanging the first two rows and then multiplying the new first row by −1. We then have the matrix

$$\begin{bmatrix} 1 & -1 & 2 & 2 & -1 & 3 \\ 0 & -1 & 3 & -1 & 0 & 2 \\ 2 & -1 & 4 & 4 & -1 & 8 \\ 1 & -2 & 5 & 1 & -1 & 5 \end{bmatrix}.$$

Next we use elementary row operations of Type 3 to reduce all elements of the first column, except this first element, to zero. More specifically, we multiply the first row by −2 and add it to the third row; also multiply the first row by −1 and add it to the fourth row. This gives us the matrix

$$\begin{bmatrix} 1 & -1 & 2 & 2 & -1 & 3 \\ 0 & -1 & 3 & -1 & 0 & 2 \\ 0 & 1 & 0 & 0 & 1 & 2 \\ 0 & -1 & 3 & -1 & 0 & 2 \end{bmatrix}.$$

Now if we add the third row to each of the other rows, and then interchange the second and third rows, we obtain

$$\begin{bmatrix} 1 & 0 & 2 & 2 & 0 & 5 \\ 0 & 1 & 0 & 0 & 1 & 2 \\ 0 & 0 & 3 & -1 & 1 & 4 \\ 0 & 0 & 3 & -1 & 1 & 4 \end{bmatrix}.$$

We next multiply the third row by −1 and add it to the last row, obtaining a row consisting entirely of zeros. We then multiply the third row by 1/3 in order to get 1 as its first nonzero element. Finally, we multiply the third row by -2 and add it to the first row. This gives the matrix

$$\begin{bmatrix} 1 & 0 & 0 & 8/3 & -2/3 & 7/3 \\ 0 & 1 & 0 & 0 & 1 & 2 \\ 0 & 0 & 1 & -1/3 & 1/3 & 4/3 \\ 0 & 0 & 0 & 0 & 0 & 0 \end{bmatrix}.$$

Since the unit vectors $(1, 0, 0)$, $(0, 1, 0)$, and $(0, 0, 1)$ of $V_3(\mathbf{Q})$ are linearly independent, it is easy to see that the first three rows of this matrix are linearly independent, and hence that its row rank is 3. Since this matrix has been obtained from the given matrix by use of elementary row operations, it follows that the matrix 14.26 also has row rank 3.

In this example, we have computed the *row* rank of the given matrix. It is obvious that we could similarly apply elementary column operations to determine the column rank of the matrix. However, the next theorem is of considerable theoretical importance and will show us that both of these ranks are known as soon as one of them has been determined.

14.27 Theorem. *The row rank of any matrix is equal to its column rank.*

Let C be the $p \times q$ matrix 14.22 over a field F, and suppose that the row rank of C is r and that its column rank is s. The main part of the proof consists in showing that any $r + 1$ column vectors of C are linearly dependent, and hence that $s \leq r$. If $r = p$, this is clearly true since, by Corollary 12.19, any $p + 1$ vectors of $V_p(F)$ are linearly dependent. Suppose, then, that $r < p$. Since the row rank is r, by Theorem 12.25(ii) there must exist r row vectors that constitute a basis of the row space of C. Let us rearrange the rows (if necessary) so that the first r rows are a basis of the row space. It is not difficult to see that this cannot change the linear dependence or independence of column vectors, and hence it does not change the column rank. As a matter of notation, we may therefore assume, without loss of generality, that the *first r* rows of C form a basis of the row space of C. Since we wish to show that the column rank s of C cannot exceed r, we may certainly assume that $q > r$ since, otherwise, there is nothing to prove. Let us now write our matrix C in a somewhat more explicit form as follows:

$$C = \begin{bmatrix} c_{11} & c_{12} & \cdots & c_{1r} & c_{1\,r+1} & \cdots & c_{1q} \\ c_{21} & c_{22} & \cdots & c_{2r} & c_{2\,r+1} & \cdots & c_{2q} \\ \cdot & \cdot & \cdot & \cdot & \cdot & \cdots & \cdot \\ c_{r1} & c_{r2} & \cdots & c_{rr} & c_{r\,r+1} & \cdots & c_{rq} \\ \cdot & \cdot & \cdot & \cdot & \cdot & \cdots & \cdot \\ c_{p1} & c_{p2} & \cdots & c_{pr} & c_{p\,r+1} & \cdots & c_{pq} \end{bmatrix}.$$

As introduced earlier, let C_1, C_2, $\cdots$, C_p be the row vectors, and C^1, C^2, $\cdots$, C^q the column vectors of C. Moreover, let

$$S^1 = \begin{bmatrix} c_{11} \\ c_{21} \\ \vdots \\ c_{r1} \end{bmatrix}, \quad S^2 = \begin{bmatrix} c_{12} \\ c_{22} \\ \vdots \\ c_{r2} \end{bmatrix}, \quad \cdots, \quad S^q = \begin{bmatrix} c_{1q} \\ c_{2q} \\ \vdots \\ c_{rq} \end{bmatrix}$$

be elements of $V_r(F)$ consisting of column vectors taken from the first r rows of C. We shall now prove the following lemma.

14.28 Lemma. *If $t_i \in F$ $(i = 1, 2, \cdots, q)$ such that*

$$\sum_{i=1}^{q} t_i S^i = 0, \quad \text{then also} \sum_{i=1}^{q} t_i C^i = 0.$$

If $T = (t_1, t_2, \cdots, t_q)$, then $\sum_{i=1}^{q} t_i S^i = 0$ can be expressed using inner products of vectors as follows:

14.29 $C_1 \cdot T = 0, \quad C_2 \cdot T = 0, \quad \cdots, \quad C_r \cdot T = 0.$

Now if C_k is an arbitrary row vector of C, then C_k is a linear combination of the vectors C_1, C_2, $\cdots$, C_r, since they form a basis of the row space of C. That is, there exist elements a_j $(j = 1, 2, \cdots, r)$ of F such that

$$C_k = a_1 C_1 + a_2 C_2 + \cdots + a_r C_r.$$

It follows from Theorem 12.35(iv) that

$$\begin{aligned} C_k \cdot T &= (a_1 C_1 + a_2 C_2 + \cdots + a_r C_r) \cdot T \\ &= a_1 (C_1 \cdot T) + a_2 (C_2 \cdot T) + \cdots + a_r (C_r \cdot T). \end{aligned}$$

Hence, in view of 14.29, we see that $C_k \cdot T = 0$. Again, changing the notation, the fact that $C_k \cdot T = 0$ for $k = 1, 2, \cdots, p$ assures us that

$$\sum_{i=1}^{q} t_i C^i = 0,$$

as we wished to prove. The lemma is therefore established.

It is now easy to complete the proof that any $r + 1$ column vectors of C are linearly dependent. Merely for convenience of notation, let us show that the first $r + 1$ column vectors C^1, C^2, $\cdots$, C^{r+1} are linearly dependent. We know that the column vectors S^1, S^2, $\cdots$, S^{r+1} must be linearly dependent since we have $r + 1$ vectors of $V_r(F)$. Hence, there exist elements b_i $(i = 1, 2, \cdots, r + 1)$ of F, not all zero, such that

$$\sum_{i=1}^{r+1} b_i S^i = 0.$$

The lemma then asserts that also

$$\sum_{i=1}^{r+1} b_i C^i = 0,$$

and since the coefficients are not all zero we have shown that the first $r + 1$ column vectors of C are linearly dependent. Similarly, any set of $r + 1$ column vectors of C is a linearly dependent set, and we have therefore shown that $s \leq r$.

We may restate what we have proved up to this point as follows. *The column rank of an arbitrary matrix cannot exceed the row rank of the matrix.* One simple way to complete the proof of the theorem is as follows. If C is the matrix 14.22, let us write a new matrix C', called the *transpose* of C, obtained from C by interchanging rows and columns. That is, C' is defined as follows:

$$C' = \begin{bmatrix} c_{11} & c_{21} & \cdots & c_{p1} \\ c_{12} & c_{22} & \cdots & c_{p2} \\ \cdot & \cdot & \cdots & \cdot \\ c_{1q} & c_{2q} & \cdots & c_{pq} \end{bmatrix}.$$

Now the row space and column space of the matrix C' are, respectively, the column space and the row space of C. Hence, the row rank of the matrix C' is s and its column rank is r. Since we have already proved that the column rank of a matrix can never exceed the row rank, we see that $r \leq s$. Moreover, we already know that $s \leq r$, and we conclude that $s = r$. This completes the proof of the theorem.

In view of this theorem, we need not distinguish between the row rank and the column rank of a matrix. Accordingly, we make the following definition.

14.30 Definition. The common value of the row rank and the column rank of a matrix is called simply the *rank* of the matrix.

We shall sometimes find it convenient to refer to the (row) rank of a matrix by which we shall mean that the truth of the statement we are making is most easily seen by consideration of the *row* rank.

EXERCISES

In each of Exercises 1–5, use elementary row operations to determine the (row) rank of the given matrix over the rational field.

1. $\begin{bmatrix} -1 & 2 & 1 \\ 1 & -1 & 2 \\ 1 & 1 & 4 \end{bmatrix}.$

2. $\begin{bmatrix} 2 & -1 & 1 \\ 3 & 1 & 2 \\ 1 & 0 & -1 \\ 0 & 1 & 0 \end{bmatrix}.$

3. $\begin{bmatrix} 1 & 3 & -1 & 2 \\ 0 & 1 & 2 & -5 \\ 2 & 3 & -8 & 19 \end{bmatrix}.$

4. $\begin{bmatrix} 0 & 1 & -1 & 2 \\ 2 & -1 & 0 & 1 \\ 1 & 1 & 1 & 1 \end{bmatrix}.$

5. $\begin{bmatrix} 1 & 2 & -1 & 3 \\ 4 & 1 & 2 & 1 \\ 3 & -1 & 1 & 2 \\ 1 & 2 & 0 & 1 \end{bmatrix}.$

6. Use elementary row operations to determine the rank of the following matrix over the field Z_5:

$$\begin{bmatrix} 2 & 1 & 1 & 3 & 4 \\ 4 & 1 & 2 & 1 & 2 \\ 1 & 2 & 1 & 1 & 2 \\ 1 & 3 & 0 & 2 & 1 \end{bmatrix}.$$

7. Show that, by use of both elementary row and column operations, the matrix

$$\begin{bmatrix} -1 & -2 & 1 & 3 \\ 1 & 0 & 1 & 1 \\ 3 & 2 & 1 & -1 \\ 1 & -4 & 5 & 9 \end{bmatrix}$$

over the rational field can be reduced to the matrix

$$\begin{bmatrix} 1 & 0 & 0 & 0 \\ 0 & 1 & 0 & 0 \\ 0 & 0 & 0 & 0 \\ 0 & 0 & 0 & 0 \end{bmatrix}.$$

8. Determine the dimension of each of the following subspaces of the appropriate vector space $V_n(\mathbf{Q})$. [Hint: Form a matrix whose row vectors are the given vectors and find the (row) rank of the matrix.]

   (a) $[(1, 2, -1), (3, 1, 2), (1, -3, 4)]$,
   (b) $[(3, -1, 4), (2, 1, 3), (1, 0, 2)]$,
   (c) $[(0, 1, 1, 2), (-2, 1, 0, 1), (3, 1, 5, 2), (1, 0, 3, -1)]$,
   (d) $[(-1, 2, -1, 0), (0, 3, 1, 2), (1, 1, -2, 2), (2, 1, 0, -1)]$.

14.4   APPLICATIONS TO SYSTEMS OF LINEAR EQUATIONS

We shall now apply the results of the preceding section to a further study of systems of linear equations.

Associated with the system 14.1 of m linear equations in n unknowns are two matrices. The $m \times n$ matrix

$$\begin{bmatrix} a_{11} & a_{12} & \cdots & a_{1n} \\ a_{21} & a_{22} & \cdots & a_{2n} \\ \cdot & \cdot & & \cdot \\ a_{m1} & a_{m2} & \cdots & a_{mn} \end{bmatrix}$$

consisting of the coefficients of the various unknowns, is called the *matrix of the coefficients* of the given system. The $m \times (n+1)$ matrix

$$\begin{bmatrix} a_{11} & a_{12} & \cdots & a_{1n} & b_1 \\ a_{21} & a_{22} & \cdots & a_{2n} & b_2 \\ \cdot & \cdot & & \cdot & \cdot \\ a_{m1} & a_{m2} & \cdots & a_{mn} & b_m \end{bmatrix}$$

is called the *augmented matrix* of the system. The augmented matrix differs from the matrix of the coefficients only in that it has an additional column which consists of the constant terms of the equation.

In the notation introduced in 14.6, the column vectors of the augmented matrix are $A^1, A^2, \cdots, A^n, B^1$. Since dim $[A^1, A^2, \cdots, A^n, B^1]$ is the (column) rank of the augmented matrix, we have at once the following consequence of Theorem 14.8.

14.31   Theorem.   *A system 14.1 of linear equations over a field F has a solution if and only if the rank of the matrix of the coefficients of the system is equal to the rank of the augmented matrix of the system.*

We can obtain some further information by again considering the reduction of a given system to an echelon system. An elementary operation on a system of linear equations, as defined in 14.10, has the same effect on the augmented matrix of the system as the corresponding elementary row operation on this matrix, as defined in 14.24. Hence, if the given system is reduced to an echelon system of equations by a sequence of elementary operations and, possibly, the deletion of zero equations, we know that the augmented matrix of the echelon system can be obtained from the augmented matrix of the given system by a sequence of elementary row operations and the possible deletion of zero rows.

In view of these observations, we see that the process of reducing a given system of linear equations to an echelon system can be carried out by working with the augmented matrix of the system. For example, suppose that we wish to solve the following system of linear equations over the rational field:

$$\begin{aligned}
x_1 + 2x_2 + 2x_3 &= 5, \\
x_1 - 3x_2 + 2x_3 &= -5, \\
2x_1 - x_2 + x_3 &= -3.
\end{aligned}$$

The augmented matrix of this system is the matrix

$$\begin{bmatrix} 1 & 2 & 2 & 5 \\ 1 & -3 & 2 & -5 \\ 2 & -1 & 1 & -3 \end{bmatrix}.$$

We omit the details, but by use of elementary row operations this matrix can be reduced to the form

$$\begin{bmatrix} 1 & 0 & 0 & -1 \\ 0 & 1 & 0 & 2 \\ 0 & 0 & 1 & 1 \end{bmatrix}.$$

This is clearly the augmented matrix of the following echelon system of equations, which must be equivalent to the given system:

$$\begin{aligned} x_1 && &= -1, \\ & x_2 & &= 2, \\ && x_3 &= 1. \end{aligned}$$

Accordingly, we conclude that the only solution of the given system is $x_1 = -1$, $x_2 = 2$, $x_3 = 1$.

As indicated by this example, there is some economy of effort in working with the augmented matrix instead of with the equations themselves. However, it is of more importance than we can apply these ideas to obtain some general theoretical results.

Since the presence or absence of a zero row cannot affect the row space of a matrix, we conclude from Theorem 14.25 that the row space of the augmented matrix of a given system of linear equations is equal to the row space of the augmented matrix of the echelon system 14.18 or 14.19 to which the given system is equivalent. Moreover, an elementary row operation on the augmented matrix of a system of linear equations induces an elementary row operation on the matrix of coefficients as well.

If a system 14.1 of linear equations has a solution, we know that it is reducible to an echelon system of the form 14.18. The (row) rank of the matrix of the coefficients, and also of the augmented matrix, of this echelon system is easily seen to be r. Hence, in view of the observations made above, and Theorem 14.25, we know that the ranks of the matrix of the coefficients and of the augmented matrix of the given system 14.1 must both be equal to r. If the given system does not have a solution, it is reducible to an echelon system of the form 14.19. For this system, the (row) rank of the matrix of coefficients is r, whereas the (row) rank of the augmented matrix is $r + 1$.

These observations, together with Theorem 14.20, yield the following result.

14.32 Theorem. *Suppose that the augmented matrix and the matrix of coefficients of a system 14.1 of linear equations over a field F both have rank r. If r is less than the number n of unknowns, certain $n - r$ of the unknowns can be assigned arbitrary values from F and the values of the other r unknowns are then uniquely determined. Moreover, all solutions can be obtained in this way. The system has a unique solution if and only if $r = n$.*

Let us now return to a consideration of the compatibility condition as defined in 14.5. We have already proved that if a system of linear equations has a solution, it is compatible. We shall now complete the proof of the following theorem.

14.33   Theorem.   *A system 14.1 of linear equations over a field F has a solution if and only if it is compatible.*

We assume that our system is compatible and shall show that it has a solution.

We continue to denote the row vectors of the matrix of coefficients of the given system by $A_1, A_2, \cdots, A_m$. It will also be convenient to denote the row vectors of the augmented matrix by (A_1, b_1), (A_2, b_2), $\cdots, (A_m, b_m)$.

Suppose that the matrix of coefficients has rank r. We shall prove that the augmented matrix also has rank r by showing that, if $r < m$, any $r + 1$ row vectors of the augmented matrix are linearly dependent. For convenience of notation, let us consider the *first* $r + 1$ row vectors. Since the coefficient matrix has rank r, we know that the $r + 1$ row vectors $A_1, A_2, \cdots, A_{r+1}$ of the coefficient matrix are linearly dependent. Accordingly, there exist elements c_i $(i = 1, 2, \cdots, r + 1)$ of F, not all of which are zero, such that

$$\sum_{i=1}^{r+1} c_i A_i = 0.$$

The compatibility condition now assures us that also

$$\sum_{i=1}^{r+1} c_i b_i = 0,$$

and we therefore conclude that

$$\sum_{i=1}^{r+1} c_i (A_i, b_i) = 0.$$

Since the c's are not all zero, we have shown that the first $r + 1$ row vectors of the augmented matrix are linearly dependent. The same argument applies to any set of $r + 1$ row vectors. This proves that the augmented matrix must have rank r, and Theorem 14.31 then shows that the system has a solution. This completes the proof of the theorem.

The next result will show that we may be able to delete some of the equations of a given system without affecting the solutions of the system. Let us now write our system of equations in the form given in 14.4, which we here repeat for convenience of reference:

14.34 $\qquad A_1 \cdot X = b_1, \quad A_2 \cdot X = b_2, \cdots, \quad A_m \cdot X = b_m.$

We shall proceed to prove the following theorem.

14.35 Theorem. *If the row vectors* $(A_{l_1}, b_{l_1}), (A_{l_2}, b_{l_2}), \cdots, (A_{l_r}, b_{l_r})$ *form a basis of the row space of the augmented matrix of the system 14.34, then the system is equivalent to the system consisting of the following r equations:*

14.36 $\qquad A_{l_1} \cdot X = b_{l_1}, \quad A_{l_2} \cdot X = b_{l_2}, \cdots, \quad A_{l_r} \cdot X = b_{l_r}.$

It is obvious that any solution of the entire system 14.34 is also a solution of the subsystem 14.36. To prove the theorem, we therefore need only show that any solution T of the system 14.36 is also a solution of the system 14.34. If $A_j \cdot X = b_j$ is an arbitrary one of the Equations 14.34, we shall show that $A_j \cdot T = b_j$. Since the row vector (A_j, b_j) is a linear combination of the given basis of the row space of the augmented matrix, there exist elements d_i $(i = 1, 2, \cdots, r)$ of F such that

$$A_j = \sum_{i=1}^{r} d_i A_{l_i}, \quad b_j = \sum_{i=1}^{r} d_i b_{l_i}.$$

Using these equations, simple properties of the inner product, and the fact that T is a solution of the system 14.36, we find that

$$A_j \cdot T = \left(\sum_{i=1}^{r} d_i A_{l_i} \right) \cdot T = \sum_{i=1}^{r} d_i (A_{l_i} \cdot T) = \sum_{i=1}^{r} d_i b_{l_i} = b_j.$$

Hence, T is, in fact, a solution of each equation of the system 14.34, and the proof is complete.

14.5 SYSTEMS OF LINEAR HOMOGENEOUS EQUATIONS

In this section we briefly discuss a special case of some importance. A linear equation is said to be *homogeneous* if its constant term is zero. A system of m linear homogeneous equations can then be written in the form 14.34 with all b's equal to zero. That is, such a system is of the form

14.37 $\qquad A_1 \cdot X = 0, \quad A_2 \cdot X = 0, \cdots, \quad A_m \cdot X = 0.$

Since the augmented matrix of this system differs from the matrix of coefficients only by having an additional zero column, the ranks of these matrices are the same. Theorem 14.31 then asserts that the system must have a solution. However, this fact is also immediately obvious from the observation that the equations are satisfied if we set $x_1 = 0$, $x_2 = 0$, $\cdots$, $x_n = 0$; otherwise expressed, $X = 0$ is a solution of the system. This solution, in which all the unknowns are assigned the value zero, is usually called the *trivial solution* of the system. Any other solution is a nontrivial solution.

The principal theorem about the solutions of a system of linear homogeneous equations is the following.

14.38   Theorem. *If r is the rank of the matrix of coefficients of a system 14.37 of linear homogeneous equations in n unknowns over a field F, then the solutions of the system form a subspace of dimension n − r of the vector space $V_n(F)$.*

First, let us verify that the set of all solutions is a subspace of $V_n(F)$. If S and T are solutions of the system 14.37, so that $A_i \cdot S = 0$ and $A_i \cdot T = 0$ for $i = 1, 2, \cdots, m$, then also

$$A_i \cdot (S + T) = A_i \cdot S + A_i \cdot T = 0,$$

so that $S + T$ is a solution. Similarly, if S is a solution and $c \in F$, then $A_i \cdot (cS) = c(A_i \cdot S) = c0 = 0$ for $i = 1, 2, \cdots, m$; and cS is also a solution. We have thus shown that the subset of $V_n(F)$ consisting of all solutions of the system 14.37 is closed under addition and scalar multiplication. This subset is then a subspace of $V_n(F)$ by Theorem 12.7. We now proceed to prove that this subspace has dimension $n − r$.

If $r = n$, we know from Theorem 14.32 that there is a unique solution, and it must therefore be the trivial solution. The subspace of all solutions is then the zero vector space and, by definition, it has dimension zero. Having disposed of this simple case, we shall henceforth assume that $r < n$.

By Theorem 14.20, we know that our system 14.37 can be reduced to an echelon system of the form 14.18 in which all the d's are zero. For convenience of notation, let us suppose that $k_1 = 1$, $k_2 = 2$, $\cdots$, $k_r = r$. Then this echelon system, which is equivalent to our given system, can be written in the form

14.39

$$
\begin{aligned}
x_1 &= c_{1\,r+1}x_{r+1} + \cdots + c_{1n}x_n, \\
x_2 &= c_{2\,r+1}x_{r+1} + \cdots + c_{2n}x_n, \\
&\;\cdot\;\cdot\;\cdot\;\cdot\;\cdot\;\cdot\;\cdot\;\cdot\;\cdot\;\cdot\;\cdot\;\cdot\;\cdot\;\cdot \\
x_r &= c_{r\,r+1}x_{r+1} + \cdots + c_{rn}x_n.
\end{aligned}
$$

where the c's are fixed elements of F. We can get a particular solution by setting $x_{r+1} = 1$, $x_{r+2} = \cdots = x_n = 0$, and solving for the corresponding values of $x_1, x_2, \cdots, x_r$. In this way we obtain the solution

$$T_1 = (c_{1\ r+1}, \cdots, c_{r\ r+1}, 1, 0, \cdots, 0).$$

In like manner, each of the following is a solution:

$$T_2 = (c_{1\ r+2}, \cdots, c_{r\ r+2}, 0, 1, \cdots, 0),$$
$$\cdot \cdot \cdot \cdot \cdot \cdot \cdot \cdot \cdot \cdot \cdot \cdot \cdot \cdot \cdot \cdot \cdot \cdot \cdot \cdot \cdot$$
$$T_{n-r} = (c_{1n}, \cdots, c_{rn}, 0, 0, \cdots, 1).$$

By a consideration of the last $n - r$ entries in these vectors, it is seen that $T_1, T_2, \cdots, T_{n-r}$ are linearly independent elements of $V_n(F)$. Moreover, if $T = (t_1, t_2, \cdots, t_n)$ is an arbitrary solution of the system 14.39, and therefore of 14.37, a straightforward calculation will show that $T = t_{r+1}T_1 + \cdots + t_n T_{n-r}$. We have therefore shown that the set $\{T_1, T_2, \cdots, T_{n-r}\}$ is a basis of the subspace of $V_n(F)$ consisting of all solutions of the system 14.37. The dimension of this subspace is thus $n - r$, and the proof of the theorem is complete.

Since a vector space of positive dimension must contain nonzero vectors, we have at once the following corollary.

14.40 Corollary. *A system of linear homogeneous equations has a nontrivial solution if and only if the rank of the matrix of coefficients of the system is less than the number of unknowns.*

The following result is an immediate consequence of the fact that the rank of a matrix cannot exceed the number of rows in the matrix.

14.41 Corollary. *A system of linear homogeneous equations with fewer equations than unknowns always has a nontrivial solution.*

EXERCISES

In each of Exercises 1–3, solve the given system of linear equations over the rational field by working only with the augmented matrix of the system.

1.
$$\begin{aligned}
x_1 - 2x_2 + x_3 &= -6, \\
3x_1 + 4x_2 + 2x_3 &= 5, \\
-x_1 + 3x_2 - x_3 &= 8.
\end{aligned}$$

2. $2x_1 - x_2 + 3x_3 \qquad = 3,$
$\qquad x_1 + 2x_2 - x_3 - 5x_4 = 4,$
$\qquad x_1 + 3x_2 - 2x_3 - 7x_4 = 5.$

3. $2x_1 - 2x_2 - x_3 + 5x_4 + x_5 = 7,$
$\qquad 3x_1 - 3x_2 + 2x_3 + 4x_4 + 2x_5 = 15,$
$\qquad x_1 - x_2 + x_3 + x_4 + x_5 = 6.$

In each of Exercises 4–7, solve the given system of linear homogeneous equations over the rational field and find a basis for the vector space of all solutions.

4. $\quad x_1 - x_2 + 2x_3 = 0,$
$\quad 2x_1 + x_2 - 5x_3 = 0,$
$\quad x_1 - 4x_2 + 11x_3 = 0.$

5. $\quad x_1 + 3x_2 - 4x_3 - 4x_4 + 9x_5 = 0,$
$\quad x_1 + x_2 - 2x_3 - x_4 + 2x_5 = 0,$
$\quad 2x_1 - x_2 + 2x_3 + 4x_4 - 8x_5 = 0.$

6. $\quad 4x_1 + 2x_2 - x_3 + 3x_4 = 0,$
$\quad x_1 - 2x_2 + 2x_3 - x_4 = 0,$
$\quad 2x_1 + 6x_2 - 5x_3 + 5x_4 = 0,$
$\quad 3x_1 + 14x_2 - 12x_3 + 11x_4 = 0.$

7. $2x_1 + 3x_2 + x_3 - x_4 = 0,$
$\qquad 3x_1 - 2x_2 - x_3 + x_4 = 0.$

In Exercises 8 and 9, solve the given system of linear homogeneous equations over the field $\mathbf{Z}_5$ and find a basis for the vector space of all solutions.

8. $2x_1 + 3x_2 + x_4 = 0,$
$\qquad x_1 + 2x_2 + 2x_4 = 0,$
$\qquad 4x_1 + 4x_2 + x_4 = 0.$

9. $\quad x_1 + 2x_2 + 3x_3 + x_4 = 0,$
$\quad 3x_1 + x_2 + x_3 + 2x_4 = 0,$
$\quad 4x_1 + 3x_2 + x_3 + 2x_4 = 0,$
$\quad x_1 + 2x_2 + 4x_3 + 3x_4 = 0.$

10. Use Corollary 14.41 to show that any $n + 1$ vectors of a vector space $V_n(F)$ are linearly dependent (12.19).

11. Show that if T is one solution of the system 14.34 of linear equations, every solution of the system is of the form $T + S$, where S is a solution of the system 14.37 of linear homogeneous equations.

DETERMINANTS

The theory of determinants, to be introduced in this chapter, had its origin in the study of systems of linear equations, but it has other applications as well. We shall establish some of the more fundamental properties of determinants and also give a new characterization of the rank of a matrix. Finally, we shall show how determinants may be used in solving a system of linear equations. A few other applications of the theory of determinants will be found in the following chapter.

15.1 PRELIMINARY REMARKS

The purpose of this section is to motivate the general definition of a determinant to be given in the next section, and to introduce some convenient notation.

The concept of a determinant arises in the attempt to find general *formulas* for the solution of a system of linear equations with the same number of equations as unknowns. Suppose, first, that we have the following system of two equations in two unknowns over a field F:

$$a_{11}x_1 + a_{12}x_2 = b_1,$$
$$a_{21}x_1 + a_{22}x_2 = b_2.$$

If, by the familiar methods of elementary algebra, we eliminate x_2 from these two equations, the resulting equation takes the form

$$(a_{11}a_{22} - a_{12}a_{21})x_1 = b_1a_{22} - b_2a_{12}.$$

Similarly, if we eliminate x_1, we obtain the equation

$$(a_{11}a_{22} - a_{12}a_{21})x_2 = b_2a_{11} - b_1a_{12}.$$

The expression $a_{11}a_{22} - a_{12}a_{21}$, which occurs as the coefficient of x_2 in this last equation, and also as the coefficient of x_1 in the preceding equation, is called the *determinant* of the matrix of coefficients of the given system of equations.

The case of two equations in two unknowns is too simple to furnish much of a hint about the general case, so let us briefly consider a system of three equations in three unknowns. Such a system may be written in the form

15.1
$$a_{11}x_1 + a_{12}x_2 + a_{13}x_3 = b_1,$$
$$a_{21}x_1 + a_{22}x_2 + a_{23}x_3 = b_2,$$
$$a_{31}x_1 + a_{32}x_2 + a_{33}x_3 = b_3.$$

It can be shown by direct calculations, although in this case the calculations would be fairly tedious, that if we eliminate any *two* of the unknowns, the coefficient of the remaining unknown in the resulting equation is as follows:

15.2 $a_{11}a_{22}a_{33} - a_{11}a_{23}a_{32} - a_{12}a_{21}a_{33} + a_{12}a_{23}a_{31} + a_{13}a_{21}a_{32} - a_{13}a_{22}a_{31}.$

This expression is called the *determinant* of the matrix of coefficients of the system 15.1. For convenience, let A be this matrix of coefficients; that is, let

$$A = \begin{bmatrix} a_{11} & a_{12} & a_{13} \\ a_{21} & a_{22} & a_{23} \\ a_{31} & a_{32} & a_{33} \end{bmatrix}.$$

Then the determinant of A, defined by 15.2, may be denoted by $|A|$.

Let us now make a few observations about $|A|$. Clearly, $|A|$ is an element of F associated with the matrix A over F. Moreover, $|A|$ consists of an algebraic sum of six terms, each of which is a product of three elements of the matrix A. In each of these products, the integers 1, 2, 3 occur, in this order, as the first subscripts; also, these three integers occur, in some order, as the second subscripts. That is, each product is a product of elements of A, one from each row and one from each column. Another way of expressing this fact is to say that a typical term of 15.2 is of the form $\pm a_{1i_1}a_{2i_2}a_{3i_3}$, where i_1, i_2, and i_3 are the integers 1, 2, and 3 in some order. Using the notation for permutations, introduced in Chapter 7, let α be the permutation of the set $\{1, 2, 3\}$ defined by $1\alpha = i_1$, $2\alpha = i_2$, $3\alpha = i_3$. Then a typical term of 15.2 can be written in the form

15.3 $$\pm a_{1\,1\alpha} a_{2\,2\alpha} a_{3\,3\alpha}.$$

Now the symmetric group S_3 on three symbols has six elements, and since there are six terms in 15.2, we see that for every α in S_3 a term of the form 15.3 occurs as a summand.

Let us now discuss the choice of sign in a term 15.3. Since, in 15.2, three of the terms are prefixed by a "$+$" sign and the other three by a "$-$" sign, it is clear that the choice of sign must depend in some way on the permutation α. We recall that a permutation is called *even* or *odd* according as it can be expressed as a product of an even or an odd number of transpositions. Moreover, we have proved, in Theorem 7.47, that half of the permutations of any symmetric group S_n are even, and half are odd. As suggested by these remarks, it is true that the choice of sign in a term 15.3 depends only on whether α is an even or an odd permutation. Before stating this fact in a more precise form, let us make the following convenient definition.

15.4 Definition. If α is a permutation of a finite set, we define

$$sign\ \alpha = \begin{cases} +1 \text{ if } \alpha \text{ is an even permutation,} \\ -1 \text{ if } \alpha \text{ is an odd permutation.} \end{cases}$$

Using this notation, we now assert that

15.5 $$|A| = \sum_{\alpha \in S_3} (\text{sign } \alpha) a_{1\,1\alpha} a_{2\,2\alpha} a_{3\,3\alpha},$$

it being understood that the sum is to be taken over all elements α of S_3. Since there are six elements in S_3, there will be six terms in this sum. To verify that this sum is exactly the expression 15.2, we need only verify that the signs of the terms are correct. For example, let us consider the product $a_{13}a_{22}a_{31}$. For this product, we have $1\alpha = 3$, $2\alpha = 2$, $3\alpha = 1$; and it follows that α is the transposition (13). Hence, this α is odd and therefore sign $\alpha = -1$. Accordingly, in the sum on the right of 15.5 we would have $-a_{13}a_{22}a_{31}$, and this product appears, with this same sign, in the expression 15.2. In like manner all the other terms may be verified. (See Exercise 4 in the next set of exercises.)

In the next section we shall give the definition of the determinant of an $n \times n$ matrix. The definition is a natural generalization of 15.5, and this is the reason that we have here gone to so much trouble to express 15.2 in the simple form 15.5.

15.2 GENERAL DEFINITION OF DETERMINANT

Unless otherwise stated, throughout this chapter the matrices with which we shall be concerned will be *square* matrices, that is, $n \times n$ matrices for some positive integer n. It is often convenient to call an $n \times n$ matrix a matrix of *order* n. Although a considerable part of what we shall do would remain valid if the elements of the matrices were elements of a commutative ring, for simplicity we shall always assume that the elements are from a field F. A matrix A, of order n, over a field F may be written in the following explicit form:

$$15.6 \qquad A = \begin{bmatrix} a_{11} & a_{12} & \cdots & a_{1n} \\ a_{21} & a_{22} & \cdots & a_{2n} \\ \cdot & \cdot & \cdot & \cdot \\ a_{n1} & a_{n2} & \cdots & a_{nn} \end{bmatrix},$$

it being understood that $a_{ij} \in F$ $(i, j = 1, 2, \cdots, n)$. If the order n is apparent from the context and therefore does not need to be mentioned explicitly, it is sometimes convenient to indicate the above matrix A by writing simply $A = (a_{ij})$.

The line joining the upper left-hand element of a square matrix and the lower right-hand element is often called the *principal diagonal* of the matrix. The elements $a_{11}, a_{22}, \cdots, a_{nn}$ of the matrix A are the elements on its principal diagonal.

We shall continue to denote by S_n the set (actually a group) of all permutations of the set $\{1, 2, \cdots, n\}$. Then, as suggested by the discussion of the preceding section, we shall make the following definition.

15.7   Definition.   If A is the matrix 15.6 of order n over a field F, the *determinant* of A, denoted by $|A|$, is defined as follows:

$$15.8 \qquad |A| = \sum_{\alpha \epsilon S_n} (\text{sign } \alpha) a_{1\,1\alpha} a_{2\,2\alpha} \cdots a_{n\,n\alpha}.$$

The determinant of A may also be denoted by $|a_{ij}|$, or by

$$\begin{vmatrix} a_{11} & a_{12} & \cdots & a_{1n} \\ a_{21} & a_{22} & \cdots & a_{2n} \\ \cdot & \cdot & \cdot & \cdot \\ a_{n1} & a_{n2} & \cdots & a_{nn} \end{vmatrix}.$$

Since the symmetric group S_n has $n!$ elements, we see that if A is a square matrix of order n, $|A|$ is a sum of $n!$ terms, each of which is a product of n elements, one from each row and one from each column of A. Moreover, half of these terms will have a "$+$" sign and the other half a "$-$" sign prefixed. We may make one other observation as follows. If in 15.8 we consider the term obtained when α is the identity permutation, which is an even permutation, we see that one of the terms is the product of the elements on the principal diagonal of A.

We shall presently develop methods for computing the determinant of a given matrix that will be much simpler than applying the definition directly. Before proceeding to do so, we shall present two simple examples to illustrate some of the ideas presented so far.

EXAMPLE 1. Suppose that the matrix A is of order 5, and let us find the sign of the term involving the product $a_{13}a_{24}a_{35}a_{42}a_{51}$ in $|A|$. For this term, we have $1\alpha = 3$, $2\alpha = 4$, $3\alpha = 5$, $4\alpha = 2$, $5\alpha = 1$. Using the notation of cycles, we find that α can be expressed in the form $\alpha = (135)(24) = (13)(15)(24)$. Hence α is an odd permutation and sign $\alpha = -1$. Accordingly, one of the terms in $|A|$ is $-a_{13}a_{24}a_{35}a_{42}a_{51}$.

EXAMPLE 2. Suppose that the matrix A is of order 6 and let us find the sign of the term involving the product $a_{45}a_{31}a_{12}a_{64}a_{23}a_{56}$ in $|A|$. As a matter of convenience, let us first rearrange this product so that the first (row) subscripts appear in their natural order. Of course, we can do so because multiplication is commutative in F. We get in this way the product $a_{12}a_{23}a_{31}a_{45}a_{56}a_{64}$. For this product, we have $1\alpha = 2$, $2\alpha = 3$, $3\alpha = 1$, $4\alpha = 5$, $5\alpha = 6$, $6\alpha = 4$; and it follows that $\alpha = (123)(456)$. This is an even permutation and therefore sign $\alpha = +1$. Accordingly, the given product occurs with a "$+$" sign.

EXERCISES

1. If A is a matrix of order 5, find the sign of the term in $|A|$ which involves each of the following products:

    (a) $a_{15}a_{24}a_{33}a_{42}a_{51}$,
    (b) $a_{13}a_{21}a_{32}a_{45}a_{54}$,
    (c) $a_{11}a_{25}a_{32}a_{43}a_{54}$,
    (d) $a_{14}a_{25}a_{33}a_{41}a_{52}$,
    (e) $a_{52}a_{41}a_{34}a_{25}a_{13}$,
    (f) $a_{24}a_{45}a_{12}a_{53}a_{31}$.

2. If the matrix B is obtained from the matrix A of order n by multiplying all elements of one row by the element c of F, show that $|B| = c|A|$.

3. Apply Definition 15.7 to show that

$$\begin{vmatrix} a & b \\ c & d \end{vmatrix} = ad - bc.$$

4. Apply Definition 15.7 to show that the expression 15.2 is actually the determinant of the matrix $A = (a_{ij})$ of order three.

5. Show that if all the elements of one row, or of one column, of a matrix A are zero, then $|A| = 0$.

6. Suppose that for the matrix A, exhibited in 15.6, all the elements above the principal diagonal are zero. Show that in this case the determinant of A is just the product of the elements on the principal diagonal.

15.3   SOME FUNDAMENTAL PROPERTIES

In the definition of the determinant of a matrix A, the rows play a role somewhat different from that of the columns. That is, we have written each term as a product of elements with the row (first) subscripts in their natural order, and have then determined the sign of the term by a consideration of the column (second) subscripts. However, we shall now show that in this definition we could just as well reverse the roles of the rows and the columns.

In the preceding chapter we have defined the *transpose* C' of any matrix C to be the matrix obtained from C by interchanging rows and columns. We shall now prove the following theorem.

15.9   Theorem.   *If A' is the transpose of the square matrix A, then $|A'| = |A|$.*

Let $A = (a_{ij})$ be the matrix of order n exhibited in 15.6. It will be helpful to set $b_{ji} = a_{ij}$ $(i, j = 1, 2, \cdots, n)$, so that $A' = (b_{ij})$ or, in more detail,

$$A' = \begin{bmatrix} b_{11} & b_{12} & \cdots & b_{1n} \\ b_{21} & b_{22} & \cdots & b_{2n} \\ \cdot & \cdot & \cdots & \cdot \\ b_{n1} & b_{n2} & \cdots & b_{nn} \end{bmatrix}.$$

Applying Definition 15.8, we see that

15.10 $$|A'| = \sum_{\alpha \in S_n} (\text{sign } \alpha) b_{1\,1\alpha} b_{2\,2\alpha} \cdots b_{n\,n\alpha}.$$

For the moment, let α be a fixed element of S_n and let us consider the following term in this sum:

15.11 $$(\text{sign } \alpha)b_{1\;1\alpha}b_{2\;2\alpha} \cdots b_{n\;n\alpha}.$$

Since multiplication is commutative in F, we can rearrange the order of the factors in this product in any way we wish. That is, if β is an arbitrary permutation of $\{1, 2, \cdots, n\}$, we can write the expression 15.11 in the form

15.12 $$(\text{sign } \alpha)b_{1\beta\;1\beta\alpha}b_{2\beta\;2\beta\alpha} \cdots b_{n\beta\;n\beta\alpha}.$$

In particular, let us choose $\beta = \alpha^{-1}$. Then, since, by a remark preceding the statement of Theorem 7.47, sign β = sign α, this expression 15.12 can be written as follows:

15.13 $$(\text{sign } \beta)b_{1\beta\;1}b_{2\beta\;2} \cdots b_{n\beta\;n}.$$

Now if α_1 and α_2 are elements of the group S_n, we know that $\alpha_1^{-1} = \alpha_2^{-1}$ if and only if $\alpha_1 = \alpha_2$. It follows that *every* element of S_n is uniquely expressible in the form β^{-1} for $\alpha \in S_n$. By the equality of the expressions 15.11 and 15.13, we can therefore rewrite 15.10 as follows:

$$|A'| = \sum_{\beta \in S_n} (\text{sign } \beta)b_{1\beta\;1}b_{2\beta\;2} \cdots b_{n\beta\;n}.$$

However, using the fact that $b_{ji} = a_{ij}$, it then follows that

$$|A'| = \sum_{\beta \in S_n} (\text{sign } \beta)a_{1\;1\beta}a_{2\;2\beta} \cdots a_{n\;n\beta}.$$

The sum on the right is clearly $|A|$, and we have therefore proved that $|A'| = |A|$.

In the next theorem we shall determine the effect on $|A|$ of an elementary operation on the square matrix A, as defined in 14.24.

15.14 Theorem. *The effect of an elementary operation of each of the three types may be described as follows:*

TYPE 1. *If the matrix B is obtained from the matrix A by interchanging two rows (columns), then $|B| = -|A|$.*

TYPE 2. *If the matrix C is obtained from the matrix A by multiplying all elements of one row (column) by the nonzero element r of F, then $|C| = r|A|$.*

TYPE 3.   *If the matrix D is obtained from the matrix A by multiplying all elements of one row (column) by an element of F and adding them to the corresponding elements of a different row (column), then* $|D| = |A|$.

First, let us observe that an elementary column operation on a matrix A induces an elementary row operation of the same type on the transpose A' of A. Hence, the preceding theorem assures us that in proving the present theorem we may limit ourselves to elementary *row* operations only.

PROOF FOR TYPE 1.   Suppose that the matrix B is obtained from the matrix A by interchanging rows k and l, $k < l$. Then $B = (b_{ij})$, where $b_{ij} = a_{ij}$ if $i \neq k$ and $i \neq l$; $b_{kj} = a_{lj}$, $b_{lj} = a_{kj}$. Then, by the definition of determinant, we have

$$|B| = \sum_{\alpha \in S_n} (\text{sign } \alpha) b_{1\,1\alpha} \cdots b_{k\,k\alpha} \cdots b_{l\,l\alpha} \cdots b_{n\,n\alpha}$$

$$= \sum_{\alpha \in S_n} (\text{sign } \alpha) a_{1\,1\alpha} \cdots a_{l\,k\alpha} \cdots a_{k\,l\alpha} \cdots a_{n\,n\alpha}$$

$$= \sum_{\alpha \in S_n} (\text{sign } \alpha) a_{1\,1\alpha} \cdots a_{k\,l\alpha} \cdots a_{l\,k\alpha} \cdots a_{n\,n\alpha}.$$

In this last sum we have merely changed the order of the factors in each product by interchanging $a_{l\,k\alpha}$ and $a_{k\,l\alpha}$ so that the first subscripts are in their natural order.

Now if $\alpha \in S_n$, let us set $\beta = (kl)\alpha$ so that $i\beta = i\alpha$ if $i \neq k$ and $i \neq l$; $k\beta = l\alpha$, $l\beta = k\alpha$. It is clear that sign $\beta = -\text{sign } \alpha$ and, moreover, every element of S_n is expressible uniquely in the form $(kl)\alpha$ with $\alpha \in S_n$. Using all these facts, and referring to the last form for $|B|$ given above, we see that

$$|B| = - \sum_{\beta \in S_n} (\text{sign } \beta) a_{1\,1\beta} \cdots a_{k\,k\beta} \cdots a_{l\,l\beta} \cdots a_{n\,n\beta} = - |A|,$$

and the proof is complete.

Before proceeding to the proof of the other two parts of the theorem, we point out the following consequence of what we have just proved.

15.15 Corollary.   *If a matrix A has two rows (columns) that are identical, then* $|A| = 0$.

Suppose, for convenience of statement, that the first two rows of A are alike. If B is obtained from A by interchanging the first two rows, clearly A and B are identical and therefore $|B| = |A|$. However, by the first part of the preceding theorem, we have $|B| = -|A|$. Accordingly, $|A| = -|A|$, and we conclude that $|A| = 0$. In this final argument we have tacitly assumed that the characteristic of the field F is different from 2. The statement of Corollary 15.15 remains true even for this case, but the proof must make direct use of the definition of a determinant. However, this case is not a very important one for our purposes, and we shall omit its proof.

We now return to a consideration of the other parts of Theorem 15.14.

PROOF FOR TYPE 2. Since each term in the sum which defines a determinant contains exactly one element from each row, the desired result follows almost immediately from the definition. Actually, the argument holds equally well even if r happens to be zero although, by the definition of elementary operations on a matrix, this would not be an elementary operation. We can, however, conclude that if all the elements of one row (column) of a matrix are zero, then the determinant of the matrix is zero. (*Cf.* Exercises 2 and 5 of the preceding set.)

PROOF FOR TYPE 3. The same argument would apply in general but, for simplicity, let us assume that the matrix D is obtained from the matrix A by multiplying the elements of the second row by $s \in F$ and adding them to the corresponding elements of the first row. If $D = (d_{ij})$, then for $j = 1, 2, \cdots, n$ we have $d_{ij} = a_{ij}$ if $i \neq 1$; $d_{1j} = a_{1j} + s a_{2j}$. Accordingly,

$$|D| = \sum_{\alpha \epsilon S_n} (\text{sign } \alpha) d_{1\,1\alpha} d_{2\,2\alpha} \cdots d_{n\,n\alpha}$$

$$= \sum_{\alpha \epsilon S_n} (\text{sign } \alpha)(a_{1\,1\alpha} + s a_{2\,1\alpha}) a_{2\,2\alpha} \cdots a_{n\,n\alpha}$$

$$= \sum_{\alpha \epsilon S_n} (\text{sign } \alpha) a_{1\,1\alpha} a_{2\,2\alpha} \cdots a_{n\,n\alpha}$$

$$+ s \sum_{\alpha \epsilon S_n} (\text{sign } \alpha) a_{2\,1\alpha} a_{2\,2\alpha} a_{3\,3\alpha} \cdots a_{n\,n\alpha}$$

$$= |A| + s \sum_{\alpha \epsilon S_n} (\text{sign } \alpha) a_{2\,1\alpha} a_{2\,2\alpha} a_{3\,3\alpha} \cdots a_{n\,n\alpha}.$$

Now this last sum is the determinant of a matrix obtained from A by replacing the first row by the second row. Since two rows are identical, the determinant of the matrix is zero by Corollary 15.15. The above calculations therefore show that $|D| = |A|$, and the proof of the theorem is complete.

If the row vectors of a matrix A are linearly dependent, a finite sequence of elementary row operations of Type 3 will reduce the matrix to one which has a zero row. The determinant of such a matrix is zero and, since the value of a determinant is not changed by elementary row operations of this type, we conclude that also $|A| = 0$. We have therefore proved the following result.

15.16 Corollary. *If the row vectors (column vectors) of the square matrix A are linearly dependent, then $|A| = 0$.*

Theorem 15.14 is exceedingly useful in actually computing the value of the determinant of a given matrix. However, this theorem is usually used in conjunction with the principal theorem of the following section, and we shall therefore postpone any further discussion of these matters until that theorem has also been established.

15.4 EXPANSION IN TERMS OF A ROW OR COLUMN

Let us make the following convenient definitions.

15.17 Definition.

(i)   A matrix obtained from a given matrix (not necessarily a square matrix) by deleting certain rows or columns, or both, is called a *submatrix* of the given matrix.

(ii) If A is a square matrix of order n, the square submatrix M_{ij} of order $n - 1$ obtained by deleting the ith row and the jth column of A is called the *minor of the element a_{ij}.*

(iii) If A is a square matrix, the *cofactor A_{ij}* of a_{ij} in $|A|$ is defined as follows: $A_{ij} = (-1)^{i+j}|M_{ij}|$.

In order to illustrate these concepts, suppose that A is the following matrix of order 4:

15.18
$$A = \begin{bmatrix} a_{11} & a_{12} & a_{13} & a_{14} \\ a_{21} & a_{22} & a_{23} & a_{24} \\ a_{31} & a_{32} & a_{33} & a_{34} \\ a_{41} & a_{42} & a_{43} & a_{44} \end{bmatrix}.$$

Then the minor of the element a_{43} in this matrix is the matrix

15.19
$$M_{43} = \begin{bmatrix} a_{11} & a_{12} & a_{14} \\ a_{21} & a_{22} & a_{24} \\ a_{31} & a_{32} & a_{34} \end{bmatrix},$$

and the cofactor A_{43} of a_{43} in $|A|$ is given by:

$$A_{43} = (-1)^7|M_{43}| = -|M_{43}|.$$

We may emphasize that a minor is a *matrix*, whereas a cofactor is an element of the underlying field F.

The reason for the name *cofactor* will be suggested by the following result.

15.20   Lemma.   *If $A = (a_{ij})$ is a square matrix of order n, the sum of all the terms in $|A|$ which contain the arbitrary fixed element a_{ij} of A is $a_{ij}A_{ij}$.*

We shall first prove this lemma for the special case in which $i = 1$ and $j = 1$. In $|A|$, the sum of all the terms which contain a_{11} can be written in the form

$$a_{11} \sum_{\substack{\alpha \in S_n \\ 1\alpha = 1}} (\text{sign } \alpha)a_{2\,2\alpha}a_{3\,3\alpha} \cdots a_{n\,n\alpha},$$

it being understood that the sum is over all permutations α of S_n such that $1\alpha = 1$. Of course, if we let S_{n-1} be the set of all permutations of the set $\{2, 3, \cdots, n\}$, this sum can be written in the form

$$a_{11} \sum_{\gamma \in S_{n-1}} (\text{sign } \gamma)a_{2\,2\gamma}a_{3\,3\gamma} \cdots a_{n\,n\gamma}.$$

Moreover, although the notation is slightly different from that which we have previously used, the sum occurring here is just the determinant of the matrix

$$\begin{bmatrix} a_{22} & a_{23} & \cdots & a_{2n} \\ a_{32} & a_{33} & \cdots & a_{3n} \\ \cdot & \cdot & \cdot & \cdot \\ a_{n2} & a_{n3} & \cdots & a_{nn} \end{bmatrix}.$$

Now this is the minor M_{11} of the element a_{11} of the matrix A; hence the sum of all the terms in $|A|$ which contain a_{11} is $a_{11}|M_{11}|$. Since, by Definition 15.17(iii), $A_{11} = (-1)^2|M_{11}| = |M_{11}|$, the sum of all these terms is $a_{11}A_{11}$. This proves the lemma for the special case in which

$i = 1$ and $j = 1$. For later reference, let us restate what we have proved in the following form. *In the determinant of an arbitrary square matrix, the sum of the terms which contain the element in the upper left-hand corner of the matrix is just this element times the determinant of its minor.* We shall make use of this fact in the proof of the lemma for the case in which i and j are arbitrary. However, let us first illustrate the method to be used by an example.

For the moment, let A be the matrix of order 4 given in 15.18, and let us show that the sum of the terms in $|A|$ which contain the element a_{43} is $a_{43}A_{43}$, where $A_{43} = -|M_{43}|$. We proceed to perform on A a finite sequence of elementary operations of Type 1 to get a matrix with a_{43} in the upper left-hand corner and, moreover, in such a way that the minor of a_{43} in this new matrix is the same as its minor in A. More specifically, we first interchange rows 3 and 4, then rows 2 and 3, and then rows 1 and 2. This gives us the following matrix in which the element a_{43} now occurs in the first row:

$$\begin{bmatrix} a_{41} & a_{42} & a_{43} & a_{44} \\ a_{11} & a_{12} & a_{13} & a_{14} \\ a_{21} & a_{22} & a_{23} & a_{24} \\ a_{31} & a_{32} & a_{33} & a_{34} \end{bmatrix}.$$

We now interchange columns 2 and 3 in this matrix, and finally columns 1 and 2. We then have the matrix B given by

$$B = \begin{bmatrix} a_{43} & a_{41} & a_{42} & a_{44} \\ a_{13} & a_{11} & a_{12} & a_{14} \\ a_{23} & a_{21} & a_{22} & a_{24} \\ a_{33} & a_{31} & a_{32} & a_{34} \end{bmatrix}.$$

Now the minor of the element a_{43} *of this matrix* B is obtained by deleting the row and column which contain a_{43}, that is, the first row and first column. This minor is therefore as follows:

$$\begin{bmatrix} a_{11} & a_{12} & a_{14} \\ a_{21} & a_{22} & a_{24} \\ a_{31} & a_{32} & a_{34} \end{bmatrix}.$$

It will be seen that this matrix is exactly the minor M_{43} of the element a_{43} *in the matrix* A, as given in 15.19. Moreover, the special case of the lemma which we have already proved, as applied to the matrix B, shows that the sum of the terms in $|B|$ which contain a_{43} is $a_{43}|M_{43}|$. To obtain the matrix B from A we applied five elementary operations of Type 1, each of which changed the sign of the determinant. Hence, $|A| = -|B|$

and the sum of all the terms in $|A|$ which contain a_{43} is $-a_{43}|M_{43}| = a_{43}A_{43}$.

Of course, it would have been possible to get from A a matrix with a_{43} in the upper left-hand corner merely by interchanging the first and fourth rows, and the first and third columns. However, had we done so, the minor of a_{43} in the matrix so obtained would not have been M_{43} and we would have had to do some more work before reaching the desired conclusion.

To complete the proof of the lemma, we use the same method as in this illustration. Again, let A be a matrix of order n, and let i and j be fixed integers, distinct or identical, from the set $\{1, 2, \cdots, n\}$. By $i - 1$ successive interchanges of adjacent rows and $j - 1$ successive interchanges of adjacent columns we can obtain a matrix C with the element a_{ij} in the upper left-hand corner and with the further important property that the minor of a_{ij} in the matrix C is exactly the minor M_{ij} of the element a_{ij} in the given matrix A. Clearly, $|C| = (-1)^{i+j-2}|A| = (-1)^{i+j}|A|$. Now, applying the special case of the lemma which has already been proved, we see that the sum of all the terms in $|C|$ which contain the element a_{ij} is $a_{ij}|M_{ij}|$. Hence, the sum of all the terms in $|A|$ which contain the element a_{ij} is $(-1)^{i+j}a_{ij}|M_{ij}| = a_{ij}A_{ij}$. This completes the proof of the lemma.

Since, by the definition of a determinant, every term contains exactly one element from the first row, it is clear that every term in $|A|$ contains exactly one of the elements $a_{11}, a_{12}, \cdots, a_{1n}$. It follows at once from the lemma that

$$|A| = a_{11}A_{11} + a_{12}A_{12} + \cdots + a_{1n}A_{1n}.$$

It is obvious that a similar argument applies to the elements of any fixed row or column, and we therefore have the following important result.

15.21 Theorem. *Let $A = (a_{ij})$ be a matrix of order n over a field. Then*

15.22
$$|A| = \sum_{j=1}^{n} a_{kj}A_{kj}, \qquad (k = 1, 2, \cdots, n),$$

and also

15.23
$$|A| = \sum_{i=1}^{n} a_{il}A_{il}, \qquad (l = 1, 2, \cdots, n).$$

It is customary to say that 15.22 gives the expansion of $|A|$ in terms of the kth row, and 15.23 the expansion in terms of the lth column. Since the cofactor of an element in $|A|$ is the determinant of a matrix of order $n - 1$, these expansions express the determinant of a matrix of order n in terms of determinants of matrices of order $n - 1$. This fact is of great value in computing the determinant of a given matrix. We shall presently give some examples, but first let us establish another result which follows easily from Theorem 15.21 and is of considerable interest in itself.

15.24   Theorem.   *Let $A = (a_{ij})$ be a matrix of order n over a field. Then, if $k \neq l$, we have*

15.25
$$\sum_{j=1}^{n} a_{kj} A_{lj} = 0,$$

and

15.26
$$\sum_{i=1}^{n} a_{ik} A_{il} = 0.$$

Theorem 15.21 states that the sum of the products of the elements of any row (column) of a matrix by their respective cofactors is the determinant of the matrix. This theorem states that the sum of the products of the elements of any row (column) by the cofactors of the corresponding elements of a *different* row (column) is always zero.

To prove 15.25, let k and l be distinct integers of the set $\{1, 2, \cdots, n\}$, and let D be the matrix obtained from A by deleting its lth row and replacing it by its kth row. Since two rows of D are identical, Corollary 15.15 assures us that $|D| = 0$. Moreover, the cofactor of an element a_{kj} of the lth row of D coincides with A_{lj}, the cofactor of the corresponding element a_{lj} of A. Accordingly, the sum appearing in 15.25 is, by the preceding theorem applied to D, the expansion of $|D|$ in terms of its lth row. Since $|D| = 0$, this proves 15.25. A similar argument, using columns instead of rows, will establish 15.26.

We now proceed to give examples which may help to clarify the theory that has been presented so far. In particular, we shall give illustrations of how certain of our results may be used in actually computing the determinant of a given matrix. It will be understood that the elements are from the field of rational numbers.

EXAMPLE 1.   Find the value of the following determinant:

$$\begin{vmatrix} 1 & 3 & 2 \\ -2 & 1 & -1 \\ 0 & 1 & 4 \end{vmatrix}.$$

We shall compute the value of this determinant in two different ways. First, let us use 15.22 to expand the determinant in terms of its first row as follows:

$$\begin{vmatrix} 1 & 3 & 2 \\ -2 & 1 & -1 \\ 0 & 1 & 4 \end{vmatrix} = 1 \cdot \begin{vmatrix} 1 & -1 \\ 1 & 4 \end{vmatrix} - 3 \cdot \begin{vmatrix} -2 & -1 \\ 0 & 4 \end{vmatrix} + 2 \cdot \begin{vmatrix} -2 & 1 \\ 0 & 1 \end{vmatrix}.$$

Of course, the minus sign in the second term is caused by the fact that the cofactor of an element in the first row and second column is $(-1)^3$ times its minor. Now it was observed in Exercise 3 at the end of Section 15.2 that

$$\begin{vmatrix} a & b \\ c & d \end{vmatrix} = ad - bc,$$

and hence it is easy to find the value of each of our determinants of order two. Doing so, we obtain as the value of the given determinant

$$1 \cdot (4 + 1) - 3(-8) + 2(-2) = 25.$$

Now let us carry out the calculation in a different way using an elementary operation as follows. If we multiply the first row by 2 and add to the second, we know by Theorem 15.14 that the determinant is unchanged. We then expand in terms of the first column. The calculations are as follows:

$$\begin{vmatrix} 1 & 3 & 2 \\ -2 & 1 & -1 \\ 0 & 1 & 4 \end{vmatrix} = \begin{vmatrix} 1 & 3 & 2 \\ 0 & 7 & 3 \\ 0 & 1 & 4 \end{vmatrix} = 1 \cdot \begin{vmatrix} 7 & 3 \\ 1 & 4 \end{vmatrix} = 25.$$

EXAMPLE 2. Find the value of the following determinant:

$$\begin{vmatrix} 5 & -3 & 12 & 2 \\ 6 & 4 & 8 & 6 \\ 3 & -1 & 8 & -1 \\ 4 & 2 & 12 & 4 \end{vmatrix}.$$

Of course, it would be possible to expand this determinant in terms of some row or column and then proceed to evaluate each of the four determinants of order three that would be involved. However, it is much less work to use elementary operations in such a way as to get all elements but one of some row or column equal to zero, and then to expand in terms of that particular row or column. One possible way to apply this procedure is indicated by the following calculations, which we shall explain briefly below:

$$\begin{vmatrix} 5 & -3 & 12 & 2 \\ 6 & 4 & 8 & 6 \\ 3 & -1 & 8 & -1 \\ 4 & 2 & 12 & 4 \end{vmatrix} = 2\begin{vmatrix} 5 & -3 & 12 & 2 \\ 3 & 2 & 4 & 3 \\ 3 & -1 & 8 & -1 \\ 4 & 2 & 12 & 4 \end{vmatrix} = 8\begin{vmatrix} 5 & -3 & 3 & 2 \\ 3 & 2 & 1 & 3 \\ 3 & -1 & 2 & -1 \\ 4 & 2 & 3 & 4 \end{vmatrix}$$

$$= 8\begin{vmatrix} -4 & -9 & 0 & -7 \\ 3 & 2 & 1 & 3 \\ -3 & -5 & 0 & -7 \\ -5 & -4 & 0 & -5 \end{vmatrix} = -8\begin{vmatrix} 4 & 9 & 0 & 7 \\ 3 & 2 & 1 & 3 \\ 3 & 5 & 0 & 7 \\ 5 & 4 & 0 & 5 \end{vmatrix} = 8\begin{vmatrix} 4 & 9 & 7 \\ 3 & 5 & 7 \\ 5 & 4 & 5 \end{vmatrix}$$

$$= 8\begin{vmatrix} 1 & 4 & 0 \\ 3 & 5 & 7 \\ 5 & 4 & 5 \end{vmatrix} = 8\begin{vmatrix} 1 & 0 & 0 \\ 3 & -7 & 7 \\ 5 & -16 & 5 \end{vmatrix} = 8\begin{vmatrix} -7 & 7 \\ -16 & 5 \end{vmatrix} = 8(77) = 616.$$

We have first used the second part of Theorem 15.14 to factor 2 from each element of the second row, then have factored 4 from each element of the third column. Next we used elementary operations of Type 3, which did not change the value of the determinant, to get all elements but one of the third column equal to zero. In order to avoid so many minus signs we then multiplied the first, third, and fourth rows by -1. Since each of these operations changed the sign of the determinant, we had to place a minus sign in front. We then expanded in terms of the third column. To evaluate the determinant of order three, we subtracted the second row from the first (multiplied by -1 and added to the first). This was done merely to get 1 in some position. The rest of the calculation should be obvious.

EXAMPLE 3.   Without expanding the determinants, show that

$$\begin{vmatrix} a & b & c \\ d & e & f \\ g & h & i \end{vmatrix} = \begin{vmatrix} c & i & f \\ b & h & e \\ a & g & d \end{vmatrix}.$$

The calculations are as follows, first using Theorem 15.9 and then using the first part of Theorem 15.14 twice:

$$\begin{vmatrix} a & b & c \\ d & e & f \\ g & h & i \end{vmatrix} = \begin{vmatrix} a & d & g \\ b & e & h \\ c & f & i \end{vmatrix} = -\begin{vmatrix} c & f & i \\ b & e & h \\ a & d & g \end{vmatrix} = \begin{vmatrix} c & i & f \\ b & h & e \\ a & g & d \end{vmatrix}.$$

EXERCISES

1.   Find the value of each of the following determinants over the rational field:

(a) $\begin{vmatrix} 1 & -3 & 2 \\ -2 & 4 & 3 \\ 3 & 1 & 2 \end{vmatrix}$,

(b) $\begin{vmatrix} 1 & 2 & 3 \\ 4 & 5 & 6 \\ 7 & 8 & 9 \end{vmatrix}$,

(c) $\begin{vmatrix} 6 & -4 & 8 \\ -2 & 3 & 5 \\ 10 & 4 & 14 \end{vmatrix}$,

(d) $\begin{vmatrix} \frac{1}{2} & \frac{2}{3} & -\frac{1}{2} \\ -\frac{2}{3} & -\frac{1}{2} & 2 \\ \frac{1}{6} & \frac{1}{2} & \frac{1}{3} \end{vmatrix}$,

(e) $\begin{vmatrix} 2 & 3 & -2 & -3 \\ 4 & 1 & 2 & 1 \\ 2 & -2 & 3 & 4 \\ 2 & 3 & -1 & 2 \end{vmatrix}$,

(f) $\begin{vmatrix} 2 & \frac{1}{2} & -\frac{1}{2} & 1 \\ \frac{2}{3} & \frac{1}{3} & -\frac{2}{3} & -\frac{1}{3} \\ 2 & -2 & 2 & -2 \\ 4 & 6 & 2 & 4 \end{vmatrix}$,

(g) $\begin{vmatrix} 2 & -3 & 1 & 2 & 3 \\ 1 & 2 & 2 & 3 & 4 \\ -1 & 1 & 1 & -1 & 1 \\ 2 & 4 & 6 & 4 & 2 \\ 3 & 2 & 1 & -3 & 2 \end{vmatrix}$.

2. Find the value of each of the following determinants over the field $\mathbf{Z}_5$:

(a) $\begin{vmatrix} 2 & 3 & 4 \\ 1 & 2 & 3 \\ 3 & 3 & 2 \end{vmatrix}$,

(b) $\begin{vmatrix} 3 & 0 & 4 \\ 1 & 2 & 4 \\ 4 & 3 & 2 \end{vmatrix}$,

(c) $\begin{vmatrix} 1 & 2 & 3 & 4 \\ 2 & 3 & 4 & 1 \\ 3 & 4 & 1 & 2 \\ 4 & 1 & 2 & 3 \end{vmatrix}$.

3. Without expansion of the determinants involved, verify the following (the elements are from any field):

$$\begin{vmatrix} a_1 & a_2 & a_3 \\ b_1 & b_2 & b_3 \\ c_1 & c_2 & c_3 \end{vmatrix} = \begin{vmatrix} c_1 + 2a_1 & b_1 & a_1 \\ c_3 + 2a_3 & b_3 & a_3 \\ c_2 + 2a_2 & b_2 & a_2 \end{vmatrix}.$$

15.5   THE DETERMINANT RANK OF A MATRIX

In this section we shall consider matrices that are not necessarily square. First we make the following definition.

15.27   Definition.   An arbitrary matrix C over a field F is said to have *determinant rank* r if there exists a square submatrix of C of order r whose determinant is different from zero, whereas every square submatrix of C of order $r + 1$ has zero determinant. If all elements of C are zero, we define its determinant rank to be zero.

We may notice that if the determinant rank of C is r, not only is the determinant of every square submatrix of order $r + 1$ equal to zero, but also the determinant of every square submatrix of order greater than r is necessarily zero. For example, consider a square submatrix M of order $r + 2$. If $|M|$ is expanded in terms of a row or column, every cofactor is, except possibly for sign, the determinant of a submatrix of C of order $r + 1$, and hence has the value zero. Accordingly, $|M| = 0$; that is, the determinant of every square submatrix of order $r + 2$ has the value zero. By the same kind of argument, the determinant of every square submatrix of order $r + 3$ must now be zero, and so on. Of course, a process of induction is actually involved here.

The following theorem justifies the use of the word *rank* in the above definition.

15.28   Theorem.   *The determinant rank of an arbitrary matrix C over a field coincides with its rank as defined in 14.30.*

Let C be the $p \times q$ matrix given by

$$C = \begin{bmatrix} c_{11} & c_{12} & \cdots & c_{1q} \\ c_{21} & c_{22} & \cdots & c_{2q} \\ \cdot & \cdot & \cdot & \cdot \\ c_{p1} & c_{p2} & \cdots & c_{pq} \end{bmatrix},$$

and let us assume that C has determinant rank r. If $r = 0$, which means that all elements of C are zero, then the dimension of the row space (or column space) of C is also zero by definition of the dimension of a zero vector space. Hence, also, the rank of C is zero, and this case is easily disposed of. Henceforth we shall assume that $r > 0$, and shall complete the proof by showing that the row rank of C is r.

It is clear that interchanging rows (or columns) of C cannot affect its row (or column) rank, and also cannot affect its determinant rank since such operations would at most change the *sign* of certain determinants. Accordingly, by making such interchanges we can be sure that the square submatrix of order r in the upper left-hand corner has determinant different from zero. As a matter of notation, let us assume that this is already true for the matrix C; that is, that the determinant of the matrix

15.29
$$\begin{bmatrix} c_{11} & c_{12} & \cdots & c_{1r} \\ c_{21} & c_{22} & \cdots & c_{2r} \\ \cdot & \cdot & \cdot & \cdot \\ c_{r1} & c_{r2} & \cdots & c_{rr} \end{bmatrix}$$

is different from zero. Now, by Corollary 15.16, the row vectors of this matrix are linearly independent; hence the first r row vectors of

C must also be linearly independent. If C_1, C_2, $\cdots$, C_p are the row vectors of C, we therefore know that the set $\{C_1, C_2, \cdots, C_r\}$ is linearly independent and we shall show that it is a basis of the row space of C. This is obviously true if $r = p$, so we henceforth assume that $r < p$. Let s be an arbitrary, but fixed, integer such that $r < s \leq p$, and let us show that C_s is a linear combination of C_1, C_2, $\cdots$, C_r. For each integer $t = 1, 2, \cdots, q$, let us consider the matrix $D(t)$ of order $r + 1$ defined as follows:

$$
D(t) = \begin{bmatrix}
c_{11} & c_{12} & \cdots & c_{1r} & c_{1t} \\
c_{21} & c_{22} & \cdots & c_{2r} & c_{2t} \\
\cdot & \cdot & \cdot & \cdot & \cdot \\
c_{r1} & c_{r2} & \cdots & c_{rr} & c_{rt} \\
c_{s1} & c_{s2} & \cdots & c_{sr} & c_{st}
\end{bmatrix}.
$$

If $t \leq r$, this matrix has two identical columns and hence $|D(t)| = 0$. On the other hand, if $t > r$, $D(t)$ is a square submatrix of C of order $r + 1$, and again $|D(t)| = 0$ since it is given that C has determinant rank r. Accordingly, $|D(t)| = 0$ for $t = 1, 2, \cdots, q$. If $d_1, d_2, \cdots, d_r, d_s$ are the cofactors of the elements of the last column of $D(t)$, it is clear that they do not depend on t, and if we expand $|D(t)|$ in terms of its last column, we find that

$$c_{1t}d_1 + c_{2t}d_2 + \cdots + c_{rt}d_r + c_{st}d_s = 0, \qquad (t = 1, 2, \cdots, q).$$

In terms of row vectors, this equation can be written in the form

$$d_1C_1 + d_2C_2 + \cdots + d_rC_r + d_sC_s = 0.$$

Moreover, $d_s \neq 0$ since it is the determinant of the matrix 15.29. It follows that C_s is a linear combination of C_1, C_2, $\cdots$, C_r. Since this is true for each s satisfying $r < s \leq p$, we have proved that $\{C_1, C_2, \cdots, C_r\}$ is indeed a basis of the row space of C, and hence that C has (row) rank r. The proof is therefore complete.

If A is a square matrix of order n, its determinant rank will be less than n if and only if $|A| = 0$. Moreover, the row (column) rank will be less than n if and only if the row vectors (column vectors) are linearly dependent. Accordingly, we have at once the following result, which completes the result of Corollary 15.16.

15.30 Corollary. *If A is a square matrix over a field, then $|A| = 0$ if and only if the row vectors (column vectors) of A are linearly dependent.*

In view of the equality of all the various ranks of a matrix, in the future we shall usually refer merely to the *rank* of a matrix to mean the row rank, the column rank, or the determinant rank.

15.6   SYSTEMS OF LINEAR EQUATIONS

We now briefly discuss applications of determinants to the problem of finding the solutions of a system of linear equations. We shall first consider a system with the same number of equations as unknowns. Let us therefore consider the following system of linear equations over a field F:

15.31
$$\sum_{j=1}^{n} a_{ij}x_j = b_i, \qquad (i = 1, 2, \cdots, n).$$

We shall denote by A the matrix of the coefficients in this system of equations and by A_{ij} the cofactor of a_{ij} in $|A|$. If $|A| \neq 0$, it follows that the matrix A has rank n and clearly the augmented matrix of the system also has rank n. We already know from Theorem 14.32 that in this case the system of equations will have a *unique* solution. As hinted at in Section 15.1, the theory of determinants gives us an easy way to write down the solution in this case. The procedure is as follows.

In order to find the value of an arbitrary unknown x_l, we multiply the first equation by A_{1l}, the second by $A_{2l}, \cdots$, the nth by A_{nl}, and add. In the resulting equation, the coefficient of x_l is

$$\sum_{i=1}^{n} a_{il}A_{il}$$

which, by Theorem 15.21, is just $|A|$. If $k \neq l$, the coefficient of x_k in this resulting equation is

$$\sum_{i=1}^{n} a_{ik}A_{il},$$

which is zero by 15.26. Accordingly, the equation takes the following form:

15.32
$$|A|x_l = \sum_{i=1}^{n} b_i A_{il}.$$

For convenience, let us define the matrix $B(l)$ to be the matrix of order n obtained from A by replacing the lth column by the column of constant terms in the system 15.31. It follows that the right side of 15.32 is the expansion of $|B(l)|$ in terms of its lth column. Using this fact, and observing that the above argument holds for each choice of l, we find that

15.33 $$|A|x_l = |B(l)|, \qquad (l = 1, 2, \cdots, n).$$

Up to this point the calculations remain valid even if $|A| = 0$, but we are here concerned with the case in which $|A| \neq 0$. In this case, the preceding equations yield at once the unique solution of our given system of equations in the following explicit form:

15.34 $$x_l = \frac{|B(l)|}{|A|}, \qquad (l = 1, 2, \cdots, n).$$

Actually, our calculations here merely show that *if* $|A| \neq 0$ and *if* the given system of equations has a solution, then that solution is given by 15.34. However, from previous results we know that if $|A| \neq 0$, the system does have a solution and it is therefore given by 15.34. It is also fairly easy to verify directly that 15.34 does furnish a solution (see Exercise 12 below). Our results may be summarized as follows.

15.35 Cramer's Rule. *If A is the matrix of the coefficients of a system 15.31 of n linear equations in n unknowns over a field, and if $|A| \neq 0$, then the system has the unique solution*

$$x_l = \frac{|B(l)|}{|A|}, \qquad (l = 1, 2, \cdots, n),$$

where $B(l)$ is the matrix obtained from A by replacing the lth column by the column of constant terms.

As an illustration of the use of Cramer's Rule, let us solve the following system of equations over the rational field:

$$\begin{aligned}
3x_1 + x_2 - x_3 &= 2, \\
x_1 + 2x_2 + x_3 &= 3, \\
-x_1 + x_2 + 4x_3 &= 9.
\end{aligned}$$

For this system, using the notation introduced above, we have

$$A = \begin{bmatrix} 3 & 1 & -1 \\ 1 & 2 & 1 \\ -1 & 1 & 4 \end{bmatrix}, \quad B(1) = \begin{bmatrix} 2 & 1 & -1 \\ 3 & 2 & 1 \\ 9 & 1 & 4 \end{bmatrix}, \quad B(2) = \begin{bmatrix} 3 & 2 & -1 \\ 1 & 3 & 1 \\ -1 & 9 & 4 \end{bmatrix},$$

and

$$B(3) = \begin{bmatrix} 3 & 1 & 2 \\ 1 & 2 & 3 \\ -1 & 1 & 9 \end{bmatrix}.$$

We omit the details but the values of the determinants of these matrices are: $|A| = 13$, $|B(1)| = 26$, $|B(2)| = -13$, and $|B(3)| = 39$. The solution of the system is therefore $x_1 = 2$, $x_2 = -1$, $x_3 = 3$.

Although Cramer's Rule applies to the solution of a system of equations involving the same number of equations as unknowns, and then only if the determinant of the coefficients is different from zero, it can frequently be used in a somewhat more general situation as follows. Suppose that we have the following system of r linear equations in n unknowns, for which the rank of the matrix of the coefficients is also r:

15.36
$$\sum_{j=1}^{n} a_{ij}x_j = b_i, \qquad (i = 1, 2, \cdots, r).$$

If $r = n$, we may apply Cramer's Rule at once, so let us assume that $r < n$. The matrix of the coefficients must have a square submatrix of order r whose determinant is different from zero. Suppose, for simplicity, that this submatrix is made up of the *first* r columns. In this case, we rewrite the system 15.36 in the following form:

15.37
$$\begin{aligned}
a_{11}x_1 + a_{12}x_2 + \cdots + a_{1\,r}x_r &= b_1 - a_{1\,r+1}x_{r+1} - \cdots - a_{1n}x_n, \\
a_{21}x_1 + a_{22}x_2 + \cdots + a_{2\,r}x_r &= b_2 - a_{2\,r+1}x_{r+1} - \cdots - a_{2n}x_n, \\
&\ \cdots \\
a_{r1}x_1 + a_{r2}x_2 + \cdots + a_{r\,r}x_r &= b_r - a_{r\,r+1}x_{r+1} - \cdots - a_{rn}x_n.
\end{aligned}$$

We then replace $x_{r+1}, \cdots, x_n$ by arbitrary elements of the underlying field and since the matrix of the coefficients of $x_1, \cdots, x_r$ has nonzero determinant, we can use Cramer's Rule to solve for the corresponding values of $x_1, \cdots, x_r$. All solutions of the system 15.37, and therefore of the system 15.36, can be obtained in this way.

We may point out that, by Theorem 14.35, any system of equations that has a solution is equivalent to a system of the form 15.36 so that, at least in theory, the present method is always available.

Let us illustrate how to solve a system of the form 15.36 by considering the following system of linear equations over the rational field:

15.38
$$\begin{aligned}
x_1 + 2x_2 - x_3 + x_4 &= 4, \\
-x_1 + x_2 + 3x_3 + x_4 &= -2, \\
x_1 + 5x_2 + x_3 + x_4 &= 2.
\end{aligned}$$

It may be verified that the matrix of the coefficients has rank 3; also that the determinant of the submatrix consisting of the first three columns is zero. However, the matrix consisting of the first, third, and fourth columns has nonzero determinant. Accordingly, we replace x_2 by the arbitrary rational number s and solve the following system by Cramer's Rule:

$$x_1 - x_3 + x_4 = 4 - 2s,$$
$$-x_1 + 3x_3 + x_4 = -2 - s,$$
$$x_1 + x_3 + x_4 = 2 - 5s.$$

We omit the details but the solution turns out to be as follows:

$$x_1 = \frac{2 - 7s}{2}, \quad x_2 = s, \quad x_3 = -\frac{2 + 3s}{2}, \quad x_4 = 2.$$

Every solution of the given system 15.38 is then of this form.

In this section we have considered applications of the theory of determinants to the problem of solving a given system of linear equations. Of course, there is no reason why the use of determinants may not be combined with the methods of the preceding chapter. In particular, it may be helpful first to simplify the system somewhat by use of elementary operations, and then at some appropriate stage to apply Cramer's Rule.

EXERCISES

In each of Exercises 1–9, apply Cramer's Rule to solve the given system of linear equations over the rational field.

1. $\quad 3x_1 - 5x_2 = 25,$
$\quad\quad x_1 + 4x_2 = -3.$

2. $\quad 3x_1 + 6x_2 = -15,$
$\quad\quad x_1 + 4x_2 = 1.$

3. $\quad 2x_1 - x_2 + x_3 = 0,$
$\quad\quad x_1 + 2x_2 - 2x_3 = 10,$
$\quad\quad 3x_1 - 3x_2 - 5x_3 = 2.$

4. $\quad 2x_1 - 4x_2 + x_3 = 4,$
$\quad\quad x_1 + 3x_2 - x_3 = 5,$
$\quad\quad 4x_1 - 2x_2 + 3x_3 = 6.$

5. $\quad x_1 - 3x_2 + x_3 = 2,$
$\quad\quad 3x_1 + x_2 + x_3 = 1,$
$\quad\quad 5x_1 + x_2 + 3x_3 = 3.$

6. $\quad 2x_1 + x_2 + 3x_3 - x_4 = 1,$
$\quad\quad x_1 - x_2 + x_3 - x_4 = -5,$
$\quad\quad 3x_1 + 2x_2 + 2x_3 - 3x_4 = 1,$
$\quad\quad -x_1 + 3x_2 - x_3 + 2x_4 = 14.$

7. $2x_1 - x_2 + 3x_3 = 4,$
$3x_1 + x_2 - 2x_3 = 3.$

8. $x_1 - 2x_2 + x_3 - x_4 = 2,$
$2x_1 + x_2 - x_3 + 2x_4 = 1,$
$x_1 + x_2 + 3x_3 - 3x_4 = 3.$

9. $x_1 - x_2 + 2x_3 - x_4 = 2,$
$2x_1 + x_2 - 3x_3 + 3x_4 = 0,$
$4x_1 - x_2 + x_3 + 2x_4 = 1.$

In each of Exercises 10 and 11, apply Cramer's Rule to solve the given system of linear equations over the field Z_3.

10. $x_1 + x_2 + 2x_3 = 0,$
$x_1 + x_2 + x_3 = 2,$
$2x_1 + 2x_2 + x_3 = 1.$

11. $x_1 + x_2 + x_3 + x_4 = 2,$
$2x_1 + x_2 + 2x_3 = 2,$
$x_1 + x_3 + x_4 = 1.$

12. Verify that 15.34 actually gives a solution of the *first* equation of the system 15.31. [Hint: By expanding in terms of the first row, show that the determinant

$$\begin{vmatrix} b_1 & a_{11} & a_{12} & \cdots & a_{1n} \\ b_1 & a_{11} & a_{12} & \cdots & a_{1n} \\ b_2 & a_{21} & a_{22} & \cdots & a_{2n} \\ \cdot & \cdot & \cdot & \cdots & \cdot \\ b_n & a_{n1} & a_{n2} & \cdots & a_{nn} \end{vmatrix}$$

has the value

$$b_1|A| - a_{11}|B(1)| - a_{12}|B(2)| - \cdots - a_{1n}|B(n)|.]$$

NOTES AND REFERENCES

We have used what might be called the traditional approach to the theory of determinants. For a variety of other points of view, see Curtis [**32**]; Finkbeiner [**33**]; Halmos [**34**]; Mostow, Sampson, Meyer [**13**]; Ames [**1**]; Maclane and Birkhoff [**12**].

XVI

LINEAR TRANSFORMATIONS AND MATRICES

In Section 12.6 we defined a homomorphism of a vector space V over a field F into a vector space W over the same field. We also introduced the descriptive notation $\mathrm{Hom}_F(V, W)$ for the set of all homomorphisms of V into W. In this chapter we shall be concerned with the important special case in which V and W coincide.

It is customary to call a homomorphism of a vector space V into itself a *linear transformation* of V. We shall adopt this terminology and, for simplicity, we shall find it convenient to denote the set of all linear transformations of a given vector space by L instead of using the notation $\mathrm{Hom}_F(V, V)$.

Let L be the set of all linear transformations of the vector space V over F. As a special case of results of Section 12.7, we know that under suitable definitions of addition and scalar multiplication L is itself a vector space over F. In the present setting, we will have also an operation of multiplication defined on L and it will turn out that L is a ring with respect to these operations of addition and multiplication. Actually, L is an example of an *algebra over F*, according to the definition to be given in Section 16.2.

For our purposes, the most important case is that in which V is a vector space of finite dimension n over F and, in this case, we shall show how to set up a one-one mapping of the set L onto the set F_n of all matrices of order n over F. This leads to natural definitions of addition, multiplication, and scalar multiplication in F_n in such a way that F_n becomes an algebra over F which is isomorphic to the algebra L. The rest of the chapter has to do with certain properties of linear transformations or of matrices and, in particular, with the interplay between these two concepts.

The topics introduced in this chapter play an important role in algebra and have been studied extensively. Our treatment gives merely a brief introduction to some of the basic ideas and methods.

16.1   NOTATION AND PRELIMINARY REMARKS

Let V be a vector space over a field F, and let us denote the unity of F by 1. Heretofore, we have denoted mappings by lower case Greek letters, but we shall henceforth denote linear transformations of a vector space by capital script letters such as $\mathcal{A}$, $\mathcal{B}$, and $\mathcal{C}$.

Using the present notation and terminology, we proceed to review briefly what we already know about linear transformations. First, we recall that a mapping $\mathcal{A} : V \to V$ of the vector space $V(F)$ into itself is, by definition, a linear transformation of V if addition and scalar multiplication are preserved under the mapping $\mathcal{A}$, that is, if the following hold:

16.1   If $X , Y \in V$, then $(X + Y)\mathcal{A} = X\mathcal{A} + Y\mathcal{A}$,

and

16.2   If $X \in V$ and $c \in F$, then $(cX)\mathcal{A} = c(X\mathcal{A})$.

From Theorem 12.31(iii), we see that if k is an arbitrary positive integer, $X_i \in V$ and $c_i \in F$ ($i = 1 , 2 , \cdots , k$), then

16.3 $(c_1X_1 + c_2X_2 + \cdots + c_kX_k)\mathcal{A}$
$$= c_1(X_1\mathcal{A}) + c_2(X_2\mathcal{A}) + \cdots + c_k(X_k\mathcal{A}).$$

Of course, both 16.1 and 16.2 are special cases of 16.3. Moreover, the special cases of 16.2 in which c is 0 or -1, respectively, show that $0\mathcal{A} = 0$ and that for each X in V, $(-X)\mathcal{A} = -(X\mathcal{A})$.

A very useful property of a linear transformation is that it maps a subspace of V onto a subspace of V. That is, as indicated in Theorem 12.31(iv), if U is a subspace of V, then $U\mathcal{A} = \{X\mathcal{A} \mid X \in U\}$ is a subspace of V. In particular, $V\mathcal{A} = V$ if and only if $\mathcal{A}$ is an onto mapping.

For later reference, let us recall the definitions of addition and scalar multiplication (12.39 and 12.40) on the set L of all linear transformations of the vector space V over F. They are, respectively, as follows, it being understood that $\mathcal{A}$ and $\mathcal{B}$ are elements of L and $c \in F$:

16.4
$$X(\alpha + \mathfrak{B}) = X\alpha + X\mathfrak{B}, \qquad\qquad X \in V,$$

and

16.5
$$X(c\alpha) = (cX)\alpha, \qquad\qquad X \in V.$$

Theorem 12.41 then shows that if addition and scalar multiplication are so defined, L is a vector space over F.

16.2 ALGEBRA OF LINEAR TRANSFORMATIONS

In order to have a convenient way to state the principal result of this section, we first make the following definition.

16.6 Definition. Let S be a nonempty set on which there are defined binary operations of addition and multiplication, and also a scalar multiplication by elements of a field H. We shall call S an *algebra* over the field H if the following conditions are satisfied:

  (i) S is a ring with respect to the operations of addition and multiplication,
  (ii) S is a vector space over H with respect to the operations of addition and scalar multiplication,
  (iii) If $u, v \in S$ and $a \in H$, then $(au)v = u(av) = a(uv)$.

It will be observed that part (iii) of this definition is a condition which involves both multiplication and scalar multiplication.

Throughout this section we shall continue to let L denote the set of all linear transformations of a vector space V over a field F. We already have (16.4 and 16.5) definitions of addition and scalar multiplication on L, and we proceed to introduce an operation of multiplication on L.

Multiplication of mappings has been defined in Section 1.3, where it was also shown that the associative law of multiplication always holds. In accordance with the general definition of multiplication of mappings, we define the product $\alpha\mathfrak{B}$ of elements of L as follows:

16.7
$$X(\alpha\mathfrak{B}) = (X\alpha)\mathfrak{B}, \qquad\qquad X \in V.$$

Certainly, $\alpha\mathfrak{B}$ is a mapping of V into V, but we must show that it is in fact a linear transformation of V. In this case, the calculations are as follows where, again, $X, Y \in V$ and $c \in F$:

$$(X + Y)(\mathcal{A}\mathcal{B}) = ((X + Y)\mathcal{A})\mathcal{B} \qquad (by \ 16.7)$$
$$= (X\mathcal{A} + Y\mathcal{A})\mathcal{B} \qquad (by \ 16.1)$$
$$= (X\mathcal{A})\mathcal{B} + (Y\mathcal{A})\mathcal{B} \qquad (by \ 16.1)$$
$$= X(\mathcal{A}\mathcal{B}) + Y(\mathcal{A}\mathcal{B}) \qquad (by \ 16.7),$$

and

$$(cX)(\mathcal{A}\mathcal{B}) = ((cX)\mathcal{A})\mathcal{B} \qquad (by \ 16.7)$$
$$= (c(X\mathcal{A}))\mathcal{B} \qquad (by \ 16.2)$$
$$= c((X\mathcal{A})\mathcal{B}) \qquad (by \ 16.2)$$
$$= c(X(\mathcal{A}\mathcal{B})) \qquad (by \ 16.7).$$

We have thus established the two defining properties of a linear transformation, and therefore $\mathcal{A}\mathcal{B} \subset L$. Hence, 16.7 actually defines an operation of multiplication on the set L.

We may now state the following important result.

16.8   Theorem.   *Using the respective Definitions 16.4, 16.7, and 16.5 of addition, multiplication, and scalar multiplication, the set L of all linear transformations of a vector space V over F is an algebra over F.*

We have already shown (Theorem 12.41) that L is a vector space over F, so part (ii) of Definition 16.6 holds. The zero of this vector space L is the linear transformation $\mathcal{O}: V \to V$ defined by

16.9 $X\mathcal{O} = 0,$ $X \in V,$

that is, it maps every element of V into the zero.

Since L is a vector space, addition in L has all the properties required of addition in a ring. Moreover, we have the associative law of multiplication since the elements of L are mappings. In order to show that L is a ring there remains only to prove the distributive laws.

Suppose that $\mathcal{A}$, $\mathcal{B}$, and $\mathcal{C}$ are elements of L, and let us prove that

16.10 $\mathcal{A}(\mathcal{B} + \mathcal{C}) = \mathcal{A}\mathcal{B} + \mathcal{A}\mathcal{C}.$

To establish this result, we shall prove that for every element X of V, X has the same image under the linear transformation $\mathcal{A}(\mathcal{B} + \mathcal{C})$ as under the linear transformation $\mathcal{A}\mathcal{B} + \mathcal{A}\mathcal{C}$. The calculations are as follows:

$$X[\mathcal{A}(\mathcal{B} + \mathcal{C})] = (X\mathcal{A})(\mathcal{B} + \mathcal{C}) \qquad (by \ 16.7)$$
$$= (X\mathcal{A})\mathcal{B} + (X\mathcal{A})\mathcal{C} \qquad (by \ 16.4)$$
$$= X(\mathcal{A}\mathcal{B}) + X(\mathcal{A}\mathcal{C}) \qquad (by \ 16.7)$$
$$= X(\mathcal{A}\mathcal{B} + \mathcal{A}\mathcal{C}) \qquad (by \ 16.4).$$

We leave as exercises the proof of the other distributive law and property (iii) of Definition 16.6.

It is quite easy to verify that the identity mapping $\mathcal{I}$ of V into V, that is, the mapping defined by

16.11 $$X\mathcal{I} = X, \qquad\qquad X \in V,$$

is a linear transformation and hence an element of L. Moreover, if $\alpha \in L$, we have that $\alpha\mathcal{I} = \mathcal{I}\alpha = \alpha$, and thus the algebra L has $\mathcal{I}$ as unity.

It is now natural to consider the question of which elements of L have multiplicative inverses. One characterization of these elements is given in the following theorem.

16.12 Theorem. *An element α of L has a multiplicative inverse α^{-1} in L if and only if α is a one-one mapping of V onto V.*

From Theorem 1.11 and remarks following the proof of that theorem, we know that there exists a *mapping* α^{-1} which is an inverse of the *mapping* α if and only if α is a one-one mapping of V onto V. There remains only to show that if α is a linear transformation which has an inverse mapping, this inverse mapping is also a linear transformation. Suppose, then, that α is a linear transformation of V which has an inverse *mapping* α^{-1}. Thus $\alpha\alpha^{-1} = \alpha^{-1}\alpha = \mathcal{I}$ and α is a one-one mapping of V onto V. In fact, α^{-1} is the mapping defined by

16.13 $$(X\alpha)\alpha^{-1} = X, \qquad\qquad X \in V.$$

We complete the proof of the theorem by verifying that the mapping α^{-1} defined by 16.13 is indeed a linear transformation and therefore an element of L.

Since α is an onto mapping, we may let $X\alpha$ and $Y\alpha$ be any elements of V. Then

$$\begin{aligned}
(X\alpha + Y\alpha)\alpha^{-1} &= [(X + Y)\alpha]\alpha^{-1} &&\text{(by 16.4)}\\
&= X + Y &&\text{(by 16.13)}\\
&= (X\alpha)\alpha^{-1} + (Y\alpha)\alpha^{-1} &&\text{(by 16.13)}.
\end{aligned}$$

This establishes property 16.1 of a linear transformation. Likewise, if $X\alpha \in V$ and $c \in F$, we have

$$\begin{aligned}
[c(X\alpha)]\alpha^{-1} &= [(cX)\alpha]\alpha^{-1} &&\text{(by 16.2)}\\
&= cX &&\text{(by 16.13)}\\
&= c[(X\alpha)\alpha^{-1}] &&\text{(by 16.13)}.
\end{aligned}$$

Hence property 16.2 is also satisfied, and α^{-1} is an element of L. This completes the proof of the theorem.

We may pause to point out one consequence of part of the calculations used to prove Theorem 16.8. Let us, for the moment, ignore scalar multiplication in V and consider V to be merely an abelian group with operation addition. Moreover, instead of linear transformations of the vector space V, let us consider group homomorphisms of V into itself, that is, we assume Property 16.1 but not Property 16.2. If we define addition and multiplication of homomorphisms by 16.4 and 16.7, respectively, the parts of the proof of Theorem 16.8 which do not involve scalar multiplication show that the set of all these homomorphisms is a ring with unity. Otherwise expressed, if $\mathrm{Hom}(G, G)$ is the set of all homomorphisms of an abelian group G into itself, $\mathrm{Hom}(G, G)$ is a ring with respect to natural definitions of addition and multiplication. In Exercises 10 and 11 below it is indicated that *every* ring is isomorphic to a subring of $\mathrm{Hom}(G, G)$ for some abelian group G. This fact plays an important role in certain parts of the theory of rings.

EXERCISES

1. Which of the following mappings of $V_2(\mathbf{R})$ into $V_2(\mathbf{R})$ are linear transformations of $V_2(\mathbf{R})$?

    (a) $(x_1, x_2)\alpha = (0, 0)$,
    (b) $(x_1, x_2)\alpha = (3x_1 + x_2, x_1 + x_2)$,
    (c) $(x_1, x_2)\alpha = (x_1 + 1, x_1 + x_2)$,
    (d) $(x_1, x_2)\alpha = (x_2, x_1)$,
    (e) $(x_1, x_2)\alpha = (2x_1 - x_2, x_1x_2)$,
    (f) $(x_1, x_2)\alpha = (x_1 - 3x_2, x_1 - 3x_2)$,
    (g) $(x_1, x_2)\alpha = (x_1, x_2)$.

2. Let $V(F)$ be a vector space with a basis $\{X_1, X_2, X_3\}$, and let α be a linear transformation of V such that

    $$X_1\alpha = X_2, \quad X_2\alpha = X_3 + X_2, \quad X_3\alpha = X_2.$$

    (i)   Determine the vector $(X_1 + 2X_2 - X_3)\alpha$.
    (ii) Find a basis of the subspace $V\alpha$ of V.
    (iii) Find a subspace U of V of dimension two such that $U\alpha = U$.
    (iv) Find a subspace U of V of dimension two such that $U\alpha \subset U$.

3. Let V be the vector space of all polynomials in an indeterminate x over a field F (Example 4, Section 12.2). Verify that each of the following mappings of V into V is a linear transformation of V:

   (a) $f(x)\alpha = -f(x)$,
   (b) $f(x)\alpha = 0$,
   (c) $f(x)\alpha = f(x)$,
   (d) $f(x)\alpha = f(-x)$,
   (e) $f(x)\alpha = f(0)$,
   (f) $f(x)\alpha = f(x^2)$,
   (g) $f(x)\alpha = f(x) + f(-x)$.

4. If $V(F)$ is the vector space of the preceding exercise, verify that the mapping defined by $f(x)\alpha = f'(x)$, where $f'(x)$ is the derivative of $f(x)$ (Exercise 11 of Section 10.2), is a linear transformation of V. Determine the subspace $V\alpha$ of V in case F has characteristic zero. Do the same thing in case F has characteristic the prime p.

5. Let α and $\mathcal{B}$ be linear transformations of the vector space $V_2(\mathbf{R})$ defined as follows:

   $$(x_1 , x_2)\alpha = (2x_1 + x_2 , x_1 - x_2),$$
   $$(x_1 , x_2)\mathcal{B} = (x_1 , x_1 + 3x_2).$$

   Exhibit in a similar manner each of the following linear transformations of $V_2(\mathbf{R})$: $\alpha + \mathcal{B}$, $\alpha\mathcal{B}$, $\mathcal{B}\alpha$, 5α, $-\alpha$, α^2.

6. If α is as in the preceding exercise, verify that $\alpha^2 - \alpha = 3\mathcal{I}$, where $\mathcal{I}$ is the unity of the algebra of all linear transformations of $V_2(\mathbf{R})$.

7. Find nonzero linear transformations $\mathcal{C}$ and $\mathcal{D}$ of $V_2(\mathbf{R})$ such that $\mathcal{C}\mathcal{D} = \mathcal{O}$.

8. Complete the proof of Theorem 16.8 by proving the other distributive law and Property (iii) of Definition 16.6.

9. If L is the algebra of all linear transformations of a vector space V over F, verify that the set of all elements of L that are one-one mappings of V onto V is a group with respect to the operation of multiplication.

10. Let R be an arbitrary ring with unity, and let G be the additive group of R. If $a \in R$, the mapping $\theta_a : G \to G$ defined by $x\theta_a = xa$, $x \in G$, is a homomorphism of G into G. Show that the mapping $a \to \theta_a$ is an isomorphism of the ring R onto a subring of Hom (G, G). [*Cf.* the proof of Theorem 7.19.]

11.   Show that every ring is isomorphic to a subring of Hom (G, G)
         for some abelian group G. [*Hint:* Use the result of Exercise 15 of
         Section 2.7.]

16.3   THE FINITE DIMENSIONAL CASE

Heretofore, we have considered linear transformations of an entirely
arbitrary vector space V over a field F. In this section we shall restrict
V to have finite dimension $n > 0$. Of course, this restriction assures us
that V has a basis consisting of n vectors, and we shall exploit the existence of a basis in obtaining the results to follow.

We begin by stating the following result, which is a special case of
Theorem 12.35, since it is important for our present purposes.

16.14   Corollary.   *If $\{X_1, X_2, \cdots, X_n\}$ is a basis of V and $Z_1, Z_2, \cdots, Z_n$
are arbitrary elements of V, there exists exactly one linear transformation
α of V such that*

16.15
$$X_i\alpha = Z_i, \qquad (i = 1, 2, \cdots, n).$$

As in the preceding section, we shall continue to let L denote the
algebra of all linear transformations of the vector space V.

We have already observed that if U is a subspace of the vector
space V and $\alpha \in L$, then $U\alpha$ is also a subspace of V. We can now say
something as follows about the dimensions of these subspaces.

16.16   Theorem.   *If U is a subspace of the vector space V of finite dimension
and $\alpha \in L$, then $\dim (U\alpha) \leq \dim U$. Moreover, if α has a multiplicative inverse α^{-1} in L, then $\dim (U\alpha) = \dim U$.*

We may remark that the theorem remains true for an arbitrary
vector space V provided only that the subspace U has finite dimension.
However, our assumption that V has finite dimension assures us that
every subspace of V necessarily has finite dimension.

The result is trivial if either U or V has dimension zero. Suppose
that $\dim U = k > 0$ and that $\{X_1, X_2, \cdots, X_k\}$ is a basis of U, so that
every element of U is expressible in the form

$$c_1X_1 + c_2X_2 + \cdots + c_kX_k, \qquad c_i \in F\ (i = 1, 2, \cdots, k).$$

Since

$$(c_1X_1 + c_2X_2 + \cdots + c_kX_k)\alpha = c_1(X_1\alpha) + c_2(X_2\alpha) + \cdots + c_k(X_k\alpha),$$

it follows at once that $U\alpha$ is generated by the k vectors $X_1\alpha$, $X_2\alpha$, $\cdots$, $X_k\alpha$. That is, in the notation of Chapter 12, we have

$$U\alpha = [X_1\alpha, X_2\alpha, \cdots, X_k\alpha].$$

Hence dim $(U\alpha) \leq k$, and since dim $U = k$, we see immediately that dim $(U\alpha) \leq$ dim U.

Now if α has a multiplicative inverse α^{-1} in L, we apply the result just established with U replaced by $U\alpha$ and α by α^{-1}. Accordingly, we find that

$$\text{dim } U = \text{dim } ((U\alpha)\alpha^{-1} \leq \text{dim } (U\alpha)).$$

Since we proved above that always dim $(U\alpha) \leq$ dim U, we conclude that dim $(U\alpha) =$ dim U, and the proof is complete.

The dimension of the subspace $V\alpha$ of V gives some important information about the linear transformation α. For convenience of reference, we therefore make the following definition.

16.17   Definition.   Suppose that dim $V = n$ and let α be a linear transformation of V. Then dim $(V\alpha)$ is called the *rank* of the linear transformation α. If the rank of α is less than n, α is said to be *singular*; if the rank of α is n, α is said to be *nonsingular*.

In the next section we shall show how matrices are related to linear transformations, and justify the use of the word "rank" in terms of the previous definition of rank of a matrix.

We now proceed to prove the following theorem.

16.18   Theorem.   *Let V be a vector space of dimension $n > 0$, and let $\{X_1, X_2, \cdots, X_n\}$ be a basis of V. If $\alpha \in L$, the following are all equivalent:*

(i) α *is a one-one mapping.*

(ii)   *If $X \in V$ such that $X\alpha = 0$, then $X = 0$.*

(iii) $\{X_1\alpha, X_2\alpha, \cdots, X_n\alpha\}$ *is a basis of V.*

(iv) α *is an onto mapping, that is, $V\alpha = V$.*

(v) α *is nonsingular.*

(vi) α *has a multiplicative inverse α^{-1} in L.*

By saying that these statements are equivalent, we mean that each one implies all the others.

It is quite easy to show as follows, without any restriction on V, that (i) and (ii) are equivalent. If (i) holds and $X\alpha = 0$, then we have $X\alpha = 0\alpha$, and thus $X = 0$. Conversely, if (ii) holds and $X\alpha = Y\alpha$, then $(X - Y)\alpha = 0$ and we conclude that $X - Y = 0$, that is, that $X = Y$.

Next, let us prove the equivalence of (ii) and (iii). If (ii) holds and $\sum c_i(X_i\alpha) = 0$, it follows that $\left(\sum c_iX_i\right)\alpha = 0$ and (ii) implies that $\sum c_iX_i = 0$. However, the X's are linearly independent, so every $c_i = 0$. This shows that $\{X_1\alpha, X_2\alpha, \cdots, X_n\alpha\}$ is a linearly independent set and, by Theorem 12.23(ii), it is a basis of V. Conversely, let us assume (iii) and prove (ii). Supposet hat $X\alpha = 0$. Since we may write $X = \sum c_iX_i$, it follows that

$$0 = X\alpha = \left(\sum c_iX_i\right)\alpha = \sum c_i(X_i\alpha).$$

But, by our assumption, $\{X_1\alpha, X_2\alpha, \cdots, X_n\alpha\}$ is a basis of V and therefore these vectors are linearly independent. We conclude that every $c_i = 0$, and hence that $X = 0$. We have thus proved the equivalence of (ii) and (iii).

Since $V\alpha = [X_1\alpha, X_2\alpha, \cdots, X_n\alpha]$, clearly (iii) implies (iv). Conversely, if $V\alpha = V$, we must have $V = [X_1\alpha, X_2\alpha, \cdots, X_n\alpha]$ and these vectors are a basis of V (by Theorem 12.23(iv)). Thus (iii) and (iv) are equivalent.

Since $V\alpha$ is a subspace of V, $V\alpha = V$ if and only if dim $(V\alpha) = $ dim V, that is, if and only if α is nonsingular. This shows the equivalence of (iv) and (v).

Finally, we have already proved in Theorem 16.12, without any restriction on V, that (vi) is equivalent to (i) and (iv) together. But, with the present restriction that V have finite dimension, what we have already proved above shows that (i) and (iv) are equivalent. This completes the proof of the theorem.

We may observe that since α is the multiplicative inverse of α^{-1}, the equivalence of (v) and (vi) shows that α^{-1} *is nonsingular if and only if α is nonsingular.*

Let us now give an example to indicate one possible way of actually computing the multiplicative inverse of a given nonsingular linear transformation.

EXAMPLE. Compute the multiplicative inverse of the linear transformation of $V_2(\mathbf{R})$ defined by $(x_1, x_2)\alpha = (x_1 - x_2, x_1 + x_2)$.

SOLUTION: The set $\{(1, 0), (0, 1)\}$ of unit vectors is a basis of $V_2(\mathbf{R})$, and we find that

$$(1, 0)\alpha = (1, 1), \quad (0, 1)\alpha = (-1, 1).$$

Now these image vectors $(1, 1)$ and $(-1, 1)$ are linearly independent and form a basis of $V_2(\mathbf{R})$. By definition of α^{-1}, we therefore have

$$(1, 1)\alpha^{-1} = (1, 0), \quad (-1, 1)\alpha^{-1} = (0, 1).$$

But an arbitrary element (x_1, x_2) of $V_2(\mathbf{R})$ can be expressed in the form

$$(x_1, x_2) = \frac{x_1 + x_2}{2} (1, 1) + \frac{x_2 - x_1}{2} (-1, 1),$$

and hence we see that α^{-1} is as follows:

$$(x_1, x_2)\alpha^{-1} = \frac{x_1 + x_2}{2} (1, 1)\alpha^{-1} + \frac{x_2 - x_1}{2} (-1, 1)\alpha^{-1}$$

$$= \frac{x_1 + x_2}{2} (1, 0) + \frac{x_2 - x_1}{2} (0, 1)$$

$$= \left(\frac{x_1 + x_2}{2}, \frac{x_2 - x_1}{2} \right).$$

The reader may check these calculations by verifying that if (x_1, x_2) is an element of $V_2(\mathbf{R})$, then

$$(x_1, x_2)\alpha\alpha^{-1} = (x_1, x_2)\alpha^{-1}\alpha = (x_1, x_2).$$

The next theorem will give some information about the rank of a product of linear transformations. For convenience, we shall designate the rank of the linear transformation α by "rank α."

16.19 Theorem.

(i) *If α, $\mathcal{B} \in L$, then rank $(\alpha\mathcal{B}) \leq$ rank α and also rank $(\alpha\mathcal{B}) \leq$ rank $\mathcal{B}$.*

(ii) *If α, $\mathcal{B} \in L$ and α is nonsingular, then rank $(\alpha\mathcal{B}) =$ rank $(\mathcal{B}\alpha) =$ rank $\mathcal{B}$.*

Let us first apply Theorem 16.16 with U replaced by $V\alpha$ and α by $\mathcal{B}$. We then have dim $((V\alpha)\mathcal{B}) \leq$ dim $(V\alpha)$. But, by the definition of the product of linear transformations, $(V\alpha)\mathcal{B} = V(\alpha\mathcal{B})$. Accordingly, we see that rank $(\alpha\mathcal{B}) \leq$ rank α.

Since $V\alpha \subseteq V$, it follows that $V(\alpha\mathcal{B}) = (V\alpha)\mathcal{B} \subseteq V\mathcal{B}$. Hence, dim $(V(\alpha\mathcal{B})) \leq$ dim $(V\mathcal{B})$, that is, rank $(\alpha\mathcal{B}) \leq$ rank $\mathcal{B}$. We have thus established part (i) of the theorem.

To prove the second part, suppose that α is nonsingular. Then, by the preceding theorem, α has a multiplicative inverse α^{-1}, and we can write $\mathcal{B} = \alpha^{-1}(\alpha\mathcal{B})$. Now the part of the theorem already proved assures us that the rank of a product does not exceed the rank of either factor. Hence, rank $\mathcal{B} \leq$ rank $(\alpha\mathcal{B})$. On the other hand, we know from part (i) of the theorem that rank $(\alpha\mathcal{B}) \leq$ rank $\mathcal{B}$, and we conclude that rank $(\alpha\mathcal{B}) =$ rank $\mathcal{B}$. To show that also rank $(\mathcal{B}\alpha) =$ rank $\mathcal{B}$, we need only write $\mathcal{B} = (\mathcal{B}\alpha)\alpha^{-1}$, and apply a similar argument.

The following important result is a special case of the second part of the theorem just proved, and is also an easy consequence of Theorem 16.18.

16.20 Corollary.   *The product of two nonsingular linear transformations of a vector space V is itself a nonsingular linear transformation of V.*

If α is a linear transformation of V, we have previously called the set of all vectors X of V such that $X\alpha = 0$ (actually a subspace of V by Theorem 12.32) the *kernel* of α. However, in the present setting it is frequently given an alternate name as follows.

16.21 Definition.   If $\alpha \in L$, the subspace of V consisting of all vectors X of V such that $X\alpha = 0$ is called the *null space* of α. The dimension of the null space of α is called the *nullity* of α.

The equivalence of conditions (ii) and (v) of Theorem 16.18 shows that if α is nonsingular (that is, has rank n), then the nullity of α is zero. This is a special case of the following theorem.

16.22 Theorem.   *If $dim\ V = n$ and α is a linear transformation of V of rank r, then α has nullity $n - r$.*

In view of the preceding remarks we may restrict attention to the case in which the nullity k of α is positive. Let $\{Y_1, \cdots, Y_k\}$ be a basis of the null space of α, and let us extend this set to a basis

$$\{Y_1, \cdots, Y_k, \cdots, Y_n\}$$

of V. Since $Y_i\alpha = 0$ $(i = 1, 2, \cdots, k)$, it follows easily that

$$V\alpha = [Y_{k+1}\alpha, \cdots, Y_n\alpha].$$

We shall now show that $\{Y_{k+1}\alpha, \cdots, Y_n\alpha\}$ is a linearly independent set and hence a basis of $V\alpha$. Suppose that

$$c_{k+1}(Y_{k+1}\alpha) + \cdots + c_n(Y_n\alpha) = 0,$$

where $c_{k+1}, \cdots, c_n$ are elements of F. It follows that

$$(c_{k+1}Y_{k+1} + \cdots + c_n Y_n)\mathfrak{a} = 0,$$

and hence that

$$c_{k+1}Y_{k+1} + \cdots + c_n Y_n$$

is in the null space of $\mathfrak{a}$. Hence, this vector is a linear combination of the basis elements $Y_1, Y_2, \cdots, Y_k$ of this null space. However, since $\{Y_1, \cdots, Y_n\}$ is a linearly independent set, we conclude that $c_{k+1} = 0, \cdots, c_n = 0$. This shows that $\{Y_{k+1}\mathfrak{a}, \cdots, Y_n\mathfrak{a}\}$ is a linearly independent set, and therefore a basis of $V\mathfrak{a}$. Accordingly, dim $(V\mathfrak{a}) = n - k$. Since $r = $ dim $(V\mathfrak{a})$, it follows that $r = n - k$ or $k = n - r$, and the proof of the theorem is complete.

EXERCISES

1. In each of the following, find the rank of the linear transformation $\mathfrak{a}$ of $V_3(\mathbf{R})$ and find a basis for the null space of $\mathfrak{a}$:

    (a) $(x_1, x_2, x_3)\mathfrak{a} = (x_1 + 2x_2 - x_3, 2x_1 + x_2 + x_3, x_2 - x_3)$,
    (b) $(x_1, x_2, x_3)\mathfrak{a} =$
    $\qquad (2x_1 - x_2 + x_3, x_1 + 2x_2 - x_3, x_1 + 7x_2 - 4x_3)$,
    (c) $(x_1, x_2, x_3)\mathfrak{a} = (x_1 + x_2, x_1 + x_2, x_1 + x_2)$.

2. In each of the following, find the multiplicative inverse of the given linear transformation of $V_2(\mathbf{R})$:

    (a) $(x_1, x_2)\mathfrak{a} = (2x_1 - x_2, x_1 + x_2)$,
    (b) $(x_1, x_2)\mathfrak{a} = (x_2, -x_1)$,
    (c) $(x_1, x_2)\mathfrak{a} = (x_1 + 2x_2, 2x_1 + x_2)$.

3. Find the multiplicative inverse of the linear transformation $\mathfrak{a}$ of $V_3(\mathbf{R})$ defined by $(x_1, x_2, x_3)\mathfrak{a} = (x_1 + x_2 + x_3, x_2 + x_3, x_3)$.

4. Let V be the vector space consisting of all polynomials of degree not greater than two, together with the zero polynomial, over the real field $\mathbf{R}$. Now let $\mathfrak{a}$ be the linear transformation of V defined by $f(x)\mathfrak{a} = f'(x)$, where $f'(x)$ is the derivative of $f(x)$.

    (a) Find the rank and the nullity of each of the following linear transformations of V: $\mathfrak{a}$, $\mathfrak{a}^2$, $\mathfrak{a}^3$, $\mathfrak{a} + \mathfrak{s}$, where $\mathfrak{s}$ is the unity.

(b) Find the multiplicative inverse of the one of these linear transformations which is nonsingular.

In Exercises 5–8 the vector space is assumed to have finite dimension.

5. If c is a nonzero element of F and $\alpha \in L$, show that the rank of $(c\alpha)$ is equal to the rank of α.

6. Prove that if α, $\mathcal{B} \in L$ and $\alpha\mathcal{B}$ is nonsingular, then both α and $\mathcal{B}$ are nonsingular.

7. Prove that if α, $\mathcal{B} \in L$ and $\alpha\mathcal{B} = \mathcal{I}$, then also $\mathcal{B}\alpha = \mathcal{I}$, and therefore $\mathcal{B} = \alpha^{-1}$.

8. If α, $\mathcal{B} \in L$, prove that rank $(\alpha + \mathcal{B}) \leq$ rank $\alpha +$ rank $\mathcal{B}$. [Hint: Using the Definition 12.26 of the sum of two subspaces, observe that $V(\alpha + \mathcal{B}) \subseteq V\alpha + V\mathcal{B}$.]

9. Let $W(F)$ be the vector space of Example 2 of Section 12.2 whose elements are infinite sequences of elements of F. Verify that the mapping $\alpha: W \to W$ defined by

$$(a_1, a_2, a_3, \cdots)\alpha = (0, a_1, a_2, \cdots)$$

is a linear transformation of W which is a one-one mapping but not an onto mapping. Similarly, verify that the mapping $\mathcal{B}:$ $W \to W$ defined by

$$(a_1, a_2, a_3, \cdots)\mathcal{B} = (a_2, a_3, \cdots)$$

is an onto mapping but not a one-one mapping. Why do these examples not violate Theorem 16.18?

16.4   ALGEBRA OF MATRICES

We have defined a basis of a vector space to be a set of vectors having certain properties, and the order of writing down these vectors was of no significance. Now, however, we wish to specify an order for the elements of a basis, and shall then speak of an *ordered basis*. Thus, for example, if $\{X_1, X_2, X_3\}$ is a basis of a vector space V of dimension three, then X_1, X_2, X_3 and X_2, X_1, X_3 would be different ordered bases of V, although the *sets* $\{X_1, X_2, X_3\}$ and $\{X_2, X_1, X_3\}$ are equal.

Throughout this section we shall let V be a vector space of dimension $n > 0$ over a field F, L the algebra of all linear transformations of V, and $X_1, X_2, \cdots, X_n$ a fixed ordered basis of V.

Suppose, now, that $\alpha \in L$. Then each of the vectors $X_i\alpha$ is uniquely expressible as a linear combination of the basis elements, so that there exist elements a_{ij} $(i,j = 1, 2, \cdots, n)$ of F, *uniquely determined* by α, such that

$$\begin{aligned}
X_1\alpha &= a_{11}X_1 + a_{12}X_2 + \cdots + a_{1n}X_n, \\
X_2\alpha &= a_{21}X_1 + a_{22}X_2 + \cdots + a_{2n}X_n, \\
&\cdots\cdots\cdots\cdots\cdots\cdots\cdots\cdots \\
X_n\alpha &= a_{n1}X_1 + a_{n2}X_2 + \cdots + a_{nn}X_n.
\end{aligned}$$

Of course, we may also write these equations in the following condensed form:

16.23 $$X_1\alpha = \sum_{j=1}^{n} a_{ij}X_j, \qquad (i = 1, 2, \cdots, n).$$

Let us restate what we have just observed in the following way. Each linear transformation α of V has associated with it, by Equations 16.23, a unique matrix $A = (a_{ij})$ of order n over F. Conversely, if $A = (a_{ij})$ is a given matrix of order n over F, Corollary 16.14 shows that there exists a unique linear transformation α of V such that α and A are related as in Equations 16.23.

Let us henceforth denote by F_n the set of all matrices of order n over F. To avoid any possible confusion, perhaps we should state that two elements of F_n are considered as equal only if they are identical. That is, if (a_{ij}) and (b_{ij}) are elements of F_n, $(a_{ij}) = (b_{ij})$ means that $a_{ij} = b_{ij}$ for all $i, j = 1, 2, \cdots, n$.

We can now state in the following precise way what we have observed above. The mapping

16.24 $$\alpha \to A = (a_{ij}), \qquad \alpha \in L,$$

defined by Equations 16.23, is a one-one mapping of L onto F_n.

Inasmuch as L is an algebra over F, it is almost obvious that we can use this one-one mapping of L onto F_n to define operations of addition, multiplication, and scalar multiplication on F_n in such a way that F_n will be an algebra over F, which is isomorphic to L. We proceed to consider each of these operations in turn.

First, let us consider addition, and let $A = (a_{ij})$ and $B = (b_{ij})$ be elements of F_n. Suppose, further, that under the mapping 16.24, $\alpha \to A$ and $\mathcal{B} \to B$. Then

$$X_i\alpha = \sum_{j=1}^{n} a_{ij}X_j, \qquad (i = 1, 2, \cdots, n),$$

and

$$X_i \mathcal{B} = \sum_{j=1}^{n} b_{ij} X_j, \qquad (i = 1, 2, \cdots, n).$$

Now, by the definition of addition of linear transformations, it follows that

$$X_i(\mathcal{A} + \mathcal{B}) = X_i \mathcal{A} + X_i \mathcal{B} = \sum_{j=1}^{n} (a_{ij} + b_{ij}) X_j, \qquad (i = 1, 2, \cdots, n).$$

Accordingly, we see that under the mapping 16.24,

$$\mathcal{A} + \mathcal{B} \to (a_{ij} + b_{ij}).$$

This leads us to *define* addition in F_n as follows:

16.25 $$(a_{ij}) + (b_{ij}) = (a_{ij} + b_{ij}).$$

That is, the element of the matrix $A + B$ in any fixed position is obtained by adding the elements of A and of B that are in that position. Taking $n = 2$, and F to be the field of rational numbers, we have as an illustration:

$$\begin{bmatrix} 4 & 0 \\ -2 & 3 \end{bmatrix} + \begin{bmatrix} -1 & 2 \\ 1 & 2 \end{bmatrix} = \begin{bmatrix} 3 & 2 \\ -1 & 5 \end{bmatrix}.$$

We next consider multiplication, and let A and B be as above. Then, using first the definition of a product of linear transformations, we have the following:

$$X_i(\mathcal{A}\mathcal{B}) = (X_i \mathcal{A})\mathcal{B} = \left(\sum_{k=1}^{n} a_{ik} X_k \right) \mathcal{B}$$

$$= \sum_{k=1}^{n} a_{ik} (X_k \mathcal{B})$$

$$= \sum_{k=1}^{n} a_{ik} \left(\sum_{j=1}^{n} b_{kj} X_j \right), \qquad (i = 1, 2, \cdots, n).$$

By rearranging the order of summation, this can be written in the form

$$X_i(\mathfrak{a}\mathfrak{B}) = \sum_{j=1}^{n} \left(\sum_{k=1}^{n} a_{ik}b_{kj} \right) X_j, \qquad (i = 1, 2, \cdots, n).$$

Hence, under the mapping 16.24,

$$\mathfrak{a}\mathfrak{B} \rightarrow \left(\sum_{k=1}^{n} a_{ik}b_{kj} \right).$$

Accordingly, we *define* multiplication in F_n as follows:

16.26
$$(a_{ij})(b_{ij}) = \left(\sum_{k=1}^{n} a_{ik}b_{kj} \right).$$

This definition may be stated in words as follows. The element in the ith row and jth column of the product AB is the sum of the products of the elements of the ith row of A by the corresponding elements of the jth column of B. This can be expressed in another way as follows. Let $A_1, A_2, \cdots, A_n$ be the row vectors of A; and let $B^1, B^2, \cdots, B^n$ be the column vectors of B. In terms of inner products of vectors, we may then write 16.26 in the following alternate form:

$$AB = (A_i \cdot B^j).$$

As a simple example of multiplication of matrices, using the same matrices as were used above to illustrate addition, we have

$$\begin{bmatrix} 4 & 0 \\ -2 & 3 \end{bmatrix} \begin{bmatrix} -1 & 2 \\ 1 & 2 \end{bmatrix}$$

$$= \begin{bmatrix} 4(-1) + 0(1) & 4(2) + 0(2) \\ -2(-1) + 3(1) & -2(2) + 3(2) \end{bmatrix} = \begin{bmatrix} -4 & 8 \\ 5 & 2 \end{bmatrix}.$$

On the other hand, the reader may verify that

$$\begin{bmatrix} -1 & 2 \\ 1 & 2 \end{bmatrix} \begin{bmatrix} 4 & 0 \\ -2 & 3 \end{bmatrix} = \begin{bmatrix} -8 & 6 \\ 0 & 6 \end{bmatrix},$$

and clearly the commutative law of multiplication does not hold in F_n.

Finally, we consider scalar multiplication. If $c \in F$ and $\mathfrak{a} \in L$, by the definition of scalar multiplication in L, we have

$$X_i(c\mathfrak{a}) = c(X_i\mathfrak{a}) = c\sum_{j=1}^{n} a_{ij}X_j = \sum_{j=1}^{n} (ca_{ij})X_j, \qquad (i = 1, 2, \cdots, n).$$

This suggests that we *define* scalar multiplication in F_n as follows:

16.27 $$c(a_{ij}) = (ca_{ij}).$$

Otherwise expressed, if $A \in F_n$, cA is the matrix obtained by multiplying every element of A by c. As a simple example, we have

$$2\begin{bmatrix} 4 & 0 \\ -2 & 3 \end{bmatrix} = \begin{bmatrix} 8 & 0 \\ -4 & 6 \end{bmatrix}.$$

We have now defined addition, multiplication, and scalar multiplication on F_n in such a way that all of these operations are preserved under the mapping 16.24. That is, if under this mapping $\alpha \to A$ and $\mathcal{B} \to B$, then $\alpha + \mathcal{B} \to A + B$, $\alpha\mathcal{B} \to AB$, and $c\alpha \to cA$ for $c \in F$. We have therefore established the following result, it being understood that an isomorphism of two algebras over F means an isomorphism as rings and also as vector spaces.

16.28 Theorem. *With addition, multiplication, and scalar multiplication defined respectively by 16.25, 16.26, and 16.27, the set F_n of all matrices of order n over F is an algebra over F. Moreover this algebra is isomorphic to the algebra L of all linear transformations of a vector space V of dimension n over F.*

It follows easily from 16.25 that the zero element of the algebra F_n is the matrix of order n *all* of whose elements are zero. We shall usually designate this zero matrix by the familiar symbol 0. Of course, this matrix is the image of the zero linear transformation under the mapping 16.24.

If $\mathcal{I}$ is the unity of L, we have $X_i\mathcal{I} = X_i$ $(i = 1, 2, \cdots, n)$, and the image of $\mathcal{I}$ under the mapping 16.24 is the matrix with 1's on the principal diagonal and zeros elsewhere. This matrix must then be the unity of F_n, as can also be verified by use of 16.26. The unity of F_n will henceforth be denoted by I. For example, if $n = 3$, we have

$$I = \begin{bmatrix} 1 & 0 & 0 \\ 0 & 1 & 0 \\ 0 & 0 & 1 \end{bmatrix}.$$

Perhaps we should emphasize that the isomorphism 16.24 of L onto F_n depends upon the ordered basis of L which is used. A different ordered basis would lead to a different isomorphism, so that there are many different isomorphisms of L onto F_n.

The matrix A which corresponds to the linear transformation α

under the mapping 16.24 may be referred to as *the matrix of* α *relative to the ordered basis* $X_1, X_2, \cdots, X_n$ *of* V. In a later section we shall determine the relationship which exists between the matrices of a linear transformation of a vector space V relative to two different ordered bases of V.

The following theorem will justify the use of some of our previous terminology.

16.29 Theorem. *The rank of a linear transformation* α *of a vector space* V *is equal to the rank of the matrix of* α *relative to any ordered basis of* V.

We use the above notation according to which α and A are related by Equations 16.23. Since $V\alpha = [X_1\alpha, X_2\alpha, \cdots, X_n\alpha]$, Theorem 12.25(ii) shows that the rank of α is the maximal number of linear independent vectors in the set $\{X_1\alpha, X_2\alpha, \cdots, X_n\alpha\}$. Similarly, the (row) rank of the matrix A is the maximum number of linearly independent vectors in the set $\{A_1, A_2, \cdots, A_n\}$ of row vectors of A. The main part of the proof that these numbers are the same is in establishing the following lemma.

16.30 Lemma.

If c_i $(i = 1, 2, \cdots, n)$ *are elements of* F, *then*

$$\sum_{i=1}^{n} c_i(X_i\alpha) = 0 \quad \text{if and only if} \quad \sum_{i=1}^{n} c_i A_i = 0.$$

To prove this lemma, we first observe that Equations 16.23 show that

$$\sum_{i=1}^{n} c_i(X_i\alpha) = \sum_{i=1}^{n} c_i \left(\sum_{j=1}^{n} a_{ij}X_j \right) = \sum_{j=1}^{n} \left(\sum_{i=1}^{n} c_i a_{ij} \right) X_j.$$

Since the X's are linearly independent, it follows that

$$\sum_{i=1}^{n} c_i(X_i\alpha) = 0 \quad \text{if and only if} \quad \sum_{i=1}^{n} c_i a_{ij} = 0 \quad \text{for} \quad j = 1, 2, \cdots, n.$$

However, this last set of equations can be written in the vector form

$\sum_{i=1}^{n} c_i A_i = 0$, and the lemma is established.

We shall leave as an exercise the application of this lemma to complete the proof of the theorem.

Just as for linear transformations, it is customary to call a matrix of order n *singular* or *nonsingular* according as its rank is less than n or equal to n.

We conclude this section with some examples illustrating how one computes the matrix of a linear transformation relative to a given ordered basis.

EXAMPLE 1.   Find the matrix of the linear transformation α of $V_2(\mathbf{R})$ defined by $(x_1, x_2)\alpha = (3x_1 + x_2, x_1 - 2x_2)$ relative to the ordered basis $(1, 0)$, $(0, 1)$ of $V_2(\mathbf{R})$. Do the same thing relative to the ordered basis $(1, 1)$, $(-1, 1)$ of $V_2(\mathbf{R})$.

SOLUTION: Equations 16.23 in this case become the following:

$$(1, 0)\alpha = (3, 1) = 3(1, 0) + (0, 1),$$
$$(0, 1)\alpha = (1, -2) = (1, 0) - 2(0, 1).$$

Thus the matrix of α relative to the ordered basis $(1, 0)$, $(0, 1)$ is as follows:

$$\begin{bmatrix} 3 & 1 \\ 1 & -2 \end{bmatrix}.$$

Let us now compute the matrix of α relative to the ordered basis $(1, 1)$, $(-1, 1)$ of $V_2(\mathbf{R})$. Some of the calculations in the example of the preceding section can be used to show that in this case we have

$$(1, 1)\alpha = (4, -1) = \tfrac{3}{2}(1, 1) - \tfrac{5}{2}(-1, 1),$$
$$(-1, 1)\alpha = (-2, -3) = -\tfrac{5}{2}(1, 1) - \tfrac{1}{2}(-1, 1).$$

Accordingly, the matrix

$$\begin{bmatrix} \tfrac{3}{2} & -\tfrac{5}{2} \\ -\tfrac{5}{2} & -\tfrac{1}{2} \end{bmatrix}$$

is the matrix of α relative to the ordered basis $(1, 1)$, $(-1, 1)$ of $V_2(\mathbf{R})$.

EXAMPLE 2.   Let V be the vector space over $\mathbf{R}$ consisting of all polynomials in an indeterminate x of degree no more than two, together with the zero polynomial. Let α be the linear transformation of V defined by $f(x)\alpha = f'(x)$, where $f'(x)$ is the derivative of $f(x)$.

(i) Find the matrix of α relative to the ordered basis x^2, x, 1 of V.
(ii) Find the matrix of α relative to the ordered basis $x + 1$, 1, $x^2 + x$ of V.

SOLUTION: (i) The following equations

$$x^2\alpha = 0 \cdot x^2 + 2x + 0,$$
$$x\alpha = 0 \cdot x^2 + 0 \cdot x + 1,$$
$$1\alpha = 0 \cdot x^2 + 0 \cdot x + 0 \cdot 1,$$

show that the matrix of α relative to the ordered basis x^2, x, 1 of V is as follows:

$$\begin{bmatrix} 0 & 2 & 0 \\ 0 & 0 & 1 \\ 0 & 0 & 0 \end{bmatrix}.$$

(ii) It is easy to verify that

$$(x + 1)\alpha = 0 \cdot (x + 1) + 1 \cdot 1 + 0 \cdot (x^2 + x),$$
$$1\alpha = 0 \cdot (x + 1) + 0 \cdot 1 + 0 \cdot (x^2 + x),$$
$$(x^2 + x)\alpha = 2 \cdot (x + 1) - 1 \cdot 1 + 0 \cdot (x^2 + x).$$

Thus the matrix of α relative to the ordered basis $x + 1$, 1, $x^2 + x$ of V is the following:

$$\begin{bmatrix} 0 & 1 & 0 \\ 0 & 0 & 0 \\ 2 & -1 & 0 \end{bmatrix}.$$

EXERCISES

1. Let A and B be the following matrices of order 3 over **Q**:

$$A = \begin{bmatrix} 1 & -1 & 2 \\ 0 & 1 & 3 \\ 2 & 1 & -2 \end{bmatrix}, \qquad B = \begin{bmatrix} 1 & -2 & 3 \\ 2 & 1 & -1 \\ 1 & 0 & 1 \end{bmatrix}.$$

Compute each of the following: AB, BA, A^2, B^2, $(A + B)^2$.

2. If A is the matrix of the preceding exercise, verify that $A^3 - 10A + 15I = 0$.

3. If A is the same matrix as above, and

$$C = -\tfrac{1}{15}\begin{bmatrix} -5 & 0 & -5 \\ 6 & -6 & -3 \\ -2 & -3 & 1 \end{bmatrix},$$

   verify with $AC = CA = I$, and hence that $C = A^{-1}$.

4. If B is an element of F_n which has an inverse B^{-1} in F_n, verify that the mapping $A \to B^{-1}AB$ $(A \in F_n)$ is an isomorphism of the algebra F_n onto itself.

5. Complete the proof of Theorem 16.29.

6. Find the matrix of each linear transformation of Exercise 1 of the preceding section relative to the ordered basis $(1,0,0)$, $(0,1,0)$, $(0,0,1)$ of $V_3(\mathbf{R})$.

7. Let V be the vector space of Example 2 above, and let $\mathcal{C}$ and $\mathcal{D}$ be linear transformations of V defined as follows: $f(x)\mathcal{C} = f(x + 1)$, $f(x)\mathcal{D} = f(x - 1)$. Find the matrix of $\mathcal{C}$ and of $\mathcal{D}$ relative to the ordered basis x^2, x, 1 of V, and verify that these matrices are multiplicative inverses of each other.

8. Let V be the vector space of all polynomials of degree not greater than three, together with the zero polynomial, over a field F. Find the matrix of each of the following linear transformations of V relative to the ordered basis 1, x, x^2, x^3 of V:

   (a) $f(x)\mathcal{a} = 2f(x)$,
   (b) $f(x)\mathcal{a} = f(-x)$,
   (c) $f(x)\mathcal{a} = f(x) + f(-x)$.

9. If A is the matrix of a linear transformation $\mathcal{a}$ relative to an ordered basis $X_1, X_2, \cdots, X_n$ of a vector space V, how would you describe the matrix of $\mathcal{a}$ relative to an ordered basis obtained from the given one by interchanging X_i and X_j $(i \neq j)$?

10. Verify directly that F_n has dimension n^2 as a vector space over F. (*Cf.* Theorems 12.42 and 16.28.)

11. Show that the subset of F_n consisting of those matrices all of whose elements below the principal diagonal are zero is a subalgebra of the algebra F_n.

12. If D is any element of F_n, let D' be the *transpose* of D. Prove that if A, $B \in F_n$, then $(A + B)' = A' + B'$ and $(AB)' = B'A'$. Prove also that if A has a multiplicative inverse, then A' has a multiplicative inverse and that $(A^{-1})' = (A')^{-1}$.

16.5 LINEAR TRANSFORMATIONS OF $V_n(F)$

As the reader may have already noticed in some of the examples and exercises, the results of the preceding section take a particularly simple form if we restrict V to be a vector space $V_n(F)$ and use the unit vectors E_1, E_2, $\cdots$, E_n (as defined in Section 12.4) as our ordered basis. The isomorphism 16.24 of L onto F_n is now given by $\alpha \to A = (a_{ij})$, where

16.31 $\qquad E_i\alpha = \sum_{j=1}^{n} a_{ij}E_j = (a_{i1}, a_{i2}, \cdots, a_{in}), \qquad (i = 1, 2, \cdots, n).$

That is, $E_i\alpha$ is just the ith row vector A_i of the matrix A, and we can write 16.31 in the simpler form

16.32 $\qquad\qquad\qquad E_i\alpha = A_i, \qquad\qquad (i = 1, 2, \cdots, n).$

An arbitrary element X of $V_n(F)$ can be written in the form

16.33 $\qquad\qquad X = (x_1, x_2, \cdots, x_n) = \sum_{i=1}^{n} x_i E_i,$

and it follows from 16.32 that

$$X\alpha = \left(\sum_{i=1}^{n} x_i E_i\right)\alpha = \sum_{i=1}^{n} x_i(E_i\alpha) = \sum_{i=1}^{n} x_i A_i.$$

Thus $(V_n(F))\alpha$ is simply the row space of the matrix A, and we observe that in this special case it is particularly evident that the rank of α is equal to the (row) rank of the corresponding matrix A.

There is still another way of writing $X\alpha$. It is in terms of the inner product of X by the column vectors of A, as follows:

16.34 $\qquad\qquad X\alpha = (X \cdot A^1, X \cdot A^2, \cdots, X \cdot A^n).$

So far we have carefully distinguished between linear transformations and matrices. However, since L and F_n are isomorphic algebras it is possible to use an identical notation for these concepts. Whenever we wish to do so we shall henceforth consider that a matrix A of order n *is* the corresponding linear transformation α of $V_n(F)$ relative to the unit vectors. That is, in view of 16.32, the linear transformation A of $V_n(F)$ is the linear transformation which maps the ith unit vector E_i onto the ith row vector A_i of A. We may then write 16.34 as follows:

16.35 $$XA = (X \cdot A^1, X \cdot A^2, \cdots, X \cdot A^n).$$

It will be observed that XA can be computed by using a "row by column" multiplication of the *vector* X of $V_n(F)$ by the *matrix* A of F_n.

Let us illustrate the use of this notation by an example. Suppose that

$$A = \begin{bmatrix} 1 & -1 & 2 \\ 0 & 1 & -1 \\ 3 & 2 & 1 \end{bmatrix}$$

is considered as a linear transformation of the vector space $V_3(\mathbf{Q})$. Then the image of the vector $(2, -1, 3)$ under the mapping A, as given by 16.35, is computed as follows:

$$(2, -1, 3) \begin{bmatrix} 1 & -1 & 2 \\ 0 & 1 & -1 \\ 3 & 2 & 1 \end{bmatrix}$$
$$= (2 \cdot 1 + (-1)0 + 3 \cdot 3, 2(-1) + (-1)1 + 3 \cdot 2,$$
$$2 \cdot 2 + (-1)(-1) + 3 \cdot 1) = (11, 3, 8).$$

16.6   ADJOINT AND INVERSE OF A MATRIX

If we think of a matrix A of order n as being a linear transformation of $V_n(F)$, it is clear from Theorem 16.18 that A has a multiplicative inverse A^{-1} in F_n if and only if it is nonsingular. Moreover, by Theorem 15.28, A is nonsingular if and only if $|A| \neq 0$. We now proceed to show how determinants may be used to compute the multiplicative inverse of a nonsingular matrix.

If $A = (a_{ij}) \in F_n$, we use the notation of the preceding chapter and let A_{ij} denote the cofactor of the element a_{ij} in $|A|$. That is, $A_{ij} = (-1)^{i+j} |M_{ij}|$, where M_{ij} is the minor of a_{ij} in the matrix A. We now consider a certain matrix whose elements are cofactors of elements of A. It will be convenient to make the following definition.

16.36 Definition. If $A \in F_n$, the *adjoint* of A (which we shall write as adj A) is the transpose of the matrix (A_{ij}) of F_n; that is,

$$\text{adj } A = \begin{bmatrix} A_{11} & A_{21} & \cdots & A_{n1} \\ A_{12} & A_{22} & \cdots & A_{n2} \\ \cdot & \cdot & \cdots & \cdot \\ A_{1n} & A_{2n} & \cdots & A_{nn} \end{bmatrix}.$$

We shall now prove the following result.

16.37 Theorem. *If $A \in F_n$, then*

$$A(adj\ A) = (adj\ A)A = |A| \cdot I.$$

Moreover, if A is nonsingular, then

$$A^{-1} = |A|^{-1} adj\ A.$$

By the definition of the product of two matrices, we see that the element in the pth row and qth column of $A(\text{adj } A)$ is $\sum_{k=1}^{n} a_{pk}A_{qk}$. By 15.25 and 15.22, this element has the value zero if $p \neq q$, and is just $|A|$ if $p = q$. Hence, each element of the principal diagonal of the matrix $A(\text{adj } A)$ is $|A|$, and all other elements are zero. That is,

$$A(\text{adj } A) = |A| \cdot I,$$

where I is the unity of F_n. A similar argument, using 15.23 and 15.26, will show that also

$$(\text{adj } A)A = |A| \cdot I,$$

and the first statement of the theorem is established. Using this result and the Definition 16.27 of scalar multiplication of matrices, we now see that

$$A(\,|A|^{-1} \text{adj } A) = (\,|A|^{-1} \text{adj } A)A = I,$$

and hence that $A^{-1} = |A|^{-1}$ adj A. This completes the proof of the theorem.

As an illustration of this theorem, let C be the matrix

$$\begin{bmatrix} 1 & -1 & 2 \\ 0 & 1 & 2 \\ 1 & -3 & -4 \end{bmatrix}$$

of order three over **Q**. Then a calculation shows that

$$\text{adj } C = \begin{bmatrix} 2 & -10 & -4 \\ 2 & -6 & -2 \\ -1 & 2 & 1 \end{bmatrix}.$$

The reader may now verify that

$$C(\text{adj } C) = (\text{adj } C)C = \begin{bmatrix} -2 & 0 & 0 \\ 0 & -2 & 0 \\ 0 & 0 & -2 \end{bmatrix} = -2I.$$

Accordingly, we have that

$$C^{-1} = -\tfrac{1}{2} \text{ adj } C = \begin{bmatrix} -1 & 5 & 2 \\ -1 & 3 & 1 \\ \tfrac{1}{2} & -1 & -\tfrac{1}{2} \end{bmatrix}.$$

Now that we have available the concept of the inverse of a matrix, it may be of interest to give a brief indication of how matrix methods may be used, in place of Cramer's Rule, to solve a system of n linear equations in n unknowns over a field F. Suppose that we have the following system of equations:

$$\sum_{j=1}^{n} a_{ij}x_j = b_i, \qquad\qquad (i = 1, 2, \cdots, n).$$

Let $A = (a_{ij})$ be the matrix of coefficients in this system of equations. Moreover, let us set $B = (b_1, b_2, \cdots, b_n)$ and $X = (x_1, x_2, \cdots, x_n)$, where we may now consider $x_1, x_2, \cdots, x_n$ as unknown elements of F. Then it may be verified that the above system can be written in the following simple form

16.38 $$XA' = B,$$

it being understood that A' is the transpose of A. Let us now assure that A is nonsingular. Hence, also, A' is nonsingular (why?), and if we multiply the preceding equation on the right by the multiplicative inverse of A', we obtain

$$(XA')(A')^{-1} = B(A')^{-1}.$$

However,

$$(XA')(A')^{-1} = X(A'(A')^{-1}) = X,$$

and therefore

16.39
$$X = B(A')^{-1}.$$

This, then, is the solution of the system 16.38. Of course, it is the same solution as would be obtained by use of Cramer's Rule (15.35).

As an example of the use of this notation, suppose that we have the following system of three linear equations in three unknowns over the field **Q** of rational numbers:

$$
\begin{aligned}
x_1 \qquad\quad + \ x_3 &= \quad 1, \\
-x_1 + \ x_2 - 3x_3 &= -2, \\
2x_1 + 2x_2 - 4x_3 &= \quad 3.
\end{aligned}
$$

This system can be written in the form 13.38 as follows:

$$(x_1, x_2, x_3)
\begin{bmatrix}
1 & -1 & 2 \\
0 & 1 & 2 \\
1 & -3 & -4
\end{bmatrix}
= (1, -2, 3).$$

The matrix appearing here is the matrix C whose inverse was computed above, and the solution 16.39 is therefore obtained by the following calculation:

$$(x_1, x_2, x_3) = (1, -2, 3)
\begin{bmatrix}
-1 & 5 & 2 \\
-1 & 3 & 1 \\
\frac{1}{2} & -1 & -\frac{1}{2}
\end{bmatrix}
= (5/2, -4, -3/2).$$

The unique solution is therefore $x_1 = 5/2$, $x_2 = -4$, $x_3 = -3/2$.

EXERCISES

1. Let the matrix

$$A =
\begin{bmatrix}
1 & 2 & 1 \\
-1 & 1 & -4 \\
-1 & 4 & -7
\end{bmatrix}$$

over **Q** be considered as a linear transformation of $V_3(\mathbf{Q})$. Verify that under this linear transformation both of the vectors $(2, 1, 3)$

and $(1, -1, 4)$ map into the vector $(-2, 17, -23)$. What does this fact tell us about the matrix A? Find a basis of the null space of A.

2. Find the adjoint and, if the matrix is nonsingular, the multiplicative inverse of each of the following matrices over **Q**:

(a) $\begin{bmatrix} 1 & 2 \\ 2 & -3 \end{bmatrix}$,   (b) $\begin{bmatrix} -2 & 1 \\ 0 & 2 \end{bmatrix}$,   (c) $\begin{bmatrix} 1 & -1 & 1 \\ -1 & 1 & 1 \\ 1 & 1 & -1 \end{bmatrix}$.

(d) $\begin{bmatrix} 2 & -1 & 0 \\ 1 & 3 & -2 \\ 2 & 1 & 1 \end{bmatrix}$,   (e) $\begin{bmatrix} 2 & -1 & 3 \\ 1 & 2 & -1 \\ 1 & -8 & 9 \end{bmatrix}$.

(f) $\begin{bmatrix} 0 & 0 & 2 \\ 1 & 0 & 3 \\ 3 & 4 & 2 \end{bmatrix}$,   (g) $\begin{bmatrix} 1 & 0 & -1 & 0 \\ 0 & 2 & 0 & -3 \\ 2 & 0 & 0 & 1 \\ 1 & 0 & 1 & 2 \end{bmatrix}$.

3. Use the method illustrated above to solve each of the following systems of linear equations over **Q**:

(a) $2x_1 - x_2 + x_3 = 2,$
    $3x_1 + x_2 - 2x_3 = -1,$
    $x_1 + 2x_2 + 3x_3 = 3.$

(b) $x_1 + x_2 - x_3 = -3,$
    $2x_1 - x_2 - x_3 = 8,$
    $x_1 - 3x_2 + x_3 = 17.$

4. Of the sixteen matrices of order two over the field $\mathbf{Z}_2$ verify that ten are singular and six are nonsingular.

5. Show that the group of all nonsingular matrices of order two over $\mathbf{Z}_2$ with operation multiplication is isomorphic to the symmetric group on three symbols.

16.7 EQUIVALENCE OF MATRICES

All matrices will be of order n over a field F, that is, elements of F_n. We now study again the elementary row and column operations, as defined in 14.24. There are three types, and we begin by introducing some notation that will be helpful in referring to specific elementary operations.

Let $\mathfrak{R}_{ij}$ stand for the operation of interchanging the ith and jth rows, let $\mathfrak{R}_i(c)$ stand for the operation of multiplying the ith row by the nonzero element c of F, and let $\mathfrak{R}_{ij}(d)$ stand for the operation of adding to the jth row d times the ith row, where $d \in F$.

In like manner, let $\mathfrak{C}_{ij}$, $\mathfrak{C}_i(c)$, and $\mathfrak{C}_{ij}(d)$ represent the corresponding *column* operations.

When we speak of an elementary operation, we shall mean either an elementary row operation or an elementary column operation.

It is an important fact that the effect of an elementary operation can always be canceled by an elementary operation. Suppose, first, that matrix B is obtained from matrix A by applying an elementary operation $\Re_{ij}$. Then, it is clear that the same operation $\Re_{ij}$ applied to B will yield A again. Likewise, if the operation $\Re_i(c)$ applied to A gives B, the operation $\Re_i(c^{-1})$ applied to B gives A. In like manner, if $\Re_{ij}(d)$ applied to A yields B, then $\Re_{ij}(-d)$ applied to B yields A. Of course, similar statements apply to the column operations as well.

We now make the following definition.

16.40 Definition. If $A, B \in F_n$, we say that A is *equivalent* to B, and write $A \sim B$, if it is possible to pass from A to B by a finite sequence of elementary operations.

From the observations just made it follows easily that if $A \sim B$, then $B \sim A$. This is one of the defining properties (1.12) of an equivalence relation. The other two properties are obviously satisfied, and hence $\sim$ is an equivalence relation defined on F_n.

We may remark that other equivalence relations are often defined on F_n, and we shall briefly consider another one in Section 16.9. However, in the theory of matrices it is customary to use the words "equivalence" and "equivalent" with reference to the particular equivalence relation now being considered.

Now that we have an equivalence relation defined on F_n, we may consider the equivalence sets relative to this equivalence relation. The main part of this section will be devoted to the determination of these equivalence sets. Otherwise expressed, we shall find conditions under which two elements of F_n will be equivalent. For convenience of reference, let us first state the following fact, which is a consequence of Theorem 14.25 and Definition 14.30.

16.41 Lemma. *If $A \sim B$, then rank A = rank B.*

We shall presently prove the converse of this lemma, from which it will follow that the elements of an equivalence set are just those matrices with some specified rank. Before proving this converse, we shall establish one more lemma.

If r is an integer ($0 \leq r \leq n$), let us denote by I_r the element of F_n which has a 1 in the first r places of the principal diagonal and zeros elsewhere. Clearly, I_0 is the zero and I_n the unity I of F_n. As an illustration of this notation, if $n = 3$, we have

$$I_1 = \begin{bmatrix} 1 & 0 & 0 \\ 0 & 0 & 0 \\ 0 & 0 & 0 \end{bmatrix} \quad \text{and} \quad I_2 = \begin{bmatrix} 1 & 0 & 0 \\ 0 & 1 & 0 \\ 0 & 0 & 0 \end{bmatrix}.$$

We are now in a position to state the following result.

16.42 Lemma. *If $A \in F_n$ and rank $A = r$, then $A \sim I_r$.*

The method of proof of this lemma is suggested by the procedure used in Chapter 14 to reduce a system of linear equations to an echelon system. However, we can here carry the simplification somewhat further since we may use column operations as well as row operations.

Before proceeding, we give an example to illustrate the method of proof and also to clarify the notation and terminology introduced so far. Let us consider the following matrix over the rational field **Q**:

$$D = \begin{bmatrix} 1 & 2 & -1 \\ 3 & 1 & 2 \\ 2 & -1 & 3 \end{bmatrix}.$$

First, we perform the operations $\mathcal{R}_{12}(-3)$ and $\mathcal{R}_{13}(-2)$. That is, we multiply the first row by -3 and add it to the second row, then multiply the first row by -2 and add it to the third row. Next, we perform the column operations $\mathcal{C}_{12}(-2)$ and $\mathcal{C}_{13}(1)$. At this stage, we have a 1 in the upper left-hand corner and zeros in all other positions of the first row and first column. Actually, we have the matrix

$$\begin{bmatrix} 1 & 0 & 0 \\ 0 & -5 & 5 \\ 0 & -5 & 5 \end{bmatrix}.$$

We now proceed to perform elementary operations that do not involve the first row or first column. In particular, the operation $\mathcal{R}_{23}(-1)$ makes the last row zero, and then the operation $\mathcal{R}_2(-1/5)$ places a 1 in the second row and second column. Finally, the column operation $\mathcal{C}_{23}(1)$ gives us the matrix I_2. We have therefore showed that $D \sim I_2$. Moreover, the elementary operations that we performed were as follows, and in this order:

16.43 $\mathcal{R}_{12}(-3), \ \mathcal{R}_{13}(-2), \ \mathcal{C}_{12}(-2), \ \mathcal{C}_{13}(1), \ \mathcal{R}_{23}(-1), \ \mathcal{R}_2(-1/5), \ \mathcal{C}_{23}(1).$

As a matter of fact, we could have obtained the same result by first performing all the specified row operations in the order in which they appear above, *followed* by the column operations in their specified order (or vice versa). However, we are here only concerned with the fact that there is at least one sequence of elementary operations by which we can pass from D to I_2.

Let us return to the proof of the lemma and let $A = (a_{ij})$ be an element of F_n. If $r = 0$, then $A = 0$, and the result is trivial; hence we assume that $r > 0$. Then A has at least one nonzero element. If necessary, we can use suitable operations $\mathcal{R}_{ij}$ and $\mathcal{C}_{ij}$ (interchanging rows and interchanging columns) in order to get a nonzero element in the upper left-hand corner. For convenience, let us assume that a_{11} itself is different from zero. Then a matrix of the form

$$B = \begin{bmatrix} 1 & 0 & 0 & \cdots & 0 \\ 0 & b_{22} & b_{23} & \cdots & b_{2n} \\ 0 & b_{32} & b_{33} & \cdots & b_{3n} \\ \cdot & \cdot & \cdot & \cdot & \cdot \\ 0 & b_{n2} & b_{n3} & \cdots & b_{nn} \end{bmatrix}$$

can be obtained from A by the following sequence of elementary operations: $\mathcal{R}_1(a_{11}^{-1})$, $\mathcal{R}_{12}(-a_{21})$, $\mathcal{R}_{13}(-a_{31})$, $\cdots$, $\mathcal{R}_{1n}(-a_{n1})$, $\mathcal{C}_{12}(-a_{11}^{-1}a_{12})$, $\mathcal{C}_{13}(-a_{11}^{-1}a_{13})$, $\cdots$, $\mathcal{C}_{1n}(-a_{11}^{-1}a_{1n})$.

If some element b_{ij} of B ($i \leq 2 \leq n$, $j \leq 2 \leq n$) is different from zero, we can get such a nonzero element in the second row and second column by suitable interchange of rows and of columns. Then, proceeding as above, working only with rows and columns other than the first, we can apply elementary operations to B and get a matrix of the form

$$C = \begin{bmatrix} 1 & 0 & 0 & \cdots & 0 \\ 0 & 1 & 0 & \cdots & 0 \\ 0 & 0 & c_{33} & \cdots & c_{3n} \\ 0 & 0 & c_{43} & \cdots & c_{4n} \\ \cdot & \cdot & \cdot & \cdot & \cdot \\ 0 & 0 & c_{n3} & \cdots & c_{nn} \end{bmatrix}.$$

If some c_{ij} is different from zero, this process can be repeated. We thus finally obtain a matrix of the form I_s with $s \leq n$. Now it was given that the rank of A is r, and it is obvious that the rank of I_s is s. Since we have $A \sim I_s$, Lemma 16.41 assures us that $r = s$, and the proof is complete.

We are now ready to prove the following result.

16.44 Theorem. *If $A, B \in F_n$, then $A \sim B$ if and only if rank A = rank B.*

Of course, one part of this theorem is merely Lemma 16.41. To prove the other part, suppose that rank A = rank B = r. Then, by the preceding lemma, $A \sim I_r$ and $B \sim I_r$. By the symmetric and transitive properties of the equivalence relation $\sim$, it follows at once that $A \sim B$.

We have now obtained one characterization of the equivalence sets relative to the equivalence relation $\sim$. The elements of an equivalence set $[A]$ are precisely those elements of F_n that have the same rank as A. A little later we shall obtain another characterization of these equivalence sets.

It is a fact of considerable importance in the theory of matrices that elementary operations can be effected by matrix multiplication. We shall briefly indicate how this is done, and then give a few simple consequences of this fact.

We begin by defining certain matrices of F_n as follows. Let E_{ij}, $E_i(c)$, and $E_{ij}(d)$ be the matrices obtained by applying the respective elementary operations $\mathcal{R}_{ij}$, $\mathcal{R}_i(c)$, and $\mathcal{R}_{ij}(d)$ to the matrix I. As examples, if $n = 3$, we have the following:

$$E_{12} = \begin{bmatrix} 0 & 1 & 0 \\ 1 & 0 & 0 \\ 0 & 0 & 1 \end{bmatrix}, \quad E_2(c) = \begin{bmatrix} 1 & 0 & 0 \\ 0 & c & 0 \\ 0 & 0 & 1 \end{bmatrix}, \quad E_{12}(d) = \begin{bmatrix} 1 & 0 & 0 \\ d & 1 & 0 \\ 0 & 0 & 1 \end{bmatrix}.$$

We now make the following definition.

16.45 Definition. A matrix of the form E_{ij}, $E_i(c)$, or $E_{ij}(d)$ is called an *elementary matrix*. It is understood that i and j are distinct integers from the set $\{1, 2, \cdots, n\}$, that c is a nonzero element of F, and that $d \in F$.

We may remark on the fact that we have defined elementary matrices in terms of *row* operations on I. However, the elementary column operations on I would yield the same set of matrices. In fact, if we apply the operations $\mathcal{C}_{ij}$, $\mathcal{C}_i(c)$, and $\mathcal{C}_{ij}(d)$ to I, it may be verified that we obtain E_{ij}, $E_i(c)$, and $E_{ji}(d)$, respectively. Note that although, by definition, the application of $\mathcal{R}_{ij}(d)$ to I gives $E_{ij}(d)$, the application of $\mathcal{C}_{ij}(d)$ to I yields $E_{ji}(d)$ with subscripts interchanged.

We now assert that an elementary row (column) operation on a matrix A can be achieved by multiplying A on the left (right) by an elementary matrix. More precisely, we have the following theorem.

16.46 Theorem. *The result of applying an elementary row operation $\mathcal{R}_{ij}$, $\mathcal{R}_i(c)$, or $\mathcal{R}_{ij}(d)$ to a matrix A is to obtain the matrix $E_{ij}A$, $E_i(c)A$, or $E_{ij}(d)A$, respectively. The result of applying an elementary column operation $\mathcal{C}_{ij}$, $\mathcal{C}_i(c)$ or $\mathcal{C}_{ij}(d)$ to a matrix A is to obtain the matrix AE_{ij}, $AE_i(c)$, or $AE_{ji}(d)$, respectively.*

If $A = (a_{ij})$ and $n = 3$, we may illustrate certain parts of this theorem by the following calculations. In each case, the matrix product is obviously the matrix obtained from A by the corresponding elementary operation:

$$E_{12}A = \begin{bmatrix} 0 & 1 & 0 \\ 1 & 0 & 0 \\ 0 & 0 & 1 \end{bmatrix} \begin{bmatrix} a_{11} & a_{12} & a_{13} \\ a_{21} & a_{22} & a_{23} \\ a_{31} & a_{32} & a_{33} \end{bmatrix} = \begin{bmatrix} a_{21} & a_{22} & a_{23} \\ a_{11} & a_{12} & a_{13} \\ a_{31} & a_{32} & a_{33} \end{bmatrix},$$

$$E_{12}(d)A = \begin{bmatrix} 1 & 0 & 0 \\ d & 1 & 0 \\ 0 & 0 & 1 \end{bmatrix} \begin{bmatrix} a_{11} & a_{12} & a_{13} \\ a_{21} & a_{22} & a_{23} \\ a_{31} & a_{32} & a_{33} \end{bmatrix}$$

$$= \begin{bmatrix} a_{11} & a_{12} & a_{13} \\ a_{21} + da_{11} & a_{22} + da_{12} & a_{23} + da_{13} \\ a_{31} & a_{32} & a_{33} \end{bmatrix},$$

$$AE_{12} = \begin{bmatrix} a_{11} & a_{12} & a_{13} \\ a_{21} & a_{22} & a_{23} \\ a_{31} & a_{32} & a_{33} \end{bmatrix} \begin{bmatrix} 0 & 1 & 0 \\ 1 & 0 & 0 \\ 0 & 0 & 1 \end{bmatrix} = \begin{bmatrix} a_{12} & a_{11} & a_{13} \\ a_{22} & a_{21} & a_{23} \\ a_{32} & a_{31} & a_{33} \end{bmatrix},$$

$$AE_{12}(d) = \begin{bmatrix} a_{11} & a_{12} & a_{13} \\ a_{21} & a_{22} & a_{23} \\ a_{31} & a_{32} & a_{33} \end{bmatrix} \begin{bmatrix} 1 & 0 & 0 \\ d & 1 & 0 \\ 0 & 0 & 1 \end{bmatrix} = \begin{bmatrix} a_{11} + da_{12} & a_{12} & a_{13} \\ a_{21} + da_{22} & a_{22} & a_{23} \\ a_{31} + da_{32} & a_{32} & a_{33} \end{bmatrix}.$$

By a separate consideration of each of the cases involved, the reader should have no difficulty in convincing himself of the truth of Theorem 16.46, or even in supplying a formal proof. Accordingly, we shall omit the proof.

Suppose, now, that we can pass from a matrix A to a matrix B by a finite sequence of elementary operations. The preceding theorem says that B can be obtained from A by successive multiplications by elementary matrices. As an example, consider the matrix D which is transformed into I_2 by the elementary operations 16.43. After applying $\Re_{12}(-3)$ to D we have the matrix $E_{12}(-3)D$, after applying $\Re_{13}(-2)$ to this matrix we have $E_{13}(-2)E_{12}(-3)D$, after applying the column operation $\mathcal{C}_{12}(-2)$ to this matrix we have $E_{13}(-2)E_{12}(-3)DE_{21}(-2)$, and so on. We finally obtain in this way that

16.47 $\quad E_2(-1/5)E_{23}(-1)E_{13}(-2)E_{12}(-3)DE_{21}(-2)E_{31}(1)E_{32}(1) = I_2.$

Now each elementary matrix is nonsingular since it is obtained from the nonsingular matrix I by an elementary operation. Moreover, we know by Corollary 16.20 that a product of nonsingular matrices is nonsingular. Hence, if we set

$$S = E_2(-1/5)E_{23}(-1)E_{13}(-2)E_{12}(-3)$$

and

$$T = E_{21}(-2)E_{31}(1)E_{32}(1),$$

S and T are nonsingular matrices and Equation 16.47 can be written in the form

16.48 $$SDT = I_2.$$

This is an illustration of one part of the following general theorem.

16.49 Theorem. *If $A, B \in F_n$, then $A \sim B$ if and only if there exist nonsingular matrices P and Q such that $B = PAQ$.*

If $B = PAQ$, where P and Q are nonsingular, it follows from Theorem 16.19 (ii) that A and B have the same rank, and Theorem 16.44 then shows that $A \sim B$.

Conversely, let us assume that $A \sim B$. In view of Theorem 16.46, this implies that there exist elementary matrices $P_1, P_2, \cdots, P_k$ and $Q_1, Q_2, \cdots, Q_l$ such that

$$B = P_k \cdots P_2 P_1 A Q_1 Q_2 \cdots Q_l.$$

If we set $P = P_k \cdots P_2 P_1$ and $Q = Q_1 Q_2 \cdots Q_l$, P and Q are nonsingular since they are products of nonsingular matrices, and $B = PAQ$ as required. The proof of the theorem is therefore complete.

This theorem shows that the equivalence set $[A]$ consists of all those elements of F_n of the form PAQ, where P and Q are nonsingular elements of F_n.

An important special case of some of the preceding results is that in which A is taken to be the unity I of F_n. Since I is nonsingular, Theorem 16.44 asserts that $I \sim B$ if and only if B is nonsingular. Moreover, Theorem 16.46, as applied in the proof of the preceding theorem, shows that $I \sim B$ if and only if B is expressible as a product of elementary matrices. We have then the following result.

16.50 Corollary. *A matrix is expressible as a product of elementary matrices if and only if it is nonsingular.*

16.8 THE DETERMINANT OF A PRODUCT

The results of the preceding section enable us to prove the following theorem about determinants.

16.51 Theorem. *If $A, B \in F_n$, then $|AB| = |A| \cdot |B|$.*

First, we dispose of the case in which A is singular. In view of Theorem 15.28, this means that $|A| = 0$. Moreover, by Theorem 16.19, we see that rank $(AB) < n$, so that also $|AB| = 0$. Hence, the theorem is true in this case.

We next show that the desired result is true if A is an elementary matrix. Let us state this special case as follows.

16.52 Lemma. *If E is an elementary matrix, then $|EB| = |E| \cdot |B|$.*

To prove this lemma, we consider, in turn, each of the three types of elementary matrices. Since each such matrix is obtained from I by an elementary operation, and $|I| = 1$, it follows from Theorem 15.14 that $|E_{ij}| = -1$, $|E_i(c)| = c$, and $|E_{ij}(d)| = 1$. Then, by again applying the same theorem and Theorem 16.46, we can verify each of the following:

$$|E_{ij}B| = -|B| = |E_{ij}| \cdot |B|,$$
$$|E_i(c)B| = c|B| = |E_i(c)| \cdot |B|,$$
$$|E_{ij}(d)B| = |B| = |E_{ij}(d)| \cdot |B|,$$

and the lemma is established.

Suppose now that A is an arbitrary nonsingular matrix. Corollary 16.50 then assures us that it can be expressed as a product of elementary matrices. The desired result is now easily completed by induction. Let S_m be the statement "For every matrix B of F_n, and for every matrix A of F_n which can be expressed as a product of m elementary matrices, we have $|AB| = |A| \cdot |B|$." Then S_1 is true by the preceding lemma. Let us now assume that S_k is true and prove that S_{k+1} is true. Suppose, then, that $A = E_1 E_2 \cdots E_{k+1}$, where these are elementary matrices. It follows that

$$
\begin{aligned}
|AB| = |E_1(E_2 E_3 \cdots E_{k+1} B)| &= |E_1| \cdot |E_2 E_3 \cdots E_{k+1} B| & \text{(by } S_1\text{)} \\
&= |E_1| \cdot |E_2 E_3 \cdots E_{k+1}| \cdot |B| & \text{(by } S_k\text{)} \\
&= |E_1 E_2 \cdots E_{k+1}| \cdot |B| & \text{(by } S_1\text{)} \\
&= |A| \cdot |B|.
\end{aligned}
$$

Hence, S_{k+1} is true, and it follows that S_m is true for every positive integer m. The theorem is therefore established.

We may observe that an alternate way of stating the result just proved is to say that multiplication is preserved under the mapping $\theta : F_n \to F$ defined by $A\theta = |A|$, $A \in F_n$. Clearly, $I\theta = 1$, where 1 is the unity of F and, moreover, we know that an element A of F_n has a multiplicative inverse in F_n if and only if $|A|$ has a multiplicative inverse in

F (that is, is not zero). Finally, we state the following corollary of the preceding theorem.

16.53   Corollary.   *If* A *is a nonsingular element of* F_n, *then* $|A^{-1}| = |A|^{-1}$.

EXERCISES

1.   For each of the following matrices over **Q**, write down a sequence of elementary operations that will reduce it to the form I_r:

(a) $\begin{bmatrix} 1 & -1 \\ 2 & 3 \end{bmatrix}$,

(b) $\begin{bmatrix} 2 & -1 \\ 4 & -2 \end{bmatrix}$,

(c) $\begin{bmatrix} 0 & -1 & 2 \\ 1 & 2 & -1 \\ 1 & -1 & 5 \end{bmatrix}$,

(d) $\begin{bmatrix} 1 & -2 & 3 \\ 2 & 1 & 4 \\ -2 & 1 & 2 \end{bmatrix}$.

2.   Show that the multiplicative inverse of each elementary matrix is also an elementary matrix.

3.   Let $E_1E_2 \cdots E_s$ be a product of elementary matrices. Since $E_1E_2 \cdots E_s = E_1E_2 \cdots E_sI$, Theorem 16.46 says that we can compute this product by first applying the elementary row operation corresponding to E_s to the matrix I, then the elementary row operation corresponding to E_{s-1} to this new matrix, and so on. Use this method to compute the matrices S and T occurring in 16.48.

4.   For each matrix A of Exercise 1, find nonsingular matrices P and Q such that $PAQ = I_r$.

5.   Express each of the nonsingular matrices of Exercise 1 as a product of elementary matrices.

6.   By actual calculation of the determinants involved, verify Theorem 16.51 for the following matrices:

$$A = \begin{bmatrix} 3 & -1 & 0 \\ 1 & 0 & 3 \\ -2 & 1 & 1 \end{bmatrix}, \quad B = \begin{bmatrix} 2 & 1 & -3 \\ 0 & 1 & 2 \\ 1 & 3 & 2 \end{bmatrix}.$$

7.   Let us write $A \equiv B$ if there exist nonsingular matrices P and Q such that $B = PAQ$. Use this definition to verify that $\equiv$ is an equivalence relation on F_n. (Of course, Theorem 16.49 shows indirectly that $\equiv$ coincides with the equivalence relation $\sim$.)

8. Let us define $A \approx B$ to mean that it is possible to pass from A to B by a finite sequence of elementary *row* operations. Prove each of the following:

   (a) $\approx$ is an equivalence relation defined on F_n,

   (b) $A \approx B$ if and only if there exists a nonsingular matrix P such that $B = PA$,

   (c) If A is nonsingular, then $A \approx I$.

9. Show that if A can be reduced to I by a sequence of elementary *row* operations, then A^{-1} is the matrix obtained by starting with the matrix I and applying in turn the same sequence of elementary row operations.

10. Use the method of the previous problem to compute the multiplicative inverse of the following matrix over **Q**:

$$\begin{bmatrix} 3 & 1 & -2 \\ 2 & 0 & 3 \\ -1 & 1 & -6 \end{bmatrix}.$$

16.9 SIMILARITY OF MATRICES

We now consider the problem, suggested by the results of Section 16.4, of determining the relationship which holds between the matrices of a linear transformation of a vector space relative to two different ordered bases of the space.

Throughout this section $X_1, X_2, \cdots, X_n$ will denote a fixed ordered basis of a vector space V of dimension $n > 0$ over a field F, and L will denote the algebra of all linear transformations of V. The word *matrix* will mean an element of F_n.

If $\alpha \in L$ and

16.54 $$X_i \alpha = \sum_{j=1}^{n} a_{ij} X_j, \qquad (i = 1, 2, \cdots, n),$$

we showed in Section 16.4 that the mapping $\alpha \rightarrow A = (a_{ij})$ is an isomorphism of L onto F_n. Let us now denote this isomorphism by ϕ, that is, $\phi: L \rightarrow F_n$ is the mapping defined by $\alpha\phi = A$, where α and A are related by 16.54. We have called A the matrix of α relative to the ordered basis $X_1, X_2, \cdots, X_n$ of V.

Now suppose that $Y_1, Y_2, \cdots, Y_n$ is another ordered basis of V and that

$$Y_i \alpha = \sum_{j=1}^{n} a_{ij}^* Y_j, \qquad (i = 1, 2, \cdots, n).$$

Then $A^* = (a_{ij}^*)$ is the matrix of the linear transformation α relative to the ordered basis $Y_1, Y_2, \cdots, Y_n$. We propose to determine how the matrices A and A^* are related.

By Corollory 16.14, there exists a unique linear transformation $\mathfrak{B}$ of V such that

16.55 $$X_i \mathfrak{B} = Y_i, \qquad (i = 1, 2, \cdots, n).$$

Then, if the c_i are elements of F, we have that

$$\left(\sum c_i X_i \right) \mathfrak{B} = \sum c_i (X_i \mathfrak{B}) = \sum c_i Y_i$$

and, since the Y's also are a basis of V, we see that $V\mathfrak{B} = V$. Thus $\mathfrak{B}$ is nonsingular and, by Theorem 16.18, it has a multiplicative inverse $\mathfrak{B}^{-1}$ in L. Clearly,

$$Y_i \mathfrak{B}^{-1} = X_i, \qquad (i = 1, 2, \cdots, n),$$

and we have

$$X_i (\mathfrak{B} \alpha \mathfrak{B}^{-1}) = (X_i \mathfrak{B})(\alpha \mathfrak{B}^{-1}) = Y_i (\alpha \mathfrak{B}^{-1}) = (Y_i \alpha) \mathfrak{B}^{-1}$$

$$= \left(\sum_{j=1}^{n} a_{ij}^* Y_j \right) \mathfrak{B}^{-1} = \sum_{j=1}^{n} a_{ij}^* X_j \qquad (i = 1, 2, \cdots, n).$$

This shows that the matrix of the linear transformation $\mathfrak{B} \alpha \mathfrak{B}^{-1}$ relative to the ordered basis $X_1, X_2, \cdots, X_n$ is precisely A^*. In the notation introduced above we therefore have

$$(\mathfrak{B} \alpha \mathfrak{B}^{-1})\phi = A^*.$$

But since ϕ is an isomorphism of L onto F_n, it follows that

$$(\mathfrak{B} \alpha \mathfrak{B}^{-1})\phi = (\mathfrak{B}\phi)(\alpha\phi)(\mathfrak{B}\phi)^{-1} = A^*.$$

If we denote $\alpha\phi$ by A and $\mathfrak{B}\phi$ by B, this equation shows that

16.56 $$BAB^{-1} = A^*.$$

We have therefore shown that if A and $A*$ are matrices of the same linear transformation relative to two different ordered bases, then there exists a nonsingular matrix B such that 16.56 holds.

Conversely, suppose we are given matrices A, $A*$, and a nonsingular matrix B such that Equation 16.56 holds. Suppose that α and $\mathcal{B}$ are the linear transformations of V such that $\alpha\phi = A$ and $\mathcal{B}\phi = B$. If we *define* the Y's by

$$Y_i = X_i\mathcal{B}, \qquad\qquad (i = 1, 2, \cdots, n),$$

Theorem 16.18 shows that Y_1, Y_2, $\cdots$, Y_n is an ordered basis of V. Moreover, our calculations above show that BAB^{-1} is the matrix of α relative to the ordered basis Y_1, Y_2, $\cdots$, Y_n of V. Since we are now assuming Equation 16.56, we have completed the proof of the following theorem.

16.57 Theorem.

(i) *If A is the matrix of a linear transformation α relative to an ordered basis $X_1, X_2, \cdots, X_n$ of V, and $A*$ is the matrix of the same linear transformation relative to an ordered basis Y_1, $Y_2, \cdots$, Y_n of V, then there exists a nonsingular matrix B such that $BAB^{-1} = A*$. In fact, B is the matrix of the nonsingular linear transformation, relative to the ordered basis $X_1, X_2, \cdots, X_n$ of V, defined by $X_i\mathcal{B} = Y_i$, $(i = 1, 2, \cdots, n)$.*

(ii) *Conversely, if matrices A and $A*$ are given and there exists a nonsingular matrix B such that $BAB^{-1} = A*$, then A and $A*$ are matrices of the same linear transformation relative to properly chosen ordered bases of V.*

Let us illustrate the above calculations by returning to Example 1 of Section 16.4. Here, using the present notation, we have $n = 2$, $V = V_2(\mathbf{R})$, $X_1 = (1, 0)$, $X_2 = (0, 1)$, $Y_1 = (1, 1)$, and $Y_2 = (-1, 1)$. Moreover,

$$A = \begin{bmatrix} 3 & 1 \\ 1 & -2 \end{bmatrix}, \quad A* = \begin{bmatrix} 3/2 & -5/2 \\ -5/2 & -1/2 \end{bmatrix}.$$

We proceed to compute the nonsingular matrix B such that $BAB^{-1} = A*$. Using 16.55 to define the linear transformation $\mathcal{B}$, we obtain

$$(1, 0)\mathcal{B} = (1, 1) = (1, 0) + (0, 1),$$
$$(0, 1)\mathcal{B} = (-1, 1) = -(1, 0) + (0, 1).$$

Thus the matrix B of $\mathcal{B}$ relative to the ordered basis $(1, 0)$, $(0, 1)$ of $V_2(R)$ is as follows:

$$B = \begin{bmatrix} 1 & 1 \\ -1 & 1 \end{bmatrix}.$$

This is the desired matrix B. The reader may verify that

$$B^{-1} = \begin{bmatrix} \frac{1}{2} & -\frac{1}{2} \\ \frac{1}{2} & \frac{1}{2} \end{bmatrix}$$

and then that $BAB^{-1} = A^*$.

We still have not justified the title of this section. Let us therefore make the following definition.

16.58 Definition. If $C, D \in F_n$, we say that C is *similar* to D if there exists a nonsingular element T of F_n such that $C = TDT^{-1}$.

We leave as an exercise the proof that similarity is an equivalence relation defined on F_n. By Theorem 16.57, the matrices in an equivalence set are precisely the matrices of a single linear transformation relative to all possible ordered bases of V. In particular, two elements of F_n are similar if and only if they are the matrices of the same linear transformation relative to two ordered bases of V. However, it is a fairly difficult problem to develop a constructive method of determining whether or not two given matrices are similar. A few partial results will be obtained in the remainder of this chapter, but we shall refer to texts on linear algebra for a full treatment of the subject.

One simple fact which follows readily from Theorem 16.57 and Corollary 16.53 is the following.

16.59 Corollary. *If C and D are similar elements of F_n, then $|C| = |D|$.*

EXERCISES

1. Prove that similarity of matrices, as defined in 16.58, satisfies the three defining properties (1.12) of an equivalence relation.

2. In Example 2 of Section 16.4 we found matrices of a given linear transformation relative to two different ordered bases of a certain vector space. If we now call these matrices A and A^*, find a nonsingular matrix B such that $BAB^{-1} = A^*$.

3. Show, by an example, that two matrices having the same determinant need not be similar. [Hint: Take one of the matrices to be I.]

4. Let V be the vector space of all polynomials in an indeterminate x over $\mathbf{Q}$ of degree no more than two, together with the zero polynomial. Let $\alpha: V \to V$ be the linear transformation of V defined by $f(x)\alpha = f(x + 1)$. (i) Find the matrix A of α relative to the ordered basis 1, x, x^2 of V. (ii) Find the matrix A^* of α relative to the ordered basis x^2, x, 1 of V. (iii) Find a nonsingular matrix B such that $BAB^{-1} = A^*$.

5. Let $A = (a_{ij})$ be the matrix of a linear transformation α of $V_n(F)$ relative to the ordered basis of unit vectors E_1, E_2, $\cdots$, E_n. If $B = (b_{ij})$ is a nonsingular element of F_n, verify that the matrix of α relative to the ordered basis B_1, B_2, $\cdots$, B_n consisting of the row vectors of B is BAB^{-1}.

16.10   INVARIANT SUBSPACES

The following concept is an important one in the further study of linear transformations.

16.60   Definition.   Let α be a linear transformation of the vector space V over the field F. A subspace V_1 of V with the property that $V_1\alpha \subseteq V_1$ is said to be *invariant under* α.

If the subspace V_1 of V is invariant under the linear transformation α of V, it is clear that α induces a linear transformation α_1 of V_1 defined by $X\alpha_1 = X\alpha$ for each X in V_1. We shall often refer to this linear transformation α_1 as "α restricted to V_1" or as "α acting on V_1."

There are two trivial subspaces of V, namely $\{0\}$ and V itself, both of which are clearly invariant under every linear transformation of V. Let us now assume that V has finite dimension $n > 0$ and that V_1 is a subspace of dimension m which is invariant under the linear transformation α of V. We shall assume that $0 < m < n$ since $m = 0$ and $m = n$ give the trivial subspaces just mentioned, and there is not much more to be said about them. By Theorem 12.24, there exists a basis $\{X_1, X_2, \cdots, X_n\}$ of V with the property that $\{X_1, X_2, \cdots, X_m\}$ is a basis of V_1. Now since V_1 is invariant under α, it follows that each of $X_1\alpha$, $X_2\alpha$, $\cdots$, $X_m\alpha$ is expressible as a linear combination of $X_1, X_2, \cdots, X_m$. In this case, Equations 16.23 which define the matrix A of the linear transformation α relative to the given basis of V take the form

$$X_1 \alpha = a_{11}X_1 + a_{12}X_2 + \cdots + a_{1m}X_m,$$
$$X_2 \alpha = a_{21}X_1 + a_{22}X_2 + \cdots + a_{2m}X_m,$$
$$\cdot \quad \cdot \quad \cdot \quad \cdot \quad \cdot \quad \cdot \quad \cdot \quad \cdot \quad \cdot \quad \cdot$$

16.61
$$X_m \alpha = a_{m1}X_1 + a_{m2}X_2 + \cdots + a_{mm}X_m,$$
$$X_{m+1} \alpha = a_{m+1\,1}X_1 + a_{m+1\,2}X_2 + \cdots\cdots + a_{m+1\,n}X_n,$$
$$\cdot \quad \cdot \quad \cdot \quad \cdot \quad \cdot \quad \cdot \quad \cdot \quad \cdot \quad \cdot \quad \cdot \quad \cdot \quad \cdot \quad \cdot$$
$$X_n \alpha = a_{n1}X_1 + a_{n2}X_2 + \cdots\cdots + a_{nn}X_n.$$

Thus, if we set $A = (a_{ij})$, we see that $a_{ij} = 0$ for $i = 1, 2, \cdots, m$ provided $j > m$. A convenient way of indicating the form of this matrix A is to write

16.62
$$A = \begin{bmatrix} A_1 & O \\ B & C \end{bmatrix}$$

where

16.63
$$A_1 = \begin{bmatrix} a_{11} & a_{12} & \cdots & a_{1m} \\ a_{21} & a_{22} & \cdots & a_{2m} \\ \cdot & \cdot & \cdot & \cdot \\ a_{m1} & a_{m2} & \cdots & a_{mm} \end{bmatrix},$$

B is a matrix with $n - m$ rows and m columns, C is a matrix with $n - m$ rows and $n - m$ columns, and O is a matrix with m rows and $n - m$ columns, all of whose elements are zero.

It is clear from Equations 16.61 that the matrix A_1 appearing in the upper left corner of A is the matrix of α restricted to V_1, relative to the ordered basis $X_1, X_2, \cdots, X_m$ of V_1.

As a simple illustration of these concepts, let α be the linear transformation of $V_3(F)$ defined by

16.64
$$(x_1, x_2, x_3) \alpha = (x_1 + 2x_2 + x_3, \; x_1 + x_2 + x_3, \; x_3),$$

and let V_1 be the subspace of $V_3(F)$ consisting of all elements of the form $(x_1, x_2, 0)$. Since, by 16.64, we see that

$$(x_1, x_2, 0) \alpha = (x_1 + 2x_2, \; x_1 + x_2, \; 0),$$

it is clear that V_1 is invariant under α. In this simple case, the unit vectors E_1, E_2, E_3 of $V_3(F)$ are such that E_1, E_2 is a basis of V_1, and Equations 16.61 become in this case:

$$E_1 \alpha = E_1 + E_2,$$
$$E_2 \alpha = 2E_1 + E_2,$$
$$E_3 \alpha = E_1 + E_2 + E_3.$$

Thus the matrix A of $\mathfrak{a}$ relative to the ordered basis E_1, E_2, E_3 of $V_3(F)$ is as follows:

$$A = \begin{bmatrix} 1 & 1 & 0 \\ 2 & 1 & 0 \\ 1 & 1 & 1 \end{bmatrix}.$$

This is the desired form 16.62 with

$$A_1 = \begin{bmatrix} 1 & 1 \\ 2 & 1 \end{bmatrix}, \quad B = [1 \ 1], \quad C = [1], \quad O = \begin{bmatrix} 0 \\ 0 \end{bmatrix}.$$

Moreover, as is to be expected from the general discussion above, A_1 is the matrix of $\mathfrak{a}$ restricted to V_1, relative to the ordered basis E_1, E_2 of V_1.

A situation of special interest is that in which V is the direct sum of two invariant subspaces. Suppose that $V = V_1 \oplus V_2$, with both V_1 and V_2 being invariant under the linear transformation $\mathfrak{a}$. If dim $V_1 = m$, then dim $V_2 = n - m$. Let X_1, X_2, $\cdots$, X_m be an ordered basis of V_1 and X_{m+1}, X_{m+2}, $\cdots$, X_n an ordered basis of V_2. Then (see Exercise 4 at end of Section 12.10)

16.65
$$X_1, X_2, \cdots, X_n$$

is an ordered basis of V, and Equations 16.61 determining the matrix A of $\mathfrak{a}$ relative to the ordered basis 16.65 of V are such that also $a_{ij} = 0$ for $i = m + 1, \cdots, n$ provided $j = 1, 2, \cdots, m$. In this case, the matrix A is of the form

16.66
$$A = \begin{bmatrix} A_1 & O \\ O & A_2 \end{bmatrix},$$

where A_i is the matrix of $\mathfrak{a}$ restricted to $V_i (i = 1, 2)$. Of course, A_i is a square matrix of order equal to the dimension of V_i.

A convenient way of writing the matrix A given by 16.66 is as follows:

$$A = \text{diag}(A_1, A_2).$$

The type of argument used above will yield the following general result whose proof we omit.

16.67 Theorem. *Let $\mathfrak{a}$ be a linear transformation of the vector space V of finite dimension. If*

$$V = V_1 \oplus V_2 \oplus \cdots \oplus V_r,$$

where each V_i is invariant under α then the matrix A of α relative to a suitably chosen ordered basis of V is of the form

$$A = \mathrm{diag}(A_1, A_2, \cdots, A_r),$$

where A_i is the matrix of α restricted to V_i (relative to an ordered basis of V_i which is a part of the chosen basis of V).

If a linear transformation α of a vector space V is given, we have as yet no information as to how one might try to find subspaces of V which are invariant under α. After developing suitable machinery, we shall make a little progress in this direction in the following section.

16.11 POLYNOMIALS IN A LINEAR TRANSFORMATION

Throughout this section we shall continue to let α be a given linear transformation of a vector space V of finite dimension $n > 0$ over a field F, and let L be the algebra of all linear transformations of V.

Let $f(x)$ be an element of the polynomial ring $F[x]$ in an indeterminate x over F. If

$$f(x) = a_0 + a_1 x + \cdots + a_k x^k,$$

we shall denote by $f(\alpha)$ the linear transformation

$$a_0 \mathcal{I} + a_1 \alpha + \cdots + a_k \alpha^k$$

of V, and call $f(\alpha)$ a *polynomial in α over F*. Let us denote by $F[\alpha]$ the set of all polynomials in α over F. Then $F[\alpha]$ is an algebra over F, actually a subalgebra of L. Moreover, $F[\alpha]$ is a *commutative* subalgebra of L. That is, multiplication is commutative in $F[\alpha]$ although it is not generally commutative in L.

The mapping $\theta: F[x] \to F[\alpha]$ defined by $f(x)\theta = f(\alpha)$ is a ring homomorphism * of $F[x]$ onto $F[\alpha]$. The Fundamental Theorem on Ring Homomorphisms then asserts that $F[\alpha] \cong F[x]/\ker \theta$. Now the ideal $\ker \theta$ in $F[x]$ consists of those polynomials $f(x)$ of $F[x]$ such that $f(\alpha) = 0$. We first prove that $\ker \theta \neq \{0\}$.

16.68 Theorem. *There exists a nonzero polynomial $f(x)$ of $F[x]$ such that $f(\alpha) = 0$.*

---

* Since scalar multiplication is also preserved under the mapping θ, we might more precisely refer to θ as a homomorphism of the *algebra $F[x]$* onto the *algebra $F[A]$*.

PROOF: By Theorem 12.42, the algebra L (considered as a vector space over F) has dimension n^2. Accordingly, the subalgebra $F[\alpha]$ of L has dimension no greater than n^2. It follows that the $n^2 + 1$ elements $\mathcal{I}$, α, α^2, $\cdots$, α^{n^2} of $F[\alpha]$ are linearly dependent over F. Thus there exists a nonzero polynomial $f(x)$ of degree no greater than n^2 such that $f(\alpha) = 0$. This $f(x)$ is in ker θ and therefore ker $\theta \neq \{0\}$.

Since every ideal in $F[x]$ is a principal ideal, we may write ker. $\theta = (m(x))$, where $m(x)$ is a polynomial of least degree such that $m(A) = 0$. Clearly, $m(\alpha) = 0$ implies that $cm(\alpha) = 0$ for every element c of F, so there is no loss of generality in assuming that $m(x)$ is a *monic* polynomial.

16.69 Definition. The unique monic polynomial $m(x)$ over F of least degree such that $f(\alpha) = 0$ is called the *minimal polynomial of* α.

We have only proved that $m(x)$ exists and that deg $m(x) \leq n^2$. It is true that always deg $m(x) \leq n$, but this is not important for our present purposes.

We shall frequently use without specific reference the following fact which is a consequence of the above observations: If $m(x)$ is the minimal polynomial of α and $g(x) \in F[x]$, then $g(\alpha) = 0$ if and only if $m(x)$ divides $g(x)$ (which we shall write $m(x) \mid g(x)$, a notation previously used in the case of integers).

We shall next prove the following result.

16.70 Theorem. *Let $m(x)$ be the minimal polynomial of the linear transformation α. Then α is nonsingular if and only if the constant term in $m(x)$ is different from zero.*

PROOF: Let

$$m(x) = c_0 + c_1 x + \cdots + c_{k-1} x^{k-1} + x^k$$

be the minimal polynomial of α, and let us first assume that $c_0 \neq 0$. If we set

$$\mathcal{B} = -[c_0^{-1} c_1 \mathcal{I} + c_0^{-1} c_2 \alpha + \cdots + c_0^{-1} \alpha^{k-1}],$$

then using the fact that $m(\alpha) = 0$, it follows by a straightforward calculation that $\alpha \mathcal{B} = \mathcal{B}\alpha = \mathcal{I}$. Thus α has a multiplicative inverse and is therefore nonsingular.

Next, suppose that $c_0 = 0$ and let us show that α is singular. Since $m(\alpha) = 0$, we now have that

$$\alpha(c_1 \mathcal{I} + c_2 \alpha + \cdots + c_{k-1}\alpha^{k-2} + \alpha^{k-1}) = 0.$$

The second factor on the left side of this equation cannot be zero, for otherwise we would have a polynomial $g(x)$ of degree $k - 1$ such that $g(\alpha) = 0$, and this is impossible in view of the fact that $m(x)$ is the minimal polynomial of α. Accordingly, α is a divisor of zero in L and therefore cannot have a multiplicative inverse in L. This shows that α is singular and completes the proof of the theorem.

We may remark that although we have been considering the minimal polynomial of a *linear transformation*, in view of the previously established isomorphism of the algebra of linear transformations of a vector space of order n over F and the algebra F_n of all matrices of order n over F, we could just as well speak of the minimal polynomial of a *matrix*. In fact, in a numerical case, it is often simpler to work with a matrix than with the corresponding linear transformation.

The following lemma will be useful in obtaining some relationships between the concept of minimal polynomial and that of invariant subspace.

16.71 Lemma. *Let α be a linear transformation of the vector space V of finite dimension, and suppose that $V = V_1 \oplus V_2$, with both V_1 and V_2 being invariant under α. Let α_i $(i = 1, 2)$ be the linear transformation α restricted to V_i, and suppose that $m_i(x)$ is the minimal polynomial of α_i. Then the minimal polynomial of α is the least common multiple of $m_1(x)$ and $m_2(x)$.*

PROOF: Let $m(x)$ be the minimal polynomial of α. Then, $m(\alpha) = 0$ implies that $Xm(\alpha) = 0$ for each X in V. In particular, $Xm(\alpha) = 0$ for each X in V_1, that is, $m(\alpha_1) = 0$ and it therefore follows that $m_1(x) \mid m(x)$. Similarly, we have that $m_2(x) \mid m(x)$.

Now suppose that $f(x) \in F[x]$ such that $m_1(x) \mid f(x)$ and $m_2(x) \mid f(x)$. Since $m_i(\alpha_i) = 0$, it follows that $Xf(\alpha_i) = 0$ for every X in V_i $(i = 1, 2)$. Now if $Y \in V$, we have $Y = Y_1 + Y_2$, with $Y_i \in V_i$. Hence

$$Yf(\alpha) = Y_1 f(\alpha) + Y_2 f(\alpha) = Y_1 f(\alpha_1) + Y_2 f(\alpha_2) = 0.$$

This implies that $f(\alpha) = 0$ and it follows that $m(x) \mid f(x)$. By definition of the least common multiple, these calculations show that $m(x)$ is indeed the least common multiple of $m_1(x)$ and $m_2(x)$, completing the proof.

We next prove another lemma as follows.

16.72 Lemma. *Let α be a linear transformation of the vector space V of finite dimension over a field F, and let $m(x)$ be the minimal polynomial of α. If $m(x) = f(x)g(x)$, where $f(x)$ and $g(x)$ are monic polynomials of positive* degrees with $(f(x), g(x)) = 1$, then there exist subspaces V_1 and V_2 of V such that the following are true:

(i) V_1 and V_2 are invariant under α.

(ii) $V = V_1 \oplus V_2$.

(iii) The minimal polynomial of α acting on V_1 is $f(x)$ and the minimal polynomial of α acting on V_2 is $g(x)$.

PROOF: We define subspaces V_1 and V_2 of V as follows and show that they have the specified properties:

$$V_1 = \{X \mid X \in V, \quad Xf(\alpha) = 0\},$$
$$V_2 = \{X \mid X \in V, \quad Xg(\alpha) = 0\}.$$

Otherwise expressed, V_1 and V_2 are, respectively, the null spaces of the linear transformations $f(\alpha)$ and $g(\alpha)$.

To prove (i), we observe that if $X \in V_1$, then $(X\alpha)f(\alpha) = (Xf(\alpha))\alpha = 0\alpha = 0$, and $X\alpha \in V_1$. Similarly, V_2 is invariant under α.

We next pass to the proof of (ii). Since $(f(x), g(x)) = 1$, there exist polynomials $r(x)$ and $s(x)$ of $F[x]$ such that $1 = r(x)f(x) + s(x)g(x)$, and it follows from this equation that $\mathcal{I} = r(\alpha)f(\alpha) + s(\alpha)g(\alpha)$. Hence, if $X \in V$, we have

16.73 $X = X\mathcal{I} = Xr(\alpha)f(\alpha) + Xs(\alpha)g(\alpha).$

But since the minimal polynomial $m(x)$ of α is equal to $f(x)g(x)$, it follows that

$$Xr(\alpha)f(\alpha) \in V_2 \quad \text{and} \quad Xs(\alpha)g(\alpha) \in V_1;$$

hence the preceding equation shows that $V = V_1 + V_2$. To show that this sum is direct, suppose that $X_1 + X_2 = 0$, with $X_1 \in V_1$ and $X_2 \in V_2$. Thus $X_1f(\alpha) = 0$ and $X_2g(\alpha) = 0$. From Equation 16.73 it follows that $X_1 = X_1s(\alpha)g(\alpha)$ and that $X_2 = X_2r(\alpha)f(\alpha)$. We therefore have

16.74 $X_1s(\alpha)g(\alpha) + X_2r(\alpha)f(\alpha) = 0.$

Multiplying by $s(\alpha)g(\alpha)$ on the right, we obtain

$$X_1[s(\alpha)g(\alpha)]^2 = 0.$$

But

$$X_1 = X_1s(\alpha)g(\alpha) = X_1[s(\alpha)g(\alpha)]^2,$$

and we conclude that $X_1 = 0$. Similarly, we may show that $X_2 = 0$, and the sum $V_1 + V_2$ is a direct sum, as we wished to show.

To prove (iii), let us denote by α_i the linear transformation α restricted to V_i, and let $m_i(x)$ be the minimal polynomial of α_i. By definition of V_1, $Xf(\alpha) = 0$ for every X in V_1, and this fact simply asserts that $f(\alpha_1)$ is the zero linear transformation on V_1, that is, that $f(\alpha_1) = 0$. This then implies that $m_1(x) \mid f(x)$. In like manner, it may be verified that $m_2(x) \mid g(x)$.

Now if $Y \in V$, we may write $Y = Y_1 + Y_2$, where $Y_i \in V_i$. Then

$$
\begin{aligned}
Ym_1(\alpha)m_2(\alpha) &= Y_1m_1(\alpha)m_2(\alpha) + Y_2m_1(\alpha)m_2(\alpha) \\
&= Y_1m_1(\alpha_1)m_2(\alpha_1) + Y_2m_1(\alpha_2)m_2(\alpha_2) \\
&= 0,
\end{aligned}
$$

since $m_i(x)$ is the minimal polynomial of α_i $(i = 1, 2)$. Hence $m_1(\alpha)m_2(\alpha) = 0$ and, since the minimal polynomial of A is $f(x)g(x)$, it follows that $f(x)g(x) \mid m_1(x)m_2(x)$. But we have already proved that $m_1(x) \mid f(x)$ and that $m_2(x) \mid g(x)$. Since all these polynomials are monic, it may be shown that $f(x) = m_1(x)$ and $g(x) = m_2(x)$. We leave the verification of this fact as an exercise. This completes the proof of the lemma.

We now briefly apply the results just obtained to a more general situation as follows. Let α be a linear transformation of the vector space V of finite dimension over the field F, and let $m(x)$ be the minimal polynomial of α. Then, by Theorem 10.36, we may write

16.75 $m(x) = [p_1(x)]^{n_1}[p_2(x)]^{n_2} \cdots [p_k(x)]^{n_k}$,

where the n_i and k are positive integers and the $p_i(x)$ are the distinct monic divisors of $m(x)$ which are prime over F. We may now apply the preceding lemma to establish the following result.

16.76 Theorem. *If the linear transformation α of V has minimal polynomial $m(x)$ which can be factored as in 16.75, then there exist subspaces V_i $(i = 1, 2, \cdots, k)$ of V, all of which are invariant under α, such that*

$$V = V_1 \oplus V_2 \oplus \cdots \oplus V_k.$$

Moreover, if α_i denotes the linear transformation α restricted to V_i, the minimal polynomial of α_i is $[p_i(x)]^{n_i}$ for $i = 1, 2, \cdots, k$.

PROOF: If the number k of distinct monic prime factors of $m(x)$ is one, there is nothing to prove, and the case in which $k = 2$ is disposed of by the preceding lemma. We now complete the proof by induction on k. Suppose, as an induction hypothesis, that the stated result is true for every linear transformation (of any vector space of finite dimension) whose minimal polynomial has $k - 1$ distinct prime factors, and let α be a linear transformation whose minimal polynomial has k distinct prime factors (given in 16.75). Now, for the moment, let $f(x) = [p_1(x)]^{n_1}$ and

$$g(x) = [p_2(x)]^{n_2} \cdots [p_k(x)]^{n_k}.$$

Then $(f(x), g(x)) = 1$ and we apply the preceding lemma to obtain subspaces V_1 and V'_1 of V, both invariant under α, and such that

$$V = V_1 \oplus V'_1.$$

By the lemma, the minimal polynomial of α restricted to V_1 is $f(x)$ and the minimal polynomial of α restricted to V'_1 is $g(x)$. Let α' denote the linear transformation α restricted to V'_1. Since the minimal polynomial of α' has $k - 1$ distinct monic prime factors, the induction hypothesis assures us that there exist subspaces $V_2, \cdots, V_k$ of V'_1, all of them invariant under α' and such that both of the following are true:

(i) $V'_1 = V_2 \oplus \cdot \cdot \oplus V_k,$

(ii) The minimal polynomial of α' restricted to V_i is $[p_i(x)]^{n_i}$ for $i = 2, 3, \cdots, k.$

Now α' is itself the restriction of α to V'_1, so α restricted to V_i is identical with α' restricted to V_i for $i = 2, 3, \cdots, k$. We leave as an exercise the verification that since $V = V_1 \oplus V'_1$, it follows from (i) above that

$$V = V_1 \oplus V_2 \oplus \cdots \oplus V_k.$$

This completes the proof of the theorem.

We may remark that, in view of Theorem 16.67, if the hypotheses of Theorem 16.76 are satisfied, the matrix of α relative to a properly chosen basis of V is of the form $\mathrm{diag}(A_1, A_2, \cdots, A_k)$, where α_i is the matrix of α restricted to V_i.

Our results show that in any further analysis of linear transformations, we could restrict attention to the special case in which the minimal polynomial of the linear transformation is a power of a prime polynomial. However, we shall not go further into these questions. Actually, the procedure of the present section is not yet very helpful in a numerical situation since we have not developed a method for calculating the minimal polynomial—we have only proved its existence. A few simple special cases in which the calculations can be carried out directly will appear in the following list of exercises.

EXERCISES

1. If $A = \begin{bmatrix} a & b \\ c & d \end{bmatrix}$ is a matrix of order two over the field **Q**, do each of the following:

    (i) Show that the minimal polynomial of A is of the first degree if and only if A is a *scalar matrix*, that is, of the form rI for some $r \in$ **Q**.

    (ii) If $h(x) = x^2 - (a + d)x + ad - bc$, verify that $h(A) = 0$.

    (iii) If A is not a scalar matrix, prove that the minimal polynomial of A is $h(x)$.

2. Use the result of the preceding exercise to write down the minimal polynomial of each of the following matrices over **Q**:

$$\begin{bmatrix} 1 & 2 \\ 1 & 0 \end{bmatrix}, \quad \begin{bmatrix} 1 & 1 \\ -1 & 2 \end{bmatrix}.$$

3. Let $E_1 = (1, 0)$ and $E_2 = (0, 1)$ be the unit vectors of $V_2(\mathbf{Q})$, and let α be the linear transformation of $V_2(\mathbf{Q})$ defined by

$$(1, 0)\alpha = (1, 2),$$
$$(0, 1)\alpha = (1, 0).$$

By the preceding exercise, the minimal polynomial of α is $x^2 - x - 2 = (x - 2)(x + 1)$. Find bases for the nullspaces V_1 and V_2 of $\alpha - 2\jmath$ and $\alpha + \jmath$, respectively, and verify (Lemma 16.72) that $V = V_1 \oplus V_2$, that each V_i is invariant under α, and that the minimal polynomial of α restricted to V_1 or to V_2 is, respectively, $x - 2$ and $x + 1$.

4. Let E_1, E_2, E_3, E_4 be the unit vectors of $V_4(\mathbf{Q})$ and let α be the linear transformation of $V_4(\mathbf{Q})$ defined by

$$E_1\alpha = E_1 + 2E_3,$$
$$E_2\alpha = E_2 + E_4,$$
$$E_3\alpha = E_1,$$
$$E_4\alpha = -E_2 + 2E_4.$$

If $V_1 = [E_1, E_3]$ and $V_2 = [E_2, E_4]$, verify that both V_1 and V_2 are invariant under α, and that $V_4(\mathbf{Q}) = V_1 \oplus V_2$. Then apply Lemma 16.71 and the results of Exercise 3 to show that the minimal polynomial of α is $(x - 2)(x + 1)(x^2 - 3x + 3)$. Verify that the matrix of α relative to the ordered basis E_1, E_3, E_2, E_4 of $V_4(\mathbf{Q})$ is of the form

$$\text{diag}\left(\begin{bmatrix} 1 & 2 \\ 1 & 0 \end{bmatrix}, \begin{bmatrix} 1 & 1 \\ -1 & 2 \end{bmatrix}\right).$$

5. Find an ordered basis of $V_4(\mathbf{Q})$ relative to which the matrix of the linear transformation A of the preceding exercise is of the form

$$\text{diag}\left([2], [-1], \begin{bmatrix} 1 & 1 \\ -1 & 2 \end{bmatrix}\right).$$

6. Prove that $F[\alpha]$ has a subalgebra which is isomorphic to F.

7. Complete the proof of part *(iii)* of Lemma 16.72 by proving in detail that $f(x) = m_1(x)$ and $g(x) = m_2(x)$.

8. Fill in the details which were omitted near the end of the proof of Theorem 16.76.

16.12 CHARACTERISTIC VECTORS AND CHARACTERISTIC ROOTS

Let V continue to be a vector space of dimension $n > 0$ over a field F, and α a linear transformation of V. Under the mapping $\alpha \colon V \to V$, the zero vector certainly maps into itself but, in general, there may very well be no other vector with this property. However, we shall here be concerned with vectors satisfying the weaker condition that they "almost" map into themselves in the sense that they map into scalar multiples of themselves. Let us give the following definition.

16.77 Definition. If $c \in F$ and X is a nonzero element of V such that

16.78 $$X\alpha = cX,$$

then X is called a *characteristic vector* of α corresponding to the *characteristic root* c of α.

Let us emphasize that a nonzero vector X is a characteristic vector of α if and only if there exists an element c of F such that 16.78 holds. Conversely, an element c of F is a characteristic root of α if and only if there exists a nonzero vector X of V such that 16.78 holds.

In the literature, a great number of adjectives, such as *latent*, *proper*, and *eigen*, have been used in place of *characteristic* in Definition 16.77.

We may observe from the definition that if X is a characteristic vector corresponding to a characteristic root c, any nonzero scalar multiple of X is also a characteristic vector corresponding to the same characteristic root. Moreover, in view of the definition of a subspace being invariant under a linear transformation, we see that the nonzero vector X is a characteristic vector of α if and only if the one-dimensional subspace $[X]$ of V is invariant under α.

Let us now consider the problem of determining the characteristic roots of a linear transformation α. If $\mathcal{J}$ is the unity linear transformation, Equation 16.78 may be written in the form

16.79 $X(\alpha - c\mathcal{J}) = 0.$

Since X is required to be a nonzero vector, Theorem 16.18 shows that the linear transformation $\alpha - c\mathcal{J}$ must be singular. Suppose that A is the matrix of α relative to some ordered basis of V. Then, by Theorem 16.29, the matrix $A - cI$ is singular, and this implies that $|A - cI| = 0$. Conversely, if this determinant is zero, the linear transformation $\alpha - c\mathcal{J}$ must be singular and there will exist a nonzero vector X satisfying Equation 16.79.

We may point out that it did not matter which matrix of α we selected above. As a matter of fact, if we had used a different ordered, basis, the results of the preceding section show that the matrix of α would be of the form BAB^{-1} for some nonsingular matrix B. However,

$$|BAB^{-1} - cI| = |B(A - cI)B^{-1}| = |A - cI|,$$

by Theorem 16.51 and Corollary 16.53.

Let us, for the moment, change our point of view as follows. If λ is an indeterminate (a customary notation in this particular setting), then

$$|A - \lambda I| = \begin{vmatrix} a_{11} - \lambda & a_{12} & \cdots & a_{1n} \\ a_{21} & a_{22} - \lambda & \cdots & a_{2n} \\ \cdot & \cdot & \cdots & \cdot \\ a_{n1} & a_{n2} & \cdots & a_{nn} - \lambda \end{vmatrix},$$

and it is not difficult to verify that this is a polynomial in λ of degree exactly n. In fact, the coefficient of λ^n is $(-1)^n$. We now make another definition as follows.

16.80 **Definition.** If $A \in F_n$ and λ is an indeterminate, the polynomial $|A - \lambda I|$ is called the *characteristic polynomial* * of A, and the roots in F of this polynomial are called the *characteristic roots* of A.

---

* It can be proved that if $f(\lambda)$ is the characteristic polynomial of A, then $f(A) = 0$. This is the well-known Cayley-Hamilton Theorem. In particular, it follows that the minimal polynomial of A is a divisor of its characteristic polynomial. See, e.g., Birkhoff and MacLane [2] or Herstein [7] for a proof of the Cayley-Hamilton Theorem.

We may state the results of our observations above as the following theorem, which will also justify the two uses of the concept of characteristic root.

16.81   Theorem.   *The characteristic roots of a linear transformation α of V are precisely the characteristic roots of the matrix of α relative to any ordered basis of V.*

Since the characteristic polynomial is of degree n, a linear transformation clearly cannot have more than n characteristic roots. Of course, it may very well have fewer than n of them.

Let us now give some examples to illustrate these concepts.

EXAMPLE 1.   Let our vector space be $V_3(\mathbf{Q})$, and let α be the linear transformation whose matrix relative to the usual ordered unit vectors is

$$A = \begin{bmatrix} 2 & 0 & 0 \\ 0 & 0 & -1 \\ 0 & -1 & 0 \end{bmatrix}.$$

Find the characteristic roots and characteristic vectors of α.

SOLUTION: We have

$$|A - \lambda I| = \begin{vmatrix} 2 - \lambda & 0 & 0 \\ 0 & -\lambda & -1 \\ 0 & -1 & -\lambda \end{vmatrix} = -(\lambda - 2)(\lambda - 1)(\lambda + 1).$$

Thus the characteristic roots of A (and of α) are 2, 1, and -1. To find a characteristic vector of α corresponding to the root 2, we use the notation introduced in Section 16.6 and seek a nonzero vector $X = (x_1, x_2, x_3)$ such that $X(A - 2I) = 0$. In more detail, this equation is the following:

$$(x_1, x_2, x_3)\begin{bmatrix} 0 & 0 & 0 \\ 0 & -2 & -1 \\ 0 & -1 & -2 \end{bmatrix} = (0, -2x_2 - x_3, -x_2 - 2x_3) = 0.$$

Accordingly, we must have $-2x_2 - x_3 = 0$ and $-x_2 - 2x_3 = 0$, and these equations imply that $x_2 = x_3 = 0$. Thus $(x_1, 0, 0)$ is a characteristic vector of A for each $x_1 \neq 0$. In particular, $(1, 0, 0)$ is a characteristic vector of A corresponding to the characteristic root 2.

We omit the calculations but the reader may verify that $(0, 1, -1)$ and $(0, 1, 1)$ are characteristic vectors corresponding, respectively, to the characteristic roots 1 and -1. Again, these vectors are uniquely determined except for a nonzero scalar multiplier. In this example, there were three distinct characteristic roots and we remark that the three characteristic vectors corresponding to these three roots are linearly independent. This fact illustrates a theorem to be proved presently.

EXAMPLE 2.   Let α be the linear transformation of $V_3(\mathbf{Q})$ whose matrix relative to the ordered unit vectors is

$$A = \begin{bmatrix} 0 & 1 & -1 \\ 0 & 3 & 0 \\ 1 & 2 & 0 \end{bmatrix}.$$

Find characteristic roots and characteristic vectors of α.

SOLUTION: In this case, we find that

$$|A - \lambda I| = \begin{vmatrix} -\lambda & 1 & -1 \\ 0 & 3 - \lambda & 0 \\ 1 & 2 & -\lambda \end{vmatrix} = -(\lambda - 3)(\lambda^2 + 1).$$

This polynomial has only the root 3 in $\mathbf{Q}$, so there is only one characteristic root. Solving the equation

$$(x_1, x_2, x_3) \begin{bmatrix} -3 & 1 & -1 \\ 0 & 0 & 0 \\ 1 & 2 & -3 \end{bmatrix} = 0,$$

we find that the only characteristic vectors corresponding to the characteristic root 3 are those of the form $(0, x_2, 0)$, where $x_2 \neq 0$. In particular, $(0, 1, 0)$ is such a characteristic vector.

The same calculations and conclusions apply if we replace the field $\mathbf{Q}$ by $\mathbf{R}$. However, if we had assumed that A was the matrix of a linear transformation of $V_3(\mathbf{C})$, we would have found three characteristic roots since, in $\mathbf{C}$, $\lambda^2 + 1 = (\lambda + i)(\lambda - i)$.

The subject which we have here just barely introduced is an extensive one, and full expositions can be found in any text on "Linear Algebra." However, we shall now prove one more theorem which is of a rather special nature as follows.

16.82   Theorem.   *Suppose that a linear transformation α of a vector space V of dimension $n > 0$ over a field F has n distinct characteristic roots λ_1, $\lambda_2, \cdots, \lambda_n$ in F. If $X_1, X_2, \cdots, X_n$ are characteristic vectors corresponding, respectively, to these characteristic roots, then $\{X_1, X_2, \cdots, X_n\}$ is a linearly independent set of vectors.*

The proof is an inductive one as follows. First, since characteristic vectors are different from zero, a set consisting of just one of these vectors is linearly independent. Let us assume that a set of any k of these vectors is linearly independent and prove that if $k < n$, the same is true for any set of $k + 1$ vectors. For convenience of notation, let us prove that $\{X_1, X_2, \cdots, X_{k+1}\}$ is a linearly independent set. Suppose that c_i $(i = 1, 2, \cdots, k + 1)$ are elements of F such that

16.83
$$c_1 X_1 + c_2 X_2 + \cdots + c_{k+1} X_{k+1} = 0.$$

If $c_1 \neq 0$, we proceed as follows. From 16.83, we must have

$$\begin{aligned} 0 &= (c_1 X_1 + c_2 X_2 + \cdots + c_{k+1} X_{k+1})\mathfrak{a} \\ &= c_1(X_1\mathfrak{a}) + c_2(X_2\mathfrak{a}) + \cdots + c_{k+1}(X_{k+1}\mathfrak{a}) \\ &= c_1\lambda_1 X_1 + c_2\lambda_2 X_2 + \cdots + c_{k+1}\lambda_{k+1} X_{k+1}. \end{aligned}$$

If we multiply 16.83 by λ_1 and subtract from this equation, we obtain

$$c_2(\lambda_2 - \lambda_1)X_2 + \cdots + c_{k+1}(\lambda_{k+1} - \lambda_1)X_{k+1} = 0.$$

Since, by our hypothesis, $\{X_2, \cdots, X_{k+1}\}$ is a linearly independent set of k vectors, we must have $c_2(\lambda_2 - \lambda_1) = \cdots = c_{k+1}(\lambda_{k+1} - \lambda_1) = 0$. However, the λ's are *distinct*, and it follows that $c_2 = \cdots = c_{k+1} = 0$. Equation 16.83 then shows that $c_1 X_1 = 0$ and we conclude that $c_1 = 0$, thus contradicting our assumption that $c_1 \neq 0$. Accordingly, we must have $c_1 = 0$. Substituting this value of c_1 in 16.83, we again use the linear independence of $\{X_2, \cdots, X_{k+1}\}$ to conclude that *all* c's are zero. Therefore, any set of $k + 1$ of our vectors is linearly independent, and this completes the proof of the theorem.

Let us draw one further conclusion from this theorem. Since $\{X_1, X_2, \cdots, X_n\}$ is a linearly independent set of vectors, it is a basis of V. The matrix of $\mathfrak{a}$ relative to the ordered basis $X_1, X_2, \cdots, X_n$ of V is determined from the following equations:

$$\begin{aligned} X_1\mathfrak{a} &= \lambda_1 X_1, \\ X_2\mathfrak{a} &= \lambda_2 X_2, \\ &\ \cdot\ \cdot\ \cdot\ \cdot\ \cdot\ \cdot\ \cdot\ \cdot \\ X_n\mathfrak{a} &= \lambda_n X_n. \end{aligned}$$

That is, the matrix of $\mathfrak{a}$ relative to this basis has $\lambda_1, \lambda_2, \cdots, \lambda_n$ down the principal diagonal and zeros elsewhere. We thus have the following corollary of the theorem just established.

16.84 Corollary. *If a linear transformation $\mathfrak{a}$ of a vector space V over F has n distinct characteristic roots in F, relative to a suitably chosen ordered* *basis of V the matrix of α has these characteristic roots on the principal diagonal and zeros elsewhere.*

Finally, in view of Theorem 16.57 and Definition 16.58, this result can be expressed in an alternate form as follows.

16.85 Corollary. *If a matrix A of F_n has n distinct characteristic roots in F, then A is similar to a matrix with these characteristic roots on the principal diagonal and zeros elsewhere.*

EXERCISES

1. If the matrix A of Example 2 above is considered to be the matrix of a linear transformation $α$ of $V_3(\mathbf{C})$, find all characteristic vectors of $α$.

2. Let $α$ be the linear transformation of $V_3(\mathbf{Q})$ whose matrix relative to the ordered unit vectors is

$$\begin{bmatrix} 2 & 0 & 1 \\ 0 & 1 & 0 \\ 0 & 0 & 2 \end{bmatrix}.$$

    Find all characteristic roots and all characteristic vectors of $α$.

3. Show that the set of all characteristic vectors of a linear transformation $α$ of a vector space V which correspond to a fixed characteristic root of $α$ is a subspace of V.

4. If A is a matrix *of order two*, use the results of Exercise 1 of the preceding set to prove that the characteristic polynomial of A coincides with the minimum polynomial of A if and only if A is not a scalar matrix. [Note: We have used different symbols for the indeterminates in the two cases, but that fact is unimportant.]

5. Let
$$A = \begin{bmatrix} 2 & -2 & 2 \\ 0 & 1 & 1 \\ -4 & 8 & 3 \end{bmatrix}$$

    be the matrix of a linear transformation $α$ of $V_3(\mathbf{Q})$ relative to the usual ordered basis of unit vectors.

    (i) Verify that $α$ has three distinct characteristic roots and find a characteristic vector corresponding to each characteristic root.

(ii) Find an ordered basis of $V_3(\mathbf{Q})$ relative to which the matrix of α has these characteristic roots on the principal diagonal and zeros elsewhere.

(iii) Find a nonsingular matrix B such that BAB^{-1} is of the form described in part (ii).

NOTES AND REFERENCES

Additional material on the general subject of this chapter, as well as alternate approaches to the results presented here, will be found in most books on linear algebra such as, for example, those listed as items [32] through [35] of the bibliography. In particular, Halmos [34] and Malcev [35] give good expositions of a number of topics not covered in this book. Herstein's text [7] on abstract algebra is also recommended for supplementary reading about matrices and linear transformations.

SOME ADDITIONAL TOPICS

The purpose of this chapter is to present a brief account of several different topics of considerable algebraic interest which have not been introduced in preceding chapters. The degree of independence of these topics will be indicated by the fact that the reader may start with Section 17.1, 17.2, 17.3 or 17.5 as desired. References for further reading on these and related topics will be found at the end of the chapter.

17.1 QUATERNIONS

Before introducing the topic of this section, let us formalize as follows a definition which was casually mentioned in the notes to Chapter 12.

17.1 Definition.   A ring R with more than one element and having a unity is said to be a *division ring* if every nonzero element of R has a multiplicative inverse in R.

It will be seen that this differs from Definition 5.1 of a field only in that the word "commutative" has been omitted. Thus, a division ring is a field if and only if it is a commutative ring. In particular, every field is a division ring.

We now wish to introduce an example of a division ring which is not a field. This division ring, introduced by Sir William R. Hamilton in 1843, is of special historical interest in that it was the first time that a noncommutative ring was studied, although the name *ring* itself was not introduced until much later.

The approach which we shall use, suggested by that of Hamilton but given a more general setting, is to consider first how one might construct an algebra over a field F, starting only with a given vector space V over F. In other words, given the vector space V, how can one define a multiplication of elements of V which will make V into an algebra over F? As a simple illustration of the ideas involved, let V be a vector space of dimension two over F, and let $\{X_1, X_2\}$ be a basis of V. The elements of V are therefore uniquely expressible in the form

17.2 $$a_1X_1 + a_2X_2, \qquad\qquad a_1, a_2 \in F.$$

In order to have a multiplication of such elements defined in such a way as to obtain an algebra, it would have to be true that

17.3 $$(a_1X_1 + a_2X_2)(b_1X_1 + b_2X_2) = a_1b_1X_1^2 + a_1b_2X_1X_2$$
$$+ a_2b_1X_2X_1 + a_2b_2X_2^2.$$

Thus, *if* we knew the products X_1^2, X_1X_2, X_2X_1, X_2^2 of the basis elements, we could use 17.3 to *define* the product of any two elements of V.

Now let us look further at this approach, and suppose that we define the products X_1^2, X_1X_2, X_2X_1, X_2^2 to be arbitrarily chosen elements of the form 17.2 and then use 17.3 to define arbitrary products of elements of V. It may be shown that all the properties of a ring hold, with the possible exception of the associative law of multiplication. Furthermore, multiplication of arbitrary elements will be associative provided multiplication of basis elements is associative.

As an almost trivial example of an algebra presented as sketched above, let $\{1, i\}$ be a basis of a vector space of dimension two over the field $\mathbf{R}$ of real numbers. The "1" is the unity of $\mathbf{R}$; and we want it to be the unity of our algebra, so we want to have $1 \cdot 1 = 1, 1 \cdot i = i \cdot 1 = i$. We also propose to define $i^2 = -1$, so we have a multiplication defined for the elements of a basis. The elements of our algebra are of the form $a + bi$, where a and b are elements of $\mathbf{R}$, and the product of any two elements of the algebra is defined (in accordance with 17.3) to be as follows:

$$(a + bi)(c + di) = ac + (ad + bc)i + bdi^2$$
$$= ac - bd + (ad + bc)i.$$

Of course, it turns out that multiplication is associative and we have the algebra of complex numbers over the reals. This algebra is itself a field, the field of complex numbers.

Hamilton tried very hard, but unsuccessfully, to do something similar to the above and obtain an algebra of dimension three, which would also be a field over the reals. Although he was not able to carry out this program for dimension three, he did succeed (by a stroke of genius) in doing a comparable thing for dimension four—only it turned out that multiplication was not commutative, so he obtained a division ring which was not a field. It is this example which we now wish to present.

Let $\{1, i, j, k\}$ be a basis of a vector space V of dimension 4 over **R**. We propose to make V into an algebra Q over **R** by defining multiplication of these basis elements and then using the analogue of 17.3 to define multiplication of arbitrary elements of V. The unity 1 of **R** is to be the unity of Q, so that we need not further specify how to multiply by 1. Following Hamilton, products of the other basis elements are defined as follows:

17.4 $$i^2 = j^2 = k^2 = -1, \quad ij = k, \quad ji = -k, \quad jk = i,$$
$$kj = -i, \quad ki = j, \quad ik = -j.$$

An easy way to remember the products of different basis elements is by use of the scheme shown in Figure 17. In this figure, the product of an element by the adjacent one in the direction of the arrows is the remaining basis element. The product in the other order is changed in sign. Thus, for example, $ki = j$ since passing from k to i is in the direction of the arrows, similarly $ik = -j$ since passing from i to k is against the direction of the arrows.

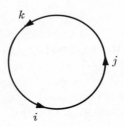

Figure 17

The elements of the algebra Q are the linear combinations of the basis elements, that is, they are of the form

17.5 $$a + bi + cj + dk, \qquad a, b, c, d \in \mathbf{R}.$$

The product of any two of these elements is defined by using 17.4 and the other properties that must hold in an algebra (as in 17.3). A detailed calculation will show that this product turns out to be as follows:

17.6 $(a_1 + b_1 i + c_1 j + d_1 k)(a_2 + b_2 i + c_2 j + d_2 k)$
$$= a_1 a_2 - b_1 b_2 - c_1 c_2 - d_1 d_2 + (a_1 b_2 + b_1 a_2 + c_1 d_2 - d_1 c_2)i$$
$$+ (a_1 c_2 + c_1 a_2 + d_1 b_2 - b_1 d_2)j + (a_1 d_2 + d_1 a_2 + b_1 c_2 - c_1 b_2)k.$$

It can be shown that the associative property of multiplication does hold and that Q is indeed an algebra over **R**. Following Hamilton, an element of Q is usually called a *quaternion* and Q is called the algebra of *real quaternions*.

If q is the element 17.5 of Q, the element

$$q^* = a - bi - cj - dk$$

may be called the *conjugate* of q. It follows easily from 17.6 that

$$q^* q = q q^* = a^2 + b^2 + c^2 + d^2.$$

Thus, if q is a nonzero element of Q, not all of the real numbers a, b, c, d can be zero; hence qq^* is a *positive real* number. It follows from the preceding equation that if $q \neq 0$, then $q^{-1} = (qq^*)^{-1} q^*$ since

$$(qq^*)^{-1} q^* q = q(qq^*)^{-1} q^* = 1.$$

This shows that every nonzero element of Q has a multiplicative inverse in Q, and Q is therefore a division ring. Since multiplication of certain quaternions (for example, i and j) is not commutative, Q is not a field. Some additional properties of this division ring Q of real quaternions will be brought out in the exercises below.

EXERCISES

1. Verify that if b, c, and d are real numbers such that $b^2 + c^2 + d^2 = 1$, the quaternion $q = bi + cj + dk$ has the property that $q^2 = -1$. Hence show that there are infinitely many real quaternions q such that $q^2 = -1$.

2. Using the notation which will distinguish between the complex number i and the quaternion i, use 17.4 and 17.6 to define an algebra over the field **C** of complex numbers. Verify that the algebra so obtained is not a division ring.

3. If q is a real quaternion, the real number qq^* is often called the *norm* of q and denoted by $N(q)$. If q_1 and q_2 are real quaternions, prove that $N(q_1 q_2) = N(q_1) N(q_2)$.

17.2 PRINCIPAL IDEAL DOMAINS

The integral domain $\mathbf{Z}$ and the integral domain $F[x]$, where F is a field and x an indeterminate, have a number of similar properties. In particular, in both of these domains there is (in a certain sense) a unique factorization of elements into a product of primes (Theorems 4.20 and 10.36). It is then natural to ask whether there might exist a general factorization theory that would include both of these as special cases. The primary purpose of this section is to show that this is indeed true.

For the present, let us introduce for an arbitrary integral domain some concepts which have been used for integers and to some extent also for polynomials over a field. A little later, we shall make a significant restriction on the integral domains considered.

Unless otherwise stated, we shall henceforth in this section let R be an arbitrary integral domain with unity e. Thus R is a commutative ring in which the cancellation law of multiplication holds for all nonzero elements.

17.7 Definition. An element of R which has a multiplicative inverse in R is called a *unit* of R.

The word "unit" is not to be confused with "unity," although the unity e of R certainly is a unit of R.

Let us denote by U the set of units of R. Since $e \in U$, U is not empty. If $a \in U$, a has a multiplicative inverse a^{-1} in R. But then a is the multiplicative inverse of a^{-1}, so that $a^{-1} \in U$. We also know that in an arbitrary ring if a and b have multiplicative inverses, then $(ab)^{-1} = b^{-1}a^{-1}$; and therefore U is closed with respect to multiplication. It follows that U is an abelian group with respect to multiplication, and that e is the identity of this group (*Cf.* Exercise 9 at the end of Section 7.1).

Just as in the case of integers, if a and b are nonzero elements of the integral domain R, and there exists an element c of R such that $a = bc$, we may say that b *divides* a or that b *is a divisor of* a, and may indicate this fact by writing $b \mid a$. It is sometimes convenient to indicate by $b \nmid a$ that b is not a divisor of a. If $u \in U$, $u \mid a$ for *every* element a of R, since $a = uu^{-1}a$.

Let us now prove the following simple, but important, result.

17.8 Lemma. *An element c of R is a unit if and only if $c \mid e$.*

To see this, suppose first that $c \mid e$; hence $e = cx$ for some x in R. Thus, $c^{-1} = x$ and c is a unit.

Conversely, if $c \in U$, then $cc^{-1} = e$ and $c \mid e$.

17.9 **Definition.** If $a = bu$, where a, $b \in R$ and $u \in U$, we say that a and b are *associates*, and each is said to be *an associate of* the other.

As suggested by the language of this definition, if a and b are associates, the relation between them is mutual. For if $a = bu$ with $u \in U$, then $b = au^{-1}$ and $u^{-1} \in U$.

It is easy to verify that the relation "is an associate of" is an equivalence relation on the set R. Moreover, the associates of e are just the units of R (the elements of U).

17.10 **Lemma.** *Nonzero elements a and b of the integral domain R are associates if and only if $a \mid b$ and $b \mid a$.*

PROOF: If $a \mid b$ and $b \mid a$, then there exist elements x and y of R such that $b = ax$ and $a = by$. Thus $a = axy$ and $e = xy$ since $a \neq 0$. It follows from Lemma 17.8 that x and y are units, and a and b are associates. Conversely, if a and b are associates, $a = ub$ for some $u \in U$, and hence $b \mid a$. Similarly, $a \mid b$, and this completes the proof.

We are now ready to give the following definition.

17.11 **Definition.** A nonzero element p of an integral domain R is said to be a *prime* if it is not a unit and its only divisors are units and associates of p.

From this definition, it follows that if q is an associate of p, then q is a prime if and only if p is a prime. Also, it is important to observe that *if p and q are primes and $p \mid q$, then p and q are associates*.

Let us now illustrate the concepts introduced so far by using the familiar cases in which R is the integral domain **Z** or the polynomial domain $F[x]$, where F is a field.

The units of **Z** are ± 1, so that $U = \{1, -1\}$ is a group of order two. Each nonzero integer a has only the two associates a and $-a$. The primes are ± 2, ± 3, ± 5, etc.

In $F[x]$, the units are the nonzero elements of F, that is, the polynomials of degree zero. In this case, $U = \{c \mid c \in F, c \neq 0\}$, so that the order of the group U is the number of nonzero elements in F in case this number is finite, and U has infinite order if F is not a finite field. The associates of an element $f(x)$ of $F[x]$ are the elements $cf(x)$, c a nonzero element of F. If $p(x)$ is a prime element of $F[x]$, that is, in our previous usage it is prime over F, then so also is $cp(x)$ for each nonzero element c of F.

We next recall that if $a \in R$, the principal ideal (a) in R, generated by a, is defined as follows:

$$(a) = \{ax \mid x \in R\}.$$

It will now be convenient to use an alternate notation for (a), namely aR. This notation will perhaps help to emphasize that the principal ideal generated by a consists of the multiples of a. That is $b \in (a) = aR$ if and only if $a \mid b$. In view of Lemma 17.10, we have at once the following result.

17.12   Lemma.   *If a and b are nonzero elements of the integral domain R, then $aR = bR$ if and only if a and b are associates.*

We have proved (Theorem 11.3) that in **Z** and in $F[x]$ every ideal is principal, and therefore these integral domains are examples of principal ideal domains, according to the following definition.

17.13   Definition.   If every ideal in an integral domain R is a principal ideal, we say that R is a *principal ideal domain.*

Henceforth in this section we shall be considering principal ideal domains, and shall let D denote such a domain.

We are now able to state the following theorem of this section which may be interpreted as showing that the unique factorization theorems for **Z** and for $F[x]$ are consequences of the fact that these are principal ideal domains.

17.14   Theorem.

(i) *Let a be a nonzero element of a principal ideal domain D with unity e. If a is not a unit of D, it can be expressed in the form*

17.15 $$a = p_1 p_2 \cdots p_r ,$$

where r is a positive integer and the p's are primes in D.

(ii) *The representation 17.15 is unique in the following sense. If also*

$$a = q_1 q_2 \cdots q_s ,$$

where the q's are primes in D, then $s = r$ and by a proper choice of notation, q_i and p_i are associates for $i = 1, 2, \cdots, r$.

The proof of part (i) of this theorem involves methods much different from those used in the case of integers (Theorem 4.20), and we shall give this part of the proof in detail. However, we shall not give a detailed proof of part (ii), but will obtain some lemmas from which it should be quite easy to adapt the inductive proof used to establish the corresponding part of Theorem 4.20.

Accordingly, we proceed to a proof of the first part of the theorem. First, we need a preliminary result which may not at first glance seem to have anything to do with our problem.

17.16 Lemma. *In a principal ideal domain D there cannot exist an infinite sequence of ideals a_1D, a_2D, a_3D, $\cdots$, such that each is properly contained in the following, that is, we cannot have*

17.17
$$A_1D \subset a_2D \subset a_3D \subset \cdots .$$

PROOF: Suppose, on the contrary, that there is an infinite sequence satisfying 17.17, and let us seek a contradiction.

We assert that the union A of all the ideals a_iD in 17.17 is itself an ideal in D. For if a, $b \in U$, we know that $a \in a_iD$ for some positive integer i and that $b \in a_jD$ for some positive integer j. Suppose, for example, that $i \leq j$. Then $a_iD \subset a_jD$ and hence, in particular, both a and b are in a_jD and therefore $a + b \in a_jD$. But $a_jD \subseteq A$, and we conclude that $a + b \in A$. Clearly, if $a \in A$, then $-a \in A$, so that A is a subring of D. Moreover, if $a \in A$ with $a \in a_iD$ and $c \in D$, then $ac \in a_iD \subseteq A$, and A is indeed an ideal in D. Since every ideal in D is a principal ideal, there exists an element a of A such that $A = aD$. Since A is the union of the ideals occurring in 17.17, this implies that $a \in a_iD$ for some positive integer i. Hence $A = aD \subseteq a_iD$ and, in particular, $a_jD \subseteq a_iD$ for each $j > i$. This gives the desired contradiction and completes the proof.

The fact that 17.17 cannot hold in a principal ideal domain is often expressed by saying that the *ascending chain condition* holds in a principal ideal domain.

Another concept which we shall find useful is the following.

17.18 Definition. *An ideal A in an arbitrary ring R is said to be a maximal ideal if there exists no ideal B in R such that $A \subset B \subset R$.*

The relation of this concept to the subject under discussion is given in the following lemma.

17.19 Lemma. *A nonzero ideal aD in a principal ideal domain D is a maximal ideal if and only if a is a prime of D.*

PROOF: Suppose, first, that a is prime. Let's assume that aD is not a maximal ideal, and seek a contradiction. Thus, by our assumption, there exists an ideal bD of D such that $aD \subset bD \subset D$. The fact that $aD \subset bD$ implies that $b \mid a$ and that b is not an associate of a since, otherwise, we would have $aD = bD$. Moreover, $bD \in D$ implies that b is not a unit. Thus b is a divisor of a and is neither a unit nor an associate of a, contradicting the assumption that a is a prime. We have thus shown that if a is prime, aD is a maximal ideal.

Conversely, suppose that aD is a maximal ideal in D. If a were not prime, it would have a divisor c, neither a unit nor an associate of a. But this would imply that $aD \subset cD \subset R$, violating our assumption that aD is a maximal ideal. We conclude that a must be prime, and the proof is complete.

We are now ready to prove the following important first step in the proof of Theorem 17.14(i).

17.20   Lemma.   *If the nonzero element a of the principal ideal domain D is not a unit, it has a prime factor.*

PROOF: If a is itself prime, there is nothing to prove. If a is not a prime, the preceding lemma shows that aD is not a maximal ideal. Thus there exists an ideal a_1D such that $aD \subset a_1D \subset D$. It follows that $a_1 \mid a$ and a_1 is not a unit. Applying the same argument to a_1 we see that if a_1 is not a prime, there exists an element a_2 of R such that $a_2 \mid a_1$ and a_2 is not a unit. In particular, we would have $aD \subset a_1D \subset a_2D \subset D$. Continuing, if a_2 is not a prime, it has a divisor a_3 such that $aD \subset a_1D \subset a_2D \subset a_3D \subset D$. By Lemma 17.16, this process must come to an end after a finite number of steps. Hence there exists a divisor, say a_n, of a such that a_n is a prime. This completes the proof of the lemma.

Using these results, let us now give a proof of part (i) of Theorem 17.14.

Let a be a nonzero element of D, not a unit. By the preceding lemma, a has a prime factor p_1 and we have $a = p_1c_1$ for some element c_1 of D. If c_1 is not a unit, we therefore have $aD \subset c_1D$. Applying the same argument to c_1, we see that there exists a prime divisor p_2 of c_1. If we write $c_1 = p_2c_2$, then $a = p_1p_2c_2$ and if c_2 is not a unit, we have $aD \subset c_1D \subset c_2D$, and also c_2 has a prime divisor p_3. At this stage, we have $a = p_1p_2p_3c_3$. This process can be continued as long as c_i is not a unit. By Lemma 17.16, there must exist a positive integer r such that c_r is a unit since, otherwise, we would have an infinite sequence c_iD of ideals in D such that

$$aD \subset c_1D \subset c_2D \subset \cdots .$$

We conclude that

$$a = p_1p_2 \cdots p_rc_r ,$$

where c_r is a unit. But then p_rc_r is an associate of p_r and is therefore a prime. Let us change the notation and call it p_r. We thus have an expression 17.15, as we wished to prove. That is, in a principal ideal domain D every nonzero element which is not a unit is expressible as a product of a finite number of primes.

We conclude this section by presenting some results from which the reader may obtain the proof of the second part of the theorem by a simple adaptation of the proof of Theorem 4.20 for the integers.

If a and b are nonzero elements of a principal ideal domain D, the element d of D is said to be a *greatest common divisor* (g.c.d.) of a and b if the following two conditions are satisfied:

(i) $d \mid a$ and $d \mid b$.

(ii) If $c \in D$ such that $c \mid a$ and $c \mid b$, then $c \mid d$.

It may be observed that if d is a g.c.d. of a and b, so also is any associate of d. In the case of the integers, we found it convenient to obtain a *unique* g.c.d. by requiring that it be positive. Similarly, for polynomials over a field we obtained a *unique* g.c.d. by requiring that it be a monic polynomial. However, in the general case here under discussion there is no obvious way to get a unique g.c.d. , so we simply get along without uniqueness since it makes no essential difference anyway.

If $a, b \in D$, it is easy to verify that the set

17.21 $\{ax + by \mid x, y \in D\}$

is an ideal in D, and therefore is a principal ideal.*

17.22   Lemma.   *If a and b are nonzero elements of the principal ideal domain D, any generator d of the ideal 17.21 is a g.c.d. of a and b.*

PROOF: We have

$$dD = \{ax + by \mid x, y \in D\},$$

and clearly $aD \subseteq dD$ and $bD \subseteq dD$, so that $d \mid a$ and $d \mid b$. Now $d \in dD$, so that there exist elements x_1 and y_1 of D such that $d = ax_1 + by_1$. From this equation, we see that if $c \mid a$ and $c \mid b$, then $c \mid d$. Accordingly, d is a g.c.d. of a and b.

The next result furnishes the essential step in the proof of our theorem.

17.23   Lemma.   *If p is a prime in the principal ideal domain D and $a; b \in D$ such that $p \mid (ab)$, then $p \mid a$ or $p \mid b$.*

PROOF: Suppose that p is a prime such that $p \mid (ab)$ and $p \nmid a$, and let us prove that $p \mid b$. Since $p \nmid a$, a g.c.d. of p and a cannot be an

---

* According to the definition given in Exercise 2 at the end of Section 11.1, this ideal is the sum $aD + bD$ of the ideals aD and bD.

associate of p; hence must be a unit. But any unit of D generates the ideal D, and therefore the ideal 17.21, with b replaced by p, is D. In particular, there exist elements x and y of D such that $ax + py = e$, e being the unity of D. Multiplying by b, we obtain

$$abx + bpy = b.$$

Since it is given that $p \mid (ab)$, it is clear that p divides the left side of this equation, and therefore divides b. This completes the proof of the lemma.

It will be observed that, after developing the appropriate machinery, the proof just given follows very closely the previously given proof of Lemma 4.18 for the case of integers.

A generalization of Lemma 17.23 to the product of any finite number of elements of D (instead of just two elements) follows by induction just as Lemma 4.19 is obtained from Lemma 4.18. We omit this proof as well as the rest of the proof of Theorem 17.14. Instead, we shall list these proofs as exercises below.

In conclusion, it may be of interest to state that there exist integral domains having elements which can be expressed as a product of primes in more than one way. Needless to say, such integral domains cannot be principal ideal domains. References will be given at the end of this chapter.

EXERCISES

1. Prove by induction that if p is a prime in the principal ideal domain D which divides a product of any finite number n of elements of D, it must divide at least one of these elements.

2. Complete the proof of Theorem 17.14(ii).

3. Define a least common multiple (l.c.m.) of two nonzero elements of a principal ideal domain. If $aD \cap bD = mD$, verify that m is a l.c.m. of a and b.

17.3 MODULES

In this section we introduce a concept which plays an increasingly important role in many aspects of modern algebra. It will be seen that the definition is obtained from the definition of a vector space except that now the scalars are not restricted to be elements of a field but are elements of an arbitrary ring R. For simplicity, we shall assume that R has a unity although, with proper care, one can get along without this restriction.

The concept which we have in mind has a formal definition as follows.

17.24 Definition. Let R be a ring with unity e, and M a nonempty set on which there is defined an operation of addition. We also assume that there is defined an operation of scalar multiplication of M by elements of R (that is, if $x \in M$ and $a \in R$, then ax is a uniquely determined element of M). The set M is called an R-*module* (or a *module over R*) if the following conditions are satisfied:

(i) M is an abelian group with respect to addition.

(ii) $a(x + y) = ax + ay$, $\qquad\qquad\qquad\qquad a \in R;\ x, y \in M$,

(iii) $(a + b)x = ax + bx$, $\qquad\qquad\qquad\quad a, b \in R;\ x \in M$,

(iv) $a(bx) = (ab)x$, $\qquad\qquad\qquad\qquad\quad a, b \in R;\ x \in M$,

(v) $ex = x$, $\qquad\qquad\qquad\qquad e$ the unity of $R;\ x \in M$.

Since we are writing the elements of R to the left of elements of M, the above might more precisely be called a *left* R-module, and a right R-module could be defined in an analogous way by writing the elements of R on the right. However, we shall consider only left R-modules and shall call them modules in accordance with the definition just given.

If the ring R remains fixed in a discussion, we shall sometimes refer simply to a module, it being understood that we mean R-module.

As indicated before the definition, if F is a field, an F-module is just a vector space over F. If R is a division ring, it is also customary to call an R-module a vector space over the division ring.

Let us now give some additional examples of modules.

EXAMPLE 1.   Let G be an abelian group with operation addition. If $n \in \mathbf{Z}$ and $a \in G$, we have a definition (given in Section 7.1) of na. Under this definition, it may be verified that G is a $\mathbf{Z}$-module. Accordingly, any abelian group may be considered to be a $\mathbf{Z}$-module.

EXAMPLE 2.   In this example, we generalize in a natural way the concept of a vector space of the form $V_n(F)$. Let R be an arbitrary ring with unity, n a positive integer, and consider the set M of all n-tuples $(a_1, a_2, \cdots, a_n)$ of elements of R. This set becomes an R-module if we define addition and scalar multiplication as follows:

$$(a_1, a_2, \cdots, a_n) + (b_1, b_2, \cdots, b_n)$$
$$= (a_1 + b_1, a_2 + b_2, \cdots, (a_n + b_n)),$$

and for $c \in R$,

$$c(a_1, a_2, \cdots, a_n) = (ca_1, ca_2, \cdots, ca_n).$$

EXAMPLE 3.   Let R be a ring with unity, and consider the polynomial ring * $R[x]$, where x is an indeterminate. Then $R[x]$ is an R-module with addition the usual addition in $R[x]$ as a ring, and for $c \in R$ and $f(x) \in R[x]$, define $cf(x)$ to be multiplication of the polynomials c and $f(x)$ in $R[x]$.

EXAMPLE 4.   Let A be a left ideal in the ring R. A is an R-module if addition in A is addition in the subring A of R and for $c \in R$ and $a \in A$, ca is the product of c by a in the ring R. In this case, properties (ii) and (iii) of Definition 17.24 are consequences of the distributive laws in R, and (iv) is implied by the associative law of multiplication in R.

EXAMPLE 5.   Again, let A be a left ideal in R. Then the additive group of A is a subgroup of the additive group of R. We now let M be the quotient group of the additive group of R by the subgroup of the additive group of A. The elements of M are therefore cosets of the form

$$r + A, \qquad\qquad r \in R,$$

and addition of cosets is well-defined by

17.25 $\qquad\qquad (r + A) + (s + A) = (r + s) + A.$

We already know that M is an abelian group with respect to this definition of addition. We propose to make M into an R-module by defining

17.26 $\qquad\qquad a(r + A) = ar + A,$

where a and r are elements of R. We leave it as an exercise to verify that scalar multiplication is well-defined by 17.26 and that M is indeed an R-module under the definitions 17.25 and 17.26.

Having given several examples of modules, we proceed to a brief presentation of a number of concepts. It will be observed that most of

---

* Since, for simplicity, we have only defined polynomial rings over a commutative ring, the reader may here assume that R is commutative or assume the true statement that the theory goes over just as well for noncommutative rings.

these are suggested by what we have already done in the special case of vector spaces. Proofs of some of the statements will be left as exercises.

A subset of an R-module M will be called a *submodule* of M if it is itself an R-module with respect to the operations of addition and scalar multiplication defined in M. A nonempty subset N of M will be a submodule of M if and only if it is closed under addition and $rx \in N$ for $r \in R$ and $x \in N$.

If $x_1, x_2, \cdots, x_n$ are elements of the R-module M, an element of M of the form

$$a_1x_1 + a_2x_2 + \cdots + a_nx_n, \qquad \text{each } a_i \in R,$$

may naturally be called a *linear combination* of $x_1, x_2, \cdots, x_n$. The set of all linear combinations of $x_1, x_2, \cdots, x_n$ is a submodule of M. It is the smallest submodule of M (in the sense of set inclusion) which contains the given elements $x_1, x_2, \cdots, x_n$. We call it the *submodule generated by* $x_1, x_2, \cdots, x_n$, and denote it by $[x_1, x_2, \cdots, x_n]$.

If there is a single element x of M which generates M, that is, if $M = [x]$ for some element x of M, we say that M is a *cyclic module* with generator x. The notation Rx is frequently used in place of $[x]$ to denote such a cyclic module. This is a suggestive notation inasmuch as $Rx = \{ax \mid a \in R\}$.

The R-module M is said to be *finitely generated* if there exists a finite set of elements $\{x_1, x_2, \cdots, x_n\}$ of M such that $M = [x_1, x_2, \cdots, x_n]$.

If $M_1, M_2, \cdots, M_k$ are submodules of an R-module M, the set of all sums of the form

17.27 $$y_1 + y_2 + \cdots + y_k, \qquad y_i \in M_i,$$

is a submodule of M which we denote by

17.28 $$M_1 + M_2 + \cdots + M_k.$$

If each element of this sum is *uniquely* expressed in the form 17.27, we call the sum a *direct sum* and write it in the form

$$M_1 \oplus M_2 \oplus \cdots \oplus M_k.$$

If, in 17.28, each M_i is cyclic and, say, $M_i = Rx_i$, then 17.28 takes the form

$$Rx_1 + Rx_2 + \cdots + Rx_k.$$

A finite set $\{x_1, x_2, \cdots, x_n\}$ of elements of the R-module M is said to be *independent* if

$$a_1 x_1 + a_2 x_2 + \cdots + a_n x_n = 0 \qquad \text{(all } a_i \in R)$$

implies that $a_i = 0$ $(i = 1, 2, \cdots, n)$. If $\{x_1, x_2, \cdots, x_n\}$ is independent and generates M, then $\{x_1, x_2, \cdots, x_n\}$ is said to be a *basis* of M. The concept of a basis is not as important in the study of arbitrary modules as it is for vector spaces since there are many finitely generated modules which do not have a basis. A module which has a basis is often called a *free* module.

The concept of homomorphism is readily applied to modules over the same ring. If M and N are R-modules, a mapping $\theta : M \to N$ is said to be an *R-homomorphism* of M into N if both addition and scalar multiplication are preserved, that is, if

$$(x + y)\theta = x\theta + y\theta \qquad\qquad x, y \in M,$$

and

$$(ax)\theta = a(x\theta) \qquad\qquad a \in R, \ x \in M.$$

If there exists an R-homomorphism of M onto N, we may say that N is an *R-homomorphic image* of M. Following our usual pattern, an R-homomorphism which is a one-one mapping is called an *R-isomorphism*. If there exists an R-isomorphism of M onto N, we also say that M and N are *R-isomorphic*. The notation $M \cong N$ may be used to indicate that M and N are R-isomorphic.

EXERCISES

1. If M is an R-module, prove each of the following:

    (i) $a0 = 0$, $a \in R$, 0 the zero of M.
    (ii) $a(-x) = -(ax)$, $a \in R$, $x \in M$.
    (iii) $(-a)x = -(ax)$, $a \in R$, $x \in M$.
    (iv) $0x = 0$, $x \in M$, 0 the zero of R and also of M.

2. If M is an R-module, show that the set $\{a \mid a \in R, \ Rx = 0$ for every $x \in M\}$ is an ideal in R.

3. Prove that a nonempty subset N of an R-module M is a submodule of M if and only if it is closed under addition and scalar multiplication.

4. Prove that scalar multiplication is well-defined by 17.26 and that M of Example 5 is an R-module under Definitions 17.25 and 17.26.

5. If θ is an R-homomorphism of the R-module M onto the R-module N, let us define ker $\theta = \{x \mid x \in M, \ x\theta = 0\}$. Show that ker θ is a submodule of M.

6. If N is a submodule of the R-module N, in a manner suggested by previous situations, introduce the concept of an R-module M/N whose elements are the cosets of the additive subgroup N of the additive group M.

7. In the notation introduced in the two preceding exercises, prove that $M/\text{ker } \theta$ is R-isomorphic to N.

8. A nonzero R-module M is said to be *irreducible* if its only submodules are $\{0\}$ and M. Prove that an irreducible R-module is cyclic.

9. Determine all irreducible **Z**-modules.

10. Find a basis for the module of Example 2.

17.4 MODULES OVER A PRINCIPAL IDEAL DOMAIN

Our purpose in this section is to introduce enough concepts to be able to state without proof an important theorem about finitely generated modules over a principal ideal domain. We will also give an indication of the generality of this result by interpreting, again without proof, what it says about finite abelian groups and also about the similarity of linear transformations of a vector space over a field. Reference to proofs will be given in the notes at the end of the chapter.

Unless otherwise stated, D will denote a principal ideal domain and M a D-module.

If $x \in M$ and there exists a nonzero element c of D such that $cx = 0$, x is said to be a *torsion element* of M. If x is a torsion element of M, the set of all elements c of D such that $cx = 0$ is an ideal A in D. Since in D every ideal is principal, we must have $A = (a)$ for some nonzero element a of D. This element a (or, equally well, any of its associates) is called the *order* of the element x. It follows that if a is the order of x, then $bx = 0$ for $b \in D$ if and only if $a \mid b$. If x has order a, we may also call a the *order* of the cyclic module Dx.

If M is a **Z**-module (an abelian group), a torsion element is what we have called an element of finite order.

A *torsion module* is a module in which each element is a torsion element. If M is a finitely generated torsion module, there exist nonzero elements c of D such that $cM = \{cx \mid x \in M\} = \{0\}$. To see this, suppose that $M = x_1 D + x_2 D + \cdots + x_n D$, and that x_i has order c_i for $i = 1, 2, \cdots, n$. Then, in particular, if $c = c_1 c_2 \cdots c_n$, we know that $c \neq 0$ since D is a division ring, and clearly $cM = 0$. The set of all elements c of R such that $cM = 0$ is again an ideal in R; it is called the *minimal annihilator* of M.

We are now ready to state the following theorem.

17.29 Theorem.

(*i*) *If M is a finitely generated torsion module over a principal ideal domain D, there exist a finite number of cyclic submodules M_1, $M_2, \cdots, M_r$ of M, each of which has order a power of a prime, such that*

17.30 $$M = M_1 \oplus M_2 \oplus \cdots \oplus M_r.$$

(*ii*) *If, in addition to 17.27, we also have*

$$M = N_1 \oplus N_2 \oplus \cdots \oplus N_s,$$

where the N's are cyclic submodules of M, each of which has order a power of a prime of D, then $s = r$ and by a suitable choice of notation, for each $i = 1, 2, \cdots, r$, the order of N_i is the same as (or, equally well, is an associate of) the order of M_i.

It will be observed that the second part of this theorem states that, in a certain sense, the expression of a module of the specified kind as a direct sum of submodules having the indicated properties is *unique*.

The orders of the submodules M_i in 17.30 (repetitions being allowed) are called the *elementary divisors* of the module M.

It can be shown that *two torsion D-modules, each of which is finitely generated, are D-isomorphic if and only if their elementary divisors coincide.*

Again, let us consider the special case of a finitely generated abelian group, each element of which has finite order. This requires the group itself to have finite order. The theorem just stated is thus a direct generalization of Theorem 8.29 for finite abelian groups. Compare, also, Theorem 8.33 in relation to the general statement made above about the D-isomorphisms of finitely generated torsion D-modules.

Let us now briefly introduce another situation in which this theorem is applicable. Let α be a fixed linear transformation of a vector space V of finite dimension over a field F. If t is an indeterminate, we can use α to make V into an $F[t]$-module in the following way. For each $f(t) \in F[t]$ and $X \in V$, we define

$$f(t)X = Xf(\alpha).$$

It may be verified that the module properties are satisfied and we do have an $F(t)$-module. Since $F(t)$ is a principal ideal domain, we may apply the results of this section. The minimal polynomial of the linear transformation α, as introduced in Section 16.11, is the minimal annihilator of the $F(t)$-module in the sense defined in the present section. A D-submodule is the same as a subspace invariant under α, as used in Section 16.10. Although, in Theorem 16.76 the submodules V_i are not necessarily cyclic, we know by Theorem 17.29 that the decomposition can be continued until one obtains *cyclic* submodules of orders a power of a prime polynomial.

The elementary divisors of this $F[t]$-module are called the *elementary divisors* of the matrix of α relative to any ordered basis of V. The next paragraph will hint at why it makes no difference which ordered basis is used.

We have not quite developed all of the machinery needed to prove the following fact, but its truth is the primary reason why the concept of elementary divisors of a matrix is important.

Two square matrices of the same order over a field are similar if and only if their elementary divisors coincide.

17.5 ZORN'S LEMMA

We introduce in this section an important tool of frequent use in algebra as well as in other branches of mathematics.

Let $\mathfrak{M}$ (German M) denote a nonempty collection of subsets of some fixed set S. A subset $\mathfrak{C}$ (German C) of $\mathfrak{M}$ is said to be a *chain* (or a *completely ordered* subset) if for $A, B \in \mathfrak{C}$, either $A \subseteq B$ or $B \subseteq A$. By the *union of the chain* $\mathfrak{C}$ we mean the union of all subsets of S which are the elements of $\mathfrak{C}$. An element M of $\mathfrak{M}$ is naturally called a *maximal* element of $\mathfrak{M}$ if it is not properly contained in any element of $\mathfrak{M}$. Although we shall take the following statement as an axiom, it is customary to call it a lemma.

17.31 **Zorn's Lemma.** *Let $\mathfrak{M}$ denote a nonempty set of subsets of a fixed set S. If the union of each chain in $\mathfrak{M}$ is an element of $\mathfrak{M}$, then $\mathfrak{M}$ contains one or more maximal elements.*

References to equivalent formulations of this statement and to its role in the theory of sets will be given at the end of this chapter. We shall here consider it to be an axiom and proceed to give two examples illustrating its use.

As a first illustration, let us prove the following result.

17.32   Theorem. *If R is a ring with unity e, and C is an ideal in R with $C \neq R$, then C is contained in at least one maximal ideal M in R.*

First, let us recall the Definition 17.18 of a maximal ideal M in R. It is an ideal with the property that there exists no ideal N in R such that $M \subset N \subset R$. In the language introduced before the statement of Zorn's Lemma, a maximal ideal in R is an ideal which is maximal in the set of all ideals other than R itself.

Accordingly, let $\mathfrak{M}$ be the set of all ideals in R which contain C but not the unity e of R. Since $C \neq R$, $e \notin C$ and therefore $C \in \mathfrak{M}$, and $\mathfrak{M}$ is not empty. Now let $\mathfrak{C}$ be a chain in $\mathfrak{M}$ and let us denote by U the union of the chain $\mathfrak{C}$. Hence U consists of all elements of R that are in any element of the chain $\mathfrak{C}$ of subsets of R. We proceed to prove that U is an ideal in R, that $e \notin U$, and therefore $U \in \mathfrak{M}$. If a, $b \in U$, there exist ideals A and B belonging to the chain $\mathfrak{C}$ such that $a \in A$ and $b \in B$. Since $\mathfrak{C}$ is a chain, we must have either $A \subseteq B$ or $B \subseteq A$. In either case, both a and b belong to the same ideal in $\mathfrak{C}$, and hence $a + b$ is an element of one of the ideals of the chain. It follows that $a + b \in U$. It is even easier to verify that if $a \in U$, then $-a \in U$; also that if $a \in U$, then $ar \in U$ and $ra \in U$ for each $r \in R$; hence U is an ideal in R. Clearly, also, $e \notin U$ since, otherwise, e would be an element of one of the ideals in $\mathfrak{C}$. But no ideal of $\mathfrak{M}$ (and therefore no ideal of $\mathfrak{C}$) contains e. Therefore, $e \notin U$, and $U \in \mathfrak{M}$ since U satisfies all conditions imposed on the elements of $\mathfrak{M}$. We have shown that the union of each chain in $\mathfrak{M}$ is an element of $\mathfrak{M}$, and Zorn's Lemma then assures us that $\mathfrak{M}$ has maximal elements. Let M be a maximal element of $\mathfrak{M}$ and N an ideal in R such that $M \subset N$. Since N is not an element of $\mathfrak{M}$, we must have $e \in N$. This implies that $N = R$ and therefore that M is indeed a maximal ideal in R. Clearly $C \subseteq M$, and the proof is complete.

As another illustration, let us prove that every vector space has a basis—in a sense now to be made precise.

Let V be a vector space over a field F (a division ring would do just as well). An arbitrary (possibly infinite) nonempty set of elements of V is said to be *linearly independent* if each finite subset is linearly independent. The subspace of V *generated* by an arbitrary nonempty set T of elements of V is the set of all linear combinations of any finite number of elements of T. A set B of elements of V is a *basis* of V if it is a linearly independent set and generates V.

We shall now use Zorn's Lemma to prove the following generalization of Theorem 12.24 for finite dimensional vector spaces, which asserts that any linear independent set of elements is a part of a basis.

17.33   Theorem.   *If T is a linearly independent set of elements of a vector space V over a field F, then there exists a basis of V which contains T.*

PROOF: Let $\mathfrak{M}$ be the set of all linearly independent subsets of V which contain the given set T. Since T is itself such a subset, $\mathfrak{M}$ is not empty. Let U be the union of a chain $\mathfrak{C}$ of elements of M. If X_1, $X_2 \in U$, then $X_1 \in A$ and $X_2 \in B$ for elements A and B of $\mathfrak{C}$. But since $\mathfrak{C}$ is a chain, either $A \subseteq B$ or $B \subseteq A$, and hence both X_1 and X_2 are elements of some one element of $\mathfrak{C}$. More generally, if for an arbitrary positive integer n, $\{X_1, X_2, \cdots, X_n\} \subseteq U$, then $\{X_1, X_2, \cdots, X_n\}$ is contained in some *one* element of $\mathfrak{C}$, and this set is therefore linearly independent. Since each finite set of elements of U is linearly independent, and clearly $T \subseteq U$, it follows that $U \in \mathfrak{M}$. The conclusion of Zorn's Lemma is therefore applicable, and therefore there exists a maximal element B of $\mathfrak{M}$. Let us show that the elements of B generate V and it will follow that B is the basis which we seek.

If $X \in B$, it is trivial that X is expressible as a linear combination of a finite number (actually one!) of elements of B. If $X \in V$, $X \notin B$, the maximal property of B shows that the union $\{X\} \cup B$ cannot be an element of $\mathfrak{M}$. This fact implies that the set $\{X\} \cup B$ cannot be linearly independent, so there must exist finitely many elements $X_1, X_2, \cdots, X_n$ of B such that $\{X, X_1, X_2, \cdots, X_n\}$ is a linearly dependent set. Since $\{X_1, X_2, \cdots, X_n\}$ is a linearly independent set, it follows that X is expressible as a linear combination of X_1, X_2, $\cdots$, X_n (*Cf.* Theorem 12.15(*iii*)). We have therefore shown that every element of V is expressible as a linear combination of a finite number of elements of B. The set B is therefore a basis of V and since $T \subseteq B$, the proof is complete.

If V is a nonzero vector space, and X_1 is a nonzero element of V, the set $\{X_1\}$ is linearly independent; hence, by the theorem just established, there is a basis of V which contains the vector X_1. In particular, *any nonzero vector space has a basis.*

17.6   REPRESENTATIONS OF BOOLEAN RINGS

On several occasions we have referred to the ring S of all subsets of some given set A, first introduced in Example 10 of Section 2.3. Throughout this section, it will be convenient to denote addition and multiplication in S by $\oplus$ and $\odot$, respectively. Thus, if c, $d \in S$, we have $c \odot d =$

$c \cap d$. There is a fairly common notation $X \setminus Y$, which we have not used heretofore, to denote the set of elements of the set X which are not elements of Y. Using this notation, we recall that our definition of addition in the ring S may be given by $c \oplus d = (c \cup d) \setminus (c \cap d)$. The empty set $\varnothing$ is the zero of the ring S, and each element of S is its own additive inverse since $c \oplus c = \varnothing$ for $c \in S$.

Any subring of S is naturally called *a ring of subsets of A*. Since in S every element c is its own additive inverse, we see that a nonempty set K of elements of S will be a subring of S, and therefore a ring of subsets of A, if and only if K is closed with respect to the operations $\oplus$ and $\odot$ in S.

We have also defined (Exercise 11 at the end of Section 2.6) a *Boolean ring R* to be a ring with the property that $a^2 = a$ for every element a of R. It is known (see this same exercise) that a Boolean ring is necessarily a commutative ring and that $a + a = 0$ for $a \in R$. We shall use these facts without further mention.

By the very definition, it follows that a ring of subsets of any given set is a Boolean ring, since always $c \odot c = c \cap c = c$. The purpose of this section is to prove the interesting fact that there are no other Boolean rings. More precisely, we shall prove the following theorem of Stone.

17.34   Theorem.   *Every Boolean ring R is isomorphic to a ring of subsets of some set.*

We leave it to the reader to verify that the theorem is trivially true if R has only one element (the zero). Accordingly, we shall henceforth tacitly assume that R has more than one element.

In order to prove the theorem, we must find a set T, some of whose subsets will turn out to form a ring which is isomorphic to R. Clearly, the set T must be related in some significant way to the ring R. Although it is unlikely that it will be obvious how to choose T, we shall show that T may be chosen to be the set of all maximal ideals in R!

We shall prove several lemmas from which the theorem will follow fairly easily. Henceforth, let R be an arbitrary Boolean ring with more than one element, and let T be the set of all maximal ideals in R. We first prove the following useful result.

17.35   Lemma.   *If M is an element of T, that is, a maximal ideal in R, and $c \notin M$, then every element of R is expressible in the form $m + cx$ for some $m \in M$ and $x \in R$.*

To prove the truth of this statement, we observe that the set $C = \{m + cx \mid m \in M,\ x \in R\}$ is an ideal in R, as is readily verified. Moreover, $M \subseteq C$ since, as a special case, x can be zero. We now assert that $c \in C$ since we obtain c by letting $m = 0$ and $x = c$. Since it was given that $c \not\subset M$, it follows that the maximal ideal M is properly contained in the ideal C. By definition of maximal ideal, this implies that $C = R$, completing the proof of the lemma.

17.36 Lemma. *If a is a nonzero element of R, there exists in R a maximal ideal M which does not contain a.*

PROOF: We leave it to the reader to verify that the set $B = \{ax + x \mid x \in R\}$ is an ideal in R. We assert that $a \not\subset B$. Suppose, on the contrary, that $a \in B$. Thus $a = ax + x$ for some x in R. Multiplying by a, we obtain

$$a = a^2 = a^2 x + ax = ax + ax = 0 \, ,$$

which contradicts the assumption that $a \not\subset 0$. Hence we conclude that $a \not\subset B$.

We proceed to apply Zorn's Lemma as follows. Let $\mathfrak{M}$ be the set of all ideals in R which contain the ideal B and do not contain the element a. We have shown above that $a \not\subset B$, so $B \in \mathfrak{M}$ and $\mathfrak{M}$ is not empty. As in the proof of 17.32, the union of any chain in $\mathfrak{M}$ is an ideal in R and it clearly does not contain a; hence is an element of $\mathfrak{M}$. By Zorn's Lemma, $\mathfrak{M}$ therefore has maximal elements. Let M be such a maximal element. Hence M is an ideal in R, and we wish to show that it is a maximal ideal in R. Accordingly, let N be an ideal such that $M \subset N$, and let us prove that N must be R itself. Suppose that $c \in N$, $c \not\subset M$. Then, as in the proof of Lemma 17.35, we see that $D = \{m + cx \mid m \in M , x \in R\}$ is an ideal in R which contains M and also contains c, hence M is properly contained in D and, by the fact that M is a maximal element of $\mathfrak{M}$, we see that we must have $a \in D$. But this implies that $ax \in D$ for every $x \in R$. Then, since $B \subseteq M \subset D$, it follows that $x \in D$ for every $x \in R$, and therefore $D = R$. But $D \subseteq N$ and thus $N = R$. This shows that the only ideal which properly contains M is R itself, and M is therefore a maximal ideal in R. Since $a \not\subset M$, this is an ideal whose existence we wished to prove.

The form of the statements of the next two lemmas is suggested by the fact that we shall presently be interested in maximal ideals that do *not* contain a given element of R.

17.37 Lemma. *If M is a maximal ideal in R and $a, b \in R$, then $ab \not\subset M$ if and only if $a \not\subset M$ and $b \not\subset M$.*

PROOF: What we wish to prove is logically equivalent to the statement that if $a, b \in R$, then $ab \in M$ if and only if $a \in M$ or

$b \in M$. Let us prove it in this form. We shall do so by assuming that $ab \in M$, $b \notin M$, and showing that we must have $a \in M$.

Since $b \notin M$, Lemma 17.35 asserts the existence of an element m of M and an element x of R such that $a = bx + m$. Multiplying by a, we obtain

$$a^2 = a = abx + am.$$

But since $ab \in M$ and $am \in M$, this equation implies that $a \in M$, completing the proof.

17.38 Lemma.   *If M is a maximal ideal in R and $a, b \in R$, then $a + b \notin M$ if and only if exactly one of the two elements a and b is an element of M.*

PROOF: Again, it is a little simpler to prove the following equivalent formulation of this lemma. If $a, b \in R$, then $a + b \in M$ if and only if both a and b are elements of M or neither of them is an element of M.

In order to prove this last statement, suppose first that $a + b \in M$. Then if $a \in M$, it follows that $b = (a + b) - a$ is also an element of M. Similarly, of course, if $b \in M$, then also $a \in M$. So $a + b \in M$ implies that either $a \in M$ and $b \in M$ or $a \notin M$ and $b \notin M$.

Conversely, if $a \in M$ and $b \in M$, it is trivial that $a + b \in M$. The only thing left to prove is that if $a \notin M$ and $b \notin M$, then $a + b \in M$. This fact we can establish as follows.

Since $b \notin M$, by Lemma 17.35, there exist $x \in R$ and $m \in M$ such that

17.39 $a = bx + m.$

We observe that $x \notin M$ since otherwise this equation would imply that $a \in M$. Multiplying Equation 17.39 by x, we obtain $ax = bx + mx$. It follows that

$$(a + b)x = ax + bx = ax - bx = mx,$$

so that $(a + b)x \in M$. Since $x \notin M$, Lemma 17.37 now assures us that $a + b \in M$, completing the proof of the lemma.

We are now ready to complete the proof of the theorem. We recall that T denotes the set of all maximal ideals in R. If $a \in R$, let us now denote by T_a the subset of T consisting of all maximal ideals in R which do *not* contain the element a. Then the two preceding lemmas can be stated in the following simple form:

$$T_{ab} = T_a \cap T_b,$$

and

$$T_{a+b} = (T_a \cup T_b) \backslash (T_a \cap T_b).$$

In terms of multiplication $\odot$ and addition $\oplus$ as defined in a ring of subsets of T, these may be written, respectively, as follows:

17.40
$$T_{ab} = T_a \odot T_b,$$

and

17.41
$$T_{a+b} = T_a \oplus T_b.$$

Now let $S = \{T_a \mid a \in R\}$; hence S is a set of subsets of T. Equations 17.40 and 17.41 show that S is closed under the operations $\odot$ and $\oplus$, and hence S is a ring of subsets of T.

Now let $\theta : R \to S$ be defined by $a\theta = T_a$, $a \in R$. By the very definition of S, this mapping is an onto mapping. Moreover, equations 17.40 and 17.41 show that θ is a homomorphism. Lemma 17.36 shows that $T_a \neq \emptyset$ if $a \neq 0$; hence that the kernel of this homomorphism is $\{0\}$. This proves that θ is indeed an isomorphism of R onto a ring of subsets of T, and the proof of the theorem is complete.

An isomorphism of a Boolean ring R onto a ring of subsets is often referred to as a *representation* of R. We conclude with this explanation of the title of this section.

NOTES AND REFERENCES

There is a famous Theorem of Frobenius which asserts that the *only* division rings which are algebras of finite dimension over the field **R** of real numbers are **R** itself, the field **C** of complex numbers, and the algebra of real quaternions. For a proof of this theorem see Chapter 7 of Herstein [7].

Another interesting and well-known Theorem of Wedderburn states that a division ring with a finite number of elements is necessarily commutative, that is, it is a field. This theorem is also proved in Chapter 7 of Herstein. See also, Paley and Weichsel [14], p. 262.

For additional discussions of principal ideal domains and unique factorization see, e.g., Ames [1], Fraleigh [5], Johnson [9], and van der Waerden [16]. For an example of an integral domain in which factorization as a product of primes is *not* unique, see p. 136 of Johnson.

Modules are presented in some detail in Ames [1], Godement [6], and MacLane and Birkhoff [12]. A proof of our Theorem 17.29 will be found in MacLane and Birkhoff [12], p. 354 and also in Rotman [25], p. 68. For further details of application of this theorem to similarity of matrices, see Herstein [7], p. 262 ff; MacLane and Birkhoff [12], p. 357.

The role of the "axiom of choice" in set theory and its equivalence to Zorn's Lemma and other related topics will be found in Birkhoff [45] and Kurosh [10]. See also Wilder [51] for the connection with "proofs by transfinite induction."

Stone's Theorem (Theorem 17.34) on the representation of Boolean rings was proved (or at least a proof outlined) from a slightly different point of view in McCoy [30] and [31]. References are given in both of these books to Stone's original article in which also the fundamental relationship between Boolean rings and what are known as Boolean algebras is developed. A good introduction to Boolean algebras will be found in Whitesit [50].

BIBLIOGRAPHY

This bibliography is by no means complete. Most of the books mentioned below have been referred to at least once in the notes at the ends of certain chapters. Others are included for a variety of reasons including one or more of the following: they are particularly readable by students with a modest background in abstract algebra, they are standard treatises and give wide coverage, they are modern in spirit, they should be interesting and challenging to the better students.

Several of the listed books have fairly extensive bibliographies which may be used as desired to supplement this one.

ABSTRACT ALGEBRA IN GENERAL

1. AMES, DENNIS B., *An Introduction to Abstract Algebra*, International, Scranton, Pa., 1969.
2. BIRKHOFF, GARRETT and SAUNDERS MACLANE, *A Survey of Modern Algebra* (third edition), Macmillan, New York, 1965.
3. DEAN, RICHARD A., *Elements of Abstract Algebra*, Wiley, New York, 1966.
4. DUBISCH, ROY, *Introduction to Abstract Algebra*, Wiley, New York, 1965.
5. FRALEIGH, JOHN B., *A First Course in Abstract Algebra*, Addison-Wesley, Reading, Mass., 1967.
6. GODEMENT, ROGER, *Algebra*, Hermann, Paris, 1968.
7. HERSTEIN, I. N., *Topics in Algebra*, Blaisdell, New York, 1964.
8. JACOBSON, NATHAN, *Lectures in Abstract Algebra*, Van Nostrand, New York, vol. 1, 1951; vol. 2, 1953; vol. 3, 1964.
9. JOHNSON, RICHARD E., *University Algebra*, Prentice-Hall, Englewood Cliffs, N. J., 1966.
10. KUROSH, A. G., *Lectures on General Algebra*, Chelsea, New York, 1963.

11. LEWIS, DONALD J., *Introduction to Algebra*, Harper, New York, 1965.

12. MACLANE, SAUNDERS and GARRETT BIRKHOFF, *Algebra*, Macmillan, New York, 1967.

13. MOSTOW, GEORGE D., JOSEPH H. SAMPSON, and JEAN-PIERRE MEYER, *Fundamental Structures of Algebra*, McGraw-Hill, New York, 1963.

14. PALEY, HIRAM and PAUL M. WEICHSEL, *A First Course in Abstract Algebra*, Holt, Rinehart, and Winston, New York, 1966.

15. PERLIS, SAM, *Introduction to Algebra*, Blaisdell, Waltham, Mass., 1966.

16. VAN DER WAERDEN, B. L., *Modern Algebra* (rev. English ed.), Ungar, New York, 1953.

GROUP THEORY

17. BURNSIDE, WILLIAM, *Theory of Groups of Finite Order* (2nd ed.) Dover, New York, 1955.

18. CARMICHAEL, ROBERT D., *Introduction to the Theory of Groups of Finite Order*, Ginn, Boston, 1937.

19. FUCHS, L., *Infinite Abelian Groups*, vol. 1, Academic Press, New York, 1970.

20. HALL, MARSHALL, Jr., *The Theory of Groups* (rev. ed.), Macmillan, New York, 1959.

21. KAPLANSKY, IRVING, *Infinite Abelian Groups* (rev. ed.), University of Michigan Press, Ann Arbor, Mich., 1968.

22. LEDERMAN, WALTER, *Introduction to the Theory of Finite Groups* (4th ed.), Interscience, New York, 1961.

23. MACDONALD, IAN D., *The Theory of Groups*, Oxford University Press, 1968.

24. MILLER, G. A., H. F. BLICHFELDT, and L. E. DICKSON, *Theory and Applications of Finite Groups*, Wiley, New York, 1916.

25. ROTMAN, JOSEPH J., *The Theory of Groups: An Introduction*, Allyn and Bacon, Boston, 1965.

RING THEORY

26. ARTIN, E., C. J. NESBITT, and R. M. THRALL, *Rings with Minimum Condition*, Univ. of Michigan Press, Ann Arbor, 1944.

27. BURTON, DAVID M., *A First Course in Rings and Ideals*, Addison-Wesley, Reading, Mass., 1970.

28. HERSTEIN, I. N., *Noncommutative Rings* (Carus Mathematical Monograph no. 15), The Mathematical Association of America, 1968.

29. JACOBSON, NATHAN, *Structure of Rings* (Colloquium Publications, no. 37), American Mathematical Society, 1956 (Revised, 1964).

30. McCOY, NEAL H., *Rings and Ideals* (Carus Mathematical Monograph no. 8), The Mathematical Association of America, 1948.

31. McCOY, NEAL H., *The Theory of Rings*, Macmillan, New York, 1964.

LINEAR ALGEBRA

32. CURTIS, CHARLES W., *Linear Algebra, An Introductory Approach*, Allyn and Bacon, Boston, Second edition 1968.
33. FINKBEINER, DANIEL T., *Introduction to Matrices and Linear Transformations*, Freeman, San Francisco, Second edition 1966.
34. HALMOS, PAUL R., *Finite-Dimensional Vector Spaces*, van Nostrand, Princeton, N. J., Second edition 1958.
35. MALCEV, A. I., *Foundations of Linear Algebra*, Freeman, San Francisco, 1963.

FIELD THEORY

36. ARTIN, EMIL, *Galois Theory* (Notre Dame Mathematical Lecture no. 2), University of Notre Dame Press, Notre Dame, Indiana, Second edition 1944.
37. POSTNIKOV, M. M., *Foundations of Galois Theory*, Macmillan (Pergamon Press), New York, 1962.
38. ZARISKI, OSCAR and PIERRE SAMUEL, *Commutative Algebra*, vol. 1, van Nostrand, Princeton, N. J., 1958.

NUMBER THEORY

39. DAVENPORT, H., *The Higher Arithmetic*, Hutchinson's University Library, London, 1952.
40. HARDY, G. H. and E. M. WRIGHT, *An Introduction to the Theory of Numbers*, Oxford University Press, Oxford, Fourth edition 1960.
41. LEVEQUE, WILLIAM J., *Elementary Theory of Numbers*, Addison-Wesley, Reading, Mass., 1962.
42. NIVEN, IVAN and HERBERT S. ZUCKERMAN, *An Introduction to the Theory of Numbers*, Wiley, New York, 1960.
43. ORE, OYSTEIN, *Number Theory and its History*, McGraw-Hill, New York, 1948.
44. SIERPINSKI, W., *Elementary Theory of Numbers*, Państwowe Wydawnictwo Naukowe, Warsaw, 1964.

MISCELLANEOUS

45. BIRKHOFF, GARRETT, *Lattice Theory* (Colloquium Publications no. 25), American Mathematical Society, Second edition 1948.
46. CURTIS, CHARLES and IRVING REINER, *Representation Theory of Finite Groups and Associative Algebras*, Interscience, New York, 1962.
47. LANDAU, EDMUND, *Foundations of Analysis*, Chelsea, New York, 1960.

48. NORTHCOTT, D. G., *An Introduction to Homological Algebra*, Cambridge University Press, Cambridge, 1960.

49. SZASZ, GABOR, *Introduction to Lattice Theory*, Academic Press, New York, Third edition 1963.

50. WHITESITT, J. E., *Boolean Algebra and its Applications*, Addison-Wesley, Reading, Mass., 1961.

51. WILDER, RAYMOND L., *Introduction to the Foundations of Mathematics*, Wiley, New York, 1952.

INDEX